Reece • Urry • Cain • Wasserman • Minorsky • Jackson

Campbell Biology, Volume 1

A Custom Edition for Hudson Valley Community College

D1399168

Taken from:
Campbell Biology, Tenth Edition
by Jane B. Reece, Lisa A. Urry, Michael L. Cain, Steven A. Wasserman,
Peter V. Minorsky, and Robert B. Jackson

Cover Art: Courtesy of Photodisc/Getty Images.

Taken from:

Campbell Biology, Tenth Edition
by Jane B. Reece, Lisa A. Urry, Michael L. Cain, Steven A. Wasserman, Peter V. Minorsky, and Robert B. Jackson
Copyright © 2014, 2011, 2008 by Pearson Education
Boston, Massachusetts 02116

This special edition published in cooperation with Pearson Learning Solutions.

All trademarks, service marks, registered trademarks, and registered service marks are the property of their respective owners and are used herein for identification purposes only.

Pearson Learning Solutions, 501 Boylston Street, Suite 900, Boston, MA 02116
A Pearson Education Company
www.pearsoned.com

Printed in the United States of America

1 2 3 4 5 6 7 8 9 10 V0UD 18 17 16 15 14

000200010271885074

RD

ISBN 10: 1-269-71597-6
ISBN 13: 978-1-269-71597-3

1

Evolution, the Themes of Biology, and Scientific Inquiry

▲ **Figure 1.1 How is the dandelion adapted to its environment?**

Inquiring About Life

The dandelions shown in **Figure 1.1** send their seeds aloft for dispersal. A seed is an embryo surrounded by a store of food and a protective coat. The dandelion's seeds, shown at the lower left, are borne on the wind by parachute-like structures made from modified flower parts. The parachutes harness the wind, which carries such seeds to new locations where conditions may favor sprouting and growth. Dandelions are very successful plants, found in temperate regions worldwide.

An organism's adaptations to its environment, such as the dandelion seed's parachute, are the result of evolution. **Evolution** is the process of change that has transformed life on Earth from its earliest beginnings to the diversity of organisms living today. Because evolution is the fundamental organizing principle of biology, it is the core theme of this book.

Although biologists know a great deal about life on Earth, many mysteries remain. For instance, what processes led to the origin of flowering among plants such as the ones pictured above? Posing questions about the living world and seeking answers through scientific inquiry are the central activities of **biology**, the scientific study of life. Biologists' questions can be ambitious. They may ask how a single tiny cell becomes a tree or a dog, how the human mind works, or how the different

▼ **Order.** This close-up of a sunflower illustrates the highly ordered structure that characterizes life.

▲ **Regulation.** The regulation of blood flow through the blood vessels of this jackrabbit's ears helps maintain a constant body temperature by adjusting heat exchange with the surrounding air.

▲ **Evolutionary adaptation.** The appearance of this pygmy sea horse camouflages the animal in its environment. Such adaptations evolve over many generations by the reproductive success of those individuals with heritable traits that are best suited to their environments.

Reproduction. Organisms (living things) reproduce their own kind.

▲ **Energy processing.** This butterfly obtains fuel in the form of nectar from flowers. The butterfly will use chemical energy stored in its food to power flight and other work.

▲ **Growth and development.** Inherited information carried by genes controls the pattern of growth and development of organisms, such as this oak seedling.

▲ **Response to the environment.** This Venus flytrap closed its trap rapidly in response to the environmental stimulus of a damselfly landing on the open trap.

▲ **Figure 1.2**
Some properties of life.

forms of life in a forest interact. Many interesting questions probably occur to you when you are out-of-doors, surrounded by the natural world. When they do, you are already thinking like a biologist. More than anything else, biology is a quest, an ongoing inquiry about the nature of life.

At the most fundamental level, we may ask: What is life? Even a child realizes that a dog or a plant is alive, while a rock or a car is not. Yet the phenomenon we call life defies a simple, one-sentence definition. We recognize life by what living things do. **Figure 1.2** highlights some of the properties and processes we associate with life.

While limited to a handful of images, Figure 1.2 reminds us that the living world is wondrously varied. How do biologists make sense of this diversity and complexity? This opening chapter sets up a framework for answering this question. The first part of the chapter provides a panoramic view of the biological "landscape," organized around some unifying themes. We then focus on biology's core theme, evolution, which accounts for life's unity and diversity. Next, we look at scientific inquiry—how scientists ask and attempt to answer questions about the natural world. Finally, we address the culture of science and its effects on society.

CONCEPT 1.1

The study of life reveals common themes

Biology is a subject of enormous scope, and exciting new biological discoveries are being made every day. How can you organize into a comprehensible framework all the information you'll encounter as you study the broad range of topics included in biology? Focusing on a few big ideas will

help. Here, we'll list five unifying themes—ways of thinking about life that will still hold true decades from now. These unifying themes are described in greater detail in the next few pages. We hope they will serve as touchstones as you proceed through this text:

- Organization
- Information
- Energy and Matter
- Interactions
- Evolution

▼ Figure 1.3
Exploring Levels of Biological Organization

◄ 1 The Biosphere

Even from space, we can see signs of Earth's life—in the green mosaic of the forests, for example. We can also see the scale of the entire biosphere, which consists of all life on Earth and all the places where life exists: most regions of land, most bodies of water, the atmosphere to an altitude of several kilometers, and even sediments far below the ocean floor.

◄ 2 Ecosystems

Our first scale change brings us to a North American forest with many deciduous trees (trees that lose their leaves and grow new ones each year). A deciduous forest is an example of an ecosystem, as are grasslands, deserts, and coral reefs. An ecosystem consists of all the living things in a particular area, along with all the nonliving components of the environment with which life interacts, such as soil, water, atmospheric gases, and light.

► 3 Communities

The array of organisms inhabiting a particular ecosystem is called a biological community. The community in our forest ecosystem includes many kinds of trees and other plants, various animals, mushrooms and other fungi, and enormous numbers of diverse microorganisms, which are living forms, such as bacteria, that are too small to see without a microscope. Each of these forms of life is called a *species*.

► 4 Populations

A population consists of all the individuals of a species living within the bounds of a specified area. For example, our forest includes a population of sugar maple trees and a population of white-tailed deer. A community is therefore the set of populations that inhabit a particular area.

▲ 5 Organisms

Individual living things are called organisms. Each of the maple trees and other plants in the forest is an organism, and so is each deer, frog, beetle, and other forest animals. The soil teems with microorganisms such as bacteria.

Theme: New Properties Emerge at Successive Levels of Biological Organization

ORGANIZATION In **Figure 1.3**, we zoom in from space to take a closer and closer look at life in a deciduous forest in Ontario, Canada. This journey shows the different levels of organization recognized by biologists: The study of life extends from the global scale of the entire living planet to the microscopic scale of cells and molecules. The numbers in the figure guide you through the hierarchy of biological organization.

Zooming in at ever-finer resolution illustrates an approach called *reductionism*, which reduces complex systems to simpler components that are more manageable to study. Reductionism is a powerful strategy in biology. For example, by studying the molecular structure of DNA that had been extracted from cells, James Watson and Francis Crick inferred the chemical basis of biological inheritance. However, although it has propelled many major discoveries, reductionism provides a necessarily incomplete view of life on Earth, as we'll discuss next.

▼ 6 Organs and Organ Systems

The structural hierarchy of life continues to unfold as we explore the architecture of more complex organisms. A maple leaf is an example of an organ, a body part that carries out a particular function in the body. Stems and roots are the other major organs of plants. The organs of complex animals and plants are organized into organ systems, each a team of organs that cooperate in a larger function. Organs consist of multiple tissues.

50 μm

◀ 7 Tissues

Viewing the tissues of a leaf requires a microscope. Each tissue is a group of cells that work together, performing a specialized function. The leaf shown here has been cut on an angle. The honeycombed tissue in the interior of the leaf (left side of photo) is the main location of photosynthesis, the process that converts light energy to the chemical energy of sugar. The jigsaw puzzle–like "skin" on the surface of the leaf is a tissue called epidermis (right side of photo). The pores through the epidermis allow entry of the gas CO_2, a raw material for sugar production.

Cell   10 μm

▶ 10 Molecules

Our last scale change drops us into a chloroplast for a view of life at the molecular level. A molecule is a chemical structure consisting of two or more units called atoms, represented as balls in this computer graphic of a chlorophyll molecule. Chlorophyll is the pigment molecule that makes a maple leaf green, and it absorbs sunlight during photosynthesis. Within each chloroplast, millions of chlorophyll molecules are organized into systems that convert light energy to the chemical energy of food.

Atoms

Chlorophyll molecule

▲ 8 Cells

The cell is life's fundamental unit of structure and function. Some organisms are single cells, while others are multicellular. A single cell performs all the functions of life, while a multicellular organism has a division of labor among specialized cells. Here we see a magnified view of cells in a leaf tissue. One cell is about 40 micrometers (μm) across—about 500 of them would reach across a small coin. As tiny as these cells are, you can see that each contains numerous green structures called chloroplasts, which are responsible for photosynthesis.

Chloroplast

▶ 9 Organelles

Chloroplasts are examples of organelles, the various functional components present in cells. This image, taken by a powerful microscope, shows a single chloroplast.

1 μm

Emergent Properties

Let's reexamine Figure 1.3, beginning this time at the molecular level and then zooming out. This approach allows us to see novel properties emerge at each level that are absent from the preceding level. These **emergent properties** are due to the arrangement and interactions of parts as complexity increases. For example, although photosynthesis occurs in an intact chloroplast, it will not take place in a disorganized test-tube mixture of chlorophyll and other chloroplast molecules. The coordinated processes of photosynthesis require a specific organization of these molecules in the chloroplast. Isolated components of living systems, serving as the objects of study in a reductionist approach to biology, lack a number of significant properties that emerge at higher levels of organization.

Emergent properties are not unique to life. A box of bicycle parts won't transport you anywhere, but if they are arranged in a certain way, you can pedal to your chosen destination. Compared with such nonliving examples, however, biological systems are far more complex, making the emergent properties of life especially challenging to study.

To explore emergent properties more fully, biologists today complement reductionism with **systems biology**, the exploration of a biological system by analyzing the interactions among its parts. In this context, a single leaf cell can be considered a system, as can a frog, an ant colony, or a desert ecosystem. By examining and modeling the dynamic behavior of an integrated network of components, systems biology enables us to pose new kinds of questions. For example, we can ask how a drug that lowers blood pressure affects the functioning of organs throughout the human body. At a larger scale, how does a gradual increase in atmospheric carbon dioxide alter ecosystems and the entire biosphere? Systems biology can be used to study life at all levels.

Structure and Function

At each level of the biological hierarchy, we find a correlation of structure and function. Consider the leaf shown in Figure 1.3: Its thin, flat shape maximizes the capture of sunlight by chloroplasts. More generally, analyzing a biological structure gives us clues about what it does and how it works. Conversely, knowing the function of something provides

insight into its structure and organization. Many examples from the animal kingdom show a correlation between structure and function. For example, the hummingbird's anatomy allows the wings to rotate at the shoulder, so hummingbirds have the ability, unique among birds, to fly backward or hover

in place. While hovering, the birds can extend their long, slender beaks into flowers and feed on nectar. The elegant match of form and function in the structures of life is explained by natural selection, which we'll explore shortly.

The Cell: An Organism's Basic Unit of Structure and Function

In life's structural hierarchy, the cell is the smallest unit of organization that can perform all activities required for life. In fact, the actions of organisms are all based on the functioning of cells. For instance, the movement of your eyes as you read this sentence results from the activities of muscle and nerve cells. Even a process that occurs on a global scale, such as the recycling of carbon atoms, is the product of cellular functions, including the photosynthetic activity of chloroplasts in leaf cells.

All cells share certain characteristics. For instance, every cell is enclosed by a membrane that regulates the passage of materials between the cell and its surroundings. Nevertheless, we recognize two main forms of cells: prokaryotic and eukaryotic. The cells of two groups of single-celled microorganisms—bacteria (singular, *bacterium*) and archaea (singular, *archaean*)—are prokaryotic. All other forms of life, including plants and animals, are composed of eukaryotic cells.

A **eukaryotic cell** contains membrane-enclosed organelles (Figure 1.4). Some organelles, such as the DNA-containing nucleus, are found in the cells of all eukaryotes; other organelles are specific to particular cell types. For example, the chloroplast in Figure 1.3 is an organelle found

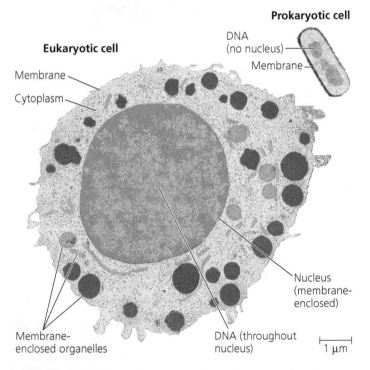

▲ Figure 1.4 **Contrasting eukaryotic and prokaryotic cells in size and complexity.**

only in eukaryotic cells that carry out photosynthesis. In contrast to eukaryotic cells, a **prokaryotic cell** lacks a nucleus or other membrane-enclosed organelles. Another distinction is that prokaryotic cells are generally smaller than eukaryotic cells, as shown in Figure 1.4.

Theme: Life's Processes Involve the Expression and Transmission of Genetic Information

INFORMATION Within cells, structures called chromosomes contain genetic material in the form of **DNA (deoxyribonucleic acid)**. In cells that are preparing to divide, the chromosomes may be made visible using a dye that appears blue when bound to the DNA **(Figure 1.5)**.

25 μm

▲ **Figure 1.5 A lung cell from a newt divides into two smaller cells that will grow and divide again.**

DNA, the Genetic Material

Each time a cell divides, the DNA is first replicated, or copied, and each of the two cellular offspring inherits a complete set of chromosomes, identical to that of the parent cell. Each chromosome contains one very long DNA molecule with hundreds or thousands of **genes**, each a section of the DNA of the chromosome. Transmitted from parents to offspring, genes are the units of inheritance. They encode the information necessary to build all of the molecules synthesized within a cell, which in turn establish that cell's identity and function. Each of us began as a single cell stocked with DNA inherited from our parents. The replication of that DNA during each round of cell division transmitted copies of the DNA to what eventually became the trillions of cells of our body. As the cells grew and divided, the genetic information encoded by the DNA directed our development **(Figure 1.6)**.

The molecular structure of DNA accounts for its ability to store information. A DNA molecule is made up of two long chains, called strands, arranged in a double helix. Each chain is made up of four kinds of chemical building blocks called nucleotides, abbreviated A, T, C, and G **(Figure 1.7)**.

▲ **Figure 1.6 Inherited DNA directs development of an organism.**

(a) **DNA double helix.** This model shows the atoms in a segment of DNA. Made up of two long chains (strands) of building blocks called nucleotides, a DNA molecule takes the three-dimensional form of a double helix.

(b) **Single strand of DNA.** These geometric shapes and letters are simple symbols for the nucleotides in a small section of one strand of a DNA molecule. Genetic information is encoded in specific sequences of the four types of nucleotides. Their names are abbreviated A, T, C, and G.

▲ **Figure 1.7 DNA: The genetic material.**

The way DNA encodes information is analogous to how we arrange the letters of the alphabet into words and phrases with specific meanings. The word *rat*, for example, evokes a rodent; the words *tar* and *art*, which contain the same letters, mean very different things. We can think of nucleotides as a four-letter alphabet. Specific sequences of these four nucleotides encode the information in genes.

Many genes provide the blueprints for making proteins, which are the major players in building and maintaining the cell and carrying out its activities. For instance, a given bacterial gene may specify a particular protein (an enzyme) required to break down a certain sugar molecule, while a human gene may denote a different protein (an antibody) that helps fight off infection.

Genes control protein production indirectly, using a related molecule called RNA as an intermediary (**Figure 1.8**). The sequence of nucleotides along a gene is transcribed into RNA, which is then translated into a linked series of protein building blocks called amino acids. These two stages result in a specific protein with a unique shape and function. The entire process, by which the information in a gene directs the manufacture of a cellular product, is called **gene expression**.

In translating genes into proteins, all forms of life employ essentially the same genetic code: A particular sequence of nucleotides says the same thing in one organism as it does in another. Differences between organisms reflect differences between their nucleotide sequences rather than between their genetic codes. Comparing the sequences in several species for a gene that codes for a particular protein can provide valuable information both about the protein and about the relationship of the species to each other, as you will see.

In addition to RNA molecules (called mRNAs) that are translated into proteins, some RNAs in the cell carry out other important tasks. For example, we have known for decades that some types of RNA are actually components of the cellular machinery that manufactures proteins. Recently, scientists have discovered whole new classes of RNA that play other roles in the cell, such as regulating the functioning of protein-coding genes. All of these RNAs are specified by genes, and the production of these RNAs is also referred to as gene expression. By carrying the instructions for making proteins and RNAs and by replicating with each cell division, DNA ensures faithful inheritance of genetic information from generation to generation.

Genomics: Large-Scale Analysis of DNA Sequences

The entire "library" of genetic instructions that an organism inherits is called its **genome**. A typical human cell has two similar sets of chromosomes, and each set has approximately 3 billion nucleotide pairs of DNA. If the one-letter abbreviations for the nucleotides of a set were written in letters the size of those you are now reading, the genetic text would fill about 700 biology textbooks.

(a) The lens of the eye (behind the pupil) is able to focus light because lens cells are tightly packed with transparent proteins called crystallin.

Lens cell

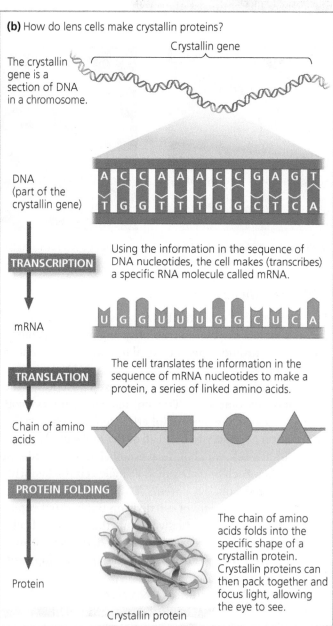

(b) How do lens cells make crystallin proteins?

Crystallin gene

The crystallin gene is a section of DNA in a chromosome.

DNA (part of the crystallin gene)

A C C A A A C C G A G T
T G G T T T G G C T C A

TRANSCRIPTION

Using the information in the sequence of DNA nucleotides, the cell makes (transcribes) a specific RNA molecule called mRNA.

mRNA

U G G U U U G G C U C A

TRANSLATION

The cell translates the information in the sequence of mRNA nucleotides to make a protein, a series of linked amino acids.

Chain of amino acids

PROTEIN FOLDING

The chain of amino acids folds into the specific shape of a crystallin protein. Crystallin proteins can then pack together and focus light, allowing the eye to see.

Protein

Crystallin protein

▲ **Figure 1.8 Gene expression: The transfer of information from a gene results in a functional protein.**

Since the early 1990s, the pace at which researchers can determine the sequence of a genome has accelerated at an astounding rate, enabled by a revolution in technology. The entire sequence of nucleotides in the human genome is now known, along with the genome sequences of many other organisms, including other animals and numerous plants, fungi, bacteria, and archaea. To make sense of the deluge of data from genome-sequencing projects and the growing catalog of known gene functions, scientists are applying a systems biology approach at the cellular and molecular levels. Rather than investigating a single gene at a time, researchers study whole sets of genes (or other DNA) in one or more species—an approach called **genomics**. Likewise, the term **proteomics** refers to the study of sets of proteins and their properties. (The entire set of proteins expressed by a given cell or group of cells is called a **proteome**).

Three important research developments have made the genomic and proteomic approaches possible. One is "high-throughput" technology, tools that can analyze many biological samples very rapidly. The second major development is **bioinformatics**, the use of computational tools to store, organize, and analyze the huge volume of data that results from high-throughput methods. The third development is the formation of interdisciplinary research teams—groups of diverse specialists that may include computer scientists, mathematicians, engineers, chemists, physicists, and, of course, biologists from a variety of fields. Researchers in such teams aim to learn how the activities of all the proteins and non-translated RNAs encoded by the DNA are coordinated in cells and in whole organisms.

Theme: Life Requires the Transfer and Transformation of Energy and Matter

ENERGY AND MATTER A fundamental characteristic of living organisms is their use of energy to carry out life's activities. Moving, growing, reproducing, and the various cellular activities of life are work, and work requires energy. The input of energy, primarily from the sun, and the transformation of energy from one form to another make life possible. A plant's leaves absorb sunlight, and molecules within the leaves convert the energy of sunlight to the chemical energy of food, such as sugars, produced during photosynthesis. The chemical energy in the food molecules is then passed along by plants and other photosynthetic organisms (**producers**) to consumers. **Consumers** are organisms, such as animals, that feed on producers and other consumers.

When an organism uses chemical energy to perform work, such as muscle contraction or cell division, some of that energy is lost to the surroundings as heat. As a result, energy flows one way *through* an ecosystem, usually entering as light and exiting as heat. In contrast, chemicals are recycled *within* an ecosystem (**Figure 1.9**). Chemicals that a plant absorbs from the air or soil may be incorporated into the plant's body and then passed to an animal that eats the plant. Eventually, these chemicals will be returned to the environment by decomposers, such as bacteria and fungi, that break down waste products, leaf litter, and the bodies of dead organisms. The chemicals are then available to be taken up by plants again, thereby completing the cycle.

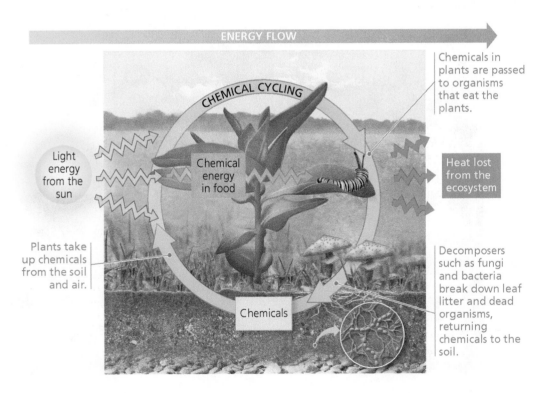

◄ **Figure 1.9 Energy flow and chemical cycling.** There is a one-way flow of energy in an ecosystem: During photosynthesis, plants convert energy from sunlight to chemical energy (stored in food molecules such as sugars), which is used by plants and other organisms to do work and is eventually lost from the ecosystem as heat. In contrast, chemicals cycle between organisms and the physical environment.

ENERGY FLOW

CHEMICAL CYCLING

Chemicals in plants are passed to organisms that eat the plants.

Light energy from the sun

Chemical energy in food

Heat lost from the ecosystem

Plants take up chemicals from the soil and air.

Chemicals

Decomposers such as fungi and bacteria break down leaf litter and dead organisms, returning chemicals to the soil.

Theme: From Ecosystems to Molecules, Interactions Are Important in Biological Systems

INTERACTIONS At any level of the biological hierarchy, interactions between the components of the system ensure smooth integration of all the parts, such that they function as a whole. This holds true equally well for the components of an ecosystem and the molecules in a cell; we'll discuss both as examples.

Ecosystems: An Organism's Interactions with Other Organisms and the Physical Environment

At the ecosystem level, each organism interacts with other organisms. For instance, an acacia tree interacts with soil microorganisms associated with its roots, insects that live on it, and animals that eat its leaves and fruit **(Figure 1.10)**. In some cases, interactions between organisms are mutually beneficial. An example is the association between a sea turtle and the so-called "cleaner fish" that hover around it. The fish feed on parasites that would otherwise harm the turtle, while gaining a meal and protection from predators. Sometimes, one species benefits and the other is harmed, as when a lion kills and eats a zebra. In yet other cases, both species are harmed—for example, when two plants compete for a soil resource that is in short supply. Interactions among organisms help regulate the functioning of the ecosystem as a whole.

Organisms also interact continuously with physical factors in their environment. The leaves of a tree, for example, absorb light from the sun, take in carbon dioxide from the air, and release oxygen to the air (see Figure 1.10). The environment is also affected by the organisms living there. For instance, in addition to taking up water and minerals from the soil, the roots of a plant break up rocks as they grow, thereby contributing to the formation of soil. On a global scale, plants and other photosynthetic organisms have generated all the oxygen in the atmosphere.

Molecules: Interactions Within Organisms

At lower levels of organization, the interactions between components that make up living organisms—organs, tissues, cells, and molecules—are crucial to their smooth operation. Consider the sugar in your blood, for instance. After a meal, the level of the sugar glucose in your blood rises **(Figure 1.11)**. The increase in blood glucose stimulates the pancreas to release insulin into the blood. Once it reaches liver or muscle cells, insulin causes excess glucose to be stored in the form of a very large carbohydrate called glycogen, reducing blood glucose level to a range that is optimal for bodily functioning. The lower blood glucose level that results no longer stimulates insulin secretion by pancreas cells. Some sugar is also used by cells for energy: When you exercise, your muscle cells increase their consumption of sugar molecules.

Interactions among the body's molecules are responsible for most of the steps in this process. For instance, like most chemical activities in the cell, those that either decompose or store sugar are accelerated at the molecular level (catalyzed) by proteins called enzymes. Each type of enzyme

▶ **Figure 1.10 Interactions of an African acacia tree with other organisms and the physical environment.**

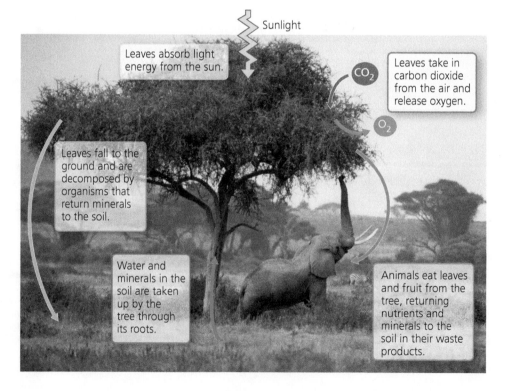

Sunlight

Leaves absorb light energy from the sun.

Leaves take in carbon dioxide from the air and release oxygen.

CO₂

O₂

Leaves fall to the ground and are decomposed by organisms that return minerals to the soil.

Water and minerals in the soil are taken up by the tree through its roots.

Animals eat leaves and fruit from the tree, returning nutrients and minerals to the soil in their waste products.

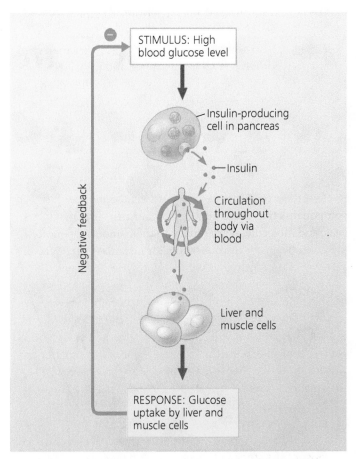

▲ **Figure 1.11 Feedback regulation.** The human body regulates the use and storage of glucose, a major cellular fuel derived from food. This figure shows negative feedback: The response (glucose uptake by cells) decreases the high glucose levels that provide the stimulus for insulin secretion, thus negatively regulating the process.

Figure labels:
STIMULUS: High blood glucose level
Insulin-producing cell in pancreas
Insulin
Circulation throughout body via blood
Liver and muscle cells
RESPONSE: Glucose uptake by liver and muscle cells
Negative feedback

catalyzes a specific chemical reaction. In many cases, these reactions are linked into chemical pathways, each step with its own enzyme. How does the cell coordinate its various chemical pathways? In our example of sugar management, how does the cell match fuel supply to demand, regulating its opposing pathways of sugar consumption and storage? The key is the ability of many biological processes to self-regulate by a mechanism called feedback.

In **feedback regulation**, the output, or product, of a process regulates that very process. The most common form of regulation in living systems is *negative feedback*, a loop in which the response reduces the initial stimulus. As seen in the example of insulin signaling (see Figure 1.11), the uptake of glucose by cells (the response) decreases blood glucose levels, eliminating the stimulus for insulin secretion and thereby shutting off the pathway. Thus, the output of the process negatively regulates that process.

Though less common than processes regulated by negative feedback, there are also many biological processes regulated by *positive feedback*, in which an end product *speeds up* its own production. The clotting of your blood

in response to injury is an example. When a blood vessel is damaged, structures in the blood called platelets begin to aggregate at the site. Positive feedback occurs as chemicals released by the platelets attract *more* platelets. The platelet pileup then initiates a complex process that seals the wound with a clot.

Feedback is a regulatory motif common to life at all levels, from the molecular level through ecosystems and the biosphere. Interactions between organisms can affect system-wide processes like the growth of a population. And as we'll see, interactions between individuals not only affect the participants, but also affect how populations evolve over time.

Evolution, the Core Theme of Biology

Having considered four of the unifying themes that run through this text (organization, information, energy and matter, and interactions), let's now turn to biology's core theme—evolution. Evolution is the one idea that makes logical sense of everything we know about living organisms. The fossil record documents the fact that life has been evolving on Earth for billions of years, resulting in a vast diversity of past and present organisms. But along with the diversity are many shared features. For example, while sea horses, jackrabbits, hummingbirds, and giraffes all look very different, their skeletons are organized in the same basic way. The scientific explanation for this unity and diversity—as well as for the adaptation of organisms to their environments—is evolution: the concept that the organisms living on Earth today are the modified descendants of common ancestors. In other words, we can explain the sharing of traits by two organisms with the premise that the organisms have descended from a common ancestor, and we can account for differences with the idea that heritable changes have occurred along the way. Many kinds of evidence support the occurrence of evolution and the theory that describes how it takes place. In the next section, we'll consider the fundamental concept of evolution in greater detail.

CONCEPT CHECK 1.1

1. Starting with the molecular level in Figure 1.3, write a sentence that includes components from the previous (lower) level of biological organization, for example: "A molecule consists of *atoms* bonded together." Continue with organelles, moving up the biological hierarchy.

2. Identify the theme or themes exemplified by (a) the sharp quills of a porcupine, (b) the development of a multicellular organism from a single fertilized egg, and (c) a hummingbird using sugar to power its flight.

3. **WHAT IF?** For each theme discussed in this section, give an example not mentioned in the text.

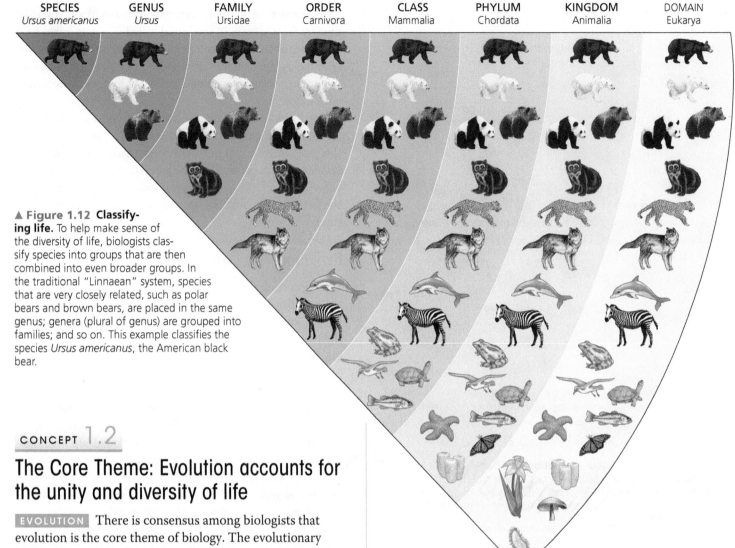

SPECIES	GENUS	FAMILY	ORDER	CLASS	PHYLUM	KINGDOM	DOMAIN
Ursus americanus	*Ursus*	Ursidae	Carnivora	Mammalia	Chordata	Animalia	Eukarya

▲ Figure 1.12 **Classifying life.** To help make sense of the diversity of life, biologists classify species into groups that are then combined into even broader groups. In the traditional "Linnaean" system, species that are very closely related, such as polar bears and brown bears, are placed in the same genus; genera (plural of genus) are grouped into families; and so on. This example classifies the species *Ursus americanus*, the American black bear.

CONCEPT 1.2

The Core Theme: Evolution accounts for the unity and diversity of life

EVOLUTION There is consensus among biologists that evolution is the core theme of biology. The evolutionary changes seen in the fossil record are observable facts. Furthermore, as we'll describe, evolutionary mechanisms account for the unity and diversity of all species on Earth. To quote one of the founders of modern evolutionary theory, Theodosius Dobzhansky, "Nothing in biology makes sense except in the light of evolution."

In addition to encompassing a hierarchy of size scales from molecules to the biosphere, biology explores the great diversity of species that have ever lived on Earth. To understand Dobzhansky's statement, we need to discuss how biologists think about this vast diversity.

Classifying the Diversity of Life

Diversity is a hallmark of life. Biologists have so far identified and named about 1.8 million species. To date, this diversity of life is known to include at least 100,000 species of fungi, 290,000 plant species, 57,000 vertebrate species (animals with backbones), and 1 million insect species (more than half of all known forms of life)—not to mention the myriad types of single-celled organisms. Researchers identify thousands of additional species each year. Estimates of the total number of species range from about 10 million to over 100 million. Whatever the actual number, the enormous variety of life gives biology a very broad scope. Biologists face a major challenge in attempting to make sense of this variety.

Grouping Species: The Basic Idea

There is a human tendency to group diverse items according to their similarities and their relationships to each other. For instance, we may speak of "squirrels" and "butterflies," though we recognize that many different species belong to each group. We may even sort groups into broader categories, such as rodents (which include squirrels) and insects (which include butterflies). Taxonomy, the branch of biology that names and classifies species, formalizes this ordering of species into groups of increasing breadth, based on the degree to which they share characteristics (**Figure 1.12**). Here, we will focus on the big picture by considering the broadest units of classification, kingdoms and domains.

The Three Domains of Life

Historically, scientists have classified the diversity of life-forms into species and broader groupings by careful comparisons of structure, function, and other obvious features. In the last few decades, new methods of assessing species relationships, such as comparisons of DNA sequences, have led to an ongoing reevaluation of the number and boundaries of kingdoms. Researchers have proposed anywhere from six kingdoms to dozens of kingdoms. While debate continues at the kingdom level, biologists agree that the kingdoms of life can be grouped into three even higher levels of classification called domains. The three domains are named Bacteria, Archaea, and Eukarya (Figure 1.13).

As you read earlier, the organisms making up two of the three domains—**Bacteria** and **Archaea**—are prokaryotic.

All the eukaryotes (organisms with eukaryotic cells) are now grouped in domain **Eukarya**. This domain includes three kingdoms of multicellular eukaryotes: kingdoms Plantae, Fungi, and Animalia. These three kingdoms are distinguished partly by their modes of nutrition. Plants produce their own sugars and other food molecules by photosynthesis, fungi absorb dissolved nutrients from their surroundings, and animals obtain food by eating and digesting other organisms. Animalia is, of course, the kingdom to which we belong. But neither plants, nor fungi, nor animals are as numerous or diverse as the single-celled eukaryotes we call protists. Although protists were once placed in a single kingdom, recent evidence shows that some protists are more closely related to plants, animals, or fungi than they are to other protists. Thus, the recent taxonomic trend has been to split the protists into several kingdoms.

▼ Figure 1.13 **The three domains of life.**

(a) Domain Bacteria

Bacteria are the most diverse and widespread prokaryotes and are now classified into multiple kingdoms. Each rod-shaped structure in this photo is a bacterial cell.

(b) Domain Archaea

Some of the prokaryotes known as **archaea** live in Earth's extreme environments, such as salty lakes and boiling hot springs. Domain Archaea includes multiple kingdoms. Each round structure in this photo is an archaeal cell.

(c) Domain Eukarya

◀ **Kingdom Animalia** consists of multicellular eukaryotes that ingest other organisms.

100 μm

▲ **Kingdom Plantae** consists of terrestrial multicellular eukaryotes (land plants) that carry out photosynthesis, the conversion of light energy to the chemical energy in food.

▶ **Kingdom Fungi** is defined in part by the nutritional mode of its members (such as this mushroom), which absorb nutrients from outside their bodies.

▶ **Protists** are mostly unicellular eukaryotes and some relatively simple multicellular relatives. Pictured here is an assortment of protists inhabiting pond water. Scientists are currently debating how to classify protists in a way that accurately reflects their evolutionary relationships.

Cross section of a cilium,
as viewed with an
electron microscope

5 µm

Cilia of *Paramecium*.
The cilia of the single-celled
Paramecium propel the
organism through pond
water.

15 µm

0.1 µm

Cilia of windpipe cells.
The cells that line the
human windpipe are
equipped with cilia that
help keep the lungs
clean by sweeping a
film of debris-trapping
mucus upward.

▲ **Figure 1.14 An example of unity underlying the diversity of life: the architecture of cilia in eukaryotes.** Cilia (singular, *cilium*) are extensions of cells that function in locomotion. They occur in eukaryotes as diverse as *Paramecium* (found in pond water) and humans. Even organisms so different share a common architecture for their cilia, which have an elaborate system of tubules that is striking in cross-sectional views.

Unity in the Diversity of Life

As diverse as life is, it also displays remarkable unity. Earlier we mentioned both the similar skeletons of different vertebrate animals and the universal genetic language of DNA (the genetic code). In fact, similarities between organisms are evident at all levels of the biological hierarchy. For example, unity is obvious in many features of cell structure, even among distantly related organisms **(Figure 1.14).**

How can we account for life's dual nature of unity and diversity? The process of evolution, explained next, illuminates both the similarities and differences in the world of life. It also introduces another important dimension of biology: historical time.

Charles Darwin and the Theory of Natural Selection

The history of life, as documented by fossils and other evidence, is the saga of a changing Earth billions of years old, inhabited by an evolving cast of living forms **(Figure 1.15).** This evolutionary view of life came into sharp focus in November 1859, when Charles Robert Darwin published one of the most important and influential books ever written.

▼ **Figure 1.15 Digging into the past.** Paleontologists carefully excavate the hind leg of a long-necked dinosaur (*Rapetosaurus krausei*) from rocks in Madagascar.

▲ **Figure 1.16 Charles Darwin as a young man.** His revolutionary book *On the Origin of Species* was first published in 1859.

Entitled *On the Origin of Species by Means of Natural Selection*, Darwin's book was an immediate bestseller and soon made "Darwinism," as it was dubbed at the time, almost synonymous with the concept of evolution **(Figure 1.16)**.

On the Origin of Species articulated two main points. The first point was that contemporary species arose from a succession of ancestors that differed from them. Darwin called this process "descent with modification." This insightful phrase captured the duality of life's unity and diversity—unity in the kinship among species that descended from common ancestors and diversity in the modifications that evolved as species branched from their common ancestors **(Figure 1.17)**.

Darwin's second main point was his proposal that "natural selection" is an evolutionary mechanism for descent with modification.

Darwin developed his theory of natural selection from observations that by themselves were neither new nor profound. Others had described the pieces of the puzzle, but Darwin saw how they fit together. He started with the following three observations from nature: First, individuals in a population vary in their traits, many of which seem to be heritable (passed on from parents to offspring). Second, a population can produce far more offspring than can survive to produce offspring of their own. With more individuals than the environment is able to support, competition is inevitable. Third, species generally suit their environments—in other words, they are adapted to their environments. For instance, a common adaptation among birds that eat tough seeds as their major food source is that they have especially thick, strong beaks.

Making inferences from these three observations, Darwin arrived at his theory of evolution. He reasoned that individuals with inherited traits that are better suited to the local environment are more likely to survive and reproduce than less well-suited individuals. Over many generations, a higher and higher proportion of individuals in a population will have the advantageous traits. Evolution occurs as the unequal reproductive success of individuals ultimately leads to adaptation to their environment, as long as the environment remains the same.

Darwin called this mechanism of evolutionary adaptation **natural selection** because the natural environment "selects" for the propagation of certain traits among naturally occurring variant traits in the population. The example

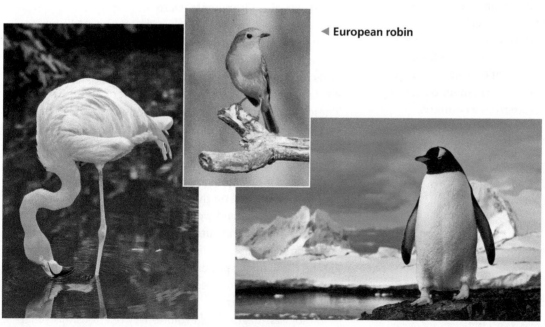

◄ **European robin**

▲ **American flamingo**   ▲ **Gentoo penguin**

◄ **Figure 1.17 Unity and diversity among birds.** These three birds are variations on a common body plan. For example, each has feathers, a beak, and wings—although these features are highly specialized for the birds' diverse lifestyles.

① Population with varied inherited traits

② Elimination of individuals with certain traits

③ Reproduction of survivors

④ Increasing frequency of traits that enhance survival and reproductive success

▲ **Figure 1.18 Natural selection.** This imaginary beetle population has colonized a locale where the soil has been blackened by a recent brush fire. Initially, the population varies extensively in the inherited coloration of the individuals, from very light gray to charcoal. For hungry birds that prey on the beetles, it is easiest to spot the beetles that are lightest in color.

in **Figure 1.18** illustrates the ability of natural selection to "edit" a population's heritable variations in color. We see the products of natural selection in the exquisite adaptations of various organisms to the special circumstances of their way of life and their environment. The wings of the bat shown in **Figure 1.19** are an excellent example of adaptation.

The Tree of Life

Take another look at the skeletal architecture of the bat's wings in Figure 1.19. These wings are not like those of feathered birds; the bat is a mammal. The bat's forelimbs, though adapted for flight, actually have all the same bones, joints, nerves, and blood vessels found in other limbs as diverse as the human arm, the foreleg of a horse, and the flipper of a whale. Indeed, all mammalian forelimbs are anatomical variations of a common architecture, much as the birds in Figure 1.17 are variations on an underlying "avian" theme. Such examples of kinship connect life's unity in diversity to the Darwinian concept of descent with modification. In this view, the unity of mammalian limb anatomy reflects inheritance of that structure from a common

ancestor—the "prototype" mammal from which all other mammals descended. The diversity of mammalian forelimbs results from modification by natural selection operating over millions of generations in different environmental contexts. Fossils and other evidence corroborate anatomical unity in supporting this view of mammalian descent from a common ancestor.

Darwin proposed that natural selection, by its cumulative effects over long periods of time, could cause an ancestral species to give rise to two or more descendant species. This could occur, for example, if one population fragmented into several subpopulations isolated in different environments. In these separate arenas of natural selection, one species could gradually radiate into multiple species as the geographically isolated populations adapted over many generations to different sets of environmental factors.

The "family tree" of 14 finches in **Figure 1.20** illustrates a famous example of adaptive radiation of new species from a common ancestor. Darwin collected specimens of these birds during his 1835 visit to the remote Galápagos Islands, 900 kilometers (km) off the Pacific coast of South America. These relatively young, volcanic islands are home to many species of plants and animals found nowhere else in the world, though many Galápagos organisms are clearly related to species on the South American mainland. After volcanoes built up the Galápagos several million years ago, finches probably diversified on the various islands from an ancestral finch species that by chance reached the archipelago from elsewhere. Years after Darwin collected the Galapagos finches, researchers began to sort out the relationships among these finch species, first from anatomical and geographic data and more recently with the help of DNA sequence comparisons.

Biologists' diagrams of evolutionary relationships generally take treelike forms, though the trees are often turned

▲ **Figure 1.19 Evolutionary adaptation.** Bats, the only mammals capable of active flight, have wings with webbing between extended "fingers." Darwin proposed that such adaptations are refined over time by natural selection.

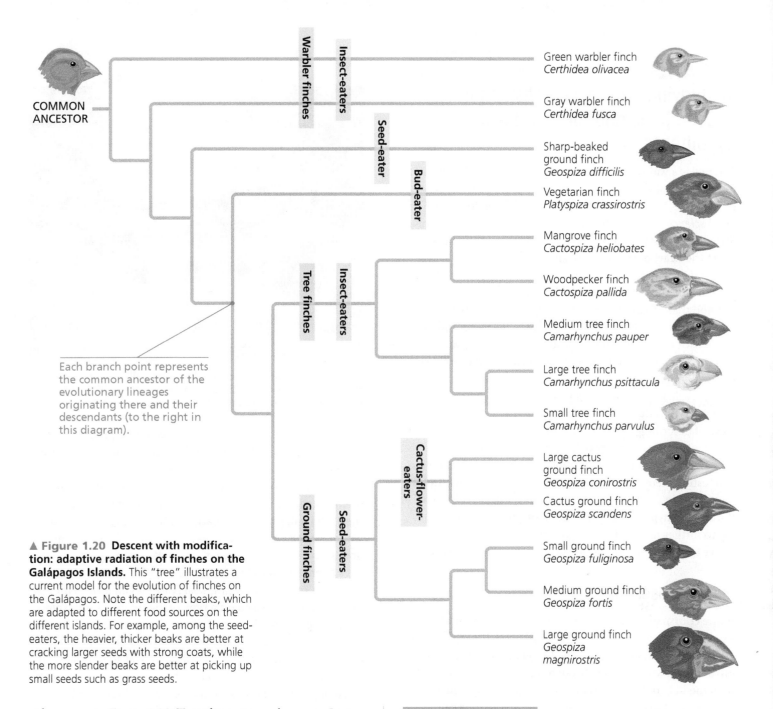

▲ **Figure 1.20 Descent with modification: adaptive radiation of finches on the Galápagos Islands.** This "tree" illustrates a current model for the evolution of finches on the Galápagos. Note the different beaks, which are adapted to different food sources on the different islands. For example, among the seed-eaters, the heavier, thicker beaks are better at cracking larger seeds with strong coats, while the more slender beaks are better at picking up small seeds such as grass seeds.

Each branch point represents the common ancestor of the evolutionary lineages originating there and their descendants (to the right in this diagram).

**Labels in figure:**

Warbler finches — Insect-eaters: Green warbler finch *Certhidea olivacea*; Gray warbler finch *Certhidea fusca*

Seed-eater: Sharp-beaked ground finch *Geospiza difficilis*

Bud-eater: Vegetarian finch *Platyspiza crassirostris*

Tree finches — Insect-eaters: Mangrove finch *Cactospiza heliobates*; Woodpecker finch *Cactospiza pallida*; Medium tree finch *Camarhynchus pauper*; Large tree finch *Camarhynchus psittacula*; Small tree finch *Camarhynchus parvulus*

Ground finches — Cactus-flower-eaters: Large cactus ground finch *Geospiza conirostris*; Cactus ground finch *Geospiza scandens*

Ground finches — Seed-eaters: Small ground finch *Geospiza fuliginosa*; Medium ground finch *Geospiza fortis*; Large ground finch *Geospiza magnirostris*

COMMON ANCESTOR

sideways as in Figure 1.20. Tree diagrams make sense: Just as an individual has a genealogy that can be diagrammed as a family tree, each species is one twig of a branching tree of life extending back in time through ancestral species more and more remote. Species that are very similar, such as the Galápagos finches, share a common ancestor at a relatively recent branch point on the tree of life. But through an ancestor that lived much farther back in time, finches are related to sparrows, hawks, penguins, and all other birds. And birds, mammals, and all other vertebrates share a common ancestor even more ancient. Trace life back far enough, and we reach the early prokaryotes that inhabited Earth over 3.5 billion years ago. We can recognize their vestiges in our own cells—in the universal genetic code, for example. Indeed, all of life is connected through its long evolutionary history.

CONCEPT CHECK 1.2

1. How is a mailing address analogous to biology's hierarchical taxonomic system?

2. Explain why "editing" is an appropriate metaphor for how natural selection acts on a population's heritable variation.

3. **WHAT IF?** The three domains you learned about in Concept 1.2 can be represented in the tree of life as the three main branches, with three subbranches on the eukaryotic branch being the kingdoms Plantae, Fungi, and Animalia. What if fungi and animals are more closely related to each other than either of these kingdoms is to plants—as recent evidence strongly suggests? Draw a simple branching pattern that symbolizes the proposed relationship between these three eukaryotic kingdoms.

In studying nature, scientists make observations and form and test hypotheses

Science is a way of knowing—an approach to understanding the natural world. It developed out of our curiosity about ourselves, other life-forms, our planet, and the universe. The word *science* is derived from a Latin verb meaning "to know." Striving to understand seems to be one of our basic urges.

At the heart of science is **inquiry**, a search for information and explanations of natural phenomena. There is no formula for successful scientific inquiry, no single scientific method that researchers must rigidly follow. As in all quests, science includes elements of challenge, adventure, and luck, along with careful planning, reasoning, creativity, patience, and the persistence to overcome setbacks. Such diverse elements of inquiry make science far less structured than most people realize. That said, it is possible to highlight certain characteristics that help to distinguish science from other ways of describing and explaining nature.

Scientists use a process of inquiry that includes making observations, forming logical, testable explanations (*hypotheses*), and testing them. The process is necessarily repetitive: In testing a hypothesis, more observations may inspire revision of the original hypothesis or formation of a new one, thus leading to further testing. In this way, scientists circle closer and closer to their best estimation of the laws governing nature.

Making Observations

In the course of their work, scientists describe natural structures and processes as accurately as possible through careful observation and analysis of data. Observation is the gathering of information, either through direct use of the senses or with the help of tools such as microscopes, thermometers, and balances that extend our senses. Observations can reveal valuable information about the natural world. For example, a series of detailed observations have shaped our understanding of cell structure, and another set of observations is currently expanding our databases of genomes of diverse species and of genes whose expression is altered in cancer and other diseases.

Recorded observations are called **data**. Put another way, data are items of information on which scientific inquiry is based. The term *data* implies numbers to many people. But some data are *qualitative*, often in the form of recorded descriptions rather than numerical measurements. For example, Jane Goodall spent decades recording her observations of chimpanzee behavior during field research in a Tanzanian jungle **(Figure 1.21)**. Along with these qualitative data, Goodall also enriched the field of animal behavior with

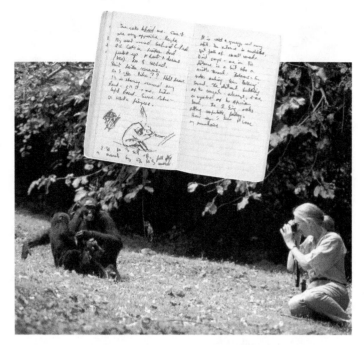

▲ **Figure 1.21 Jane Goodall collecting qualitative data on chimpanzee behavior.** Goodall recorded her observations in field notebooks, often with sketches of the animals' behavior.

volumes of *quantitative* data, such as the frequency and duration of specific behaviors for different members of a group of chimpanzees in a variety of situations. Quantitative data are generally expressed as numerical measurements and often organized into tables and graphs. Scientists analyze their data using a type of mathematics called statistics to test whether their results are significant or merely due to random fluctuations. (Note that all results presented in this text have been shown to be statistically significant.)

Collecting and analyzing observations can lead to important conclusions based on a type of logic called **inductive reasoning**. Through induction, we derive generalizations from a large number of specific observations. "The sun always rises in the east" is an example. And so is "All organisms are made of cells." Careful observations and data analyses, along with generalizations reached by induction, are fundamental to our understanding of nature.

Forming and Testing Hypotheses

Our innate curiosity often stimulates us to pose questions about the natural basis for the phenomena we observe in the world. What *caused* the different chimpanzee behaviors that Goodall observed in different situations? What *causes* the roots of a plant seedling to grow downward? In science, such inquiry usually involves the forming and testing of hypothetical explanations—that is, hypotheses.

In science, a **hypothesis** is a tentative answer to a well-framed question—an explanation on trial. It is usually a rational account for a set of observations, based on the available data and guided by inductive reasoning. A scientific hypothesis must lead to predictions that can be tested by

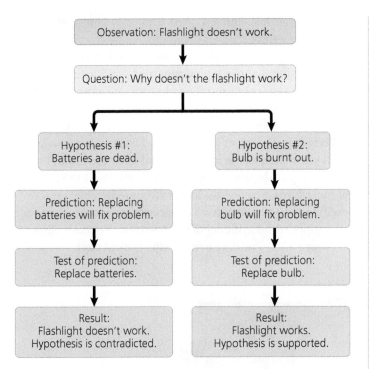

Observation: Flashlight doesn't work.

↓

Question: Why doesn't the flashlight work?

```
        ┌──────────────────────────┴──────────────────────────┐
        ↓                                                      ↓
Hypothesis #1:                                         Hypothesis #2:
Batteries are dead.                                    Bulb is burnt out.
        ↓                                                      ↓
Prediction: Replacing                                  Prediction: Replacing
batteries will fix problem.                            bulb will fix problem.
        ↓                                                      ↓
Test of prediction:                                    Test of prediction:
Replace batteries.                                     Replace bulb.
        ↓                                                      ↓
Result:                                                Result:
Flashlight doesn't work.                               Flashlight works.
Hypothesis is contradicted.                            Hypothesis is supported.
```

▲ **Figure 1.22 A simplified view of the scientific process.** The idealized process sometimes called the "scientific method" is shown in this flow chart, using a campground example of hypothesis testing.

making additional observations or by performing experiments. An *experiment* is a scientific test, carried out under controlled conditions.

We all use observations and develop questions and hypotheses in solving everyday problems. Let's say, for example, that your flashlight fails while you are camping. That's an observation. The question is obvious: Why doesn't the flashlight work? Two reasonable hypotheses based on your experience are that (1) the batteries in the flashlight are dead or (2) the bulb is burnt out. Each of these alternative hypotheses leads to predictions you can test with informal experiments. For example, the dead-battery hypothesis predicts that replacing the batteries will fix the problem. **Figure 1.22** diagrams this campground inquiry. Figuring things out like this, by systematic trial and error, is a hypothesis-based approach.

Sometimes we can't carry out an experiment but can test a hypothesis using observations. Let's say you don't have a spare bulb or spare batteries. How could you figure out which hypothesis is more likely? You could examine the bulb and see if it looks burnt out. You could also check the expiration date on the battery. Experiments are great ways to test hypotheses, but when experiments aren't possible, we can often test a hypothesis in other ways.

Deductive Reasoning

A type of logic called deduction is also built into the use of hypotheses in science. While induction entails reasoning from a set of specific observations to reach a general

conclusion, **deductive reasoning** involves logic that flows in the opposite direction, from the general to the specific. From general premises, we extrapolate to the specific results we should expect if the premises are true. In the scientific process, deductions usually take the form of predictions of results that will be found if a particular hypothesis (premise) is correct. We then test the hypothesis by carrying out experiments or observations to see whether or not the results are as predicted. This deductive testing takes the form of "*If . . . then*" logic. In the case of the flashlight example: *If* the dead-battery hypothesis is correct, *then* the flashlight should work if you replace the batteries with new ones.

The flashlight inquiry demonstrates two other key points about the use of hypotheses in science. First, the initial observations may give rise to multiple hypotheses. The ideal plan is to design experiments to test all these candidate explanations. For instance, another of the many possible alternative hypotheses to explain our dead flashlight is that *both* the batteries *and* the bulb are bad, and you could design an experiment to test this.

Second, we can never *prove* that a hypothesis is true. Based on the experiments shown in Figure 1.22, the burnt-out bulb hypothesis stands out as the most likely explanation. The results support that hypothesis but do not absolutely prove it is correct. Perhaps the first bulb was simply loose, so it wasn't making electrical contact, and the new bulb was inserted correctly. We could attempt to test the burnt-out bulb hypothesis again by trying another experiment—removing the original bulb and carefully reinstalling it. If the flashlight still doesn't work, the burnt-out bulb hypothesis is supported by another line of evidence—but still not proven. For example, the bulb may have another defect not related to being burnt out. Testing a hypothesis in various ways, producing different sorts of data, can increase our confidence in it tremendously, but no amount of experimental testing can *prove* a hypothesis beyond a shadow of doubt.

Questions That Can and Cannot Be Addressed by Science

Scientific inquiry is a powerful way to learn about nature, but there are limitations to the kinds of questions it can answer. A scientific hypothesis must be *testable*; there must be some observation or experiment that could reveal if such an idea is likely to be true or false. The hypothesis that dead batteries are the sole cause of the broken flashlight could be (and was) tested by replacing the old batteries with new ones.

Not all hypotheses meet the criteria of science: You wouldn't be able to test the hypothesis that invisible campground ghosts are fooling with your flashlight! Because science only deals with natural, testable explanations for natural phenomena, it can neither support nor contradict the invisible ghost hypothesis, nor whether spirits, elves, or fairies, either benevolent or evil, cause storms, rainbows, illnesses, and cures. Such supernatural explanations, because they cannot be tested, are simply outside the bounds of science. For the same reason, science does not deal with religious matters, which are issues of personal faith. Science and religion are not mutually exclusive or contradictory, they are simply concerned with different issues.

The Flexibility of the Scientific Process

The flashlight example of Figure 1.22 traces an idealized process of inquiry sometimes called *the scientific method.* We can recognize the elements of this process in most of the research articles published by scientists, but rarely in such structured form. Very few scientific inquiries adhere rigidly to the sequence of steps prescribed by the "textbook"

scientific method, which is often applied in hindsight, after the experiment or study is completed. For example, a scientist may start to design an experiment, but then backtrack after realizing that more preliminary observations are necessary. In other cases, puzzling observations simply don't prompt well-defined questions until other research places those observations in a new context. For example, Darwin collected specimens of the Galápagos finches, but it wasn't until years later, as the idea of natural selection began to gel, that biologists began asking key questions about the history of those birds. Science is a lot more unpredictable—and exciting—than lock-step adherence to any five-step method.

A more realistic model of the scientific process is shown in **Figure 1.23.** The core activity (the central circle in the

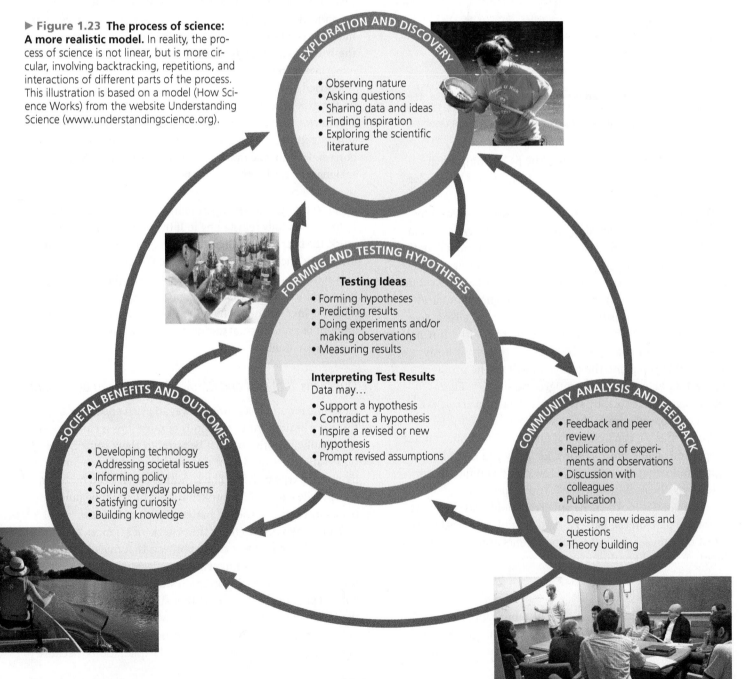

▶ **Figure 1.23 The process of science: A more realistic model.** In reality, the process of science is not linear, but is more circular, involving backtracking, repetitions, and interactions of different parts of the process. This illustration is based on a model (How Science Works) from the website Understanding Science (www.understandingscience.org).

EXPLORATION AND DISCOVERY
- Observing nature
- Asking questions
- Sharing data and ideas
- Finding inspiration
- Exploring the scientific literature

FORMING AND TESTING HYPOTHESES

Testing Ideas
- Forming hypotheses
- Predicting results
- Doing experiments and/or making observations
- Measuring results

Interpreting Test Results
Data may...
- Support a hypothesis
- Contradict a hypothesis
- Inspire a revised or new hypothesis
- Prompt revised assumptions

COMMUNITY ANALYSIS AND FEEDBACK
- Feedback and peer review
- Replication of experiments and observations
- Discussion with colleagues
- Publication
- Devising new ideas and questions
- Theory building

SOCIETAL BENEFITS AND OUTCOMES
- Developing technology
- Addressing societal issues
- Informing policy
- Solving everyday problems
- Satisfying curiosity
- Building knowledge

figure) is the forming and testing of hypotheses. This is the most fundamental aspect of science and is the reason that science does such a reliable job of explaining phenomena in the natural world. However, there is much more to the scientific process than just testing. The choice of ideas to test, the interpretation and evaluation of results, and the decision about which ideas to pursue for further study are influenced by three other arenas as well.

First, well-framed questions, new hypotheses, and good study designs do not spring to life out of thin air; they are inspired and nurtured by the sorts of endeavors associated with exploration and discovery (the upper circle in Figure 1.23). Second, testing is not performed in a social vacuum; community analysis and feedback play an important role (lower right circle). Interactions within the scientific community influence which hypotheses are tested and how, provoke reinterpretations of test results, provide independent assessments of the validity of study designs, and much more. Finally, the process of science is interwoven with the fabric of society (lower left circle). A societal need—for example, to understand the process of climate change—may inspire a flurry of hypotheses and studies. Similarly, well-supported hypotheses may wind up enabling an important technological innovation or encouraging a particular policy, which may, in turn, inspire new scientific questions. Though testing hypotheses and interpreting data are at the heart of science, these pursuits represent only part of the picture.

A Case Study in Scientific Inquiry: Investigating Coat Coloration in Mouse Populations

Now that we have highlighted the key features of scientific inquiry—making observations and forming and testing hypotheses—you should be able to recognize these features in a case study of actual scientific research.

The story begins with a set of observations and inductive generalizations. Color patterns of animals vary widely in nature, sometimes even among members of the same species. What accounts for such variation? An illustrative example is found in two populations of mice that belong to the same species (*Peromyscus polionotus*) but have different color patterns and reside in different environments (Figure 1.24). The beach mouse lives along the Florida seashore, a habitat of brilliant white sand dunes with sparse clumps of beach grass. The inland mouse lives on darker, more fertile soil farther inland. Even a brief glance at the photographs in Figure 1.24 reveals a striking match of mouse coloration to its habitat. The natural predators of these mice, including

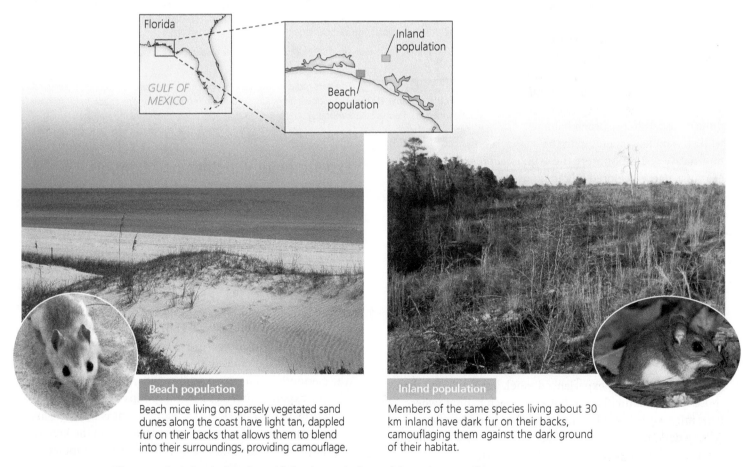

Beach population

Beach mice living on sparsely vegetated sand dunes along the coast have light tan, dappled fur on their backs that allows them to blend into their surroundings, providing camouflage.

Inland population

Members of the same species living about 30 km inland have dark fur on their backs, camouflaging them against the dark ground of their habitat.

▲ Figure 1.24 **Different coloration in beach and inland populations of *Peromyscus polionotus*.**

hawks, owls, foxes, and coyotes, are all visual hunters (they use their eyes to look for prey). It was logical, therefore, for Francis Bertody Sumner, a naturalist studying populations of these mice in the 1920s, to form the hypothesis that their coloration patterns had evolved as adaptations that camouflage the mice in their native environments, protecting them from predation.

As obvious as the camouflage hypothesis may seem, it still required testing. In 2010, biologist Hopi Hoekstra of Harvard University and a group of her students headed to Florida to test the prediction that mice with coloration that did not match their habitat would be preyed on more heavily than the native, well-matched mice. **Figure 1.25** summarizes this field experiment.

The researchers built hundreds of plasticine models of mice and spray-painted them to resemble either beach mice (light colored) or inland mice (darker colored), so that the models differed only in their color patterns. The researchers placed equal numbers of these model mice randomly in both habitats and left them overnight. The mouse models resembling the native mice in the habitat were the *control* group (for instance, light-colored beach mouse models in the beach habitat), while the mouse models with the non-native coloration were the *experimental* group (for example, darker-colored inland mouse models in the beach habitat). The following morning, the team counted and recorded signs of predation events, which ranged from bites and gouge marks on some models to the outright disappearance of others. Judging by the shape of the predator's bites and the tracks surrounding the experimental sites, the predators appeared to be split fairly evenly between mammals (such as foxes and coyotes) and birds (such as owls, herons, and hawks).

For each environment, the researchers then calculated the percentage of predation events that targeted camouflaged mouse models. The results were clear: Camouflaged models experienced much less predation than those lacking camouflage in both the beach habitat (where light mice were less vulnerable) and the inland habitat (where dark mice were less vulnerable). The data thus fit the key prediction of the camouflage hypothesis.

▼ Figure 1.25 | Inquiry

Does camouflage affect predation rates on two populations of mice?

Experiment Hopi Hoekstra and colleagues wanted to test the hypothesis that coloration of beach and inland mice (*Peromyscus polionotus*) provides camouflage that protects them from predation in their respective habitats. The researchers spray-painted mouse models with either light or dark color patterns that matched those of the beach and inland mice and then placed models with both patterns in each of the habitats. The next morning, they counted damaged or missing models.

Results For each habitat, the researchers calculated the percentage of attacked models that were camouflaged or non-camouflaged. In both habitats, the models whose pattern did not match their surroundings suffered much higher "predation" than did the camouflaged models.

Conclusion The results are consistent with the researchers' prediction: that mouse models with camouflage coloration would be preyed on less often than non-camouflaged mouse models. Thus, the experiment supports the camouflage hypothesis.

Source: S. N. Vignieri, J. G. Larson, and H. E. Hoekstra, The selective advantage of crypsis in mice, *Evolution* 64:2153–2158 (2010).

INTERPRET THE DATA *The bars indicate the percentage of the attacked models that were either light or dark. Assume 100 mouse models were attacked in each habitat. For the beach habitat, how many were light models? Dark models? Answer the same questions for the inland habitat.*

Experimental Variables and Controls

Earlier in this section, we described an experiment as a scientific test carried out under controlled conditions. More specifically, an **experiment** involves manipulation of one factor in a system in order to see the effects of changing it. Both the factor that is manipulated and the effects that are measured are types of experimental **variables**—factors that vary in an experiment.

The mouse camouflage experiment described in Figure 1.25 is an example of a **controlled experiment**, one that is designed to compare an experimental group (the non-camouflaged mice, in this case) with a control group (the camouflaged mice normally resident in the area). Ideally, the experimental and control groups are designed to differ only in the one factor the experiment is testing—in our example, the effect of mouse coloration on the behavior of predators. Here, mouse color is the factor manipulated by the researchers; it is called the the **independent variable**. The amount of predation is the **dependent variable**, a factor that is measured in the experiment. Without the control group, the researchers would not have been able to rule out other factors as causes of the more frequent attacks on the non-camouflaged mice—such as different numbers of predators or different temperatures in the different test areas. The clever experimental design left coloration as the only factor that could account for the low predation rate on the camouflaged mice placed in their normal environment.

A common misconception is that the term *controlled experiment* means that scientists control the experimental environment to keep everything strictly constant except the one variable being tested. But that's impossible in field research and not realistic even in highly regulated laboratory environments. Researchers usually "control" unwanted variables not by *eliminating* them through environmental regulation, but by *canceling out* their effects by using control groups.

Theories in Science

Our everyday use of the term *theory* often implies an untested speculation: "It's just a theory!" But the term *theory* has a different meaning in science. What is a scientific theory, and how is it different from a hypothesis or from mere speculation?

First, a scientific **theory** is much broader in scope than a hypothesis. This is a hypothesis: "Fur coloration well-matched to their habitat is an adaptation that protects mice from predators." But *this* is a theory: "Evolutionary adaptations arise by natural selection." This theory proposes that natural selection is the evolutionary mechanism that accounts for an enormous variety of adaptations, of which coat color in mice is but one example.

Second, a theory is general enough to spin off many new, specific hypotheses that can be tested. For example, two researchers at Princeton University, Peter and Rosemary Grant, were motivated by the theory of natural selection to test the specific hypothesis that the beaks of Galápagos finches evolve in response to changes in the types of available food.

And third, compared with any hypothesis, a theory is generally supported by a much greater body of evidence. The theory of natural selection has been supported by a vast quantity of evidence, with more being found every day, and has not been contradicted by any scientific data. Other similarly supported theories include the theory of gravity and the theory that the Earth revolves around the sun. Those theories that become widely adopted in science explain a great range of observations and are supported by a vast accumulation of evidence. In fact, scrutiny of theories continues through testing of the specific hypotheses they generate.

In spite of the body of evidence supporting a widely accepted theory, scientists will modify or even reject theories when new research produces results that don't fit. For example, the theory of biological diversity that lumped bacteria and archaea together as a kingdom of prokaryotes began to erode when new methods for comparing cells and molecules made it possible to test some of the hypothetical relationships between organisms that were based on the theory. If there is "truth" in science, it is at best conditional, based on the preponderance of available evidence.

CONCEPT CHECK 1.3

1. Contrast inductive reasoning with deductive reasoning.
2. In the mouse camouflage experiment, what is the independent variable? The dependent variable? Explain.
3. Why is natural selection called a theory?
4. **WHAT IF?** In the deserts of the southwestern United States, the soils are mostly sandy, with occasional large regions of black rock derived from lava flows that occurred 1.7 million years ago. Mice are found in both sandy and rocky areas, and owls are known predators. What might you expect about coat color in these two mouse populations? Explain. How would you use this ecosystem to further test the camouflage hypothesis?

CONCEPT 1.4

Science benefits from a cooperative approach and diverse viewpoints

Movies and cartoons sometimes portray scientists as loners working in isolated labs. In reality, science is an intensely social activity. Most scientists work in teams, which often include both graduate and undergraduate students. And to succeed in science, it helps to be a good communicator. Research results have no impact until shared with a community of peers through seminars, publications, and websites.

Building on the Work of Others

The great scientist Isaac Newton once said: "To explain all nature is too difficult a task for any one man or even for any one age. 'Tis much better to do a little with certainty, and leave the rest for others that come after you. . . ." Anyone who becomes a scientist, driven by curiosity about how nature works, is sure to benefit greatly from the rich storehouse of discoveries by others who have come before. In fact, Hopi Hoekstra's experiment benefited from the work of another researcher, D. W. Kaufman, 40 years earlier. You

Interpreting a Pair of Bar Graphs

How Much Does Camouflage Affect Predation on Mice by Owls with and without Moonlight? D. W. Kaufman investigated the effect of prey camouflage on predation. Kaufman tested the hypothesis that the amount of contrast between the coat color of a mouse and the color of its surroundings would affect the rate of nighttime predation by owls. He also hypothesized that the color contrast would be affected by the amount of moonlight. In this exercise, you will analyze data from his owl-mouse predation studies.

How the Experiment Was Done Pairs of mice (*Peromyscus polionotus*) with different coat colors, one light brown and one dark brown, were released simultaneously into an enclosure that contained a hungry owl. The researcher recorded the color of the mouse that was first caught by the owl. If the owl did not catch either mouse within 15 minutes, the test was recorded as a zero. The release trials were repeated multiple times in enclosures with either a dark-colored soil surface or a light-colored soil surface. The presence or absence of moonlight during each assay was recorded.

Data from the Experiment

Interpret the Data

1. First, make sure you understand how the graphs are set up. Graph A shows data from the light-colored soil enclosure and graph B from the dark-colored enclosure, but in all other respects the graphs are the same. (a) There is more than one independent variable in these graphs. What are the independent variables, the variables that were tested by the researcher? Which axis of the graphs has the independent variables? (b) What is the dependent variable, the response to the variables being tested? Which axis of the graphs has the dependent variable?

2. (a) How many dark brown mice were caught in the light-colored soil enclosure on a moonlit night? (b) How many dark brown mice were caught in the dark-colored soil enclosure on a moonlit night? (c) On a moonlit night, would a dark brown mouse be more likely to escape predation by owls on dark- or light-colored soil? Explain your answer.

3. (a) Is a dark brown mouse on dark-colored soil more likely to escape predation under a full moon or with no moon? (b) A light brown mouse on light-colored soil? Explain.

4. (a) Under which conditions would a dark brown mouse be most likely to escape predation at night? (b) A light brown mouse?

5. (a) What combination of independent variables led to the highest predation level in enclosures with light-colored soil? (b) What combination of independent variables led to the highest predation level in enclosures with dark-colored soil? (c) What relationship, if any, do you see in your answers to parts (a) and (b)?

6. What conditions are most deadly for both light brown and dark brown mice?

7. Combining the data shown in both graphs, estimate the total number of mice caught in moonlight versus no-moonlight conditions. Which condition is optimal for predation by the owl on mice? Explain your answer.

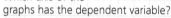 A version of this Scientific Skills Exercise can be assigned in MasteringBiology.

Data from D. W. Kaufman, Adaptive coloration in *Peromyscus polionotus*: Experimental selection by owls, *Journal of Mammalogy* 55:271–283 (1974).

can study the design of Kaufman's experiment and interpret the results in the Scientific Skills Exercise.

Scientific results are continually vetted through the repetition of observations and experiments. Scientists working in the same research field often check one another's claims by attempting to confirm observations or repeat experiments. If experimental results cannot be repeated by scientific colleagues, this failure may reflect some underlying weakness in the original claim, which will then have to be revised. In this sense, science polices itself. Integrity and adherence to high professional standards in reporting results are central to the scientific endeavor. After all, the validity of experimental data is key to designing further lines of inquiry.

It is not unusual for several scientists to converge on the same research question. Some scientists enjoy the challenge of being first with an important discovery or key experiment, while others derive more satisfaction from cooperating with fellow scientists working on the same problem.

Cooperation is facilitated when scientists use the same organism. Often it is a widely used **model organism**—a species that is easy to grow in the lab and lends itself particularly well to the questions being investigated. Because all species are evolutionarily related, such an organism may be viewed as a model for understanding the biology of other species and their diseases. For example, genetic studies of the fruit fly *Drosophila melanogaster* have taught us a lot about how genes work in other species, even humans. Some other popular model organisms are the mustard plant *Arabidopsis thaliana*, the soil worm *Caenorhabditis elegans*, the zebrafish *Danio rerio*, the mouse *Mus musculus*, and the bacterium *Escherichia coli*. As you read through this book, note the many contributions that these and other model organisms have made to the study of life.

Biologists may approach interesting questions from different angles. Some biologists focus on ecosystems, while others study natural phenomena at the level of organisms or cells. This text is divided into units that look at biology at different levels. Yet any given problem can be addressed from many perspectives, which in fact complement each other. For example, Hoekstra's work uncovered at least one genetic mutation that underlies the differences between beach and inland mouse coloration. Her lab includes biologists specializing at different biological levels, allowing links to be made between the evolutionary adaptations she focuses on and their molecular basis in DNA sequences.

As a biology student, you can benefit from making connections between the different levels of biology. You can develop this skill by noticing when certain topics crop up again and again in different units. One such topic is sickle-cell disease, a well-understood genetic condition that is prevalent among native inhabitants of Africa and other warm regions and their descendants. Sickle-cell disease will appear in several units of the text, each time addressed at a new level. In addition, we have designed a number of figures that make connections between the content in different chapters, as well as questions that ask you to make the connections yourselves. We hope these features will help you integrate the material you're learning and enhance your enjoyment of biology by encouraging you to keep the big picture in mind.

Science, Technology, and Society

The research community is part of society at large, and the relationship of science to society becomes clearer when we add technology to the picture (see Figure 1.23). Though science and technology sometimes employ similar inquiry patterns, their basic goals differ. The goal of science is to understand natural phenomena, while that of **technology** is to *apply* scientific knowledge for some specific purpose. Biologists and other scientists usually speak of "discoveries," while engineers and other technologists more often speak of "inventions." Because scientists put new technology to work in their research, science and technology are interdependent.

The potent combination of science and technology can have dramatic effects on society. Sometimes, the applications of basic research that turn out to be the most beneficial come out of the blue, from completely unanticipated observations in the course of scientific exploration. For example, discovery of the structure of DNA by Watson and Crick 60 years ago and subsequent achievements in DNA science led to the technologies of DNA manipulation that are transforming applied fields such as medicine, agriculture, and forensics **(Figure 1.26)**. Perhaps Watson and Crick

▲ **Figure 1.26 DNA technology and crime scene investigation.** In 2011, forensic analysis of DNA samples from a crime scene led to the release of Michael Morton from prison after he had served nearly 25 years for a crime he didn't commit, the brutal murder of his wife. The DNA analysis linked another man, also charged in a second murder, to the crime. The photo shows Mr. Morton hugging his parents after his conviction was overturned.

envisioned that their discovery would someday lead to important applications, but it is unlikely that they could have predicted exactly what all those applications would be.

The directions that technology takes depend less on the curiosity that drives basic science than on the current needs and wants of people and on the social environment of the times. Debates about technology center more on "*should* we do it" than "*can* we do it." With advances in technology come difficult choices. For example, under what circumstances is it acceptable to use DNA technology to find out if particular people have genes for hereditary diseases? Should such tests always be voluntary, or are there circumstances when genetic testing should be mandatory? Should insurance companies or employers have access to the information, as they do for many other types of personal health data? These questions are becoming much more urgent as the sequencing of individual genomes becomes quicker and cheaper.

Ethical issues raised by such questions have as much to do with politics, economics, and cultural values as with science and technology. All citizens—not only professional scientists—have a responsibility to be informed about how science works and about the potential benefits and risks of technology. The relationship between science, technology, and society increases the significance and value of any biology course.

The Value of Diverse Viewpoints in Science

Many of the technological innovations with the most profound impact on human society originated in settlements along trade routes, where a rich mix of different cultures ignited new ideas. For example, the printing press, which helped spread knowledge to all social classes and ultimately led to the book in your hands, was invented by the German

Johannes Gutenberg around 1440. This invention relied on several innovations from China, including paper and ink. Paper traveled along trade routes from China to Baghdad, where technology was developed for its mass production. This technology then migrated to Europe, as did water-based ink from China, which was modified by Gutenberg to become oil-based ink. We have the cross-fertilization of diverse cultures to thank for the printing press, and the same can be said for other important inventions.

Along similar lines, science stands to gain much from embracing a diversity of backgrounds and viewpoints among its practitioners. But just how diverse a population are scientists in relation to gender, race, ethnicity, and other attributes?

The scientific community reflects the cultural standards and behaviors of the society around it. It is therefore not surprising that until recently, women and certain minorities have faced huge obstacles in their pursuit to become professional scientists in many countries around the world. Over the past 50 years, changing attitudes about career choices have increased the proportion of women in biology and some other sciences, so that now women constitute

roughly half of undergraduate biology majors and biology Ph.D. students. The pace has been slow at higher levels in the profession, however, and women and many racial and ethnic groups are still significantly underrepresented in many branches of science. This lack of diversity hampers the progress of science. The more voices that are heard at the table, the more robust, valuable, and productive the scientific interchange will be. The authors of this text welcome all students to the community of biologists, wishing you the joys and satisfactions of this exciting field of science.

CONCEPT CHECK 1.4

1. How does science differ from technology?
2. **MAKE CONNECTIONS** The gene that causes sickle-cell disease is present in a higher percentage of residents of sub-Saharan Africa than among those of African descent living in the United States. This gene provides some protection from malaria, a serious disease that is widespread in sub-Saharan Africa. Discuss an evolutionary process that could account for the different percentages among residents of the two regions. (See Concept 1.2.)

1 Chapter Review

SUMMARY OF KEY CONCEPTS

CONCEPT 1.1

The study of life reveals common themes (pp. 2–9)

Organization Theme: New Properties Emerge at Successive Levels of Biological Organization

- The hierarchy of life unfolds as follows: biosphere > ecosystem > community > population > organism > organ system > organ > tissue > cell > organelle > molecule > atom. With each step upward from atoms, new **emergent properties** result from interactions among components at the lower levels. In an approach called reductionism, complex systems are broken down to simpler components that are more manageable to study. In **systems biology**, scientists attempt to model the dynamic behavior of whole biological systems by studying the interactions among the system's parts.
- The structure and function of biological components are interrelated. The cell, an organism's basic unit of structure and function, is the lowest level of organization that can perform all activities required for life. Cells are either prokaryotic or eukaryotic. **Eukaryotic cells** contain membrane-enclosed organelles, including a DNA-containing nucleus. **Prokaryotic cells** lack membrane-enclosed organelles.

Information Theme: Life's Processes Involve the Expression and Transmission of Genetic Information

- Genetic information is encoded in the nucleotide sequences of **DNA**. It is DNA that transmits heritable information from parents to offspring. DNA sequences called **genes** program a cell's protein production by being transcribed into mRNAs and then translated into specific proteins, a process called **gene expression**. Gene expression also results in RNAs that are not translated into protein but serve other important functions. **Genomics** is the large-scale analysis of the DNA sequences of a species (its **genome**) as well as the comparison of genomes between species. **Bioinformatics** uses computational tools to deal with huge volumes of sequence data.

Energy and Matter Theme: Life Requires the Transfer and Transformation of Energy and Matter

- Energy flows through an ecosystem. All organisms must perform work, which requires energy. Producers convert energy from sunlight to chemical energy, some of which is then passed on to consumers. (The rest is lost as heat energy.) Chemicals cycle between organisms and the environment.

Interactions Theme: From Ecosystems to Molecules, Interactions Are Important in Biological Systems

- Organisms interact continuously with physical factors. Plants take up nutrients from the soil and chemicals from the air and use energy from the sun. Interactions among plants, animals, and other organisms affect the participants in various ways.

- In **feedback regulation,** a process is regulated by its output or end product. In negative feedback, accumulation of the end product slows its production. In positive feedback, an end product speeds up its own production. Feedback is a type of regulation common to life at all levels, from molecules to ecosystems.

Evolution, the Core Theme of Biology

- **Evolution**, the process of change that has transformed life on Earth, accounts for the unity and diversity of life. It also explains evolutionary adaptation— the match of organisms to their environments.

? *Why is evolution considered the core theme of biology?*

CONCEPT 1.2

The Core Theme: Evolution accounts for the unity and diversity of life (pp. 10–15)

- Biologists classify species according to a system of broader and broader groups. Domain **Bacteria** and domain **Archaea** consist of prokaryotes. Domain **Eukarya**, the eukaryotes, includes various groups of protists and the kingdoms Plantae, Fungi, and Animalia. As diverse as life is, there is also evidence of remarkable unity, which is revealed in the similarities between different kinds of organisms.
- Darwin proposed **natural selection** as the mechanism for evolutionary adaptation of populations to their environments.

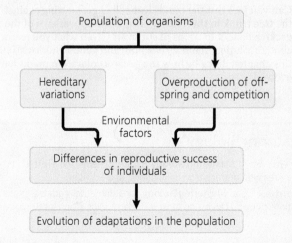

- Each species is one twig of a branching tree of life extending back in time through ancestral species more and more remote. All of life is connected through its long evolutionary history.

? *How could natural selection have led to the evolution of adaptations such as the parachute-like structure carrying a seed shown on the first page of this chapter?*

CONCEPT 1.3

In studying nature, scientists make observations and form and test hypotheses (pp. 16–21)

- In scientific **inquiry**, scientists make observations (collect **data**) and use **inductive reasoning** to draw a general conclusion, which can be developed into a testable **hypothesis**. **Deductive reasoning** makes predictions that can be used to test hypotheses. Hypotheses must be testable; science can address neither the possibility of supernatural phenomena nor the validity of religious beliefs. Hypotheses can be tested by experimentation or, when that is not possible, by making observations. In the process of science, the core activity is testing ideas. This endeavor is influenced by three arenas: exploration and discovery, community analysis and feedback, and societal benefits and outcomes. Testing ideas, in turn, affects each of these three pursuits as well.
- **Controlled experiments**, such as the study investigating coat coloration in mouse populations, are designed to demonstrate the effect of one variable by testing control groups and experimental groups that differ in only that one variable.
- A scientific **theory** is broad in scope, generates new hypotheses, and is supported by a large body of evidence.

? *What are the roles of gathering and interpreting data in the process of scientific inquiry?*

CONCEPT 1.4

Science benefits from a cooperative approach and diverse viewpoints (pp. 21–24)

- Science is a social activity. The work of each scientist builds on the work of others that have come before. Scientists must be able to repeat each other's results, so integrity is key. Biologists approach questions at different levels; their approaches complement each other.
- **Technology** consists of any method or device that applies scientific knowledge for some specific purpose that affects society. The ultimate impact of basic research is not always immediately obvious.
- Diversity among scientists promotes progress in science.

? *Explain why different approaches and diverse backgrounds among scientists are important.*

TEST YOUR UNDERSTANDING

LEVEL 1: KNOWLEDGE/COMPREHENSION

1. All the organisms on your campus make up
   a. an ecosystem.
   b. a community.
   c. a population.
   d. a taxonomic domain.

2. Which of the following is a correct sequence of levels in life's hierarchy, proceeding downward from an individual animal?
   a. organism, brain, organ system, nerve cell
   b. organ system, nervous tissue, brain, nerve cell
   c. organism, organ system, tissue, cell, organ
   d. nervous system, brain, nervous tissue, nerve cell

3. Which of the following is *not* an observation or inference on which Darwin's theory of natural selection is based?
   a. Poorly adapted individuals never produce offspring.
   b. There is heritable variation among individuals.
   c. Because of overproduction of offspring, there is competition for limited resources.
   d. A population can become adapted to its environment over time.

4. Systems biology is mainly an attempt to
   a. analyze genomes from different species.
   b. simplify complex problems by reducing the system into smaller, less complex units.
   c. understand the behavior of entire biological systems by studying interactions among its component parts.
   d. build high-throughput machines for the rapid acquisition of biological data.

5. Protists and bacteria are grouped into different domains because
   a. protists eat bacteria.
   b. bacteria are not made of cells.
   c. protists have a membrane-bounded nucleus.
   d. protists are photosynthetic.

6. Which of the following best demonstrates the unity among all organisms?
   a. emergent properties
   b. descent with modification
   c. the structure and function of DNA
   d. natural selection

7. A controlled experiment is one that
   a. proceeds slowly enough that a scientist can make careful records of the results.
   b. tests experimental and control groups in parallel.
   c. is repeated many times to make sure the results are accurate.
   d. keeps all variables constant.

8. Which of the following statements best distinguishes hypotheses from theories in science?
   a. Theories are hypotheses that have been proved.
   b. Hypotheses are guesses; theories are correct answers.
   c. Hypotheses usually are relatively narrow in scope; theories have broad explanatory power.
   d. Theories are proved true; hypotheses are often contradicted by experimental results.

LEVEL 2: APPLICATION/ANALYSIS

9. Which of the following is an example of qualitative data?
   a. The fish swam in a zigzag motion.
   b. The contents of the stomach are mixed every 20 seconds.
   c. The temperature decreased from 20°C to 15°C.
   d. The six pairs of robins hatched an average of three chicks each.

10. Which of the following best describes the logic of scientific inquiry?
    a. If I generate a testable hypothesis, tests and observations will support it.
    b. If my prediction is correct, it will lead to a testable hypothesis.
    c. If my observations are accurate, they will support my hypothesis.
    d. If my hypothesis is correct, I can expect certain test results.

11. DRAW IT With rough sketches, draw a biological hierarchy similar to the one in Figure 1.3 but using a coral reef as the ecosystem, a fish as the organism, its stomach as the organ, and DNA as the molecule. Include all levels in the hierarchy.

LEVEL 3: SYNTHESIS/EVALUATION

12. EVOLUTION CONNECTION
    A typical prokaryotic cell has about 3,000 genes in its DNA, while a human cell has almost 21,000 genes. About 1,000 of these genes are present in both types of cells. Based on your understanding of evolution, explain how such different organisms could have this same subset of 1,000 genes. What sorts of functions might these shared genes have?

13. SCIENTIFIC INQUIRY
    Based on the results of the mouse coloration case study, suggest another hypothesis researchers might use to further study the role of predators in the natural selection process.

14. WRITE ABOUT A THEME: EVOLUTION
    In a short essay (100–150 words), discuss Darwin's view of how natural selection resulted in both unity and diversity of life on Earth. Include in your discussion some of his evidence. (See a suggested grading rubric and tips for writing good essays in the Study Area of MasteringBiology under "Write About a Theme.")

15. SYNTHESIZE YOUR KNOWLEDGE

Can you pick out the mossy leaf-tailed gecko lying against the tree trunk in this photo? How is the appearance of the gecko a benefit in terms of survival? Given what you learned about evolution, natural selection, and genetic information in this chapter, describe how the gecko's coloration might have evolved.

MasteringBiology®

Students Go to **MasteringBiology** for assignments, the eText, and the Study Area with practice tests, animations, and activities.

Instructors Go to **MasteringBiology** for automatically graded tutorials and questions that you can assign to your students, plus Instructor Resources.

2

The Chemical Context of Life

▲ Figure 2.1 **What weapon are these wood ants shooting into the air?**

A Chemical Connection to Biology

Like other animals, ants have structures and mechanisms that defend them from attack. Wood ants live in colonies of hundreds or thousands, and the colony as a whole has a particularly effective mechanism for dealing with enemies. When threatened, the ants shoot volleys of formic acid into the air from their abdomens, and the acid rains down upon the potential invaders (**Figure 2.1**). This substance is produced by many species of ants and in fact got its name from the Latin word for ant, *formica*. For quite a few ant species, the formic acid isn't shot out, but probably serves as a disinfectant that protects the ants against microbial parasites. Scientists have long known that chemicals play a major role in insect communication, the attraction of mates, and defense against predators.

Research on ants and other insects is a good example of how relevant chemistry is to the study of life. Unlike college courses, nature is not neatly packaged into individual sciences—biology, chemistry, physics, and so forth. Biologists specialize in the study of life, but organisms and their environments are natural systems to which the concepts of chemistry and physics apply. Biology is multidisciplinary.

This unit of chapters introduces some basic concepts of chemistry that apply to the study of life. Somewhere in the transition from molecules to cells, we will cross the blurry boundary between nonlife and life. This chapter focuses on the chemical components that make up all matter.

Matter consists of chemical elements in pure form and in combinations called compounds

Organisms are composed of **matter**, which is anything that takes up space and has mass.* Matter exists in many forms. Rocks, metals, oils, gases, and living organisms are a few examples of what seems to be an endless assortment of matter.

Elements and Compounds

Matter is made up of elements. An **element** is a substance that cannot be broken down to other substances by chemical reactions. Today, chemists recognize 92 elements occurring in nature; gold, copper, carbon, and oxygen are examples. Each element has a symbol, usually the first letter or two of its name. Some symbols are derived from Latin or German; for instance, the symbol for sodium is Na, from the Latin word *natrium.*

A **compound** is a substance consisting of two or more different elements combined in a fixed ratio. Table salt, for example, is sodium chloride (NaCl), a compound composed of the elements sodium (Na) and chlorine (Cl) in a 1:1 ratio. Pure sodium is a metal, and pure chlorine is a poisonous gas. When chemically combined, however, sodium and chlorine form an edible compound. Water (H_2O), another compound, consists of the elements hydrogen (H) and oxygen (O) in a 2:1 ratio. These are simple examples of organized matter having emergent properties: A compound has characteristics different from those of its elements **(Figure 2.2)**.

Sodium **Chlorine** **Sodium chloride**

▲ **Figure 2.2 The emergent properties of a compound.** The metal sodium combines with the poisonous gas chlorine, forming the edible compound sodium chloride, or table salt.

---

*In everyday language we tend to substitute the term weight for mass, although the two are not identical. Mass is the amount of matter in an object, whereas the weight of an object is how strongly that mass is pulled by gravity. The weight of an astronaut walking on the moon is approximately ⅙ the astronaut's weight on Earth, but his or her mass is the same. However, as long as we are earthbound, the weight of an object is a measure of its mass; in everyday language, therefore, we tend to use the terms interchangeably.

The Elements of Life

Of the 92 natural elements, about 20–25% are **essential elements** that an organism needs to live a healthy life and reproduce. The essential elements are similar among organisms, but there is some variation—for example, humans need 25 elements, but plants need only 17.

Just four elements—oxygen (O), carbon (C), hydrogen (H), and nitrogen (N)—make up 96% of living matter. Calcium (Ca), phosphorus (P), potassium (K), sulfur (S), and a few other elements account for most of the remaining 4% of an organism's mass. **Trace elements** are required by an organism in only minute quantities. Some trace elements, such as iron (Fe), are needed by all forms of life; others are required only by certain species. For example, in vertebrates (animals with backbones), the element iodine (I) is an essential ingredient of a hormone produced by the thyroid gland. A daily intake of only 0.15 milligram (mg) of iodine is adequate for normal activity of the human thyroid. An iodine deficiency in the diet causes the thyroid gland to grow to abnormal size, a condition called goiter. Where it is available, eating seafood or iodized salt reduces the incidence of goiter. All the elements needed by the human body are listed in **Table 2.1**.

Some naturally occurring elements are toxic to organisms. In humans, for instance, the element arsenic has been linked to numerous diseases and can be lethal. In some areas of the world, arsenic occurs naturally and can make its way into the groundwater. As a result of using water from drilled

Table 2.1 Elements in the Human Body

Element	Symbol	Percentage of Body Mass (including water)	
Oxygen	O	65.0%	
Carbon	C	18.5%	96.3%
Hydrogen	H	9.5%	
Nitrogen	N	3.3%	
Calcium	Ca	1.5%	
Phosphorus	P	1.0%	
Potassium	K	0.4%	
Sulfur	S	0.3%	3.7%
Sodium	Na	0.2%	
Chlorine	Cl	0.2%	
Magnesium	Mg	0.1%	

Trace elements (less than 0.01% of mass): Boron (B), chromium (Cr), cobalt (Co), copper (Cu), fluorine (F), iodine (I), iron (Fe), manganese (Mn), molybdenum (Mo), selenium (Se), silicon (Si), tin (Sn), vanadium (V), zinc (Zn)

INTERPRET THE DATA *Given what you know about the human body, what do you think could account for the high percentage of oxygen (65.0%)?*

▲ Figure 2.3 Serpentine plant community.
These plants are growing on serpentine soil, which contains elements that are usually toxic to plants. The insets show a close-up of serpentine rock and one of the plants, a Tiburon Mariposa lily.

wells in southern Asia, millions of people have been inadvertently exposed to arsenic-laden water. Efforts are under way to reduce arsenic levels in their water supply.

Case Study: Evolution of Tolerance to Toxic Elements

EVOLUTION   Some species have become adapted to environments containing elements that are usually toxic; an example is serpentine plant communities. Serpentine is a jade-like mineral that contains elevated concentrations of elements such as chromium, nickel, and cobalt. Although most plants cannot survive in soil that forms from serpentine rock, a small number of plant species have adaptations that allow them to do so (**Figure 2.3**). Presumably, variants of ancestral, nonserpentine species arose that could survive in serpentine soils, and subsequent natural selection resulted in the distinctive array of species we see in these areas today. Researchers are studying whether serpentine-adapted plants could take up toxic heavy metals in contaminated areas, concentrating them for safer disposal.

CONCEPT CHECK 2.1

1. **MAKE CONNECTIONS** Explain how table salt has emergent properties. (See Concept 1.1.)

2. Is a trace element an essential element? Explain.

3. **WHAT IF?** In humans, iron is a trace element required for the proper functioning of hemoglobin, the molecule that carries oxygen in red blood cells. What might be the effects of an iron deficiency?

4. **MAKE CONNECTIONS** Explain how natural selection might have played a role in the evolution of species that are tolerant of serpentine soils. (Review Concept 1.2.)

An element's properties depend on the structure of its atoms

Each element consists of a certain type of atom that is different from the atoms of any other element. An **atom** is the smallest unit of matter that still retains the properties of an element. Atoms are so small that it would take about a million of them to stretch across the period printed at the end of this sentence. We symbolize atoms with the same abbreviation used for the element that is made up of those atoms. For example, the symbol C stands for both the element carbon and a single carbon atom.

Subatomic Particles

Although the atom is the smallest unit having the properties of an element, these tiny bits of matter are composed of even smaller parts, called *subatomic particles.* Using high-energy collisions, physicists have produced more than a hundred types of particles from the atom, but only three kinds of particles are relevant here: **neutrons**, **protons**, and **electrons**. Protons and electrons are electrically charged. Each proton has one unit of positive charge, and each electron has one unit of negative charge. A neutron, as its name implies, is electrically neutral.

Protons and neutrons are packed together tightly in a dense core, or **atomic nucleus,** at the center of an atom; protons give the nucleus a positive charge. The rapidly moving electrons form a "cloud" of negative charge around the nucleus, and it is the attraction between opposite charges that keeps the electrons in the vicinity of the nucleus. **Figure 2.4**

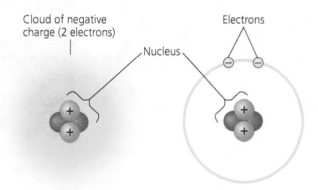

(a) This model represents the two electrons as a cloud of negative charge.

(b) In this more simplified model, the electrons are shown as two small yellow spheres on a circle around the nucleus.

▲ Figure 2.4 Simplified models of a helium (He) atom. The helium nucleus consists of 2 neutrons (brown) and 2 protons (pink). Two electrons (yellow) exist outside the nucleus. These models are not to scale; they greatly overestimate the size of the nucleus in relation to the electron cloud.

shows two commonly used models of the structure of the helium atom as an example.

The neutron and proton are almost identical in mass, each about 1.7×10^{-24} gram (g). Grams and other conventional units are not very useful for describing the mass of objects that are so minuscule. Thus, for atoms and subatomic particles (and for molecules, too), we use a unit of measurement called the **dalton**, in honor of John Dalton, the British scientist who helped develop atomic theory around 1800. (The dalton is the same as the *atomic mass unit*, or *amu*, a unit you may have encountered elsewhere.) Neutrons and protons have masses close to 1 dalton. Because the mass of an electron is only about 1/2,000 that of a neutron or proton, we can ignore electrons when computing the total mass of an atom.

Atomic Number and Atomic Mass

Atoms of the various elements differ in their number of subatomic particles. All atoms of a particular element have the same number of protons in their nuclei. This number of protons, which is unique to that element, is called the **atomic number** and is written as a subscript to the left of the symbol for the element. The abbreviation $_2\text{He}$, for example, tells us that an atom of the element helium has 2 protons in its nucleus. Unless otherwise indicated, an atom is neutral in electrical charge, which means that its protons must be balanced by an equal number of electrons. Therefore, the atomic number tells us the number of protons and also the number of electrons in an electrically neutral atom.

We can deduce the number of neutrons from a second quantity, the **mass number**, which is the sum of protons plus neutrons in the nucleus of an atom. The mass number is written as a superscript to the left of an element's symbol. For example, we can use this shorthand to write an atom of helium as $_2^4\text{He}$. Because the atomic number indicates how many protons there are, we can determine the number of neutrons by subtracting the atomic number from the mass number. Accordingly, the helium atom $_2^4\text{He}$ has 2 neutrons. For sodium (Na):

Mass number = number of protons + neutrons
= 23 for sodium

$_{11}^{23}\text{Na}$

Atomic number = number of protons
= number of electrons in a neutral atom
= 11 for sodium

Number of neutrons = mass number − atomic number
= 23 − 11 = 12 for sodium

The simplest atom is hydrogen $_1^1\text{H}$, which has no neutrons; it consists of a single proton with a single electron.

Because the contribution of electrons to mass is negligible, almost all of an atom's mass is concentrated in its nucleus. And since neutrons and protons each have a mass very close to 1 dalton, the mass number is an approximation of the total mass of an atom, called its **atomic mass**. So we might say that the atomic mass of sodium ($_{11}^{23}\text{Na}$) is 23 daltons, although more precisely it is 22.9898 daltons.

Isotopes

All atoms of a given element have the same number of protons, but some atoms have more neutrons than other atoms of the same element and therefore have greater mass. These different atomic forms of the same element are called **isotopes** of the element. In nature, an element occurs as a mixture of its isotopes. As an explanatory example, let's consider the three naturally occurring isotopes of the element carbon, which has the atomic number 6. The most common isotope is carbon-12, $_6^{12}\text{C}$, which accounts for about 99% of the carbon in nature. The isotope $_6^{12}\text{C}$ has 6 neutrons. Most of the remaining 1% of carbon consists of atoms of the isotope $_6^{13}\text{C}$, with 7 neutrons. A third, even rarer isotope, $_6^{14}\text{C}$, has 8 neutrons. Notice that all three isotopes of carbon have 6 protons; otherwise, they would not be carbon. Although the isotopes of an element have slightly different masses, they behave identically in chemical reactions. (The number usually given as the atomic mass of an element, such as 12.01 daltons for carbon, is actually an average of the atomic masses of all the element's naturally occurring isotopes, weighted according to the abundance of each.)

Both ^{12}C and ^{13}C are stable isotopes, meaning that their nuclei do not have a tendency to lose subatomic particles, a process called decay. The isotope ^{14}C, however, is unstable, or radioactive. A **radioactive isotope** is one in which the nucleus decays spontaneously, giving off particles and energy. When the radioactive decay leads to a change in the number of protons, it transforms the atom to an atom of a different element. For example, when an atom of carbon-14 (^{14}C) decays, it becomes an atom of nitrogen (^{14}N). Radioactive isotopes have many useful applications in biology.

Radioactive Tracers

Radioactive isotopes are often used as diagnostic tools in medicine. Cells can use radioactive atoms just as they would use nonradioactive isotopes of the same element. The radioactive isotopes are incorporated into biologically active molecules, which are then used as tracers to track atoms during metabolism, the chemical processes of an organism. For example, certain kidney disorders are diagnosed by injecting small doses of radioactively-labeled substances into the blood and then analyzing the tracer molecules excreted in the urine. Radioactive tracers are also used in combination with sophisticated imaging instruments, such as PET

◀ **Figure 2.5 A PET scan, a medical use for radioactive isotopes.** PET, an acronym for positron-emission tomography, detects locations of intense chemical activity in the body. The bright yellow spot marks an area with an elevated level of radioactively labeled glucose, which in turn indicates high metabolic activity, a hallmark of cancerous tissue.

Cancerous throat tissue

scanners that can monitor growth and metabolism of cancers in the body (**Figure 2.5**).

Although radioactive isotopes are very useful in biological research and medicine, radiation from decaying isotopes also poses a hazard to life by damaging cellular molecules. The severity of this damage depends on the type and amount of radiation an organism absorbs. One of the most serious environmental threats is radioactive fallout from nuclear accidents. The doses of most isotopes used in medical diagnosis, however, are relatively safe.

Radiometric Dating

EVOLUTION Researchers measure radioactive decay in fossils to date these relics of past life. Fossils provide a large body of evidence for evolution, documenting differences between organisms from the past and those living at present and giving us insight into species that have disappeared over time. While the layering of fossil beds establishes that deeper fossils are older than more shallow ones, the actual age (in years) of the fossils in each layer cannot be determined by position alone. This is where radioactive isotopes come in.

A "parent" isotope decays into its "daughter" isotope at a fixed rate, expressed as the **half-life** of the isotope—the time it takes for 50% of the parent isotope to decay. Each radioactive isotope has a characteristic half-life that is not affected by temperature, pressure, or any other environmental variable. Using a process called **radiometric dating**, scientists measure the ratio of different isotopes and calculate how many half-lives (in years) have passed since an organism was fossilized or a rock was formed. Half-life values range from very short for some isotopes, measured in seconds or days, to extremely long—uranium-238 has a half-life of 4.5 billion years! Each isotope can best "measure" a particular range of years: Uranium 238 was used to determine that moon rocks are approximately 4.5 billion years old, similar to the estimated age of Earth. In the Scientific Skills Exercise, you can work with data from an experiment that used carbon-14 to determine the age of an important fossil.

The Energy Levels of Electrons

The simplified models of the atom in Figure 2.4 greatly exaggerate the size of the nucleus relative to that of the whole atom. If an atom of helium were the size of a typical football stadium, the nucleus would be the size of a pencil eraser in the center of the field. Moreover, the electrons would be like two tiny gnats buzzing around the stadium. Atoms are mostly empty space. When two atoms approach each other during a chemical reaction, their nuclei do not come close enough to interact. Of the three subatomic particles we have discussed, only electrons are directly involved in chemical reactions.

An atom's electrons vary in the amount of energy they possess. **Energy** is defined as the capacity to cause change—for instance, by doing work. **Potential energy** is the energy that matter possesses because of its location or structure. For example, water in a reservoir on a hill has potential energy because of its altitude. When the gates of the reservoir's dam are opened and the water runs downhill, the energy can be used to do work, such as moving the blades of turbines to generate electricity. Because energy has been expended, the water has less energy at the bottom of the hill than it did in the reservoir. Matter has a natural tendency to move toward the lowest possible state of potential energy; in our example, the water runs downhill. To restore the potential energy of a reservoir, work must be done to elevate the water against gravity.

The electrons of an atom have potential energy due to their distance from the nucleus (**Figure 2.6**). The negatively

(a) A ball bouncing down a flight of stairs provides an analogy for energy levels of electrons, because the ball can come to rest only on each step, not between steps.

Third shell (highest energy level in this model)

Second shell (next highest energy level)

First shell (lowest energy level)

Energy absorbed

Energy lost

Atomic nucleus

(b) An electron can move from one shell to another only if the energy it gains or loses is exactly equal to the difference in energy between the energy levels of the two shells. Arrows in this model indicate some of the stepwise changes in potential energy that are possible.

▲ **Figure 2.6 Energy levels of an atom's electrons.** Electrons exist only at fixed levels of potential energy called electron shells.

Calibrating a Standard Radioactive Isotope Decay Curve and Interpreting Data

When Did Neanderthals Become Extinct? Neanderthals (*Homo neanderthalensis*) were living in Europe by 350,000 years ago, perhaps coexisting with early *Homo sapiens* in parts of Eurasia for hundreds or thousands of years. Researchers sought to more accurately determine the extent of their overlap by pinning down when Neanderthals became extinct. They used carbon-14 dating to determine the age of a Neanderthal fossil from the most recent (uppermost) archeological layer containing Neanderthal bones. In this exercise you will calibrate a standard carbon-14 decay curve and use it to determine the age of this Neanderthal fossil. The age will help you approximate the last time the two species may have coexisted at the site where this fossil was collected.

How the Experiment Was Done Carbon-14 (^{14}C) is a radioactive isotope of carbon that decays to ^{14}N at a constant rate. ^{14}C is present in the atmosphere in small amounts at a constant ratio with both ^{13}C and ^{12}C, two other isotopes of carbon. When carbon is taken up from the atmosphere by a plant during photosynthesis, ^{12}C, ^{13}C, and ^{14}C isotopes are incorporated into the plant in the same proportions in which they were present in the atmosphere. These proportions remain the same in the tissues of an animal that eats the plant. While an organism is alive, the ^{14}C in its body constantly decays to ^{14}N but is constantly replaced by new carbon from the environment. Once an organism dies, it stops taking in new ^{14}C but the ^{14}C in its tissues continues to decay, while the ^{12}C in its tissues remains the same because it is not radioactive and does not decay. Thus, scientists can calculate how long the pool of original ^{14}C has been decaying in a fossil by measuring the ratio of ^{14}C to ^{12}C and comparing it to the ratio of ^{14}C to ^{12}C present originally in the atmosphere. The fraction of ^{14}C in a fossil compared to the original fraction of ^{14}C can be converted to years because we know that the half-life of ^{14}C is 5,730 years—in other words, half of the ^{14}C in a fossil decays every 5,730 years.

Data from the Experiment The researchers found that the Neanderthal fossil had approximately 0.0078 (or, in scientific notation, 7.8×10^{-3}) as much ^{14}C as the atmosphere. The questions will guide you through translating this fraction into the age of the fossil.

Interpret the Data

1. A standard graph of radioactive isotope decay is shown at the top of the right column. The graph line shows the fraction of the radioactive isotope over time (before present) in units of half-lives. Recall that a half-life is the amount of time it takes for half of the radioactive isotope to decay. Labeling each data point with the corresponding fractions will help orient you to this graph. Draw an arrow to the data point for half-life = 1 and write the fraction of ^{14}C that will remain after one half-life. Calculate the fraction of ^{14}C remaining at each half-life and write the fractions on the graph near arrows pointing to the data points. Convert each fraction to a decimal number and round off to a maximum of three significant digits (zeros at the

Neanderthal fossils

Fraction of isotope remaining in fossil (y-axis: 0 to 1.0) vs. *Time before present (half-lives)* (x-axis: 0 to 10)

beginning of the number do not count as significant digits). Also write each decimal number in scientific notation.

2. Recall that ^{14}C has a half-life of 5,730 years. To calibrate the x-axis for ^{14}C decay, write the time before present in years below each half-life.

3. The researchers found that the Neanderthal fossil had approximately 0.0078 as much ^{14}C as found originally in the atmosphere. (a) Using the numbers on your graph, determine how many half-lives have passed since the Neanderthal died. (b) Using your ^{14}C calibration on the x-axis, what is the approximate age of the Neanderthal fossil in years (round off to the nearest thousand)? (c) Approximately when did Neanderthals become extinct according to this study? (d) The researchers cite evidence that modern humans (*H. sapiens*) became established in the same region as the last Neanderthals approximately 39,000–42,000 years ago. What does this suggest about the overlap of Neanderthals and modern humans?

4. Carbon-14 dating works for fossils up to about 75,000 years old; fossils older than that contain too little ^{14}C to be detected. Most dinosaurs went extinct 65.5 million years ago. (a) Can ^{14}C be used to date dinosaur bones? Explain. (b) Radioactive uranium-235 has a half-life of 704 million years. If it was incorporated into dinosaur bones, could it be used to date the dinosaur fossils? Explain.

(MB) A version of this Scientific Skills Exercise can be assigned in MasteringBiology.

Data from R. Pinhasi et al., Revised age of late Neanderthal occupation and the end of the Middle Paleolithic in the northern Caucasus, *Proceedings of the National Academy of Sciences USA* 147:8611–8616 (2011). doi 10.1073/pnas.1018938108

charged electrons are attracted to the positively charged nucleus. It takes work to move a given electron farther away from the nucleus, so the more distant an electron is from the nucleus, the greater its potential energy. Unlike the continuous flow of water downhill, changes in the potential energy of electrons can occur only in steps of fixed amounts. An electron having a certain amount of energy is something like a ball on a staircase (**Figure 2.6a**). The ball can have different amounts of potential energy, depending on which step it is on, but it cannot spend much time between the steps.

Similarly, an electron's potential energy is determined by its energy level. An electron can exist only at certain energy levels, not between them.

An electron's energy level is correlated with its average distance from the nucleus. Electrons are found in different **electron shells**, each with a characteristic average distance and energy level. In diagrams, shells can be represented by concentric circles (**Figure 2.6b**). The first shell is closest to the nucleus, and electrons in this shell have the lowest potential energy. Electrons in the second shell have more energy, and electrons in the third shell even more energy. An electron can move from one shell to another, but only by absorbing or losing an amount of energy equal to the difference in potential energy between its position in the old shell and that in the new shell. When an electron absorbs energy, it moves to a shell farther out from the nucleus. For example, light energy can excite an electron to a higher energy level. (Indeed, this is the first step taken when plants harness the energy of sunlight for photosynthesis, the process that produces food from carbon dioxide and water. You'll learn more about photosynthesis in Chapter 11.) When an electron loses energy, it "falls back" to a shell closer to the nucleus, and the lost energy is usually released to the environment as heat. For example, sunlight excites electrons in the surface of a car to higher energy levels. When the electrons fall back to their original levels, the car's surface heats up. This thermal energy can be transferred to the air or to your hand if you touch the car.

Electron Distribution and Chemical Properties

The chemical behavior of an atom is determined by the distribution of electrons in the atom's electron shells. Beginning with hydrogen, the simplest atom, we can imagine building the atoms of the other elements by adding 1 proton and 1 electron at a time (along with an appropriate number of neutrons). **Figure 2.7**, an abbreviated version of what is called the *periodic table of the elements*, shows this distribution of electrons for the first 18 elements, from hydrogen ($_1$H) to argon ($_{18}$Ar). The elements are arranged in three rows, or *periods*, corresponding to the number of electron shells in their atoms. The left-to-right sequence of elements in each row corresponds to the sequential addition of electrons and protons.

Hydrogen's 1 electron and helium's 2 electrons are located in the first shell. Electrons, like all matter, tend to exist in the lowest available state of potential energy. In an atom, this state is in the first shell. However, the first shell can hold no more than 2 electrons; thus, hydrogen and helium are the only elements in the first row of the table. In an atom with more than 2 electrons, the additional electrons must occupy higher shells because the first shell is full. The next element, lithium, has 3 electrons. Two of these electrons fill the first shell, while the third electron occupies the second shell. The second shell holds a maximum of 8 electrons. Neon, at the

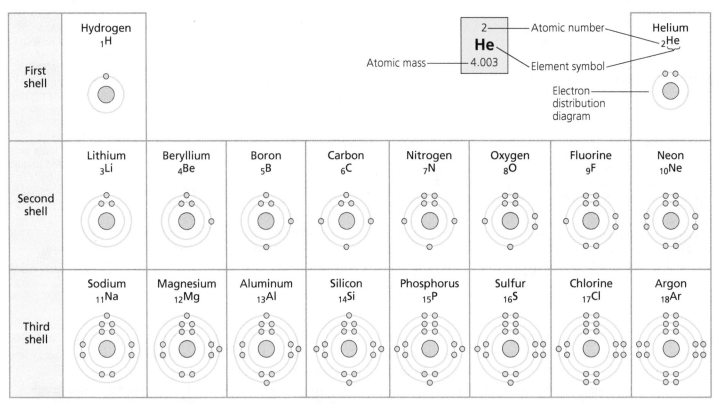

▲ **Figure 2.7 Electron distribution diagrams for the first 18 elements in the periodic table.** In a standard periodic table, information for each element is presented as shown for helium in the inset. In the diagrams in this table, electrons are represented as yellow dots and electron shells as concentric circles. These diagrams are a convenient way to picture the distribution of an atom's electrons among its electron shells, but these simplified models do not accurately represent the shape of the atom or the location of its electrons. The elements are arranged in rows, each representing the filling of an electron shell. As electrons are added, they occupy the lowest available shell.

[?] *What is the atomic number of magnesium? How many protons and electrons does it have? How many electron shells? How many valence electrons?*

end of the second row, has 8 electrons in the second shell, giving it a total of 10 electrons.

The chemical behavior of an atom depends mostly on the number of electrons in its *outermost* shell. We call those outer electrons **valence electrons** and the outermost electron shell the **valence shell**. In the case of lithium, there is only 1 valence electron, and the second shell is the valence shell. Atoms with the same number of electrons in their valence shells exhibit similar chemical behavior. For example, fluorine (F) and chlorine (Cl) both have 7 valence electrons, and both form compounds when combined with the element sodium (Na): Sodium fluoride (NaF) is commonly added to toothpaste to prevent tooth decay, and, as described earlier, NaCl is table salt (see Figure 2.2). An atom with a completed valence shell is unreactive; that is, it will not interact readily with other atoms. At the far right of the periodic table are helium, neon, and argon, the only three elements shown in Figure 2.7 that have full valence shells. These elements are said to be *inert*, meaning chemically unreactive. All the other atoms in Figure 2.7 are chemically reactive because they have incomplete valence shells.

Electron Orbitals

In the early 1900s, the electron shells of an atom were visualized as concentric paths of electrons orbiting the nucleus, somewhat like planets orbiting the sun. It is still convenient to use two-dimensional concentric-circle diagrams, as in Figure 2.7, to symbolize three-dimensional electron shells. However, you need to remember that each concentric circle represents only the *average* distance between an electron in that shell and the nucleus. Accordingly, the concentric-circle diagrams do not give a real picture of an atom. In reality, we can never know the exact location of an electron. What we can do instead is describe the space in which an electron spends most of its time. The three-dimensional space where an electron is found 90% of the time is called an **orbital**.

Each electron shell contains electrons at a particular energy level, distributed among a specific number of orbitals of distinctive shapes and orientations. **Figure 2.8** shows the orbitals of neon as an example, with its electron distribution diagram for reference. You can think of an orbital as a component of an electron shell. The first electron shell has only one spherical *s* orbital (called 1*s*), but the second shell has four orbitals: one large spherical *s* orbital (called 2*s*) and three dumbbell-shaped *p* orbitals (called 2*p* orbitals). (The third shell and other higher electron shells also have *s* and *p* orbitals, as well as orbitals of more complex shapes.)

No more than 2 electrons can occupy a single orbital. The first electron shell can therefore accommodate up to 2 electrons in its *s* orbital. The lone electron of a hydrogen atom occupies the 1*s* orbital, as do the 2 electrons of a helium atom. The four orbitals of the second electron shell can hold

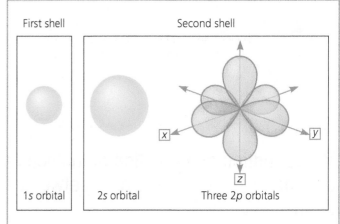

(a) Electron distribution diagram. An electron distribution diagram is shown here for a neon atom, which has a total of 10 electrons. Each concentric circle represents an electron shell, which can be subdivided into electron orbitals.

First shell | Second shell

1*s* orbital | 2*s* orbital | Three 2*p* orbitals

(b) Separate electron orbitals. The three-dimensional shapes represent electron orbitals—the volumes of space where the electrons of an atom are most likely to be found. Each orbital holds a maximum of 2 electrons. The first electron shell, on the left, has one spherical (*s*) orbital, designated 1*s*. The second shell, on the right, has one larger *s* orbital (designated 2*s* for the second shell) plus three dumbbell-shaped orbitals called *p* orbitals (2*p* for the second shell). The three 2*p* orbitals lie at right angles to one another along imaginary *x*-, *y*-, and *z*-axes of the atom. Each 2*p* orbital is outlined here in a different color.

1*s*, 2*s*, and 2*p* orbitals

(c) Superimposed electron orbitals. To reveal the complete picture of the electron orbitals of neon, we superimpose the 1*s* orbital of the first shell and the 2*s* and three 2*p* orbitals of the second shell.

▲ **Figure 2.8 Electron orbitals.**

up to 8 electrons, 2 in each orbital. Electrons in each of the four orbitals have nearly the same energy, but they move in different volumes of space.

The reactivity of an atom arises from the presence of unpaired electrons in one or more orbitals of its valence shell. As you will see in the next section, atoms interact in a way that completes their valence shells. When they do so, it is the *unpaired* electrons that are involved.

1. A lithium atom has 3 protons and 4 neutrons. What is its mass number?

2. A nitrogen atom has 7 protons, and the most common isotope of nitrogen has 7 neutrons. A radioactive isotope of nitrogen has 8 neutrons. Write the atomic number and mass number of this radioactive nitrogen as a chemical symbol with a subscript and superscript.

3. How many electrons does fluorine have? How many electron shells? Name the orbitals that are occupied. How many electrons are needed to fill the valence shell?

4. **WHAT IF?** In Figure 2.7, if two or more elements are in the same row, what do they have in common? If two or more elements are in the same column, what do they have in common?

CONCEPT 2.3

The formation and function of molecules depend on chemical bonding between atoms

Now that we have looked at the structure of atoms, we can move up the hierarchy of organization and see how atoms combine to form molecules and ionic compounds. Atoms with incomplete valence shells can interact with certain other atoms in such a way that each partner completes its valence shell: The atoms either share or transfer valence electrons. These interactions usually result in atoms staying close together, held by attractions called **chemical bonds**. The strongest kinds of chemical bonds are covalent bonds and ionic bonds (when in dry ionic compounds).

Covalent Bonds

A **covalent bond** is the sharing of a pair of valence electrons by two atoms. For example, let's consider what happens when two hydrogen atoms approach each other. Recall that hydrogen has 1 valence electron in the first shell, but the shell's capacity is 2 electrons. When the two hydrogen atoms come close enough for their $1s$ orbitals to overlap, they can share their electrons (**Figure 2.9**). Each hydrogen atom is now associated with 2 electrons in what amounts to a completed valence shell. Two or more atoms held together by covalent bonds constitute a **molecule**, in this case a hydrogen molecule.

Figure 2.10a shows several ways of representing a hydrogen molecule. Its *molecular formula*, H_2, simply indicates that the molecule consists of two atoms of hydrogen. Electron sharing can be depicted by an electron distribution diagram or by a *Lewis dot structure*, in which element symbols are surrounded by dots that represent the valence electrons (H:H). We can also use a *structural formula*, H—H, where

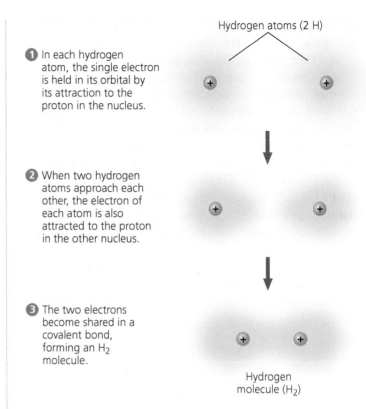

Hydrogen atoms (2 H)

❶ In each hydrogen atom, the single electron is held in its orbital by its attraction to the proton in the nucleus.

❷ When two hydrogen atoms approach each other, the electron of each atom is also attracted to the proton in the other nucleus.

❸ The two electrons become shared in a covalent bond, forming an H_2 molecule.

Hydrogen molecule (H_2)

▲ **Figure 2.9 Formation of a covalent bond.**

the line represents a **single bond**, a pair of shared electrons. A space-filling model comes closest to representing the actual shape of the molecule. You may also be familiar with ball-and-stick models, which are shown in Figure 2.15.

Oxygen has 6 electrons in its second electron shell and therefore needs 2 more electrons to complete its valence shell. Two oxygen atoms form a molecule by sharing *two* pairs of valence electrons (**Figure 2.10b**). The atoms are thus joined by what is called a **double bond** (O=O).

Each atom that can share valence electrons has a bonding capacity corresponding to the number of covalent bonds the atom can form. When the bonds form, they give the atom a full complement of electrons in the valence shell. The bonding capacity of oxygen, for example, is 2. This bonding capacity is called the atom's **valence** and usually equals the number of unpaired electrons required to complete the atom's outermost (valence) shell. See if you can determine the valences of hydrogen, oxygen, nitrogen, and carbon by studying the electron distribution diagrams in Figure 2.7. You can see that the valence of hydrogen is 1; oxygen, 2; nitrogen, 3; and carbon, 4. However, the situation is more complicated for elements in the third row of the periodic table. Phosphorus, for example, can have a valence of 3, as we would predict from the presence of 3 unpaired electrons in its valence shell. In some molecules that are biologically important, however, phosphorus can form three single bonds and one double bond. Therefore, it can also have a valence of 5.

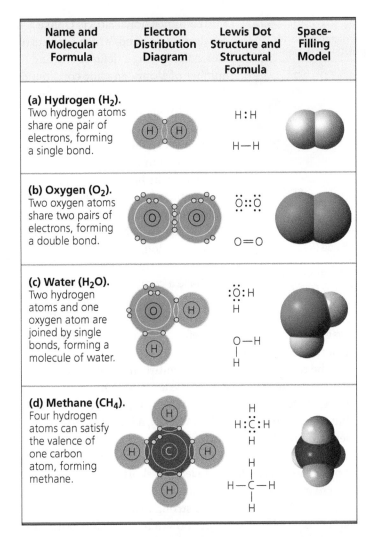

Name and Molecular Formula	Electron Distribution Diagram	Lewis Dot Structure and Structural Formula	Space-Filling Model
(a) Hydrogen (H₂). Two hydrogen atoms share one pair of electrons, forming a single bond.		H:H H—H	
(b) Oxygen (O₂). Two oxygen atoms share two pairs of electrons, forming a double bond.		Ö::Ö O=O	
(c) Water (H₂O). Two hydrogen atoms and one oxygen atom are joined by single bonds, forming a molecule of water.		:Ö:H H O—H | H	

(d) Methane (CH₄). Four hydrogen atoms can satisfy the valence of one carbon atom, forming methane.		H
		H:C:H
		   H
		
		   H
		   |
		H—C—H
		   |
		   H	

▲ **Figure 2.10 Covalent bonding in four molecules.** The number of electrons required to complete an atom's valence shell generally determines how many covalent bonds that atom will form. This figure shows several ways of indicating covalent bonds.

The molecules H_2 and O_2 are pure elements rather than compounds because a compound is a combination of two or more *different* elements. Water, with the molecular formula H_2O, is a compound. Two atoms of hydrogen are needed to satisfy the valence of one oxygen atom. **Figure 2.10c** shows the structure of a water molecule. (Water is so important to life that Chapter 3 is devoted entirely to its structure and behavior.)

Methane, the main component of natural gas, is a compound with the molecular formula CH_4. It takes four hydrogen atoms, each with a valence of 1, to complement one atom of carbon, with its valence of 4 **(Figure 2.10d)**. (We will look at many other compounds of carbon in Chapter 4.)

Atoms in a molecule attract shared bonding electrons to varying degrees, depending on the element. The attraction of a particular atom for the electrons of a covalent bond is called its **electronegativity**. The more electronegative an atom is, the more strongly it pulls shared electrons toward

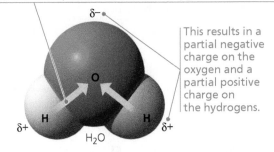

Because oxygen (O) is more electronegative than hydrogen (H), shared electrons are pulled more toward oxygen.

This results in a partial negative charge on the oxygen and a partial positive charge on the hydrogens.

▲ **Figure 2.11 Polar covalent bonds in a water molecule.**

itself. In a covalent bond between two atoms of the same element, the electrons are shared equally because the two atoms have the same electronegativity—the tug-of-war is at a standoff. Such a bond is called a **nonpolar covalent bond**. For example, the single bond of H_2 is nonpolar, as is the double bond of O_2. However, when an atom is bonded to a more electronegative atom, the electrons of the bond are not shared equally. This type of bond is called a **polar covalent bond**. Such bonds vary in their polarity, depending on the relative electronegativity of the two atoms. For example, the bonds between the oxygen and hydrogen atoms of a water molecule are quite polar **(Figure 2.11)**.

Oxygen is one of the most electronegative elements, attracting shared electrons much more strongly than hydrogen does. In a covalent bond between oxygen and hydrogen, the electrons spend more time near the oxygen nucleus than they do near the hydrogen nucleus. Because electrons have a negative charge and are pulled toward oxygen in a water molecule, the oxygen atom has a partial negative charge (indicated by the Greek letter δ with a minus sign, $\delta-$, or "delta minus"), and each hydrogen atom has a partial positive charge ($\delta+$, or "delta plus"). In contrast, the individual bonds of methane (CH_4) are much less polar because the electronegativities of carbon and hydrogen are similar.

Ionic Bonds

In some cases, two atoms are so unequal in their attraction for valence electrons that the more electronegative atom strips an electron completely away from its partner. The two resulting oppositely charged atoms (or molecules) are called **ions**. A positively charged ion is called a **cation**, while a negatively charged ion is called an **anion**. Because of their opposite charges, cations and anions attract each other; this attraction is called an ionic bond. Note that the transfer of an electron is not, by itself, the formation of a bond; rather, it allows a bond to form because it results in two ions of opposite charge. Any two ions of opposite charge can form an **ionic bond**. The ions do not need to have acquired their charge by an electron transfer with each other.

① The lone valence electron of a sodium atom is transferred to join the 7 valence electrons of a chlorine atom.

② Each resulting ion has a completed valence shell. An ionic bond can form between the oppositely charged ions.

Na
Sodium atom

Cl
Chlorine atom

Na⁺
Sodium ion
(a cation)

Cl⁻
Chloride ion
(an anion)

Sodium chloride (NaCl)

▲ **Figure 2.12 Electron transfer and ionic bonding.** The attraction between oppositely charged atoms, or ions, is an ionic bond. An ionic bond can form between any two oppositely charged ions, even if they have not been formed by transfer of an electron from one to the other.

This is what happens when an atom of sodium ($_{11}$Na) encounters an atom of chlorine ($_{17}$Cl) **(Figure 2.12)**. A sodium atom has a total of 11 electrons, with its single valence electron in the third electron shell. A chlorine atom has a total of 17 electrons, with 7 electrons in its valence shell. When these two atoms meet, the lone valence electron of sodium is transferred to the chlorine atom, and both atoms end up with their valence shells complete. (Because sodium no longer has an electron in the third shell, the second shell is now the valence shell.) The electron transfer between the two atoms moves one unit of negative charge from sodium to chlorine. Sodium, now with 11 protons but only 10 electrons, has a net electrical charge of 1+; the sodium atom has become a cation. Conversely, the chlorine atom, having gained an extra electron, now has 17 protons and 18 electrons, giving it a net electrical charge of 1−; it has become a chloride ion—an anion.

Compounds formed by ionic bonds are called **ionic compounds**, or **salts**. We know the ionic compound sodium chloride (NaCl) as table salt **(Figure 2.13)**. Salts are often found in nature as crystals of various sizes and shapes. Each salt crystal is an aggregate of vast numbers of cations and anions bonded by their electrical attraction and arranged in

▲ **Figure 2.13 A sodium chloride (NaCl) crystal.** The sodium ions (Na⁺) and chloride ions (Cl⁻) are held together by ionic bonds. The formula NaCl tells us that the ratio of Na⁺ to Cl⁻ is 1:1.

— Na⁺
— Cl⁻

a three-dimensional lattice. Unlike a covalent compound, which consists of molecules having a definite size and number of atoms, an ionic compound does not consist of molecules. The formula for an ionic compound, such as NaCl, indicates only the ratio of elements in a crystal of the salt. "NaCl" by itself is not a molecule.

Not all salts have equal numbers of cations and anions. For example, the ionic compound magnesium chloride (MgCl₂) has two chloride ions for each magnesium ion. Magnesium ($_{12}$Mg) must lose 2 outer electrons if the atom is to have a complete valence shell, so it has a tendency to become a cation with a net charge of 2+ (Mg²⁺). One magnesium cation can therefore form ionic bonds with two chloride anions (Cl⁻).

The term *ion* also applies to entire molecules that are electrically charged. In the salt ammonium chloride (NH₄Cl), for instance, the anion is a single chloride ion (Cl⁻), but the cation is ammonium (NH₄⁺), a nitrogen atom covalently bonded to four hydrogen atoms. The whole ammonium ion has an electrical charge of 1+ because it has given up 1 electron and thus is 1 electron short.

Environment affects the strength of ionic bonds. In a dry salt crystal, the bonds are so strong that it takes a hammer and chisel to break enough of them to crack the crystal in two. If the same salt crystal is dissolved in water, however, the ionic bonds are much weaker because each ion is partially shielded by its interactions with water molecules. Most drugs are manufactured as salts because they are quite stable when dry but can dissociate (come apart) easily in water. (In the next chapter, you will learn how water dissolves salts.)

Weak Chemical Bonds

In organisms, most of the strongest chemical bonds are covalent bonds, which link atoms to form a cell's molecules. But weaker bonding within and between molecules is also indispensable, contributing greatly to the emergent properties of life. Many large biological molecules are held in their functional form by weak bonds. In addition, when two molecules in the cell make contact, they may adhere temporarily by weak bonds. The reversibility of weak bonding can be an advantage: Two molecules can come together, respond to one another in some way, and then separate.

Several types of weak chemical bonds are important in organisms. One is the ionic bond as it exists between ions dissociated in water, which we just discussed. Hydrogen bonds and van der Waals interactions are also crucial to life.

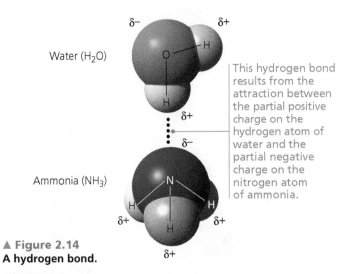

Water (H_2O) δ− δ+

This hydrogen bond results from the attraction between the partial positive charge on the hydrogen atom of water and the partial negative charge on the nitrogen atom of ammonia.

Ammonia (NH_3)

▲ **Figure 2.14**
A hydrogen bond.

DRAW IT *Draw five water molecules. (Use structural formulas; show partial charges.) Show how they make hydrogen bonds with each other.*

Hydrogen Bonds

Among weak chemical bonds, hydrogen bonds are so central to the chemistry of life that they deserve special attention. When a hydrogen atom is covalently bonded to an electronegative atom, the hydrogen atom has a partial positive charge that allows it to be attracted to a different electronegative atom nearby. This attraction between a hydrogen and an electronegative atom is called a **hydrogen bond**. In living cells, the electronegative partners are usually oxygen or nitrogen atoms. Refer to **Figure 2.14** to examine the simple case of hydrogen bonding between water (H_2O) and ammonia (NH_3).

Van der Waals Interactions

Even a molecule with nonpolar covalent bonds may have positively and negatively charged regions. Electrons are not always evenly distributed; at any instant, they may accumulate by chance in one part of a molecule or another. The results are ever-changing regions of positive and negative charge that enable all atoms and molecules to stick to one another. These **van der Waals interactions** are individually weak and occur only when atoms and molecules are very close together. When many such interactions occur simultaneously, however, they can be powerful: Van der Waals interactions allow a gecko lizard (below) to walk straight up a wall! The anatomy of the gecko's foot—including many minuscule hair-like projections from the toes and strong tendons underlying the skin—strikes a balance between maximum surface contact with the wall and necessary stiffness of the foot. The van der Waals interactions between the foot molecules and the molecules of the wall's surface are so numerous that despite their individual weakness, together they can support the

gecko's body weight. This discovery has inspired development of an artificial adhesive called Geckskin™: A patch the size of an index card can hold a 700 pound weight to a wall!

Van der Waals interactions, hydrogen bonds, ionic bonds in water, and other weak bonds may form not only between molecules but also between parts of a large molecule, such as a protein. The cumulative effect of weak bonds is to reinforce the three-dimensional shape of the molecule. (You will learn more about the very important biological roles of weak bonds in Chapter 5.)

Molecular Shape and Function

A molecule has a characteristic size and precise shape, which are crucial to its function in the living cell. A molecule consisting of two atoms, such as H_2 or O_2, is always linear, but most molecules with more than two atoms have more complicated shapes. These shapes are determined by the positions of the atoms' orbitals (**Figure 2.15**). When an

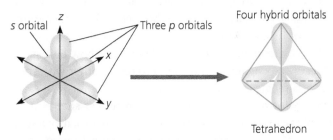

(a) Hybridization of orbitals. The single *s* and three *p* orbitals of a valence shell involved in covalent bonding combine to form four teardrop-shaped hybrid orbitals. These orbitals extend to the four corners of an imaginary tetrahedron (outlined in pink).

Space-Filling Model	Ball-and-Stick Model	Hybrid-Orbital Model (with ball-and-stick model superimposed)
Water (H_2O)	104.5°	Unbonded electron pair
Methane (CH_4)		

(b) Molecular-shape models. Three models representing molecular shape are shown for water and methane. The positions of the hybrid orbitals determine the shapes of the molecules.

▲ **Figure 2.15 Molecular shapes due to hybrid orbitals.**

atom forms covalent bonds, the orbitals in its valence shell undergo rearrangement. For atoms with valence electrons in both *s* and *p* orbitals (review Figure 2.8), the single *s* and three *p* orbitals form four new hybrid orbitals shaped like identical teardrops extending from the region of the atomic nucleus (Figure 2.15a). If we connect the larger ends of the teardrops with lines, we have the outline of a geometric shape called a tetrahedron, a pyramid with a triangular base.

For water molecules (H_2O), two of the hybrid orbitals in the oxygen's valence shell are shared with hydrogens (Figure 2.15b). The result is a molecule shaped roughly like a V, with its two covalent bonds at an angle of 104.5°.

The methane molecule (CH_4) has the shape of a completed tetrahedron because all four hybrid orbitals of the carbon atom are shared with hydrogen atoms (see Figure 2.15b). The carbon nucleus is at the center, with its four covalent bonds radiating to hydrogen nuclei at the corners of the tetrahedron. Larger molecules containing multiple carbon atoms, including many of the molecules that make up living matter, have more complex overall shapes. However, the tetrahedral shape of a carbon atom bonded to four other atoms is often a repeating motif within such molecules.

Molecular shape is crucial: It determines how biological molecules recognize and respond to one another with specificity. Biological molecules often bind temporarily to each other by forming weak bonds, but only if their shapes are complementary. Consider the effects of opiates, drugs such as morphine and heroin derived from opium. Opiates relieve pain and alter mood by weakly binding to specific receptor molecules on the surfaces of brain cells. Why would brain cells carry receptors for opiates, compounds that are not made by the body? In 1975, the discovery of endorphins answered this question. Endorphins are signaling molecules made by the pituitary gland that bind to the receptors, relieving pain and producing euphoria durisng times of stress, such as intense exercise. Opiates have shapes similar to endorphins and mimic them by binding to endorphin receptors in the brain. That is why opiates and endorphins have similar effects (Figure 2.16). The role of molecular shape in brain chemistry illustrates how biological organization leads to a match between structure and function, one of biology's unifying themes.

CONCEPT CHECK 2.3

1. Why does the structure H—C=C—H fail to make sense chemically?

2. What holds the atoms together in a crystal of magnesium chloride ($MgCl_2$)?

3. **WHAT IF?** If you were a pharmaceutical researcher, why would you want to learn the three-dimensional shapes of naturally occurring signaling molecules?

Key

Carbon   Nitrogen

Hydrogen   Sulfur

Oxygen

Natural endorphin

Morphine

(a) Structures of endorphin and morphine. The boxed portion of the endorphin molecule (left) binds to receptor molecules on target cells in the brain. The boxed portion of the morphine molecule (right) is a close match.

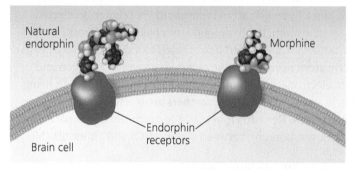

Natural endorphin

Morphine

Endorphin receptors

Brain cell

(b) Binding to endorphin receptors. Both endorphin and morphine can bind to endorphin receptors on the surface of a brain cell.

▲ **Figure 2.16 A molecular mimic.** Morphine affects pain perception and emotional state by mimicking the brain's natural endorphins.

CONCEPT 2.4

Chemical reactions make and break chemical bonds

The making and breaking of chemical bonds, leading to changes in the composition of matter, are called **chemical reactions**. An example is the reaction between hydrogen and oxygen molecules that forms water:

$2 H_2$	+	O_2		$2 H_2O$
Reactants			**Reaction**	**Products**

This reaction breaks the covalent bonds of H_2 and O_2 and forms the new bonds of H_2O. When we write a chemical reaction, we use an arrow to indicate the conversion of the starting materials, called the **reactants**, to the **products**. The coefficients indicate the number of molecules involved; for example, the coefficient 2 in front of the H_2 means that the reaction starts with two molecules of hydrogen. Notice that all atoms of the reactants must be accounted for in the products. Matter is conserved in a chemical reaction: Reactions cannot create or destroy atoms but can only rearrange (redistribute) the electrons among them.

Photosynthesis, which takes place within the cells of green plant tissues, is an important biological example of how chemical reactions rearrange matter. Humans and other animals ultimately depend on photosynthesis for food and oxygen, and this process is at the foundation of almost all ecosystems. The following chemical shorthand summarizes the process of photosynthesis:

$$6\ CO_2 + 6\ H_2O \rightarrow C_6H_{12}O_6 + 6\ O_2$$

The raw materials of photosynthesis are carbon dioxide (CO_2), which is taken from the air, and water (H_2O), which is absorbed from the soil. Within the plant cells, sunlight powers the conversion of these ingredients to a sugar called glucose ($C_6H_{12}O_6$) and oxygen molecules (O_2), a by-product that the plant releases into the surroundings (**Figure 2.17**). Although photosynthesis is actually a sequence of many chemical reactions, we still end up with the same number and types of atoms that we had when we started. Matter has simply been rearranged, with an input of energy provided by sunlight.

All chemical reactions are reversible, with the products of the forward reaction becoming the reactants for the reverse reaction. For example, hydrogen and nitrogen molecules can combine to form ammonia, but ammonia can also decompose to regenerate hydrogen and nitrogen:

$$3\ H_2 + N_2 \rightleftharpoons 2\ NH_3$$

The two opposite-headed arrows indicate that the reaction is reversible.

One of the factors affecting the rate of a reaction is the concentration of reactants. The greater the concentration of reactant molecules, the more frequently they collide with one another and have an opportunity to react and form products. The same holds true for products. As products accumulate, collisions resulting in the reverse reaction become more frequent. Eventually, the forward and reverse reactions occur at the same rate, and the relative concentrations of products and reactants stop changing. The point at which the reactions offset one another exactly is called **chemical equilibrium**. This is a dynamic equilibrium; reactions are still going on, but with no net effect on the concentrations of reactants and products. Equilibrium does *not* mean that

▲ **Figure 2.17 Photosynthesis: a solar-powered rearrangement of matter.** *Elodea*, a freshwater plant, produces sugar by rearranging the atoms of carbon dioxide and water in the chemical process known as photosynthesis, which is powered by sunlight. Much of the sugar is then converted to other food molecules. Oxygen gas (O_2) is a by-product of photosynthesis; notice the bubbles of O_2-containing gas escaping from the leaves submerged in water.

? *Explain how this photo relates to the reactants and products in the equation for photosynthesis given in the text. (You will learn more about photosynthesis in Chapter 11.)*

the reactants and products are equal in concentration, but only that their concentrations have stabilized at a particular ratio. The reaction involving ammonia reaches equilibrium when ammonia decomposes as rapidly as it forms. In some chemical reactions, the equilibrium point may lie so far to the right that these reactions go essentially to completion; that is, virtually all the reactants are converted to products.

We will return to the subject of chemical reactions after more detailed study of the various types of molecules that are important to life. In the next chapter, we focus on water, the substance in which all the chemical processes of organisms occur.

CONCEPT CHECK 2.4

1. **MAKE CONNECTIONS** Consider the reaction between hydrogen and oxygen that forms water, shown with ball-and-stick models at the beginning of Concept 2.4. Study Figure 2.10 and draw the Lewis dot structures representing this reaction.

2. Which type of chemical reaction occurs faster at equilibrium, the formation of products from reactants or reactants from products?

3. Write an equation that uses the products of photosynthesis as reactants and the reactants of photosynthesis as products. Add energy as another product. This new equation describes a process that occurs in your cells. Describe this equation in words. How does this equation relate to breathing?

CONCEPT 2.1

Matter consists of chemical elements in pure form and in combinations called compounds (pp. 29–30)

- **Elements** cannot be broken down chemically to other substances. A **compound** contains two or more different elements in a fixed ratio. Oxygen, carbon, hydrogen, and nitrogen make up approximately 96% of living matter.

? *In what way does the need for iodine or iron in your diet differ from your need for calcium or phosphorus?*

CONCEPT 2.2

An element's properties depend on the structure of its atoms (pp. 30–36)

- An **atom**, the smallest unit of an element, has the following components:

Nucleus

Protons (+ charge) determine element

Neutrons (no charge) determine isotope

Electrons (– charge) form negative cloud and determine chemical behavior

Atom

- An electrically neutral atom has equal numbers of electrons and protons; the number of protons determines the **atomic number**. The **atomic mass** is measured in **daltons** and is roughly equal to the **mass number**, the sum of protons plus neutrons. **Isotopes** of an element differ from each other in neutron number and therefore mass. Unstable isotopes give off particles and energy as radioactivity.
- In an atom, electrons occupy specific **electron shells**; the electrons in a shell have a characteristic energy level. Electron distribution in shells determines the chemical behavior of an atom. An atom that has an incomplete outer shell, the **valence shell**, is reactive.
- Electrons exist in **orbitals**, three-dimensional spaces with specific shapes that are components of electron shells.

DRAW IT *Draw the electron distribution diagrams for neon ($_{10}$Ne) and argon ($_{18}$Ar). Use these diagrams to explain why these elements are chemically unreactive.*

CONCEPT 2.3

The formation and function of molecules depend on chemical bonding between atoms (pp. 36–40)

- **Chemical bonds** form when atoms interact and complete their valence shells. **Covalent bonds** form when pairs of electrons are shared.

H· + H· ⟶ H:H
Single covalent bond

:Ö· + ·Ö: ⟶ Ö::Ö
Double covalent bond

- **Molecules** consist of two or more covalently bonded atoms. The attraction of an atom for the electrons of a covalent bond is its **electronegativity**. If both atoms are the same, they have the same electronegativity and share a **nonpolar covalent bond**. Electrons of a **polar covalent bond** are pulled closer to the more electronegative atom.
- An **ion** forms when an atom or molecule gains or loses an electron and becomes charged. An **ionic bond** is the attraction between two oppositely charged ions.

Ionic bond

Electron transfer forms ions

Na
Sodium atom

Cl
Chlorine atom

Na⁺
Sodium ion (a cation)

Cl⁻
Chloride ion (an anion)

- Weak bonds reinforce the shapes of large molecules and help molecules adhere to each other. A **hydrogen bond** is an attraction between a hydrogen atom carrying a partial positive charge (δ+) and an electronegative atom (δ−). **Van der Waals interactions** occur between transiently positive and negative regions of molecules.
- A molecule's shape is determined by the positions of its atoms' valence orbitals. Covalent bonds result in hybrid orbitals, which are responsible for the shapes of H_2O, CH_4, and many more complex biological molecules. Shape is usually the basis for the recognition of one biological molecule by another.

? *In terms of electron sharing between atoms, compare nonpolar covalent bonds, polar covalent bonds, and the formation of ions.*

CONCEPT 2.4

Chemical reactions make and break chemical bonds (pp. 40–41)

- **Chemical reactions** change **reactants** into **products** while conserving matter. All chemical reactions are theoretically reversible. **Chemical equilibrium** is reached when the forward and reverse reaction rates are equal.

? *What would happen to the concentration of products if more reactants were added to a reaction that was in chemical equilibrium? How would this addition affect the equilibrium?*

LEVEL 1: KNOWLEDGE/COMPREHENSION

1. In the term *trace element*, the adjective *trace* means that
   a. the element is required in very small amounts.
   b. the element can be used as a label to trace atoms through an organism's metabolism.
   c. the element is very rare on Earth.
   d. the element enhances health but is not essential for the organism's long-term survival.

2. Compared with ^{31}P, the radioactive isotope ^{32}P has
   a. a different atomic number.
   b. one more proton.
   c. one more electron.
   d. one more neutron.

3. The reactivity of an atom arises from
   a. the average distance of the outermost electron shell from the nucleus.
   b. the existence of unpaired electrons in the valence shell.
   c. the sum of the potential energies of all the electron shells.
   d. the potential energy of the valence shell.

4. Which statement is true of all atoms that are anions?
   a. The atom has more electrons than protons.
   b. The atom has more protons than electrons.
   c. The atom has fewer protons than does a neutral atom of the same element.
   d. The atom has more neutrons than protons.

5. Which of the following statements correctly describes any chemical reaction that has reached equilibrium?
   a. The concentrations of products and reactants are equal.
   b. The reaction is now irreversible.
   c. Both forward and reverse reactions have halted.
   d. The rates of the forward and reverse reactions are equal.

LEVEL 2: APPLICATION/ANALYSIS

6. We can represent atoms by listing the number of protons, neutrons, and electrons—for example, $2p^+$, $2n^0$, $2e^-$ for helium. Which of the following represents the ^{18}O isotope of oxygen?
   a. $7p^+$, $2n^0$, $9e^-$
   b. $8p^+$, $10n^0$, $8e^-$
   c. $9p^+$, $9n^0$, $9e^-$
   d. $10p^+$, $8n^0$, $9e^-$

7. The atomic number of sulfur is 16. Sulfur combines with hydrogen by covalent bonding to form a compound, hydrogen sulfide. Based on the number of valence electrons in a sulfur atom, predict the molecular formula of the compound.
   a. HS   c. H_2S
   b. HS_2 d. H_4S

8. What coefficients must be placed in the following blanks so that all atoms are accounted for in the products?

   $$C_6H_{12}O_6 \rightarrow \underline{\quad} C_2H_6O + \underline{\quad} CO_2$$

   a. 2; 1   c. 1; 3
   b. 3; 1   d. 2; 2

9. **DRAW IT** Draw Lewis dot structures for each hypothetical molecule shown below, using the correct number of valence electrons for each atom. Determine which molecule makes sense because each atom has a complete valence shell and each bond has the correct number of electrons. Explain what makes the other molecules nonsensical, considering the number of bonds each type of atom can make.

   (a) H—O—C—C=O with H atoms
   (b) H—C—H—C=O with H atoms

LEVEL 3: SYNTHESIS/EVALUATION

10. EVOLUTION CONNECTION

The percentages of naturally occurring elements making up the human body (see Table 2.1) are similar to the percentages of these elements found in other organisms. How could you account for this similarity among organisms?

11. SCIENTIFIC INQUIRY

Female silkworm moths (*Bombyx mori*) attract males by emitting chemical signals that spread through the air. A male hundreds of meters away can detect these molecules and fly toward their source. The sensory organs responsible for this behavior are the comblike antennae visible in the photograph shown here. Each filament of an antenna is equipped with

thousands of receptor cells that detect the sex attractant. Based on what you learned in this chapter, propose a hypothesis to account for the ability of the male moth to detect a specific molecule in the presence of many other molecules in the air. What predictions does your hypothesis make? Design an experiment to test one of these predictions.

12. WRITE ABOUT A THEME: ORGANIZATION

While waiting at an airport, Neil Campbell once overheard this claim: "It's paranoid and ignorant to worry about industry or agriculture contaminating the environment with their chemical wastes. After all, this stuff is just made of the same atoms that were already present in our environment." Drawing on your knowledge of electron distribution, bonding, and emergent properties (see Concept 1.1), write a short essay (100–150 words) countering this argument.

13. SYNTHESIZE YOUR KNOWLEDGE

This bombardier beetle is spraying a boiling hot liquid that contains irritating chemicals, used as a defense mechanism against its enemies. The beetle stores two sets of chemicals separately in its glands. Using what you learned about chemistry in this chapter, propose a possible explanation for why the beetle is not harmed by the chemicals it stores and what causes the explosive discharge.

MasteringBiology®

Students Go to **MasteringBiology** for assignments, the eText, and the Study Area with practice tests, animations, and activities.

Instructors Go to **MasteringBiology** for automatically graded tutorials and questions that you can assign to your students, plus Instructor Resources.

3

Water and Life

▲ **Figure 3.1 How does the habitat of a whooper swan depend on the chemistry of water?**

The Molecule That Supports All of Life

Life on Earth began in water and evolved there for 3 billion years before spreading onto land. Water is the substance that makes possible life as we know it here on Earth. All organisms familiar to us are made mostly of water and live in an environment dominated by water. Water is the biological medium here on Earth, and possibly on other planets as well.

Three-quarters of Earth's surface is covered by water. Although most of this water is in liquid form, water is also present on Earth as a solid (ice) and a gas (water vapor). Water is the only common substance to exist in the natural environment in all three physical states of matter. Furthermore, the solid state of water floats on the liquid, a rare property emerging from the chemistry of the water molecule. All three states of water can be seen in **Figure 3.1**, which shows water vapor rising from hot springs that feed into a partially frozen lake in Hokkaido, Japan. The lake is a migratory stop for the elegant whooper swan (*Cygnus cygnus*). The growing young require a watery habitat because their legs can't support their body weight on land for long periods of time.

In this chapter, you will learn how the structure of a water molecule allows it to interact with other molecules, including other water molecules. This ability leads to water's unique emergent properties that help make Earth suitable for life.

▲ A young whooper swan paddles after its parent.

CONCEPT 3.1

Polar covalent bonds in water molecules result in hydrogen bonding

Water is so familiar to us that it is easy to overlook its many extraordinary qualities. Following the theme of emergent properties, we can trace water's unique behavior to the structure and interactions of its molecules.

Studied on its own, the water molecule is deceptively simple. It is shaped like a wide V, with its two hydrogen atoms joined to the oxygen atom by single covalent bonds. Oxygen is more electronegative than hydrogen, so the electrons of the covalent bonds spend more time closer to oxygen than to hydrogen; these are **polar covalent bonds** (see Figure 2.11). This unequal sharing of electrons and water's V-like shape make it a **polar molecule**, meaning that its overall charge is unevenly distributed. In water, the oxygen region of the molecule has a partial negative charge ($\delta-$), and each hydrogen has a partial positive charge ($\delta+$).

The properties of water arise from attractions between oppositely charged atoms of different water molecules: The slightly positive hydrogen of one molecule is attracted to the slightly negative oxygen of a nearby molecule. The two molecules are thus held together by a hydrogen bond **(Figure 3.2)**. When water is in its liquid form, its hydrogen bonds are very fragile, each only about 1/20 as strong as a covalent bond. . The hydrogen bonds form, break, and re-form with great

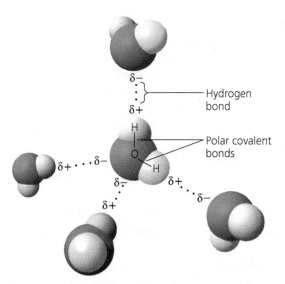

▲ **Figure 3.2 Hydrogen bonds between water molecules.** The charged regions in a water molecule are due to its polar covalent bonds. Oppositely charged regions of neighboring water molecules are attracted to each other, forming hydrogen bonds. Each molecule can hydrogen-bond to multiple partners, and these associations are constantly changing.

DRAW IT *Draw partial charges on the water molecule at the far left, and draw two more water molecules hydrogen-bonded to it.*

frequency. Each lasts only a few trillionths of a second, but the molecules are constantly forming new hydrogen bonds with a succession of partners. Therefore, at any instant, most of the water molecules are hydrogen-bonded to their neighbors. The extraordinary properties of water emerge from this hydrogen bonding , which organizes water molecules into a higher level of structural order.

CONCEPT CHECK 3.1

1. **MAKE CONNECTIONS** What is electronegativity, and how does it affect interactions between water molecules? (Review Figure 2.11.)

2. Why is it unlikely that two neighboring water molecules would be arranged like this?

$$O \diagdown_{\substack{H\ H}}^{}\diagup O$$

3. **WHAT IF?** What would be the effect on the properties of the water molecule if oxygen and hydrogen had equal electronegativity?

CONCEPT 3.2

Four emergent properties of water contribute to Earth's suitability for life

We will examine four emergent properties of water that contribute to Earth's suitability as an environment for life: cohesive behavior, ability to moderate temperature, expansion upon freezing, and versatility as a solvent.

Cohesion of Water Molecules

Water molecules stay close to each other as a result of hydrogen bonding. Although the arrangement of molecules in a sample of liquid water is constantly changing, at any given moment many of the molecules are linked by multiple hydrogen bonds. These linkages make water more structured than most other liquids. Collectively, the hydrogen bonds hold the substance together, a phenomenon called **cohesion**.

Cohesion due to hydrogen bonding contributes to the transport of water and dissolved nutrients against gravity in plants. Water from the roots reaches the leaves through a network of water-conducting cells **(Figure 3.3)**. As water evaporates from a leaf, hydrogen bonds cause water molecules leaving the veins to tug on molecules farther down, and the upward pull is transmitted through the water-conducting cells all the way to the roots. **Adhesion**, the clinging of one substance to another, also plays a role. Adhesion of

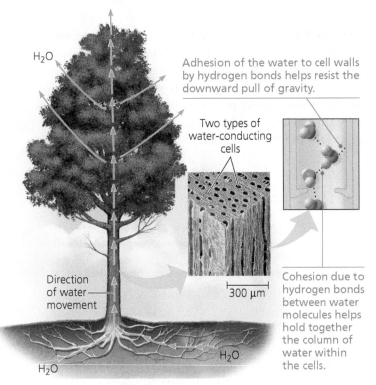

H₂O

Adhesion of the water to cell walls by hydrogen bonds helps resist the downward pull of gravity.

Two types of water-conducting cells

Direction of water movement

300 μm

Cohesion due to hydrogen bonds between water molecules helps hold together the column of water within the cells.

H₂O

H₂O

▲ Figure 3.3 **Water transport in plants.** Evaporation from leaves pulls water upward from the roots through water-conducting cells. Because of the properties of cohesion and adhesion, the tallest trees can transport water more than 100 m upward—approximately one-quarter the height of the Empire State Building in New York City.

ANIMATION **BioFlix** Visit the Study Area in **MasteringBiology** for the BioFlix ® 3-D Animation on Water Transport in Plants.

water by hydrogen bonds to the molecules of cell walls helps counter the downward pull of gravity (see Figure 3.3).

Related to cohesion is **surface tension**, a measure of how difficult it is to stretch or break the surface of a liquid. At the interface between water and air is an ordered arrangement of water molecules, hydrogen-bonded to one another and to the water below. This gives water an unusually high surface tension, making it behave as though it were coated with an invisible film. You can observe the surface tension of water by slightly overfilling a drinking glass; the water will stand above the rim. The spider in **Figure 3.4** takes advantage of the surface tension of water to walk across a pond without breaking the surface.

▼ Figure 3.4 **Walking on water.** The high surface tension of water, resulting from the collective strength of its hydrogen bonds, allows this raft spider to walk on the surface of a pond.

Moderation of Temperature by Water

Water moderates air temperature by absorbing heat from air that is warmer and releasing the stored heat to air that is cooler. Water is effective as a heat bank because it can absorb or release a relatively large amount of heat with only a slight change in its own temperature. To understand this capability of water, let's first look at temperature and heat.

Temperature and Heat

Anything that moves has **kinetic energy**, the energy of motion. Atoms and molecules have kinetic energy because they are always moving, although not necessarily in any particular direction. The faster a molecule moves, the greater its kinetic energy. The kinetic energy associated with the random movement of atoms or molecules is called **thermal energy**. Thermal energy is related to temperature, but they are not the same thing. **Temperature** is a measure of energy that represents the *average* kinetic energy of the molecules in a body of matter, regardless of volume, whereas the *total* thermal energy depends in part on the matter's volume. When water is heated in a coffeemaker, the average speed of the molecules increases, and the thermometer records this as a rise in temperature of the liquid. The total amount of thermal energy also increases in this case. Note, however, that although the pot of coffee has a much higher temperature than, say, the water in a swimming pool, the swimming pool contains more thermal energy because of its much greater volume.

Whenever two objects of different temperature are brought together, thermal energy passes from the warmer to the cooler object until the two are the same temperature. Molecules in the cooler object speed up at the expense of the thermal energy of the warmer object. An ice cube cools a drink not by adding coldness to the liquid, but by absorbing thermal energy from the liquid as the ice itself melts. Thermal energy in transfer from one body of matter to another is defined as **heat**.

One convenient unit of heat used in this book is the **calorie (cal)**. A calorie is the amount of heat it takes to raise the temperature of 1 g of water by 1°C. Conversely, a calorie is also the amount of heat that 1 g of water releases when it cools by 1°C. A **kilocalorie (kcal)**, 1,000 cal, is the quantity of heat required to raise the temperature of 1 kilogram (kg) of water by 1°C. (The "calories" on food packages are actually kilocalories.) Another energy unit used in this book is the **joule (J)**. One joule equals 0.239 cal; one calorie equals 4.184 J.

Water's High Specific Heat

The ability of water to stabilize temperature stems from its relatively high specific heat. The **specific heat** of a substance is defined as the amount of heat that must be absorbed or lost for 1 g of that substance to change its temperature by 1°C. We already know water's specific heat because we have defined a calorie as the amount of heat that causes 1 g of water to change its temperature by 1°C. Therefore, the specific heat of water is 1 calorie per gram and per degree Celsius, abbreviated as 1 cal/g · °C. Compared with most other substances, water has an unusually high specific heat. For example, ethyl alcohol, the type of alcohol in alcoholic beverages, has a specific heat of 0.6 cal/g · °C; that is, only 0.6 cal is required to raise the temperature of 1 g of ethyl alcohol by 1°C.

Because of the high specific heat of water relative to other materials, water will change its temperature less than other liquids when it absorbs or loses a given amount of heat. The reason you can burn your fingers by touching the side of an iron pot on the stove when the water in the pot is still lukewarm is that the specific heat of water is ten times greater than that of iron. In other words, the same amount of heat will raise the temperature of 1 g of the iron much faster than it will raise the temperature of 1 g of the water. Specific heat can be thought of as a measure of how well a substance resists changing its temperature when it absorbs or releases heat. Water resists changing its temperature; when it does change its temperature, it absorbs or loses a relatively large quantity of heat for each degree of change.

We can trace water's high specific heat, like many of its other properties, to hydrogen bonding. Heat must be absorbed in order to break hydrogen bonds; by the same token, heat is released when hydrogen bonds form. A calorie of heat causes a relatively small change in the temperature of water because much of the heat is used to disrupt hydrogen bonds before the water molecules can begin moving faster. And when the temperature of water drops slightly, many additional hydrogen bonds form, releasing a considerable amount of energy in the form of heat.

What is the relevance of water's high specific heat to life on Earth? A large body of water can absorb and store a huge amount of heat from the sun in the daytime and during summer while warming up only a few degrees. At night and during winter, the gradually cooling water can warm the air. This capability of water serves to moderate air temperatures in coastal areas (Figure 3.5). The high specific heat of water also tends to stabilize ocean temperatures, creating a favorable environment for marine life. Thus, because of its high specific heat, the water that covers most of Earth keeps temperature fluctuations on land and in water within limits that permit life. Also, because organisms are made primarily of water, they are better able to resist changes in their own temperature than if they were made of a liquid with a lower specific heat.

Evaporative Cooling

Molecules of any liquid stay close together because they are attracted to one another. Molecules moving fast enough to overcome these attractions can depart the liquid and enter the air as a gas (vapor). This transformation from a liquid to a gas is called vaporization, or evaporation. Recall that the speed of molecular movement varies and that temperature is the *average* kinetic energy of molecules. Even at low temperatures, the speediest molecules can escape into the air. Some evaporation occurs at any temperature; a glass of water at room temperature, for example, will eventually evaporate completely. If a liquid is heated, the average kinetic energy of molecules increases and the liquid evaporates more rapidly.

Heat of vaporization is the quantity of heat a liquid must absorb for 1 g of it to be converted from the liquid to the gaseous state. For the same reason that water has a high specific heat, it also has a high heat of vaporization relative to most other liquids. To evaporate 1 g of water at 25°C, about 580 cal of heat is needed—nearly double the amount needed to vaporize a gram of alcohol or ammonia. Water's high heat of vaporization is another emergent property resulting from the strength of its hydrogen bonds, which must be broken before the molecules can exit from the liquid in the form of water vapor (see Figure 3.1).

The high amount of energy required to vaporize water has a wide range of effects. On a global scale, for example, it helps moderate Earth's climate. A considerable amount of solar heat absorbed by tropical seas is consumed during the evaporation of surface water. Then, as moist tropical air circulates poleward, it releases heat as it condenses and forms rain. On an organismal level, water's high heat of vaporization accounts for the severity of steam burns. These burns are caused by the heat energy released when steam condenses into liquid on the skin.

As a liquid evaporates, the surface of the liquid that remains behind cools down (its temperature decreases). This **evaporative cooling** occurs because the "hottest" molecules, those with the greatest kinetic energy, are the most likely to leave as gas. It is as if the hundred fastest runners at a college transferred to another school; the average speed of the remaining students would decline.

Evaporative cooling of water contributes to the stability of temperature in lakes and ponds and also provides a mechanism that prevents terrestrial organisms from overheating. For example, evaporation of water from the leaves of a plant

▲ **Figure 3.5 Temperatures for the Pacific Ocean and Southern California on an August day.**

INTERPRET THE DATA *Explain the pattern of temperatures shown in this diagram.*

helps keep the tissues in the leaves from becoming too warm in the sunlight. Evaporation of sweat from human skin dissipates body heat and helps prevent overheating on a hot day or when excess heat is generated by strenuous activity. High humidity on a hot day increases discomfort because the high concentration of water vapor in the air inhibits the evaporation of sweat from the body.

Floating of Ice on Liquid Water

Water is one of the few substances that are less dense as a solid than as a liquid. In other words, ice floats on liquid water. While other materials contract and become denser when they solidify, water expands. The cause of this exotic behavior is, once again, hydrogen bonding. At temperatures above 4°C, water behaves like other liquids, expanding as it warms and contracting as it cools. As the temperature falls from 4°C to 0°C, water begins to freeze because more and more of its molecules are moving too slowly to break hydrogen bonds. At 0°C, the molecules become locked into a crystalline lattice, each water molecule hydrogen-bonded to four partners (Figure 3.6). The hydrogen bonds keep the molecules at "arm's length," far enough apart to make ice about 10% less dense (10% fewer molecules for the same volume) than liquid water at 4°C. When ice absorbs enough heat for its temperature to rise above 0°C, hydrogen bonds between molecules are disrupted. As the crystal collapses, the ice melts, and molecules are free to slip closer together. Water reaches its greatest density at 4°C and then begins to expand as the molecules move faster. Even in liquid water, many of the molecules are connected by hydrogen bonds, though only transiently: The hydrogen bonds are constantly breaking and re-forming.

The ability of ice to float due to its lower density is an important factor in the suitability of the environment for life. If ice sank, then eventually all ponds, lakes, and even oceans would freeze solid, making life as we know it impossible on Earth. During

summer, only the upper few inches of the ocean would thaw. Instead, when a deep body of water cools, the floating ice insulates the liquid water below, preventing it from freezing and allowing life to exist under the frozen surface, as shown in the photo in Figure 3.6. Besides insulating the water below, ice also provides a solid habitat for some animals, such as polar bears and seals.

Many scientists are worried that these bodies of ice are at risk of disappearing. Global warming, which is caused by carbon dioxide and other "greenhouse" gases in the atmosphere, is having a profound effect on icy environments around the globe. In the Arctic, the average air temperature has risen 1.4°C just since 1961. This temperature increase has affected the seasonal balance between Arctic sea ice and liquid water, causing ice to form later in the year, to melt earlier, and to cover a smaller area. The rate at which glaciers and Arctic sea ice are disappearing is posing an extreme challenge to animals that depend on ice for their survival.

Water: The Solvent of Life

A sugar cube placed in a glass of water will dissolve with a little stirring. The glass will then contain a uniform mixture of sugar and water; the concentration of dissolved sugar will be the same everywhere in the mixture. A liquid that is a completely homogeneous mixture of two or more substances is called a **solution**. The dissolving agent of a solution is the **solvent**, and the substance that is dissolved is the **solute**. In this case, water is the solvent and sugar is the solute. An **aqueous solution** is one in which the solute is dissolved in water; water is the solvent.

Water is a very versatile solvent, a quality we can trace to the polarity of the water molecule. Suppose, for example, that a spoonful of table salt, the ionic compound sodium chloride (NaCl), is placed in water (Figure 3.7). At the surface of each grain, or crystal, of salt, the sodium and chloride ions are exposed to the solvent. These ions and regions of the water molecules are attracted to each other due to their opposite

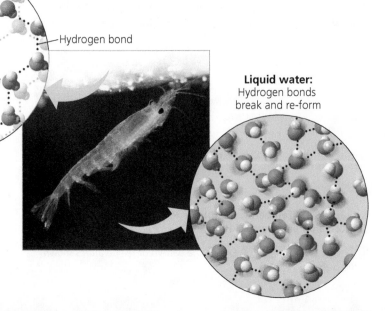

▶ Figure 3.6 **Ice: crystalline structure and floating barrier.** In ice, each molecule is hydrogen-bonded to four neighbors in a three-dimensional crystal. Because the crystal is spacious, ice has fewer molecules than an equal volume of liquid water. In other words, ice is less dense than liquid water. Floating ice becomes a barrier that insulates the liquid water below from the colder air. The marine organism shown here is a type of shrimp called krill; it was photographed beneath floating ice in the Southern Ocean near Antarctica.

WHAT IF? *If water did not form hydrogen bonds, what would happen to the shrimp's habitat, shown here?*

Hydrogen bond

Ice:
Hydrogen bonds
are stable

Liquid water:
Hydrogen bonds
break and re-form

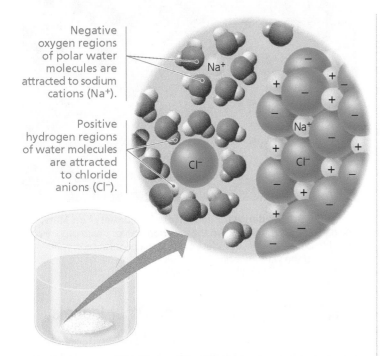

Negative oxygen regions of polar water molecules are attracted to sodium cations (Na⁺).

Positive hydrogen regions of water molecules are attracted to chloride anions (Cl⁻).

▲ **Figure 3.7 Table salt dissolving in water.** A sphere of water molecules, called a hydration shell, surrounds each solute ion.

WHAT IF? *What would happen if you heated this solution for a long time?*

charges. The oxygen regions of the water molecules are negatively charged and are attracted to sodium cations. The hydrogen regions are positively charged and are attracted to chloride anions. As a result, water molecules surround the individual sodium and chloride ions, separating and shielding them from one another. The sphere of water molecules around each dissolved ion is called a **hydration shell**. Working inward from the surface of each salt crystal, water eventually dissolves all the ions. The result is a solution of two solutes, sodium cations and chloride anions, homogeneously mixed with water, the solvent. Other ionic compounds also dissolve in water. Seawater, for instance, contains a great variety of dissolved ions, as do living cells.

A compound does not need to be ionic to dissolve in water; many compounds made up of nonionic polar molecules, such as the sugar in the sugar cube mentioned earlier, are also water-soluble. Such compounds dissolve when water molecules surround each of the solute molecules, forming hydrogen bonds with them. Even molecules as large as proteins can dissolve in water if they have ionic and polar regions on their surface (**Figure 3.8**). Many different kinds of polar

compounds are dissolved (along with ions) in the water of such biological fluids as blood, the sap of plants, and the liquid within all cells. Water is the solvent of life.

Hydrophilic and Hydrophobic Substances

Any substance that has an affinity for water is said to be **hydrophilic** (from the Greek *hydro*, water, and *philos*, loving). In some cases, substances can be hydrophilic without actually dissolving. For example, some molecules in cells are so large that they do not dissolve. Another example of a hydrophilic substance that does not dissolve is cotton, a plant product. Cotton consists of giant molecules of cellulose, a compound with numerous regions of partial positive and partial negative charges that can form hydrogen bonds with water. Water adheres to the cellulose fibers. Thus, a cotton towel does a great job of drying the body, yet it does not dissolve in the washing machine. Cellulose is also present in the walls of water-conducting cells in a plant; you read earlier how the adhesion of water to these hydrophilic walls helps water move up the plant against gravity.

There are, of course, substances that do not have an affinity for water. Substances that are nonionic and nonpolar (or otherwise cannot form hydrogen bonds) actually seem to repel water; these substances are said to be **hydrophobic** (from the Greek *phobos*, fearing). An example from the kitchen is vegetable oil, which, as you know, does not mix stably with water-based substances such as vinegar. The hydrophobic behavior of the oil molecules results from a prevalence of relatively nonpolar covalent bonds, in this case bonds between carbon and hydrogen, which share electrons almost equally. Hydrophobic molecules related to oils are major ingredients of cell membranes. (Imagine what would happen to a cell if its membrane dissolved!)

This oxygen is attracted to a slight positive charge on the lysozyme molecule.

This hydrogen is attracted to a slight negative charge on the lysozyme molecule.

▶ **Figure 3.8 A water-soluble protein.** Human lysozyme is a protein found in tears and saliva that has antibacterial action. This model shows the lysozyme molecule (purple) in an aqueous environment. Ionic and polar regions on the protein's surface attract water molecules.

Solute Concentration in Aqueous Solutions

Most of the chemical reactions in organisms involve solutes dissolved in water. To understand such reactions, we must know how many atoms and molecules are involved and calculate the concentration of solutes in an aqueous solution (the number of solute molecules in a volume of solution).

When carrying out experiments, we use mass to calculate the number of molecules. We must first calculate the **molecular mass**, which is the sum of the masses of all the atoms in a molecule. As an example, let's calculate the molecular mass of table sugar (sucrose), $C_{12}H_{22}O_{11}$. In round numbers of daltons, the mass of a carbon atom is 12, the mass of a hydrogen atom is 1, and the mass of an oxygen atom is 16. Thus, sucrose has a molecular mass of $(12 \times 12) + (22 \times 1) + (11 \times 16) = 342$ daltons. Because we can't weigh out small numbers of molecules, we usually measure substances in units called moles. Just as a dozen always means 12 objects, a **mole (mol)** represents an exact number of objects: 6.02×10^{23}, which is called Avogadro's number. Because of the way in which Avogadro's number and the unit *dalton* were originally defined, there are 6.02×10^{23} daltons in 1 g. Once we determine the molecular mass of a molecule such as sucrose, we can use the same number (342), but with the unit *gram*, to represent the mass of 6.02×10^{23} molecules of sucrose, or 1 mol of sucrose (this is sometimes called the *molar mass*). To obtain 1 mol of sucrose in the lab, therefore, we weigh out 342 g.

The practical advantage of measuring a quantity of chemicals in moles is that a mole of one substance has exactly the same number of molecules as a mole of any other substance. If the molecular mass of substance A is 342 daltons and that of substance B is 10 daltons, then 342 g of A will have the same number of molecules as 10 g of B. A mole of ethyl alcohol (C_2H_6O) also contains 6.02×10^{23} molecules, but its mass is only 46 g because the mass of a molecule of ethyl alcohol is less than that of a molecule of sucrose. Measuring in moles makes it convenient for scientists working in the laboratory to combine substances in fixed ratios of molecules.

How would we make a liter (L) of solution consisting of 1 mol of sucrose dissolved in water? We would measure out 342 g of sucrose and then gradually add water, while stirring, until the sugar was completely dissolved. We would then add enough water to bring the total volume of the solution up to 1 L. At that point, we would have a 1-molar (1 *M*) solution of sucrose. **Molarity**—the number of moles of solute per liter of solution—is the unit of concentration most often used by biologists for aqueous solutions.

Water's capacity as a versatile solvent complements the other properties discussed in this chapter. Since these remarkable properties allow water to support life on Earth so well, scientists who seek life elsewhere in the universe look for water as a sign that a planet might sustain life.

▲ **Figure 3.9 Evidence for subsurface liquid water on Mars.** The dark streaks running down the lower portion of the photo are proposed to be streams of subsurface flowing water because they appear only during the warm season. The gullies in the middle of the photo could have been formed by flowing water.

Possible Evolution of Life on Other Planets

EVOLUTION Biologists who look for life elsewhere in the universe (known as *astrobiologists*) have concentrated their search on planets that might have water. More than 800 planets have been found outside our solar system, and there is evidence for the presence of water vapor on a few of them. In our own solar system, Mars has been a focus of study. Like Earth, Mars has an ice cap at both poles. Images from spacecraft sent to Mars show that ice is present just under the surface of Mars and enough water vapor exists in its atmosphere for frost to form. **Figure 3.9** shows streaks that form along steep slopes during the Mars spring and summer, features that vanish during the winter. Some scientists have proposed that these are seasonal streams of flowing water occurring when subsurface ice melts during the warm season, while others think they are the result of CO_2 rather than water. Drilling below the surface may be the next step in the search for signs of life on Mars. If any life-forms or fossils are found, their study will shed light on the process of evolution from an entirely new perspective.

CONCEPT CHECK **3.2**

1. Describe how properties of water contribute to the upward movement of water in a tree.
2. Explain the saying "It's not the heat; it's the humidity."
3. How can the freezing of water crack boulders?
4. **WHAT IF?** A water strider (which can walk on water) has legs that are coated with a hydrophobic substance. What might be the benefit? What would happen if the substance were hydrophilic?
5. **INTERPRET THE DATA** The concentration of the appetite-regulating hormone ghrelin is about 1.3×10^{-10} *M* in the blood of a fasting person. How many molecules of ghrelin are in 1 L of blood?

CONCEPT 3.3

Acidic and basic conditions affect living organisms

Occasionally, a hydrogen atom participating in a hydrogen bond between two water molecules shifts from one molecule to the other. When this happens, the hydrogen atom leaves its electron behind, and what is actually transferred is a **hydrogen ion** (H^+), a single proton with a charge of 1+. The water molecule that lost a proton is now a **hydroxide ion** (OH^-), which has a charge of 1−. The proton binds to the other water molecule, making that molecule a **hydronium ion** (H_3O^+). We can picture the chemical reaction as follows:

$$2\ H_2O$$

Hydronium
ion (H_3O^+)

Hydroxide
ion (OH^-)

By convention, H^+ (the hydrogen ion) is used to represent H_3O^+ (the hydronium ion), and we follow that practice in this book. Keep in mind, though, that H^+ does not exist on its own in an aqueous solution. It is always associated with a water molecule in the form of H_3O^+.

As indicated by the double arrows, this is a reversible reaction that reaches a state of dynamic equilibrium when water molecules dissociate at the same rate that they are being reformed from H^+ and OH^-. At this equilibrium point, the concentration of water molecules greatly exceeds the concentrations of H^+ and OH^-. In pure water, only one water molecule in every 554 million is dissociated; the concentration of each ion in pure water is $10^{-7}\ M$ (at 25°C). This means there is only one ten-millionth of a mole of hydrogen ions per liter of pure water and an equal number of hydroxide ions. (Even so, this is a huge number—over 60,000 *trillion*—of each ion.)

Although the dissociation of water is reversible and statistically rare, it is exceedingly important in the chemistry of life. H^+ and OH^- are very reactive. Changes in their concentrations can drastically affect a cell's proteins and other complex molecules. As we have seen, the concentrations of H^+ and OH^- are equal in pure water, but adding certain kinds of solutes, called acids and bases, disrupts this balance. Biologists use something called the pH scale to describe how acidic or basic (the opposite of acidic) a solution is. In the remainder of this chapter, you will learn about acids, bases, and pH and why changes in pH can adversely affect organisms.

Acids and Bases

What would cause an aqueous solution to have an imbalance in H^+ and OH^- concentrations? When acids dissolve in water, they donate additional H^+ to the solution. An **acid** is a substance that increases the hydrogen ion concentration of a solution. For example, when hydrochloric acid (HCl) is added to water, hydrogen ions dissociate from chloride ions:

$$HCl \rightarrow H^+ + Cl^-$$

This source of H^+ (dissociation of water is the other source) results in an acidic solution—one having more H^+ than OH^-.

A substance that reduces the hydrogen ion concentration of a solution is called a **base**. Some bases reduce the H^+ concentration directly by accepting hydrogen ions. Ammonia (NH_3), for instance, acts as a base when the unshared electron pair in nitrogen's valence shell attracts a hydrogen ion from the solution, resulting in an ammonium ion (NH_4^+):

$$NH_3 + H^+ \rightleftharpoons NH_4^+$$

Other bases reduce the H^+ concentration indirectly by dissociating to form hydroxide ions, which combine with hydrogen ions and form water. One such base is sodium hydroxide (NaOH), which in water dissociates into its ions:

$$NaOH \rightarrow Na^+ + OH^-$$

In either case, the base reduces the H^+ concentration. Solutions with a higher concentration of OH^- than H^+ are known as basic solutions. A solution in which the H^+ and OH^- concentrations are equal is said to be neutral.

Notice that single arrows were used in the reactions for HCl and NaOH. These compounds dissociate completely when mixed with water, so hydrochloric acid is called a strong acid and sodium hydroxide a strong base. In contrast, ammonia is a weak base. The double arrows in the reaction for ammonia indicate that the binding and release of hydrogen ions are reversible reactions, although at equilibrium there will be a fixed ratio of NH_4^+ to NH_3.

Weak acids are acids that reversibly release and accept back hydrogen ions. An example is carbonic acid:

$$\underset{\text{Carbonic acid}}{H_2CO_3} \rightleftharpoons \underset{\text{Bicarbonate ion}}{HCO_3^-} + \underset{\text{Hydrogen ion}}{H^+}$$

Here the equilibrium so favors the reaction in the left direction that when carbonic acid is added to pure water, only 1% of the molecules are dissociated at any particular time. Still, that is enough to shift the balance of H^+ and OH^- from neutrality.

The pH Scale

In any aqueous solution at 25°C, the *product* of the H^+ and OH^- concentrations is constant at 10^{-14}. This can be written

$$[H^+][OH^-] = 10^{-14}$$

In such an equation, brackets indicate molar concentration. In a neutral solution at 25°C (close to room temperature), $[H^+] = 10^{-7}$ and $[OH^-] = 10^{-7}$, so in this case, 10^{-14} is the product of 10^{-7} and 10^{-7}. If enough acid is added to a solution to increase $[H^+]$ to 10^{-5} M, then $[OH^-]$ will decline by an equivalent factor to 10^{-9} M (note that $10^{-5} \times 10^{-9} = 10^{-14}$). This constant relationship expresses the behavior of acids and bases in an aqueous solution. An acid not only adds hydrogen ions to a solution, but also removes hydroxide ions because of the tendency for H^+ to combine with OH^-, forming water. A base has the opposite effect, increasing OH^- concentration but also reducing H^+ concentration by the formation of water. If enough of a base is added to raise the OH^- concentration to 10^{-4} M, it will cause the H^+ concentration to drop to 10^{-10} M. Whenever we know the concentration of either H^+ or OH^- in an aqueous solution, we can deduce the concentration of the other ion.

Because the H^+ and OH^- concentrations of solutions can vary by a factor of 100 trillion or more, scientists have developed a way to express this variation more conveniently than in moles per liter. The pH scale (**Figure 3.10**) compresses the range of H^+ and OH^- concentrations by employing

logarithms. The **pH** of a solution is defined as the negative logarithm (base 10) of the hydrogen ion concentration:

$$pH = -\log [H^+]$$

For a neutral aqueous solution, $[H^+]$ is 10^{-7} M, giving us

$$-\log 10^{-7} = -(-7) = 7$$

Notice that pH *declines* as H^+ concentration *increases*. Notice, too, that although the pH scale is based on H^+ concentration, it also implies OH^- concentration. A solution of pH 10 has a hydrogen ion concentration of 10^{-10} M and a hydroxide ion concentration of 10^{-4} M.

The pH of a neutral aqueous solution at 25°C is 7, the midpoint of the pH scale. A pH value less than 7 denotes an acidic solution; the lower the number, the more acidic the solution. The pH for basic solutions is above 7. Most biological fluids, such as blood and saliva, are within the range of pH 6–8. There are a few exceptions, however, including the strongly acidic digestive juice of the human stomach, which has a pH of about 2.

Remember that each pH unit represents a tenfold difference in H^+ and OH^- concentrations. It is this mathematical feature that makes the pH scale so compact. A solution of pH 3 is not twice as acidic as a solution of pH 6, but a thousand times ($10 \times 10 \times 10$) more acidic. When the pH of a solution changes slightly, the actual concentrations of H^+ and OH^- in the solution change substantially.

Buffers

The internal pH of most living cells is close to 7. Even a slight change in pH can be harmful, because the chemical processes of the cell are very sensitive to the concentrations of hydrogen and hydroxide ions. The pH of human blood is very close to 7.4, which is slightly basic. A person cannot survive for more than a few minutes if the blood pH drops to 7 or rises to 7.8, and a chemical system exists in the blood that maintains a stable pH. If 0.01 mol of a strong acid is added to a liter of pure water, the pH drops from 7.0 to 2.0. If the same amount of acid is added to a liter of blood, however, the pH decrease is only from 7.4 to 7.3. Why does the addition of acid have so much less of an effect on the pH of blood than it does on the pH of water?

The presence of substances called buffers allows biological fluids to maintain a relatively constant pH despite the addition of acids or bases. A **buffer** is a substance that minimizes changes in the concentrations of H^+ and OH^- in a solution. It does so by accepting hydrogen ions from the solution when they are in excess and donating hydrogen ions to the solution when they have been depleted. Most buffer solutions contain a weak acid and its corresponding base, which combine reversibly with hydrogen ions.

Several buffers contribute to pH stability in human blood and many other biological solutions. One of these is

▲ **Figure 3.10** **The pH scale and pH values of some aqueous solutions.**

carbonic acid (H_2CO_3), which is formed when CO_2 reacts with water in blood plasma. As mentioned earlier, carbonic acid dissociates to yield a bicarbonate ion (HCO_3^-) and a hydrogen ion (H^+):

$$\underset{\substack{\text{H}^+ \text{ donor}\\ \text{(acid)}}}{H_2CO_3} \underset{\substack{\text{Response to}\\ \text{a drop in pH}}}{\overset{\substack{\text{Response to}\\ \text{a rise in pH}}{\rightleftharpoons}}} \underset{\substack{\text{H}^+ \text{ acceptor}\\ \text{(base)}}}{HCO_3^-} + \underset{\substack{\text{Hydrogen}\\ \text{ion}}}{H^+}$$

The chemical equilibrium between carbonic acid and bicarbonate acts as a pH regulator, the reaction shifting left or right as other processes in the solution add or remove hydrogen ions. If the H^+ concentration in blood begins to fall (that is, if pH rises), the reaction proceeds to the right and more carbonic acid dissociates, replenishing hydrogen ions. But when the H^+ concentration in blood begins to rise (when pH drops), the reaction proceeds to the left, with HCO_3^- (the base) removing the hydrogen ions from the solution and forming H_2CO_3. Thus, the carbonic acid–bicarbonate buffering system consists of an acid and a base in equilibrium with each other. Most other buffers are also acid-base pairs.

Acidification: A Threat to Water Quality

Among the many threats to water quality posed by human activities is the burning of fossil fuels, which releases gaseous compounds into the atmosphere. When certain of these compounds react with water, the water becomes more acidic, altering the delicate balance of conditions for life on Earth. Carbon dioxide is the main product of fossil fuel combustion. About 25% of human-generated CO_2 is absorbed by the oceans. In spite of the huge volume of water in the oceans, scientists worry that the absorption of so much CO_2 will harm marine ecosystems.

Recent data have shown that such fears are well founded. When CO_2 dissolves in seawater, it reacts with water to form carbonic acid, which lowers ocean pH, a process known as **ocean acidification**. Based on measurements of CO_2 levels in air bubbles trapped in ice over thousands of years, scientists calculate that the pH of the oceans is 0.1 pH unit lower now than at any time in the past 420,000 years. Recent studies predict that it will drop another 0.3–0.5 pH unit by the end of this century.

As seawater acidifies, the extra hydrogen ions combine with carbonate ions (CO_3^{2-}) to form bicarbonate ions (HCO_3^-), thereby reducing the carbonate ion concentration **(Figure 3.11)**. Scientists predict that ocean acidification will cause the carbonate ion concentration to decrease by 40% by the year 2100. This is of great concern because carbonate ions are required for calcification, the production of calcium carbonate ($CaCO_3$) by many marine organisms, including reef-building corals and animals that build shells. The Scientific Skills Exercise allows you to work with data

Some carbon dioxide (CO_2) in the atmosphere dissolves in the ocean, where it reacts with water to form carbonic acid (H_2CO_3).

$CO_2 + H_2O \rightarrow H_2CO_3$

Carbonic acid dissociates into hydrogen ions (H^+) and bicarbonate ions (HCO_3^-).

$H_2CO_3 \rightarrow H^+ + HCO_3^-$

The added H^+ combines with carbonate ions (CO_3^{2-}), forming more HCO_3^-.

$H^+ + CO_3^{2-} \rightarrow HCO_3^-$

Less CO_3^{2-} is available for calcification—the formation of calcium carbonate ($CaCO_3$)—by marine organisms such as corals.

$CO_3^{2-} + Ca^{2+} \rightarrow CaCO_3$

▲ **Figure 3.11 Atmospheric CO_2 from human activities and its fate in the ocean.**

from an experiment examining the effect of carbonate ion concentration on coral reefs. Coral reefs are sensitive ecosystems that act as havens for a great diversity of marine life. The disappearance of coral reef ecosystems would be a tragic loss of biological diversity.

If there is any reason for optimism about the future quality of water resources on our planet, it is that we have made progress in learning about the delicate chemical balances in oceans, lakes, and rivers. Continued progress can come only from the actions of informed individuals, like yourselves, who are concerned about environmental quality. This requires understanding the crucial role that water plays in the suitability of the environment for continued life on Earth.

CONCEPT CHECK 3.3

1. Compared with a basic solution at pH 9, the same volume of an acidic solution at pH 4 has _____ times as many hydrogen ions (H^+).

2. HCl is a strong acid that dissociates in water: $HCl \rightarrow H^+ + Cl^-$. What is the pH of 0.01 M HCl?

3. Acetic acid (CH_3COOH) can be a buffer, similar to carbonic acid. Write the dissociation reaction, identifying the acid, base, H^+ acceptor, and H^+ donor.

4. **WHAT IF?** Given a liter of pure water and a liter solution of acetic acid, what would happen to the pH if you added 0.01 mol of a strong acid to each? Use the reaction equation from question 3 to explain the result.

Interpreting a Scatter Plot with a Regression Line

How Does the Carbonate Ion Concentration of Seawater Affect the Calcification Rate of a Coral Reef? Scientists predict that acidification of the ocean due to higher levels of atmospheric CO_2 will lower the concentration of dissolved carbonate ions, which living corals use to build calcium carbonate reef structures. In this exercise, you will analyze data from a controlled experiment that examined the effect of carbonate ion concentration ($[CO_3^{2-}]$) on calcium carbonate deposition, a process called calcification.

How the Experiment Was Done The Biosphere 2 aquarium in Arizona contains a large coral reef system that behaves like a natural reef. For several years, a group of researchers measured the rate of calcification by the reef organisms and examined how the calcification rate changed with differing amounts of dissolved carbonate ions in the seawater.

Data from the Experiment The black data points in the graph form a scatter plot. The red line, known as a linear regression line, is the best-fitting straight line for these points.

Interpret the Data

1. When presented with a graph of experimental data, the first step in analysis is to determine what each axis represents. (a) In words, explain what is being shown on the *x*-axis. Be sure to include the units. (b) What is being shown on the *y*-axis (including units)? (c) Which variable is the independent variable—the variable that was *manipulated* by the researchers? (d) Which variable is the dependent variable—the variable that responded to or depended on the treatment, which was *measured* by the researchers?

2. Based on the data shown in the graph, describe in words the relationship between carbonate ion concentration and calcification rate.

3. (a) If the seawater carbonate ion concentration is 270 µmol/kg, what is the approximate rate of calcification, and approximately how many days would it take 1 square meter of reef to accumulate 30 mmol of calcium carbonate ($CaCO_3$)? (b) If the seawater carbonate ion

concentration is 250 µmol/kg, what is the approximate rate of calcification, and approximately how many days would it take 1 square meter of reef to accumulate 30 mmol of calcium carbonate? (c) If carbonate ion concentration decreases, how does the calcification rate change, and how does that affect the time it takes coral to grow?

4. (a) Referring to the equations in Figure 3.11, determine which step of the process is measured in this experiment. (b) Are the results of this experiment consistent with the hypothesis that increased atmospheric $[CO_2]$ will slow the growth of coral reefs? Why or why not?

MB A version of this Scientific Skills Exercise can be assigned in MasteringBiology.

Data from C. Langdon et al., Effect of calcium carbonate saturation state on the calcification rate of an experimental coral reef, *Global Biogeochemical Cycles* 14:639–654 (2000).

---

3 Chapter Review

SUMMARY OF KEY CONCEPTS

CONCEPT 3.1

Polar covalent bonds in water molecules result in hydrogen bonding (p. 45)

- Water is a **polar molecule**. A hydrogen bond forms when the slightly negatively charged oxygen of one water molecule is attracted to the slightly positively charged hydrogen of a nearby water molecule. Hydrogen bonding between water molecules is the basis for water's properties.

DRAW IT *Label a hydrogen bond and a polar covalent bond in this figure. Is a hydrogen bond a covalent bond? Explain.*

CONCEPT 3.2

Four emergent properties of water contribute to Earth's suitability for life (pp. 45–50)

- Hydrogen bonding keeps water molecules close to each other, and this **cohesion** helps pull water upward in the microscopic water-conducting cells of plants. Hydrogen bonding is also responsible for water's **surface tension**.
- Water has a high **specific heat**: Heat is absorbed when hydrogen bonds break and is released when hydrogen bonds form. This helps keep temperatures relatively steady, within limits that permit life. **Evaporative cooling** is based on water's high **heat of vaporization**. The evaporative loss of the most energetic water molecules cools a surface.
- Ice floats because it is less dense than liquid water. This property allows life to exist under the frozen surfaces of lakes and polar seas.
- Water is an unusually versatile **solvent** because its polar molecules are attracted to ions and polar substances that can form

hydrogen bonds. **Hydrophilic** substances have an affinity for water; **hydrophobic** substances do not. **Molarity**, the number of moles of **solute** per liter of **solution**, is used as a measure of solute concentration in solutions. A **mole** is a certain number of molecules of a substance. The mass of a mole of a substance in grams is the same as the **molecular mass** in daltons.

- The emergent properties of water support life on Earth and may contribute to the potential for life to have evolved on other planets.

? *Describe how different types of solutes dissolve in water. Explain what a solution is.*

CONCEPT 3.3

Acidic and basic conditions affect living organisms (pp. 51–54)

- A water molecule can transfer an H^+ to another water molecule to form H_3O^+ (represented simply by H^+) and OH^-.
- The concentration of H^+ is expressed as **pH**; $pH = -\log [H^+]$. A **buffer** consists of an acid-base pair that combines reversibly with hydrogen ions, allowing it to resist pH changes.
- The burning of fossil fuels increases the amount of CO_2 in the atmosphere. Some CO_2 dissolves in the oceans, causing **ocean acidification**, which has potentially grave consequences for coral reefs.

Acidic
$[H^+] > [OH^-]$

Acids donate H^+ in aqueous solutions.

Neutral
$[H^+] = [OH^-]$

Bases donate OH^- or accept H^+ in aqueous solutions.

Basic
$[H^+] < [OH^-]$

0

7

14

? *Explain how increasing amounts of CO_2 dissolving in the ocean leads to ocean acidification. How does this change in pH affect carbonate ion concentration and the rate of calcification?*

TEST YOUR UNDERSTANDING

LEVEL 1: KNOWLEDGE/COMPREHENSION

1. Which of the following is a hydrophobic material?
   a. paper
   b. table salt
   c. wax
   d. sugar

2. We can be sure that a mole of table sugar and a mole of vitamin C are equal in their
   a. mass.
   b. volume.
   c. number of atoms.
   d. number of molecules.

3. Measurements show that the pH of a particular lake is 4.0. What is the hydrogen ion concentration of the lake?
   a. $4.0\ M$
   b. $10^{-10}\ M$
   c. $10^{-4}\ M$
   d. $10^4\ M$

4. What is the *hydroxide* ion concentration of the lake described in question 3?
   a. $10^{-10}\ M$
   b. $10^{-4}\ M$
   c. $10^{-7}\ M$
   d. $10.0\ M$

LEVEL 2: APPLICATION/ANALYSIS

5. A slice of pizza has 500 kcal. If we could burn the pizza and use all the heat to warm a 50-L container of cold water, what would be the approximate increase in the temperature of the water? (*Note*: A liter of cold water weighs about 1 kg.)
   a. 50°C
   b. 5°C
   c. 100°C
   d. 10°C

6. **DRAW IT** Draw the hydration shells that form around a potassium ion and a chloride ion when potassium chloride (KCl) dissolves in water. Label the positive, negative, and partial charges on the atoms.

LEVEL 3: SYNTHESIS/EVALUATION

7. In agricultural areas, farmers pay close attention to the weather forecast. Right before a predicted overnight freeze, farmers spray water on crops to protect the plants. Use the properties of water to explain how this method works. Be sure to mention why hydrogen bonds are responsible for this phenomenon.

8. **EVOLUTION CONNECTION**
   This chapter explains how the emergent properties of water contribute to the suitability of the environment for life. Until fairly recently, scientists assumed that other physical requirements for life included a moderate range of temperature, pH, atmospheric pressure, and salinity, as well as low levels of toxic chemicals. That view has changed with the discovery of organisms known as extremophiles, which have been found flourishing in hot, acidic sulfur springs, around hydrothermal vents deep in the ocean, and in soils with high levels of toxic metals. Why would astrobiologists be interested in studying extremophiles? What does the existence of life in such extreme environments say about the possibility of life on other planets?

9. **SCIENTIFIC INQUIRY**
   Design a controlled experiment to test the hypothesis that water acidification caused by acidic rain would inhibit the growth of *Elodea*, a freshwater plant (see Figure 2.17).

10. **WRITE ABOUT A THEME: ORGANIZATION**
    Several emergent properties of water contribute to the suitability of the environment for life. In a short essay (100–150 words), describe how the ability of water to function as a versatile solvent arises from the structure of water molecules.

11. **SYNTHESIZE YOUR KNOWLEDGE**

How do cats drink? While dogs form their tongues into spoons and scoop water into their mouths, scientists using high-speed video have shown that cats use a different technique to drink aqueous substances like water and milk. Four times a second, the cat touches the tip of its tongue to the water and draws a column of water up into its mouth (as you can see in the photo), which then shuts before gravity can pull the water back down. Describe how the properties of water allow cats to drink in this fashion, including how water's molecular structure contributes to the process.

MasteringBiology®

Students Go to **MasteringBiology** for assignments, the eText, and the Study Area with practice tests, animations, and activities.

Instructors Go to **MasteringBiology** for automatically graded tutorials and questions that you can assign to your students, plus Instructor Resources.

4

Carbon and the Molecular Diversity of Life

KEY CONCEPTS

4.1 Organic chemistry is the study of carbon compounds

4.2 Carbon atoms can form diverse molecules by bonding to four other atoms

4.3 A few chemical groups are key to molecular function

▲ Carbon can bond to four other atoms or groups of atoms, making a large variety of molecules possible.

▲ **Figure 4.1 What properties make carbon the basis of all life?**

Carbon: The Backbone of Life

Living organisms, such as the plants and the Qinling golden snub-nosed monkeys shown in **Figure 4.1**, are made up of chemicals based mostly on the element carbon. Carbon enters the biosphere through the action of plants and other photosynthetic organisms. Plants use solar energy to transform atmospheric CO_2 into the molecules of life, which are then taken in by plant-eating animals.

Of all the chemical elements, carbon is unparalleled in its ability to form molecules that are large, complex, and varied, making possible the diversity of organisms that have evolved on Earth. Proteins, DNA, carbohydrates, and other molecules that distinguish living matter from inanimate material are all composed of carbon atoms bonded to one another and to atoms of other elements. Hydrogen (H), oxygen (O), nitrogen (N), sulfur (S), and phosphorus (P) are other common ingredients of these compounds, but it is the element carbon (C) that accounts for the enormous variety of biological molecules.

Large biological molecules, such as proteins, are the main focus of Chapter 5. In this chapter, we investigate the properties of smaller molecules. We will use these small molecules to illustrate concepts of molecular architecture that will help explain why carbon is so important to life, at the same time highlighting the theme that emergent properties arise from the organization of matter in living organisms.

CONCEPT 4.1

Organic chemistry is the study of carbon compounds

For historical reasons, compounds containing carbon are said to be organic, and their study is called **organic chemistry**. By the early 1800s, chemists had learned to make simple compounds in the laboratory by combining elements under the right conditions. Artificial synthesis of the complex molecules extracted from living matter seemed impossible, however. Organic compounds were thought to arise only in living organisms, which were believed to contain a life force beyond the jurisdiction of physical and chemical laws.

Chemists began to chip away at this notion when they learned to synthesize organic compounds in the laboratory. In 1828, Friedrich Wöhler, a German chemist, tried to make an "inorganic" salt, ammonium cyanate, by mixing solutions of ammonium ions (NH_4^+) and cyanate ions (CNO^-). Wöhler was astonished to find that instead he had made urea, an organic compound present in the urine of animals.

The next few decades saw laboratory synthesis of increasingly complex organic compounds, supporting the view that physical and chemical laws govern the processes of life. Organic chemistry was redefined as the study of carbon compounds, regardless of origin. Organic compounds range from simple molecules, such as methane (CH_4), to colossal ones, such as proteins, with thousands of atoms.

Organic Molecules and the Origin of Life on Earth

EVOLUTION In 1953, Stanley Miller, a graduate student of Harold Urey's at the University of Chicago, helped bring the abiotic (nonliving) synthesis of organic compounds into the context of evolution. Study **Figure 4.2** to learn about his classic experiment. From his results, Miller concluded that complex organic molecules could arise spontaneously under conditions thought at that time to have existed on the early Earth. You can work with the data from a related experiment in the Scientific Skills Exercise. These experiments support the idea that abiotic synthesis of organic compounds, perhaps near volcanoes, could have been an early stage in the origin of life.

The overall percentages of the major elements of life—C, H, O, N, S, and P—are quite uniform from one organism to another, reflecting the common evolutionary origin of all life. Because of carbon's ability to form four bonds, however, this limited assortment of atomic building blocks can be used to build an inexhaustible variety of organic molecules. Different species of organisms, and different individuals within a species, are distinguished by variations in the types

▼ Figure 4.2 | Inquiry

Can organic molecules form under conditions estimated to simulate those on the early Earth?

Experiment In 1953, Stanley Miller set up a closed system to mimic conditions thought at that time to have existed on the early Earth. A flask of water simulated the primeval sea. The water was heated so that some vaporized and moved into a second, higher flask containing the "atmosphere"—a mixture of gases. Sparks were discharged in the synthetic atmosphere to mimic lightning.

❶ The water mixture in the "sea" flask was heated; vapor entered the "atmosphere" flask.

❷ The "atmosphere" contained a mixture of hydrogen gas (H_2), methane (CH_4), ammonia (NH_3), and water vapor.

❸ Sparks were discharged to mimic lightning.

❹ A condenser cooled the atmosphere, raining water and dissolved molecules into the sea flask.

❺ As material cycled through the apparatus, Miller periodically collected samples for analysis.

Results Miller identified a variety of organic molecules that are common in organisms. These included simple compounds, such as formaldehyde (CH_2O) and hydrogen cyanide (HCN), and more complex molecules, such as amino acids and long chains of carbon and hydrogen known as hydrocarbons.

Conclusion Organic molecules, a first step in the origin of life, may have been synthesized abiotically on the early Earth. Although new evidence indicates that the early Earth's atmosphere was different from the "atmosphere" used by Miller in this experiment, recent experiments using the revised list of chemicals also produced organic molecules.

Source: S. L. Miller, A production of amino acids under possible primitive Earth conditions, *Science* 117:528–529 (1953).

WHAT IF? *If Miller had increased the concentration of NH_3 in his experiment, how might the relative amounts of the products HCN and CH_2O have differed?*

Working with Moles and Molar Ratios

Could the First Biological Molecules Have Formed Near Volcanoes on Early Earth? In 2007, Jeffrey Bada, a former graduate student of Stanley Miller's, discovered some vials of samples that had never been analyzed from an experiment performed by Miller in 1958. In this experiment, Miller used hydrogen sulfide gas (H_2S) as one of the gases in the reactant mixture. Since H_2S is released by volcanoes, the H_2S experiment was designed to mimic conditions near volcanoes on early Earth. In 2011, Bada and colleagues published the results of their analysis of these "lost" samples. In this exercise, you will make calculations using the molar ratios of reactants and products from the H_2S experiment.

How the Experiment Was Done According to his laboratory notebook, Miller used the same apparatus as in his original experiment (see Figure 4.2), but the mixture of gaseous reactants included methane (CH_4), carbon dioxide (CO_2), hydrogen sulfide (H_2S), and ammonia (NH_3). After three days of simulated volcanic activity, he collected samples of the liquid, partially purified the chemicals, and sealed the samples in sterile vials. In 2011, Bada's research team used modern analytical methods to analyze the products in the vials for the presence of amino acids, the building blocks of proteins.

Data from the Experiment The table below shows 4 of the 23 amino acids detected in the samples from Miller's 1958 H_2S experiment.

Product Compound	Molecular Formula	Molar Ratio (Relative to Glycine)
Glycine	$C_2H_5NO_2$	1.0
Serine	$C_3H_7NO_3$	3.0×10^{-2}
Methionine	$C_5H_{11}NO_2S$	1.8×10^{-3}
Alanine	$C_3H_7NO_2$	1.1

Interpret the Data

1. A *mole* is the number of grams of a substance that equals its molecular (or atomic) mass in daltons. There are 6.02×10^{23} molecules (or atoms) in 1.0 mole (Avogadro's number; see Concept 3.2). The data table shows the "molar ratios" of some of the products from the Miller H_2S experiment. In a molar ratio, each unitless value is expressed relative to a standard for that experiment. Here, the standard is the number of moles of the amino acid glycine, which is set to a value of 1.0. For instance, serine has a molar ratio of 3.0×10^{-2}, meaning that for every mole of glycine, there is 3.0×10^{-2} mole of serine. (a) Give the molar ratio of methionine to glycine and explain what it means. (b) How many molecules of glycine are present in 1.0 mole? (c) For every 1.0 mole of glycine in the sample, how many molecules of methionine are present? (Recall that to multiply two

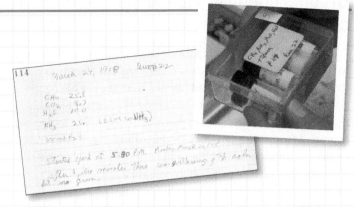

▲ Some of Stanley Miller's notes from his 1958 hydrogen sulfide (H_2S) experiment along with his original vials.

numbers with exponents, you add their exponents; to divide them, you subtract the exponent in the denominator from that in the numerator.)

2. (a) Which amino acid is present in higher amounts than glycine? (b) How many more molecules of that amino acid are present than the number of molecules in 1.0 mole of glycine?

3. The synthesis of products is limited by the amount of reactants. (a) If one mole each of CH_4, NH_3, H_2S, and CO_2 is added to 1 liter of water (= 55.5 moles of H_2O) in a flask, how many moles of hydrogen, carbon, oxygen, nitrogen, and sulfur are in the flask? (b) Looking at the molecular formula in the table, how many moles of each element would be needed to make 1.0 mole of glycine? (c) What is the maximum number of moles of glycine that could be made in that flask, with the specified ingredients, if no other molecules were made? Explain. (d) If serine or methionine were made individually, which element(s) would be used up first for each? How much of each product could be made?

4. The earlier published experiment carried out by Miller did not include H_2S in the reactants (see Figure 4.2). Which of the compounds shown in the data table can be made in the H_2S experiment but could not be made in the earlier experiment?

(MB) A version of this Scientific Skills Exercise can be assigned in MasteringBiology.

Data from E. T. Parker et al., Primordial synthesis of amines and amino acids in a 1958 Miller H_2S-rich spark discharge experiment, *Proceedings of the National Academy of Sciences USA* 108:5526-5531 (2011). www.pnas.org/cgi/doi/10.1073/pnas.1019191108.

of organic molecules they make. In a sense, the great diversity of living organisms we see on the planet (and in fossil remains) is made possible by the unique chemical versatility of the element carbon.

CONCEPT CHECK 4.1

1. Why was Wöhler astonished to find he had made urea?

2. **WHAT IF?** Miller carried out a control experiment without the electrical discharge and found no organic compounds. What might explain this result?

Carbon atoms can form diverse molecules by bonding to four other atoms

The key to an atom's chemical characteristics is its electron configuration. This configuration determines the kinds and number of bonds an atom will form with other atoms. Recall that it is the valence electrons, those in the outermost shell, that are available to form bonds with other atoms.

Molecule and Molecular Shape	Molecular Formula	Structural Formula	Ball-and-Stick Model (molecular shape in pink)	Space-Filling Model
(a) Methane. When a carbon atom has four single bonds to other atoms, the molecule is tetrahedral.	CH₄	H—C—H with H on top and bottom		
(b) Ethane. A molecule may have more than one tetrahedral group of single-bonded atoms. (Ethane consists of two such groups.)	C₂H₆	H—C—C—H with H above and below each C		
(c) Ethene (ethylene). When two carbon atoms are joined by a double bond, all atoms attached to those carbons are in the same plane, and the molecule is flat.	C₂H₄	H₂C=CH₂ structural formula		

▲ Figure 4.3 **The shapes of three simple organic molecules.**

The Formation of Bonds with Carbon

Carbon has 6 electrons, with 2 in the first electron shell and 4 in the second shell; thus, it has 4 valence electrons in a shell that can hold up to 8 electrons. A carbon atom usually completes its valence shell by sharing its 4 electrons with other atoms so that 8 electrons are present. Each pair of shared electrons constitutes a covalent bond (see Figure 2.10d). In organic molecules, carbon usually forms single or double covalent bonds. Each carbon atom acts as an intersection point from which a molecule can branch off in as many as four directions. This enables carbon to form large, complex molecules.

When a carbon atom forms four single covalent bonds, the arrangement of its four hybrid orbitals causes the bonds to angle toward the corners of an imaginary tetrahedron. The bond angles in methane (CH₄) are 109.5° **(Figure 4.3a)**, and they are roughly the same in any group of atoms where carbon has four single bonds. For example, ethane (C₂H₆) is shaped like two overlapping tetrahedrons **(Figure 4.3b)**. In molecules with more carbons, every grouping of a carbon bonded to four other atoms has a tetrahedral shape. But when two carbon atoms are joined by a double bond, as in ethene (C₂H₄), the bonds from both carbons are all in the same plane, so the atoms joined to those carbons are in the same plane as well **(Figure 4.3c)**. We find it convenient to write molecules as structural formulas, as if the molecules being represented are two-dimensional, but keep in mind that molecules are three-dimensional and that the shape of a molecule is central to its function.

Hydrogen (valence = 1)	Oxygen (valence = 2)	Nitrogen (valence = 3)	Carbon (valence = 4)
H·	·Ö:	·N̈·	·C̈·

▲ Figure 4.4 **Valences of the major elements of organic molecules.** Valence is the number of covalent bonds an atom can form. It is generally equal to the number of electrons required to complete the valence (outermost) shell (see Figure 2.7). All the electrons are shown for each atom in the electron distribution diagrams (top). Only the valence shell electrons are shown in the Lewis dot structures (bottom). Note that carbon can form four bonds.

MAKE CONNECTIONS *Draw the Lewis dot structures for sodium, phosphorus, sulfur, and chlorine. (Refer to Figure 2.7.)*

The electron configuration of carbon gives it covalent compatibility with many different elements. **Figure 4.4** shows the valences of carbon and its most frequent bonding partners—hydrogen, oxygen, and nitrogen. These are the four major atomic components of organic molecules. These valences are the basis for the rules of covalent bonding in organic chemistry—the building code for the architecture of organic molecules.

How do the rules of covalent bonding apply to carbon atoms with partners other than hydrogen? We'll look at two examples, the simple molecules carbon dioxide and urea.

In the carbon dioxide molecule (CO_2), a single carbon atom is joined to two atoms of oxygen by double covalent bonds. The structural formula for CO_2 is shown here:

$$O=C=O$$

Each line in a structural formula represents a pair of shared electrons. Thus, the two double bonds in CO_2 have the same number of shared electrons as four single bonds. The arrangement completes the valence shells of all atoms in the molecule. Because CO_2 is a very simple molecule and lacks hydrogen, it is often considered inorganic, even though it contains carbon. Whether we call CO_2 organic or inorganic, however, it is clearly important to the living world as the source of carbon for all organic molecules in organisms.

Urea, $CO(NH_2)_2$, is the organic compound found in urine that Wöhler synthesized in the early 1800s. Again, each atom has the required number of covalent bonds. In this case, one carbon atom participates in both single and double bonds.

Urea

Urea and carbon dioxide are molecules with only one carbon atom. But as Figure 4.3 shows, a carbon atom can also use one or more valence electrons to form covalent bonds to other carbon atoms, each of which can also form four bonds. Thus, the atoms can be linked into chains of seemingly infinite variety.

Molecular Diversity Arising from Variation in Carbon Skeletons

Carbon chains form the skeletons of most organic molecules. The skeletons vary in length and may be straight, branched, or arranged in closed rings (Figure 4.5). Some carbon skeletons have double bonds, which vary in number and location. Such variation in carbon skeletons is one important source of the molecular complexity and diversity that characterize living matter. In addition, atoms of other elements can be bonded to the skeletons at available sites.

Hydrocarbons

All of the molecules that are shown in Figures 4.3 and 4.5 are **hydrocarbons**, organic molecules consisting of only carbon and hydrogen. Atoms of hydrogen are attached to the carbon skeleton wherever electrons are available for covalent bonding. Hydrocarbons are the major components of petroleum, which is called a fossil fuel because it consists of the partially decomposed remains of organisms that lived millions of years ago.

Although hydrocarbons are not prevalent in most living organisms, many of a cell's organic molecules have regions consisting of only carbon and hydrogen. For example, the

▼ **Figure 4.5 Four ways that carbon skeletons can vary.**

(a) Length

Carbon skeletons vary in length.

(b) Branching

Skeletons may be unbranched or branched.

(c) Double bond position

The skeleton may have double bonds, which can vary in location.

(d) Presence of rings

Some carbon skeletons are arranged in rings. In the abbreviated structural formula for each compound (at the right), each corner represents a carbon and its attached hydrogens.

molecules known as fats have long hydrocarbon tails attached to a nonhydrocarbon component (Figure 4.6). Neither petroleum nor fat dissolves in water; both are hydrophobic compounds because the great majority of their bonds are relatively nonpolar carbon-to-hydrogen linkages. Another characteristic of hydrocarbons is that they can undergo reactions that release a relatively large amount of energy. The gasoline that fuels a car consists of hydrocarbons, and the hydrocarbon tails of fats serve as stored fuel for plant embryos (seeds) and animals.

Nucleus

Fat droplets

10 μm

(a) Part of a human adipose cell **(b) A fat molecule**

▲ **Figure 4.6 The role of hydrocarbons in fats. (a)** Mammalian adipose cells stockpile fat molecules as a fuel reserve. This colorized micrograph shows part of a human adipose cell with many fat drop-lets, each containing a large number of fat molecules. **(b)** A fat mol-ecule consists of a small, nonhydrocarbon component joined to three hydrocarbon tails that account for the hydrophobic behavior of fats. The tails can be broken down to provide energy. (Black = carbon; gray = hydrogen; red = oxygen.)

MAKE CONNECTIONS *How do the tails account for the hydro-phobic nature of fats? (See Concept 3.2.)*

Isomers

Variation in the architecture of organic molecules can be seen in **isomers**, compounds that have the same numbers of atoms of the same elements but different structures and hence different properties. We will examine three types of isomers: structural isomers, *cis-trans* isomers, and enantiomers.

Structural isomers differ in the covalent arrangements of their atoms. Compare, for example, the two five-carbon compounds in **Figure 4.7a**. Both have the molecular formula C_5H_{12}, but they differ in the covalent arrangement of their carbon skeletons. The skeleton is straight in one compound but branched in the other. The number of possible isomers increases tremendously as carbon skeletons increase in size. There are only three forms of C_5H_{12} (two of which are shown in Figure 4.7a), but there are 18 variations of C_8H_{18} and 366,319 possible structural isomers of $C_{20}H_{42}$. Structural isomers may also differ in the location of double bonds.

In *cis-trans* isomers (formerly called *geometric isomers*), carbons have covalent bonds to the same atoms, but these atoms differ in their spatial arrangements due to the inflex-ibility of double bonds. Single bonds allow the atoms they join to rotate freely about the bond axis without changing the compound. In contrast, double bonds do not permit such rotation. If a double bond joins two carbon atoms, and each C also has two different atoms (or groups of atoms) attached to it, then two distinct *cis-trans* isomers are possible. Consider a simple molecule with two double-bonded carbons, each of which has an H and an X attached to it **(Figure 4.7b)**. The ar-rangement with both Xs on the same side of the double bond is called a *cis isomer*, and that with the Xs on opposite sides is

▼ **Figure 4.7 Three types of isomers, compounds with the same molecular formula but different structures.**

(a) Structural isomers

Pentane

2-methyl butane

Structural isomers differ in covalent partners, as shown in this example of two isomers of C_5H_{12}.

(b) *Cis-trans* isomers

cis isomer: The two Xs are on the same side.

trans isomer: The two Xs are on opposite sides.

Cis-trans isomers differ in arrangement about a double bond. In these diagrams, X represents an atom or group of atoms attached to a double-bonded carbon.

(c) Enantiomers

CO₂H

CO₂H

L isomer

D isomer

Enantiomers differ in spatial arrangement around an asymmetric carbon, resulting in molecules that are mirror images, like left and right hands. The two isomers here are designated the L and D isomers from the Latin for "left" and "right" (*levo* and *dextro*). Enantiomers cannot be superimposed on each other.

© Pearson Education, Inc.

DRAW IT *There are three structural isomers of C_5H_{12}; draw the one not shown in (a).*

called a *trans isomer*. The subtle difference in shape between such isomers can dramatically affect the biological activities of organic molecules. For example, the biochemistry of vi-sion involves a light-induced change of retinal, a chemical compound in the eye, from the *cis* isomer to the *trans* isomer. Another example involves *trans* fats, which are discussed in Chapter 5.

Enantiomers are isomers that are mirror images of each other and that differ in shape due to the presence of an *asymmetric carbon*, one that is attached to four differ-ent atoms or groups of atoms. (See the middle carbon in

© Pearson Education, Inc.

Drug	Effects	Effective Enantiomer	Ineffective Enantiomer
Ibuprofen	Reduces inflammation and pain	S-Ibuprofen	R-Ibuprofen
Albuterol	Relaxes bronchial (airway) muscles, improving airflow in asthma patients	R-Albuterol	S-Albuterol

▲ Figure 4.8 **The pharmacological importance of enantiomers.** Ibuprofen and albuterol are drugs whose enantiomers have different effects. (S and R are used here to distinguish between enantiomers.) Ibuprofen is commonly sold as a mixture of the two enantiomers; the S enantiomer is 100 times more effective than the R form. Albuterol is synthesized and sold only as the R form of the drug; the S form counteracts the active R form.

the ball-and-stick models shown in **Figure 4.7c**.) The four groups can be arranged in space around the asymmetric carbon in two different ways that are mirror images. Enantiomers are, in a way, left-handed and right-handed versions of the molecule. Just as your right hand won't fit into a left-handed glove, a "right-handed" molecule won't fit into the same space as the "left-handed" version. Usually, only one isomer is biologically active because only that form can bind to specific molecules in an organism.

The concept of enantiomers is important in the pharmaceutical industry because the two enantiomers of a drug may not be equally effective, as is the case for both ibuprofen and the asthma medication albuterol (**Figure 4.8**). Methamphetamine also occurs in two enantiomers that have very different effects. One enantiomer is the highly addictive stimulant drug known as "crank," sold illegally in the street drug trade. The other has a much weaker effect and is the active ingredient in an over-the-counter vapor inhaler for treatment of nasal congestion. The differing effects of enantiomers in the body demonstrate that organisms are sensitive to even the most subtle variations in molecular architecture. Once again, we see that molecules have emergent properties that depend on the specific arrangement of their atoms.

CONCEPT CHECK 4.2

1. **DRAW IT** (a) Draw a structural formula for C_2H_4. (b) Draw the *trans* isomer of $C_2H_2Cl_2$.
2. Which molecules in Figure 4.5 are isomers? For each pair, identify the type of isomer.
3. How are gasoline and fat chemically similar?
4. Can propane (C_3H_8) form isomers? Explain.

A few chemical groups are key to molecular function

The properties of an organic molecule depend not only on the arrangement of its carbon skeleton but also on the chemical groups attached to that skeleton. We can think of hydrocarbons, the simplest organic molecules, as the underlying framework for more complex organic molecules. A number of chemical groups can replace one or more hydrogens of the hydrocarbon. These groups may participate in chemical reactions or may contribute to function indirectly by their effects on molecular shape; they help give each molecule its unique properties.

The Chemical Groups Most Important in the Processes of Life

Consider the differences between estradiol (a type of estrogen) and testosterone. These compounds are female and male sex hormones, respectively, in humans and other vertebrates. Both are steroids, organic molecules with a common carbon skeleton in the form of four fused rings. They differ only in the chemical groups attached to the rings (shown here in abbreviated form); the distinctions in molecular architecture are shaded in blue:

Estradiol   **Testosterone**

The different actions of these two molecules on many targets throughout the body are the basis of gender, producing the contrasting features of male and female vertebrates. In this case, the chemical groups are important because they affect molecular shape, contributing to function.

In other cases, chemical groups are directly involved in chemical reactions; such groups are known as **functional groups**. Each has certain properties, such as shape and charge, that cause it to participate in chemical reactions in a characteristic way.

The seven chemical groups most important in biological processes are the hydroxyl, carbonyl, carboxyl, amino, sulfhydryl, phosphate, and methyl groups. The first six groups can be chemically reactive; of these, all except the sulfhydryl group are also hydrophilic and thus increase the solubility of organic compounds in water. The methyl group is not reactive, but instead often serves as a recognizable tag on biological molecules. Study **Figure 4.9** to become familiar with these biologically important chemical groups.

▼ Figure 4.9 **Some biologically important chemical groups.**

Chemical Group	Group Properties and Compound Name	Examples
Hydroxyl group (—OH) —OH (may be written HO—)	Is polar due to electronegative oxygen. Forms hydrogen bonds with water, helping dissolve compounds such as sugars. Compound name: Alcohol (specific name usually ends in -ol)	**Ethanol**, the alcohol present in alcoholic beverages
Carbonyl group ($>$C$=$O) $-\overset{O}{\overset{\|}{C}}-$	Sugars with ketone groups are called ketoses; those with aldehydes are called aldoses. Compound name: Ketone (carbonyl group is within a carbon skeleton) or aldehyde (carbonyl group is at the end of a carbon skeleton)	**Acetone**, the simplest ketone **Propanal**, an aldehyde
Carboxyl group (—COOH) $-\overset{O}{\overset{\|\|}{C}}-OH$	Acts as an acid (can donate H⁺) because the covalent bond between oxygen and hydrogen is so polar. Compound name: Carboxylic acid, or organic acid	**Acetic acid**, which gives vinegar its sour taste Ionized form of —COOH (carboxylate ion), found in cells
Amino group (—NH₂) $-\overset{H}{\underset{H}{N}}$	Acts as a base; can pick up an H⁺ from the surrounding solution (water, in living organisms). Compound name: Amine	**Glycine**, an amino acid (note its carboxyl group) Ionized form of —NH₂, found in cells
Sulfhydryl group (—SH) —SH (may be written HS —)	Two —SH groups can react, forming a "cross-link" that helps stabilize protein structure. Hair protein cross-links maintain the straightness or curliness of hair; in hair salons, permanent treatments break cross-links, then re-form them while the hair is in the desired shape. Compound name: Thiol	**Cysteine**, a sulfur-containing amino acid
Phosphate group (—OPO₃²⁻) $-O-\overset{O}{\underset{O^-}{\overset{\|\|}{P}}}-O^-$	Contributes negative charge (1– when positioned inside a chain of phosphates; 2– when at the end). When attached, confers on a molecule the ability to react with water, releasing energy. Compound name: Organic phosphate	**Glycerol phosphate**, which takes part in many important chemical reactions in cells
Methyl group (—CH₃) $-\overset{H}{\underset{H}{\overset{\|}{C}}}-H$	Affects the expression of genes when on DNA or on proteins bound to DNA. Affects the shape and function of male and female sex hormones. Compound name: Methylated compound	**5-Methyl cytosine**, a component of DNA that has been modified by addition of a methyl group

ATP: An Important Source of Energy for Cellular Processes

The "Phosphate group" row in Figure 4.9 shows a simple example of an organic phosphate molecule. A more complicated organic phosphate, **adenosine triphosphate**, or **ATP**, is worth mentioning here because its function in the cell is so important. ATP consists of an organic molecule called adenosine attached to a string of three phosphate groups:

Where three phosphates are present in series, as in ATP, one phosphate may be split off as a result of a reaction with water. This inorganic phosphate ion, $HOPO_3^{2-}$, is often abbreviated Ⓟᵢ in this book, and a phosphate group in an organic molecule is often written as Ⓟ. Having lost one phosphate, ATP becomes adenosine *di*phosphate, or ADP. Although ATP is sometimes said to store energy, it is more accurate to think of it as storing the potential to react with water. This reaction releases energy that can be used by the cell. You will learn about this in more detail in Chapter 9.

ATP   Inorganic   ADP
phosphate

CONCEPT CHECK 4.3

1. What does the term *amino acid* signify about the structure of such a molecule?

2. What chemical change occurs to ATP when it reacts with water and releases energy?

3. **WHAT IF?** Suppose you had an organic molecule such as cysteine (see Figure 4.9, sulfhydryl group example), and you chemically removed the —NH_2 group and replaced it with —COOH. Draw the structural formula for this molecule and speculate about its chemical properties. Is the central carbon asymmetric before the change? After?

The Chemical Elements of Life: *A Review*

Living matter, as you have learned, consists mainly of carbon, oxygen, hydrogen, and nitrogen, with smaller amounts of sulfur and phosphorus. These elements all form strong covalent bonds, an essential characteristic in the architecture of complex organic molecules. Of all these elements, carbon is the virtuoso of the covalent bond. The versatility of carbon makes possible the great diversity of organic molecules, each with particular properties that emerge from the unique arrangement of its carbon skeleton and the chemical groups appended to that skeleton. This variation at the molecular level provides the foundation for the rich biological diversity found on our planet.

---

4   Chapter Review

SUMMARY OF KEY CONCEPTS

CONCEPT 4.1

Organic chemistry is the study of carbon compounds (pp. 57–58)

- Organic compounds, once thought to arise only within living organisms, were finally synthesized in the laboratory.
- Living matter is made mostly of carbon, oxygen, hydrogen, and nitrogen. Biological diversity results from carbon's ability to form a huge number of molecules with particular shapes and properties.

  ? *How did Stanley Miller's experiments support the idea that, even at life's origins, physical and chemical laws govern the processes of life?*

CONCEPT 4.2

Carbon atoms can form diverse molecules by bonding to four other atoms (pp. 58–62)

- Carbon, with a valence of 4, can bond to various other atoms, including O, H, and N. Carbon can also bond to other carbon atoms, forming the carbon skeletons of organic compounds. These skeletons vary in length and shape and have bonding sites for atoms of other elements.
- **Hydrocarbons** consist of carbon and hydrogen.
- **Isomers** are compounds that have the same molecular formula but different structures and therefore different properties. Three types of isomers are **structural isomers**, *cis-trans* isomers, and **enantiomers**.

  ? *Refer back to Figure 4.9. What type of isomers are acetone and propanal? How many asymmetric carbons are present in acetic acid, glycine, and glycerol phosphate? Can these three molecules exist as forms that are enantiomers?*

CONCEPT 4.3

A few chemical groups are key to molecular function (pp. 62–64)

- Chemical groups attached to the carbon skeletons of organic molecules participate in chemical reactions (**functional groups**) or contribute to function by affecting molecular shape (see Figure 4.9).
- **ATP (adenosine triphosphate)** consists of adenosine attached to three phosphate groups. ATP can react with water, forming

inorganic phosphate and ADP (adenosine diphosphate). This reaction releases energy that can be used by the cell.

P—P—P—Adenosine $\xrightarrow[\text{with } H_2O]{\text{Reacts}}$ Pᵢ + P—P—Adenosine + Energy

ATP   Inorganic   ADP
phosphate

? *In what ways does a methyl group differ chemically from the other six important chemical groups shown in Figure 4.9?*

TEST YOUR UNDERSTANDING

LEVEL 1: KNOWLEDGE/COMPREHENSION

1. Organic chemistry is currently defined as
   a. the study of compounds made only by living cells.
   b. the study of carbon compounds.
   c. the study of natural (as opposed to synthetic) compounds.
   d. the study of hydrocarbons.

2. Which functional group is *not* present in this molecule?
   a. carboxyl
   b. sulfhydryl
   c. hydroxyl
   d. amino

3. **MAKE CONNECTIONS** Which chemical group is most likely to be responsible for an organic molecule behaving as a base (see Concept 3.3)?
   a. hydroxyl
   b. carbonyl
   c. amino
   d. phosphate

LEVEL 2: APPLICATION/ANALYSIS

4. Which of the following hydrocarbons has a double bond in its carbon skeleton?
   a. C_3H_8 c. C_2H_4
   b. C_2H_6 d. C_2H_2

5. Choose the term that correctly describes the relationship between these two sugar molecules:
   a. structural isomers
   b. *cis-trans* isomers
   c. enantiomers
   d. isotopes

6. Identify the asymmetric carbon in this molecule:

7. Which action could produce a carbonyl group?
   a. the replacement of the —OH of a carboxyl group with hydrogen
   b. the addition of a thiol to a hydroxyl
   c. the addition of a hydroxyl to a phosphate
   d. the replacement of the nitrogen of an amine with oxygen

8. Which of the molecules shown in question 5 has an asymmetric carbon? Which carbon is asymmetric?

LEVEL 3: SYNTHESIS/EVALUATION

9. **EVOLUTION CONNECTION**
   DRAW IT Some scientists think that life elsewhere in the universe might be based on the element silicon, rather than on carbon, as on Earth. Look at the electron distribution diagram for silicon in Figure 2.7 and draw the Lewis dot structure for silicon. What properties does silicon share with carbon that would make silicon-based life more likely than, say, neon-based life or aluminum-based life?

10. **SCIENTIFIC INQUIRY**
    50 years ago, pregnant women who were prescribed thalidomide for morning sickness gave birth to children with birth defects. Thalidomide is a mixture of two enantiomers; one reduces morning sickness, but the other causes severe birth defects. Today, the FDA has approved this drug for non-pregnant individuals with Hansen's disease (leprosy) or newly diagnosed multiple myeloma, a blood and bone marrow cancer. The beneficial enantiomer can be synthesized and given to patients, but over time, both the beneficial *and* the harmful enantiomer can be detected in the body. Propose a possible explanation for the presence of the harmful enantiomer.

11. **WRITE ABOUT A THEME: ORGANIZATION**
    In 1918, an epidemic of sleeping sickness caused an unusual rigid paralysis in some survivors, similar to symptoms of advanced Parkinson's disease. Years later, L-dopa (below, left), a chemical used to treat Parkinson's disease, was given to some of these patients. L-dopa was remarkably effective at eliminating the paralysis, at least temporarily. However, its enantiomer, D-dopa (right), was subsequently shown to have no effect at all, as is the case for Parkinson's disease. In a short essay (100–150 words), discuss how the effectiveness of one enantiomer and not the other illustrates the theme of structure and function.

L-dopa   **D-dopa**

12. **SYNTHESIZE YOUR KNOWLEDGE**

Explain how the chemical structure of the carbon atom accounts for the differences between the male and female lions seen in the photo.

MasteringBiology®

Students Go to **MasteringBiology** for assignments, the eText, and the Study Area with practice tests, animations, and activities.

Instructors Go to **MasteringBiology** for automatically graded tutorials and questions that you can assign to your students, plus Instructor Resources.

5

The Structure and Function of Large Biological Molecules

▲ **Figure 5.1** Why is the structure of a protein important for its function?

The Molecules of Life

Given the rich complexity of life on Earth, it might surprise you that the most important large molecules found in all living things—from bacteria to elephants—can be sorted into just four main classes: carbohydrates, lipids, proteins, and nucleic acids. On the molecular scale, members of three of these classes—carbohydrates, proteins, and nucleic acids—are huge and are therefore called **macromolecules**. For example, a protein may consist of thousands of atoms that form a molecular colossus with a mass well over 100,000 daltons. Considering the size and complexity of macromolecules, it is noteworthy that biochemists have determined the detailed structure of so many of them. The image in **Figure 5.1** is a molecular model of a protein called alcohol dehydrogenase, which breaks down alcohol in the body.

The architecture of a large biological molecule plays an essential role in its function. Like water and simple organic molecules, large biological molecules exhibit unique emergent properties arising from the orderly arrangement of their atoms. In this chapter, we'll first consider how macromolecules are built. Then we'll examine the structure and function of all four classes of large biological molecules: carbohydrates, lipids, proteins, and nucleic acids.

Macromolecules are polymers, built from monomers

The macromolecules in three of the four classes of life's organic compounds—carbohydrates, proteins, and nucleic acids, all except lipids—are chain-like molecules called polymers (from the Greek *polys*, many, and *meros*, part). A **polymer** is a long molecule consisting of many similar or identical building blocks linked by covalent bonds, much as a train consists of a chain of cars. The repeating units that serve as the building blocks of a polymer are smaller molecules called **monomers** (from the Greek *monos*, single). Some monomers also have other functions of their own.

The Synthesis and Breakdown of Polymers

Although each class of polymer is made up of a different type of monomer, the chemical mechanisms by which cells make and break down polymers are basically the same in all cases. In cells, these processes are facilitated by **enzymes**, specialized macromolecules that speed up chemical reactions. Monomers are connected by a reaction in which two molecules are covalently bonded to each other, with the loss of a water molecule; this is known as a **dehydration reaction** **(Figure 5.2a)**. When a bond forms between two monomers, each monomer contributes part of the water molecule that is released during the reaction: One monomer provides a hydroxyl group (—OH), while the other provides a hydrogen (—H). This reaction is repeated as monomers are added to the chain one by one, making a polymer.

Polymers are disassembled to monomers by **hydrolysis**, a process that is essentially the reverse of the dehydration reaction **(Figure 5.2b)**. Hydrolysis means water breakage (from the Greek *hydro*, water, and *lysis*, break). The bond between monomers is broken by the addition of a water molecule, with a hydrogen from water attaching to one monomer and the hydroxyl group attaching to the other. An example of hydrolysis within our bodies is the process of digestion. The bulk of the organic material in our food is in the form of polymers that are much too large to enter our cells. Within the digestive tract, various enzymes attack the polymers, speeding up hydrolysis. Released monomers are then absorbed into the bloodstream for distribution to all body cells. Those cells can then use dehydration reactions to assemble the monomers into new, different polymers that can perform specific functions required by the cell.

The Diversity of Polymers

A cell has thousands of different macromolecules; the collection varies from one type of cell to another. The inherited

▼ **Figure 5.2 The synthesis and breakdown of polymers.**

(a) Dehydration reaction: synthesizing a polymer

(b) Hydrolysis: breaking down a polymer

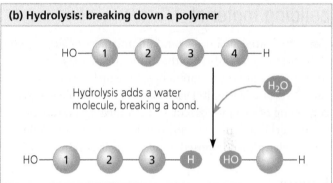

differences between close relatives such as human siblings reflect small variations in polymers, particularly DNA and proteins. Molecular differences between unrelated individuals are more extensive, and those between species greater still. The diversity of macromolecules in the living world is vast, and the possible variety is effectively limitless.

What is the basis for such diversity in life's polymers? These molecules are constructed from only 40 to 50 common monomers and some others that occur rarely. Building a huge variety of polymers from such a limited number of monomers is analogous to constructing hundreds of thousands of words from only 26 letters of the alphabet. The key is arrangement—the particular linear sequence that the units follow. However, this analogy falls far short of describing the great diversity of macromolecules because most biological polymers have many more monomers than the number of letters a word, even the longest ones. Proteins, for example, are built from 20 kinds of amino acids arranged in chains that are typically hundreds of amino acids long. The molecular logic of life is simple but elegant: Small molecules common to all organisms are ordered into unique macromolecules.

Despite this immense diversity, molecular structure and function can still be grouped roughly by class. Let's examine each of the four major classes of large biological molecules. For each class, the large molecules have emergent properties not found in their individual building blocks.

1. What are the four main classes of large biological molecules? Which class does not consist of polymers?

2. How many molecules of water are needed to completely hydrolyze a polymer that is ten monomers long?

3. **WHAT IF?** If you eat a piece of fish, what reactions must occur for the amino acid monomers in the protein of the fish to be converted to new proteins in your body?

CONCEPT 5.2

Carbohydrates serve as fuel and building material

Carbohydrates include sugars and polymers of sugars. The simplest carbohydrates are the monosaccharides, or simple sugars; these are the monomers from which more complex carbohydrates are built. Disaccharides are double sugars, consisting of two monosaccharides joined by a covalent bond. Carbohydrate macromolecules are polymers called polysaccharides, composed of many sugar building blocks.

Sugars

Monosaccharides (from the Greek *monos*, single, and *sacchar*, sugar) generally have molecular formulas that are some multiple of the unit CH_2O. Glucose ($C_6H_{12}O_6$), the most common monosaccharide, is of central importance in the chemistry of life. In the structure of glucose, we can see the trademarks of a sugar: The molecule has a carbonyl group (CO) and multiple hydroxyl groups (—OH) **(Figure 5.3)**. Depending on the location of the carbonyl group, a sugar is either an aldose (aldehyde sugar) or a ketose (ketone sugar). Glucose, for example, is an aldose; fructose, an isomer of glucose, is a ketose. (Most names for sugars end in *-ose*.) Another criterion for classifying sugars is the size of the carbon skeleton, which ranges from three to seven carbons long. Glucose, fructose, and other sugars that have six carbons are called hexoses. Trioses (three-carbon sugars) and pentoses (five-carbon sugars) are also common.

Still another source of diversity for simple sugars is in the spatial arrangement of their parts around asymmetric carbons. (Recall that an asymmetric carbon is a carbon attached to four different atoms or groups of atoms.) Glucose and galactose, for example, differ only in the placement of parts around one asymmetric carbon (see the purple boxes in Figure 5.3). What seems like a small difference is significant enough to give the two sugars distinctive shapes and binding activities, thus different behaviors.

Although it is convenient to draw glucose with a linear carbon skeleton, this representation is not completely accurate.

▲ **Figure 5.3 The structure and classification of some monosaccharides.** Sugars vary in the location of their carbonyl groups (orange), the length of their carbon skeletons, and the spatial arrangement around asymmetric carbons (compare, for example, the purple portions of glucose and galactose).

MAKE CONNECTIONS *In the 1970s, a process was developed that converts the glucose in corn syrup to its sweeter-tasting isomer, fructose. High-fructose corn syrup, a common ingredient in soft drinks and processed food, is a mixture of glucose and fructose. What type of isomers are glucose and fructose? (See Figure 4.7.)*

(a) **Linear and ring forms.** Chemical equilibrium between the linear and ring structures greatly favors the formation of rings. The carbons of the sugar are numbered 1 to 6, as shown. To form the glucose ring, carbon 1 (magenta) bonds to the oxygen (blue) attached to carbon 5.

(b) **Abbreviated ring structure.** Each unlabeled corner represents a carbon. The ring's thicker edge indicates that you are looking at the ring edge-on; the components attached to the ring lie above or below the plane of the ring.

▲ **Figure 5.4 Linear and ring forms of glucose.**

DRAW IT *Start with the linear form of fructose (see Figure 5.3) and draw the formation of the fructose ring in two steps. First, number the carbons starting at the top of the linear structure. Then draw the molecule in the same orientation as the glucose in the middle of (a) above, attaching carbon 5 via its oxygen to carbon 2. Compare the number of carbons in the fructose and glucose rings.*

In aqueous solutions, glucose molecules, as well as most other five- and six-carbon sugars, form rings (Figure 5.4).

Monosaccharides, particularly glucose, are major nutrients for cells. In the process known as cellular respiration, cells extract energy from glucose molecules by breaking them down in a series of reactions. Not only are simple-sugar molecules a major fuel for cellular work, but their carbon skeletons also serve as raw material for the synthesis of other types of small organic molecules, such as amino acids and fatty acids. Sugar molecules that are not immediately used in these ways are generally incorporated as monomers into disaccharides or polysaccharides.

A **disaccharide** consists of two monosaccharides joined by a **glycosidic linkage**, a covalent bond formed between two monosaccharides by a dehydration reaction. For example, maltose is a disaccharide formed by the linking of two molecules of glucose (Figure 5.5a). Also known as malt sugar, maltose is an ingredient used in brewing beer. The most prevalent disaccharide is sucrose, which is table sugar. Its two monomers are glucose and fructose (Figure 5.5b). Plants generally transport carbohydrates from leaves to roots and other nonphotosynthetic organs in the form of sucrose. Lactose, the sugar present in milk, is another disaccharide, in this case a glucose molecule joined to a galactose molecule.

(a) **Dehydration reaction in the synthesis of maltose.** The bonding of two glucose units forms maltose. The 1–4 glycosidic linkage joins the number 1 carbon of one glucose to the number 4 carbon of the second glucose. Joining the glucose monomers in a different way would result in a different disaccharide.

Glucose   Glucose   Maltose

(b) **Dehydration reaction in the synthesis of sucrose.** Sucrose is a disaccharide formed from glucose and fructose. Notice that fructose forms a five-sided ring, though it is a hexose like glucose.

Glucose   Fructose   Sucrose

▲ **Figure 5.5 Examples of disaccharide synthesis.**

DRAW IT *Referring to Figures 5.3 and 5.4, number the carbons in each sugar in this figure. Insert arrows linking the carbons to show how the numbering is consistent with the name of each glycosidic linkage.*

Polysaccharides

Polysaccharides are macromolecules, polymers with a few hundred to a few thousand monosaccharides joined by glycosidic linkages. Some polysaccharides serve as storage material, hydrolyzed as needed to provide sugar for cells. Other polysaccharides serve as building material for structures that protect the cell or the whole organism. The architecture and function of a polysaccharide are determined by its sugar monomers and by the positions of its glycosidic linkages.

Storage Polysaccharides

Both plants and animals store sugars for later use in the form of storage polysaccharides **(Figure 5.6)**. Plants store **starch**, a polymer of glucose monomers, as granules within cellular structures known as plastids, which include chloroplasts. Synthesizing starch enables the plant to stockpile surplus glucose. Because glucose is a major cellular fuel, starch represents stored energy. The sugar can later be withdrawn from this carbohydrate "bank" by hydrolysis, which breaks the bonds between the glucose monomers. Most animals, including humans, also have enzymes that can hydrolyze plant starch, making glucose available as a nutrient for cells. Potato tubers and grains are the major sources of starch in the human diet.

Most of the glucose monomers in starch are joined by 1–4 linkages (number 1 carbon to number 4 carbon), like the glucose units in maltose (see Figure 5.5a). The simplest form of starch, amylose, is unbranched. Amylopectin, a more complex starch, is a branched polymer with 1–6 linkages at the branch points. Both of these starches are shown in **Figure 5.6a**.

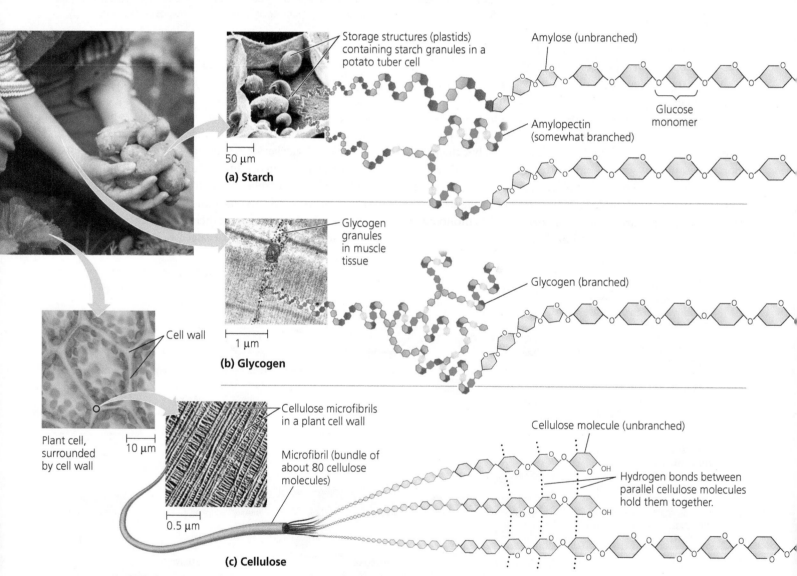

▲ **Figure 5.6 Polysaccharides of plants and animals. (a)** Starch stored in plant cells, **(b)** glycogen stored in muscle cells, and **(c)** structural cellulose fibers in plant cell walls are all polysaccharides composed entirely of glucose monomers (green hexagons). In starch and glycogen, the polymer chains tend to form helices in unbranched regions because of the angle of the linkages between glucose molecules. There are two kinds of starch: amylose and amylopectin. Cellulose, with a different kind of glucose linkage, is always unbranched.

Animals store a polysaccharide called **glycogen**, a polymer of glucose that is like amylopectin but more extensively branched (**Figure 5.6b**). Vertebrates store glycogen mainly in liver and muscle cells. Hydrolysis of glycogen in these cells releases glucose when the demand for sugar increases. This stored fuel cannot sustain an animal for long, however. In humans, for example, glycogen stores are depleted in about a day unless they are replenished by consumption of food. This is an issue of concern in low-carbohydrate diets, which can result in weakness and fatigue.

Structural Polysaccharides

Organisms build strong materials from structural polysaccharides. For example, the polysaccharide called **cellulose** is a major component of the tough walls that enclose plant cells (**Figure 5.6c**). On a global scale, plants produce almost 10^{14} kg (100 billion tons) of cellulose per year; it is the most abundant organic compound on Earth.

Like starch, cellulose is a polymer of glucose, but the glycosidic linkages in these two polymers differ. The difference is based on the fact that there are actually two slightly different ring structures for glucose (**Figure 5.7a**). When glucose forms a ring, the hydroxyl group attached to the number 1 carbon is positioned either below or above the plane of the ring. These two ring forms for glucose are called alpha (α) and beta (β), respectively. (Greek letters are often used as a "numbering" system for different versions of biological structures, much as we use the letters a, b, c, and so on for the parts of a question or a figure.) In starch, all the glucose monomers are in the α configuration (**Figure 5.7b**), the

arrangement we saw in Figures 5.4 and 5.5. In contrast, the glucose monomers of cellulose are all in the β configuration, making every glucose monomer "upside down" with respect to its neighbors (**Figure 5.7c**; see also Figure 5.6c).

The differing glycosidic linkages in starch and cellulose give the two molecules distinct three-dimensional shapes. Whereas certain starch molecules are largely helical, a cellulose molecule is straight. Cellulose is never branched, and some hydroxyl groups on its glucose monomers are free to hydrogen-bond with the hydroxyls of other cellulose molecules lying parallel to it. In plant cell walls, parallel cellulose molecules held together in this way are grouped into units called microfibrils (see Figure 5.6c). These cable-like microfibrils are a strong building material for plants and an important substance for humans because cellulose is the major constituent of paper and the only component of cotton.

Enzymes that digest starch by hydrolyzing its α linkages are unable to hydrolyze the β linkages of cellulose due to the different shapes of these two molecules. In fact, few organisms possess enzymes that can digest cellulose. Almost all animals, including humans, do not; the cellulose in our food passes through the digestive tract and is eliminated with the feces. Along the way, the cellulose abrades the wall of the digestive tract and stimulates the lining to secrete mucus, which aids in the smooth passage of food through the tract. Thus, although cellulose is not a nutrient for humans, it is an important part of a healthful diet. Most fruits, vegetables, and whole grains are rich in cellulose. On food packages, "insoluble fiber" refers mainly to cellulose.

Some microorganisms can digest cellulose, breaking it down into glucose monomers. A cow harbors

(a) α and β glucose ring structures. These two interconvertible forms of glucose differ in the placement of the hydroxyl group (highlighted in blue) attached to the number 1 carbon.

α Glucose

β Glucose

(b) Starch: 1–4 linkage of α glucose monomers. All monomers are in the same orientation. Compare the positions of the —OH groups highlighted in yellow with those in cellulose (c).

(c) Cellulose: 1–4 linkage of β glucose monomers. In cellulose, every β glucose monomer is upside down with respect to its neighbors. (See the highlighted —OH groups.)

▲ **Figure 5.7 Starch and cellulose structures.**

CH₂OH

◀ The structure of the chitin monomer

◀ Chitin, embedded in proteins, forms the exoskeleton of arthropods. This cicada is molting—shedding its old exoskeleton and emerging in adult form.

▶ Chitin is used to make a strong and flexible surgical thread that decomposes after the wound or incision heals.

▲ Figure 5.8 **Chitin, a structural polysaccharide.**

CONCEPT CHECK 5.2

1. Write the formula for a monosaccharide that has three carbons.
2. A dehydration reaction joins two glucose molecules to form maltose. The formula for glucose is $C_6H_{12}O_6$. What is the formula for maltose?
3. **WHAT IF?** After a cow is given antibiotics to treat an infection, a vet gives the animal a drink of "gut culture" containing various prokaryotes. Why is this necessary?

CONCEPT 5.3

Lipids are a diverse group of hydrophobic molecules

Lipids are the one class of large biological molecules that does not include true polymers, and they are generally not big enough to be considered macromolecules. The compounds called **lipids** are grouped with each other because they share one important trait: They mix poorly, if at all, with water. The hydrophobic behavior of lipids is based on their molecular structure. Although they may have some polar bonds associated with oxygen, lipids consist mostly of hydrocarbon regions. Lipids are varied in form and function. They include waxes and certain pigments, but we will focus on the types of lipids that are most biologically important: fats, phospholipids, and steroids.

Fats

Although fats are not polymers, they are large molecules assembled from smaller molecules by dehydration reactions. A **fat** is constructed from two kinds of smaller molecules: glycerol and fatty acids (**Figure 5.9a**). Glycerol is an alcohol; each of its three carbons bears a hydroxyl group. A **fatty acid** has a long carbon skeleton, usually 16 or 18 carbon atoms in length. The carbon at one end of the skeleton is part of a carboxyl group, the functional group that gives these molecules the name fatty *acid*. The rest of the skeleton consists of a hydrocarbon chain. The relatively nonpolar C—H bonds in the hydrocarbon chains of fatty acids are the reason fats are hydrophobic. Fats separate from water because the water molecules hydrogen-bond to one another and exclude the fats. This is the reason that vegetable oil (a liquid fat) separates from the aqueous vinegar solution in a bottle of salad dressing.

In making a fat, three fatty acid molecules are each joined to glycerol by an ester linkage, a bond formed by a dehydration reaction between a hydroxyl group and a carboxyl group. The resulting fat, also called a **triacylglycerol**, thus consists of three fatty acids linked to one glycerol molecule.

cellulose-digesting prokaryotes and protists in its gut. These microbes hydrolyze the cellulose of hay and grass and convert the glucose to other compounds that nourish the cow. Similarly, a termite, which is unable to digest cellulose by itself, has prokaryotes or protists living in its gut that can make a meal of wood. Some fungi can also digest cellulose in soil and elsewhere, thereby helping recycle chemical elements within Earth's ecosystems.

Another important structural polysaccharide is **chitin**, the carbohydrate used by arthropods (insects, spiders, crustaceans, and related animals) to build their exoskeletons (**Figure 5.8**). An exoskeleton is a hard case that surrounds the soft parts of an animal. Made up of chitin embedded in a layer of proteins, the case is leathery and flexible at first, but becomes hardened when the proteins are chemically linked to each other (as in insects) or encrusted with calcium carbonate (as in crabs). Chitin is also found in fungi, which use this polysaccharide rather than cellulose as the building material for their cell walls. Chitin is similar to cellulose, with β linkages, except that the glucose monomer of chitin has a nitrogen-containing appendage (see Figure 5.8, top right).

Fatty acid
(in this case, palmitic acid)

Glycerol

(a) One of three dehydration reactions in the synthesis of a fat

Ester linkage

(b) Fat molecule (triacylglycerol)

▲ **Figure 5.9 The synthesis and structure of a fat, or triacyl-glycerol.** The molecular building blocks of a fat are one molecule of glycerol and three molecules of fatty acids. **(a)** One water molecule is removed for each fatty acid joined to the glycerol. **(b)** A fat molecule with three fatty acid units, two of them identical. The carbons of the fatty acids are arranged zigzag to suggest the actual orientations of the four single bonds extending from each carbon (see Figure 4.3a).

(Still another name for a fat is *triglyceride,* a word often found in the list of ingredients on packaged foods.) The fatty acids in a fat can all be the same, or they can be of two or three different kinds, as in **Figure 5.9b.**

The terms *saturated* fats and *unsaturated* fats are commonly used in the context of nutrition **(Figure 5.10)**. These terms refer to the structure of the hydrocarbon chains of the fatty acids. If there are no double bonds between carbon atoms composing a chain, then as many hydrogen atoms as possible are bonded to the carbon skeleton. Such a structure is said to be *saturated* with hydrogen, and the resulting fatty acid is therefore called a **saturated fatty acid** (Figure 5.10a). An **unsaturated fatty acid** has one or more double bonds, with one fewer hydrogen atom on each double-bonded carbon. Nearly all double bonds in naturally occurring fatty acids are *cis* double bonds, which cause a kink in the hydrocarbon chain wherever they occur **(Figure 5.10b)**. (See Figure 4.7b to remind yourself about *cis* and *trans* double bonds.)

A fat made from saturated fatty acids is called a saturated fat. Most animal fats are saturated: The hydrocarbon chains of their fatty acids—the "tails" of the fat molecules—lack double bonds, and their flexibility allows the fat molecules to pack together tightly. Saturated animal fats—such as lard

(a) Saturated fat

At room temperature, the molecules of a saturated fat, such as the fat in butter, are packed closely together, forming a solid.

Structural formula of a saturated fat molecule (Each hydrocarbon chain is represented as a zigzag line, where each bend represents a carbon atom and hydrogens are not shown.)

Space-filling model of stearic acid, a saturated fatty acid (red = oxygen, black = carbon, gray = hydrogen)

(b) Unsaturated fat

At room temperature, the molecules of an unsaturated fat such as olive oil cannot pack together closely enough to solidify because of the kinks in some of their fatty acid hydrocarbon chains.

Structural formula of an unsaturated fat molecule

Space-filling model of oleic acid, an unsaturated fatty acid

Cis double bond causes bending.

and butter—are solid at room temperature. In contrast, the fats of plants and fishes are generally unsaturated, meaning that they are built of one or more types of unsaturated fatty acids. Usually liquid at room temperature, plant and fish fats are referred to as oils—olive oil and cod liver oil are examples. The kinks where the *cis* double bonds are located prevent the molecules from packing together closely enough to solidify at room temperature. The phrase "hydrogenated vegetable oils" on food labels means that unsaturated fats have been synthetically converted to saturated fats by adding hydrogen. Peanut butter, margarine, and many other products are hydrogenated to prevent lipids from separating out in liquid (oil) form.

A diet rich in saturated fats is one of several factors that may contribute to the cardiovascular disease known as atherosclerosis. In this condition, deposits called plaques develop within the walls of blood vessels, causing inward bulges that impede blood flow and reduce the resilience of the vessels. Recent studies have shown that the process of hydrogenating vegetable oils produces not only saturated fats but also unsaturated fats with *trans* double bonds. These **trans fats** may contribute more than saturated fats to atherosclerosis and other problems. Because trans fats are especially common in baked goods and processed foods, the U.S. Department of Agriculture requires nutritional labels to include information on trans fat content. Some U.S. cities and at least two countries—Denmark and Switzerland—have even banned the use of trans fats in restaurants.

The major function of fats is energy storage. The hydrocarbon chains of fats are similar to gasoline molecules and just as rich in energy. A gram of fat stores more than twice as much energy as a gram of a polysaccharide, such as starch. Because plants are relatively immobile, they can function with bulky energy storage in the form of starch. (Vegetable oils are generally obtained from seeds, where more compact storage is an asset to the plant.) Animals, however, must carry their energy stores with them, so there is an advantage to having a more compact reservoir

of fuel—fat. Humans and other mammals stock their long-term food reserves in adipose cells (see Figure 4.6a), which swell and shrink as fat is deposited and withdrawn from storage. In addition to storing energy, adipose tissue also cushions such vital organs as the kidneys, and a layer of fat beneath the skin insulates the body. This subcutaneous layer is especially thick in whales, seals, and most other marine mammals, protecting them from cold ocean water.

Phospholipids

Cells as we know them could not exist without another type of lipid—phospholipids. Phospholipids are essential for cells because they are major constituents of cell membranes. Their structure provides a classic example of how form fits function at the molecular level. As shown in **Figure 5.11**, a **phospholipid** is similar to a fat molecule but has only two fatty acids attached to glycerol rather than three. The third hydroxyl group of glycerol is joined to a phosphate group, which has a negative electrical charge in the cell. Typically, an additional small charged or polar molecule is also linked to the phosphate group. Choline is one such molecule (see Figure 5.11), but there are many others as well, allowing formation of a variety of phospholipids that differ from each other.

The two ends of phospholipids show different behavior toward water. The hydrocarbon tails are hydrophobic and are excluded from water. However, the phosphate group and its attachments form a hydrophilic head that has an affinity for water. When phospholipids are added to water, they self-assemble into double-layered structures called

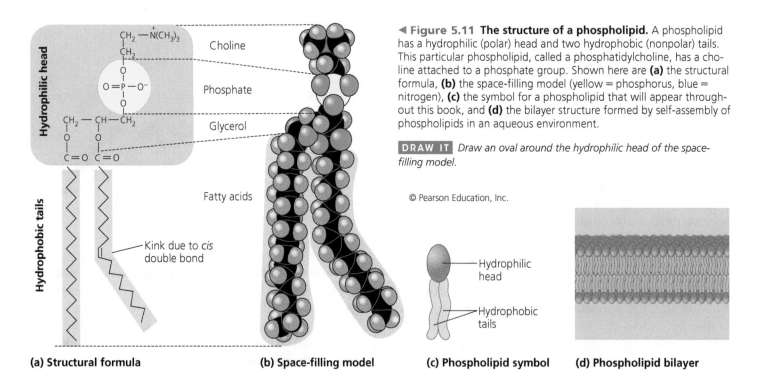

◄ **Figure 5.11 The structure of a phospholipid.** A phospholipid has a hydrophilic (polar) head and two hydrophobic (nonpolar) tails. This particular phospholipid, called a phosphatidylcholine, has a choline attached to a phosphate group. Shown here are **(a)** the structural formula, **(b)** the space-filling model (yellow = phosphorus, blue = nitrogen), **(c)** the symbol for a phospholipid that will appear throughout this book, and **(d)** the bilayer structure formed by self-assembly of phospholipids in an aqueous environment.

DRAW IT *Draw an oval around the hydrophilic head of the space-filling model.*

© Pearson Education, Inc.

(a) Structural formula   (b) Space-filling model   (c) Phospholipid symbol   (d) Phospholipid bilayer "bilayers," shielding their hydrophobic portions from water (Figure 5.11d).

At the surface of a cell, phospholipids are arranged in a similar bilayer. The hydrophilic heads of the molecules are on the outside of the bilayer, in contact with the aqueous solutions inside and outside of the cell. The hydrophobic tails point toward the interior of the bilayer, away from the water. The phospholipid bilayer forms a boundary between the cell and its external environment; in fact, the existence of cells depends on the properties of phospholipids.

Steroids

Steroids are lipids characterized by a carbon skeleton consisting of four fused rings. Different steroids are distinguished by the particular chemical groups attached to this ensemble of rings. **Cholesterol**, a type of steroid, is a crucial molecule in animals (Figure 5.12). It is a common component of animal cell membranes and is also the precursor from which other steroids, such as the vertebrate sex hormones, are synthesized. In vertebrates, cholesterol is synthesized in the liver and is also obtained from the diet. A high level of cholesterol in the blood may contribute to atherosclerosis. In fact, both saturated fats and trans fats exert their negative impact on health by affecting cholesterol levels.

▲ **Figure 5.12 Cholesterol, a steroid.** Cholesterol is the molecule from which other steroids, including the sex hormones, are synthesized. Steroids vary in the chemical groups attached to their four interconnected rings (shown in gold).

MAKE CONNECTIONS *Compare cholesterol with the sex hormones shown in the figure at the beginning of Concept 4.3. Circle the chemical groups that cholesterol has in common with estradiol; put a square around the chemical groups that cholesterol has in common with testosterone.*

CONCEPT CHECK 5.3

1. Compare the structure of a fat (triglyceride) with that of a phospholipid.
2. Why are human sex hormones considered lipids?
3. WHAT IF? Suppose a membrane surrounded an oil droplet, as it does in the cells of plant seeds and in some animal cells. Describe and explain the form it might take.

Proteins include a diversity of structures, resulting in a wide range of functions

Nearly every dynamic function of a living being depends on proteins. In fact, the importance of proteins is underscored by their name, which comes from the Greek word *proteios*, meaning "first," or "primary." Proteins account for more than 50% of the dry mass of most cells, and they are instrumental in almost everything organisms do. Some proteins speed up chemical reactions, while others play a role in defense, storage, transport, cellular communication, movement, or structural support. **Figure 5.13** shows examples of proteins with these functions, which you'll learn more about in later chapters.

Life would not be possible without enzymes, most of which are proteins. Enzymatic proteins regulate metabolism by acting as **catalysts**, chemical agents that selectively speed up chemical reactions without being consumed by the reaction. Because an enzyme can perform its function over and over again, these molecules can be thought of as workhorses that keep cells running by carrying out the processes of life.

A human has tens of thousands of different proteins, each with a specific structure and function; proteins, in fact, are the most structurally sophisticated molecules known. Consistent with their diverse functions, they vary extensively in structure, each type of protein having a unique three-dimensional shape.

Diverse as proteins are, they are all constructed from the same set of 20 amino acids, linked in unbranched polymers. The bond between amino acids is called a peptide bond, so a polymer of amino acids is called a **polypeptide**. A **protein** is a biologically functional molecule made up of one or more polypeptides, each folded and coiled into a specific three-dimensional structure.

Amino Acid Monomers

All amino acids share a common structure. An **amino acid** is an organic molecule with both an amino group and a carboxyl group (see Figure 4.9). The figure at the right shows the general formula for an amino acid. At the center of the amino acid is an asymmetric carbon atom called the *alpha* (α) *carbon*. Its four different partners are an amino group, a carboxyl group, a hydrogen atom, and a variable group symbolized by R. The R group, also called the side chain, differs with each amino acid.

Side chain (R group)

R

α carbon

Amino group

Carboxyl group

▼ Figure 5.13 An overview of protein functions.

Enzymatic proteins

Function: Selective acceleration of chemical reactions

Example: Digestive enzymes catalyze the hydrolysis of bonds in food molecules.

Defensive proteins

Function: Protection against disease

Example: Antibodies inactivate and help destroy viruses and bacteria.

Storage proteins

Function: Storage of amino acids

Examples: Casein, the protein of milk, is the major source of amino acids for baby mammals. Plants have storage proteins in their seeds. Ovalbumin is the protein of egg white, used as an amino acid source for the developing embryo.

Ovalbumin Amino acids for embryo

Transport proteins

Function: Transport of substances

Examples: Hemoglobin, the iron-containing protein of vertebrate blood, transports oxygen from the lungs to other parts of the body. Other proteins transport molecules across membranes, as shown here.

Cell membrane

Hormonal proteins

Function: Coordination of an organism's activities

Example: Insulin, a hormone secreted by the pancreas, causes other tissues to take up glucose, thus regulating blood sugar concentration.

High blood sugar   Insulin secreted   Normal blood sugar

Receptor proteins

Function: Response of cell to chemical stimuli

Example: Receptors built into the membrane of a nerve cell detect signaling molecules released by other nerve cells.

Signaling molecules   Receptor protein

Contractile and motor proteins

Function: Movement

Examples: Motor proteins are responsible for the undulations of cilia and flagella. Actin and myosin proteins are responsible for the contraction of muscles.

Actin   Myosin

Muscle tissue   30 μm

Structural proteins

Function: Support

Examples: Keratin is the protein of hair, horns, feathers, and other skin appendages. Insects and spiders use silk fibers to make their cocoons and webs, respectively. Collagen and elastin proteins provide a fibrous framework in animal connective tissues.

Collagen

Connective tissue   60 μm

Figure 5.14 shows the 20 amino acids that cells use to build their thousands of proteins. Here the amino groups and carboxyl groups are all depicted in ionized form, the way they usually exist at the pH found in a cell.

The physical and chemical properties of the side chain determine the unique characteristics of a particular amino acid, thus affecting its functional role in a polypeptide. In Figure 5.14, the amino acids are grouped according to the properties of their side chains. One group consists of amino acids with nonpolar side chains, which are hydrophobic.

Another group consists of amino acids with polar side chains, which are hydrophilic. Acidic amino acids are those with side chains that are generally negative in charge due to the presence of a carboxyl group, which is usually dissociated (ionized) at cellular pH. Basic amino acids have amino groups in their side chains that are generally positive in charge. (Notice that *all* amino acids have carboxyl groups and amino groups; the terms *acidic* and *basic* in this context refer only to groups in the side chains.) Because they are charged, acidic and basic side chains are also hydrophilic.

▼ Figure 5.14 The 20 amino acids of proteins. The amino acids are grouped here according to the properties of their side chains (R groups) and shown in their prevailing ionic forms at pH 7.2, the pH within a cell. The three-letter and one-letter abbreviations for the amino acids are in parentheses. All of the amino acids used in proteins are L enantiomers (see Figure 4.7c).

Nonpolar side chains; hydrophobic

Polar side chains; hydrophilic

Electrically charged side chains; hydrophilic

Polypeptides (Amino Acid Polymers)

Now that we have examined amino acids, let's see how they are linked to form polymers (**Figure 5.15**). When two amino acids are positioned so that the carboxyl group of one is adjacent to the amino group of the other, they can become joined by a dehydration reaction, with the removal of a water molecule. The resulting covalent bond is called a **peptide bond**. Repeated over and over, this process yields a polypeptide, a polymer of many amino acids linked by peptide bonds.

The repeating sequence of atoms highlighted in purple in Figure 5.15 is called the *polypeptide backbone*. Extending from this backbone are the different side chains (R groups) of the amino acids. Polypeptides range in length from a few amino acids to a thousand or more. Each specific polypeptide has a unique linear sequence of amino acids. Note that one end of the polypeptide chain has a free amino group, while

the opposite end has a free carboxyl group. Thus, a polypeptide of any length has a single amino end (N-terminus) and a single carboxyl end (C-terminus). In a polypeptide of any significant size, the side chains far outnumber the terminal groups, so the chemical nature of the molecule as a whole is determined by the kind and sequence of the side chains. The immense variety of polypeptides in nature illustrates an important concept introduced earlier—that cells can make many different polymers by linking a limited set of monomers into diverse sequences.

Protein Structure and Function

The specific activities of proteins result from their intricate three-dimensional architecture, the simplest level of which is the sequence of their amino acids. The pioneer in determining the amino acid sequence of proteins was Frederick Sanger, who, with his colleagues at Cambridge University in England, worked on the hormone insulin in the late 1940s and early 1950s. He used agents that break polypeptides at specific places, followed by chemical methods to determine the amino acid sequence in these small fragments. Sanger and his co-workers were able, after years of effort, to reconstruct the complete amino acid sequence of insulin. Since then, the steps involved in sequencing a polypeptide have been automated.

Once we have learned the amino acid sequence of a polypeptide, what can it tell us about the three-dimensional structure (commonly referred to simply as the "structure") of the protein and its function? The term *polypeptide* is not synonymous with the term *protein*. Even for a protein consisting of a single polypeptide, the relationship is somewhat analogous to that between a long strand of yarn and a sweater of particular size and shape that can be knit from the yarn. A functional protein is not *just* a polypeptide chain, but one or more polypeptides precisely twisted, folded, and coiled into a molecule of unique shape, which can be shown in several different types of models (**Figure 5.16**). And it is the amino acid sequence of each polypeptide that determines what three-dimensional structure the protein will have under normal cellular conditions.

When a cell synthesizes a polypeptide, the chain may fold spontaneously, assuming the functional structure for that protein. This folding is driven and reinforced by the formation of various bonds between parts of the chain, which in turn depends on the sequence of amino acids. Many proteins are roughly spherical (*globular proteins*), while others are shaped like long fibers (*fibrous proteins*). Even within these broad categories, countless variations exist.

A protein's specific structure determines how it works. In almost every case, the function of a protein depends on its ability to recognize and bind to some other molecule. In an especially striking example of the marriage of form and

▲ **Figure 5.15 Making a polypeptide chain.** Peptide bonds are formed by dehydration reactions, which link the carboxyl group of one amino acid to the amino group of the next. The peptide bonds are formed one at a time, starting with the amino acid at the amino end (N-terminus). The polypeptide has a repetitive backbone (purple) to which the amino acid side chains (yellow and green) are attached.

DRAW IT *Label the three amino acids in the upper part of the figure using three-letter and one-letter codes. Circle and label the carboxyl and amino groups that will form the new peptide bond.*

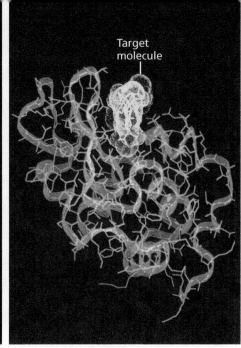

(a) A **ribbon model** shows how the single polypeptide chain folds and coils to form the functional protein. (The yellow lines represent disulfide bridges that stabilize the protein's shape.)

(b) A **space-filling model** shows more clearly the globular shape seen in many proteins, as well as the specific three-dimensional structure unique to lysozyme.

(c) In this view, a ribbon model is superimposed on a **wireframe model**, which shows the backbone with the side chains extending from it. The yellow structure is the target molecule.

▲ **Figure 5.16 Structure of a protein, the enzyme lysozyme.** Present in our sweat, tears, and saliva, lysozyme is an enzyme that helps prevent infection by binding to and catalyzing the destruction of specific molecules on the surface of many kinds of bacteria. The groove is the part of the protein that recognizes and binds to the target molecules on bacterial walls.

function, **Figure 5.17** shows the exact match of shape between an antibody (a protein in the body) and the particular foreign substance on a flu virus that the antibody binds to and marks for destruction. You'll learn more about how the immune system generates antibodies that match the shapes of specific foreign molecules so well. Also, you may recall from Chapter 2 that natural signaling molecules called endorphins bind to specific receptor proteins on the surface of brain cells in humans, producing euphoria and relieving pain. Morphine, heroin, and other opiate drugs are able to mimic endorphins because they all share a similar shape with endorphins and can thus fit into and bind to endorphin receptors in the brain. This fit is very specific, something like a lock and key (see Figure 2.16). Thus, the function of a protein—for instance, the ability of a receptor protein to bind to a particular pain-relieving signaling molecule—is an emergent property resulting from exquisite molecular order.

▲ **Figure 5.17 An antibody binding to a protein from a flu virus.** A technique called X-ray crystallography was used to generate a computer model of an antibody protein (blue and orange, left) bound to a flu virus protein (green and yellow, right). Computer software was then used to back the images away from each other, revealing the exact complementarity of shape between the two protein surfaces.

Four Levels of Protein Structure

With the goal of understanding the function of a protein, learning about its structure is often productive. In spite of their great diversity, all proteins share three superimposed levels of structure, known as primary, secondary, and tertiary structure. A fourth level, quaternary structure, arises when a protein consists of two or more polypeptide chains. **Figure 5.18** describes these four levels of protein structure. Be sure to study this figure thoroughly before going on to the next section.

Primary Structure

Linear chain of amino acids

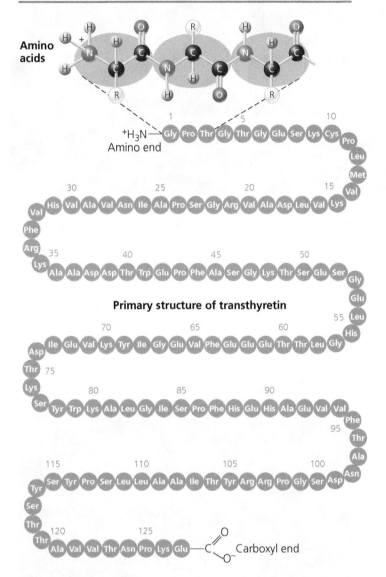

Primary structure of transthyretin

The **primary structure** of a protein is its sequence of amino acids. As an example, let's consider transthyretin, a globular blood protein that transports vitamin A and one of the thyroid hormones throughout the body. Transthyretin is made up of four identical polypeptide chains, each composed of 127 amino acids. Shown here is one of these chains unraveled for a closer look at its primary structure. Each of the 127 positions along the chain is occupied by one of the 20 amino acids, indicated here by its three-letter abbreviation.

The primary structure is like the order of letters in a very long word. If left to chance, there would be 20^{127} different ways of making a polypeptide chain 127 amino acids long. However, the precise primary structure of a protein is determined not by the random linking of amino acids, but by inherited genetic information. The primary structure in turn dictates secondary and tertiary structure, due to the chemical nature of the backbone and the side chains (R groups) of the amino acids along the polypeptide.

Secondary Structure

Regions stabilized by hydrogen bonds between atoms of the polypeptide backbone

Most proteins have segments of their polypeptide chains repeatedly coiled or folded in patterns that contribute to the protein's overall shape. These coils and folds, collectively referred to as **secondary structure**, are the result of hydrogen bonds between the repeating constituents of the polypeptide backbone (not the amino acid side chains). Within the backbone, the oxygen atoms have a partial negative charge, and the hydrogen atoms attached to the nitrogens have a partial positive charge (see Figure 2.14); therefore, hydrogen bonds can form between these atoms. Individually, these hydrogen bonds are weak, but because there are so many of them over a relatively long region of the polypeptide chain, they can support a particular shape for that part of the protein.

One such secondary structure is the **α helix**, a delicate coil held together by hydrogen bonding between every fourth amino acid, as shown above. Although each transthyretin polypeptide has only one α helix region (see tertiary structure), other globular proteins have multiple stretches of α helix separated by nonhelical regions (see hemoglobin on the next page). Some fibrous proteins, such as α-keratin, the structural protein of hair, have the α helix structure over most of their length.

The other main type of secondary structure is the **β pleated sheet**. As shown above, in this structure two or more segments of the polypeptide chain lying side by side (called β strands) are connected by hydrogen bonds between parts of the two parallel segments of the polypeptide backbone. β pleated sheets make up the core of many globular proteins, as is the case for transthyretin (see tertiary structure), and dominate some fibrous proteins, including the silk protein of a spider's web. The teamwork of so many hydrogen bonds makes each spider silk fiber stronger than a steel strand of the same weight.

▼ Spiders secrete silk fibers made of a structural protein containing β pleated sheets, which allow the spider web to stretch and recoil.

Tertiary Structure

Three-dimensional shape stabilized by interactions between side chains

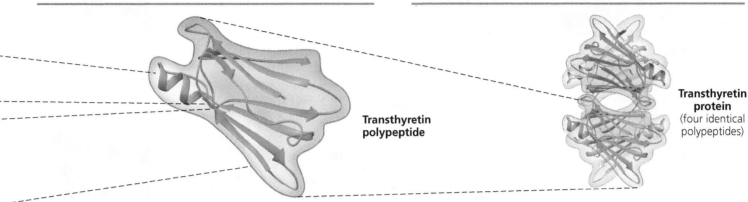

Transsthyretin polypeptide

Quaternary Structure

Association of two or more polypeptides (some proteins only)

Transthyretin protein (four identical polypeptides)

Superimposed on the patterns of secondary structure is a protein's tertiary structure, shown above in a ribbon model of the transthyretin polypeptide. While secondary structure involves interactions between backbone constituents, **tertiary structure** is the overall shape of a polypeptide resulting from interactions between the side chains (R groups) of the various amino acids. One type of interaction that contributes to tertiary structure is called—somewhat misleadingly— a **hydrophobic interaction**. As a polypeptide folds into its functional shape, amino acids with hydrophobic (nonpolar) side chains usually end up in clusters at the core of the protein, out of contact with water. Thus, a "hydrophobic interaction" is actually caused by the exclusion of nonpolar substances by water molecules. Once nonpolar amino acid side chains are close together, van der Waals interactions help hold them together. Meanwhile, hydrogen bonds between polar side chains and ionic bonds between positively and negatively charged side chains also help stabilize tertiary structure. These are all weak interactions in the aqueous cellular environment, but their cumulative effect helps give the protein a unique shape.

Covalent bonds called **disulfide bridges** may further reinforce the shape of a protein. Disulfide bridges form where two cysteine monomers, which have sulfhydryl groups (—SH) on their side chains (see Figure 4.9), are brought close together by the folding of the protein. The sulfur of one cysteine bonds to the sulfur of the second, and the disulfide bridge (—S—S—) rivets parts of the protein together (see the yellow lines in Figure 5.16a). All of these different kinds of interactions can contribute to the tertiary structure of a protein, as shown here in a small part of a hypothetical protein:

Some proteins consist of two or more polypeptide chains aggregated into one functional macromolecule. **Quaternary structure** is the overall protein structure that results from the aggregation of these polypeptide subunits. For example, shown above is the complete globular transthyretin protein, made up of its four polypeptides.

Another example is collagen, shown below, which is a fibrous protein that has three identical helical polypeptides intertwined into a larger triple helix, giving the long fibers great strength. This suits collagen fibers to their function as the girders of connective tissue in skin, bone, tendons, ligaments, and other body parts. (Collagen accounts for 40% of the protein in a human body.)

Collagen

Hemoglobin, the oxygen-binding protein of red blood cells shown below, is another example of a globular protein with quaternary structure. It consists of four polypeptide subunits, two of one kind (α) and two of another kind (β). Both α and β subunits consist primarily of α-helical secondary structure. Each subunit has a nonpolypeptide component, called heme, with an iron atom that binds oxygen.

Heme

Iron

β subunit

α subunit

α subunit

β subunit

Hemoglobin

Hydrogen bond

Hydrophobic interactions and van der Waals interactions

Disulfide bridge

Ionic bond

Polypeptide backbone

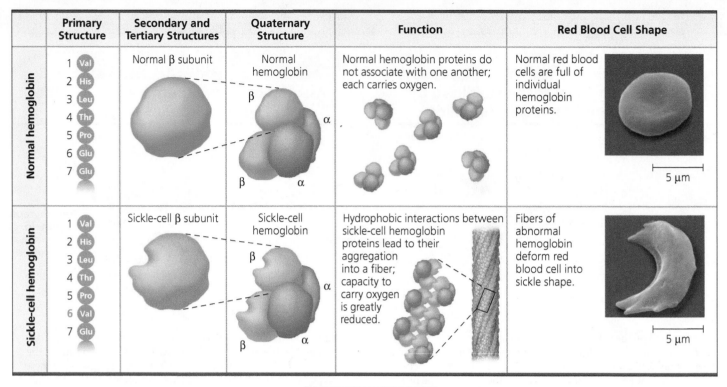

	Primary Structure	Secondary and Tertiary Structures	Quaternary Structure	Function	Red Blood Cell Shape
Normal hemoglobin	1 Val 2 His 3 Leu 4 Thr 5 Pro 6 Glu 7 Glu	Normal β subunit	Normal hemoglobin β α β α	Normal hemoglobin proteins do not associate with one another; each carries oxygen.	Normal red blood cells are full of individual hemoglobin proteins. 5 μm
Sickle-cell hemoglobin	1 Val 2 His 3 Leu 4 Thr 5 Pro 6 Val 7 Glu	Sickle-cell β subunit	Sickle-cell hemoglobin β α β α	Hydrophobic interactions between sickle-cell hemoglobin proteins lead to their aggregation into a fiber; capacity to carry oxygen is greatly reduced.	Fibers of abnormal hemoglobin deform red blood cell into sickle shape. 5 μm

▲ **Figure 5.19 A single amino acid substitution in a protein causes sickle-cell disease.**

MAKE CONNECTIONS *Considering the chemical characteristics of the amino acids valine and glutamic acid (see Figure 5.14), propose a possible explanation for the dramatic effect on protein function that occurs when valine is substituted for glutamic acid.*

Sickle-Cell Disease: A Change in Primary Structure

Even a slight change in primary structure can affect a protein's shape and ability to function. For instance, **sickle-cell disease**, an inherited blood disorder, is caused by the substitution of one amino acid (valine) for the normal one (glutamic acid) at a particular position in the primary structure of hemoglobin, the protein that carries oxygen in red blood cells. Normal red blood cells are disk-shaped, but in sickle-cell disease, the abnormal hemoglobin molecules tend to aggregate into chains, deforming some of the cells into a sickle shape **(Figure 5.19)**. A person with the disease has periodic "sickle-cell crises" when the angular cells clog tiny blood vessels, impeding blood flow. The toll taken on such patients is a dramatic example of how a simple change in protein structure can have devastating effects on protein function.

What Determines Protein Structure?

You've learned that a unique shape endows each protein with a specific function. But what are the key factors determining protein structure? You already know most of the answer: A polypeptide chain of a given amino acid sequence can be arranged into a three-dimensional shape determined by the interactions responsible for secondary and tertiary structure. This folding normally occurs as the protein is being synthesized in the crowded environment within a cell, aided by other proteins. However, protein structure also depends on the physical and chemical conditions of the protein's environment. If the pH, salt concentration, temperature, or other aspects of its environment are altered, the weak chemical bonds and interactions within a protein may be destroyed, causing the protein to unravel and lose its native shape, a change called **denaturation (Figure 5.20)**. Because it is misshapen, the denatured protein is biologically inactive.

Most proteins become denatured if they are transferred from an aqueous environment to a nonpolar solvent, such as ether or chloroform; the polypeptide chain refolds so that its hydrophobic regions face outward toward the solvent. Other denaturation agents include chemicals that disrupt

Normal protein   Denatured protein

▲ **Figure 5.20 Denaturation and renaturation of a protein.** High temperatures or various chemical treatments will denature a protein, causing it to lose its shape and hence its ability to function. If the denatured protein remains dissolved, it may renature when the chemical and physical aspects of its environment are restored to normal.

the hydrogen bonds, ionic bonds, and disulfide bridges that maintain a protein's shape. Denaturation can also result from excessive heat, which agitates the polypeptide chain enough to overpower the weak interactions that stabilize the structure. The white of an egg becomes opaque during cooking because the denatured proteins are insoluble and solidify. This also explains why excessively high fevers can be fatal: Proteins in the blood tend to denature at very high body temperatures.

When a protein in a test-tube solution has been denatured by heat or chemicals, it can sometimes return to its functional shape when the denaturing agent is removed. (Sometimes this is not possible: For example, a fried egg will not become liquefied when placed back into the refrigerator!) We can conclude that the information for building specific shape is intrinsic to the protein's primary structure. The sequence of amino acids determines the protein's shape—where an α helix can form, where β pleated sheets can exist, where disulfide bridges are located, where ionic bonds can form, and so on. But how does protein folding occur in the cell?

Protein Folding in the Cell

Biochemists now know the amino acid sequence for more than 24 million proteins, with about 1 million added each month, and the three-dimensional shape for more than 25,000. Researchers have tried to correlate the primary structure of many proteins with their three-dimensional structure to discover the rules of protein folding. Unfortunately, however, the protein-folding process is not that simple. Most proteins probably go through several intermediate structures on their way to a stable shape, and looking at the mature structure does not reveal the stages of folding required to achieve that form. However, biochemists have developed methods for tracking a protein through such stages.

Crucial to the folding process are **chaperonins** (also called chaperone proteins), protein molecules that assist in the proper folding of other proteins **(Figure 5.21)**. Chaperonins do not specify the final structure of a polypeptide.

Instead, they keep the new polypeptide segregated from disruptive chemical conditions in the cytoplasmic environment while it folds spontaneously. The chaperonin shown in Figure 5.21, from the bacterium *E. coli*, is a giant multiprotein complex shaped like a hollow cylinder. The cavity provides a shelter for folding polypeptides, and recent research suggests that minute amounts of water are present, ensuring a hydrophilic environment that aids the folding process. Molecular systems have been identified that interact with chaperonins and check whether proper folding has occurred. Such systems either refold the misfolded proteins correctly or mark them for destruction.

Misfolding of polypeptides is a serious problem in cells that has come under increasing scrutiny by medical researchers. Many diseases—such as cystic fibrosis, Alzheimer's, Parkinson's, and mad cow disease—are associated with an accumulation of misfolded proteins. In fact, misfolded versions of the transthyretin protein featured in Figure 5.18 have been implicated in several diseases, including one form of senile dementia.

Even when scientists have a correctly folded protein in hand, determining its exact three-dimensional structure is not simple, for a single protein molecule has thousands of atoms. The first 3-D structures were worked out in the late 1950s for hemoglobin and a related protein called myoglobin. The method that made these feats possible was **X-ray crystallography**, which has since been used to determine the 3-D structure of many other proteins. In a recent example, Roger Kornberg and his colleagues at Stanford University used this method to elucidate the structure of RNA polymerase, an enzyme that plays a crucial role in the expression of genes **(Figure 5.22)**. Another method for analyzing protein structure is nuclear magnetic resonance (NMR) spectroscopy, which does not require protein crystallization. A still newer approach employs bioinformatics (see Concept 5.6) to predict the 3-D structure of polypeptides from their amino acid sequence. X-ray crystallography, NMR spectroscopy, and bioinformatics are complementary approaches to understanding protein structure and function.

▶ **Figure 5.21 A chaperonin in action.** The computer graphic (left) shows a large chaperonin protein complex from the bacterium *E. coli*. It has an interior space that provides a shelter for the proper folding of newly made polypeptides. The complex consists of two proteins: One is a hollow cylinder; the other is a cap that can fit on either end. The steps of chaperonin activity are shown at the right.

Cap

Hollow cylinder

Chaperonin (fully assembled)

Polypeptide

❶ An unfolded polypeptide enters the cylinder from one end.

Correctly folded protein

❷ Cap attachment causes the cylinder to change shape, creating a hydrophilic environment for polypeptide folding.

❸ The cap comes off, and the properly folded protein is released.

▼ Figure 5.22 Inquiry

What can the 3-D shape of the enzyme RNA polymerase II tell us about its function?

Experiment In 2006, Roger Kornberg was awarded the Nobel Prize in Chemistry for using X-ray crystallography to determine the 3-D shape of RNA polymerase II, which binds to the DNA double helix and synthesizes RNA. After crystallizing a complex of all three components, Kornberg and his colleagues aimed an X-ray beam through the crystal. The atoms of the crystal diffracted (bent) the X-rays into an orderly array that a digital detector recorded as a pattern of spots called an X-ray diffraction pattern.

Results Using data from X-ray diffraction patterns, as well as the amino acid sequence determined by chemical methods, the researchers built a 3-D model of the complex with the help of computer software.

Conclusion Analysis of the model led to a hypothesis about the functions of different regions of RNA polymerase II. For example, the region above the DNA may act as a clamp that holds the nucleic acids in place. (You'll learn more about this enzyme in Chapter 17.)

Source: A. L. Gnatt et al., Structural basis of transcription: an RNA polymerase II elongation complex at 3.3Å, *Science* 292:1876–1882 (2001). Computer graphic copyright © 2001 by AAAS. Reprinted with permission.

WHAT IF? *Looking at the model, can you identify any elements of secondary structure?*

CONCEPT CHECK 5.4

1. What parts of a polypeptide participate in the bonds that hold together secondary structure? Tertiary structure?

2. Thus far in the chapter, the Greek letters α and β have been used to specify at least three different pairs of structures. Name and briefly describe them.

3. **WHAT IF?** Where would you expect a polypeptide region rich in the amino acids valine, leucine, and isoleucine to be located in a folded polypeptide? Explain.

CONCEPT 5.5

Nucleic acids store, transmit, and help express hereditary information

If the primary structure of polypeptides determines a protein's shape, what determines primary structure? The amino acid sequence of a polypeptide is programmed by a discrete unit of inheritance known as a **gene**. Genes consist of DNA, which belongs to the class of compounds called nucleic acids. **Nucleic acids** are polymers made of monomers called nucleotides.

The Roles of Nucleic Acids

The two types of nucleic acids, **deoxyribonucleic acid (DNA)** and **ribonucleic acid (RNA)**, enable living organisms to reproduce their complex components from one generation to the next. Unique among molecules, DNA provides directions for its own replication. DNA also directs RNA synthesis and, through RNA, controls protein synthesis; this entire process is called **gene expression (Figure 5.23)**.

DNA is the genetic material that organisms inherit from their parents. Each chromosome contains one long DNA molecule, usually carrying several hundred or more genes. When a cell reproduces itself by dividing, its DNA molecules are copied and passed along from one generation of

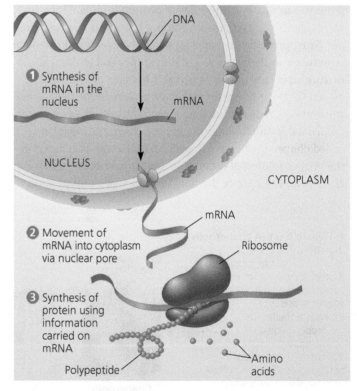

▲ **Figure 5.23 Gene expression: DNA → RNA → protein.** In a eukaryotic cell, DNA in the nucleus programs protein production in the cytoplasm by dictating synthesis of messenger RNA (mRNA).

cells to the next. Encoded in the structure of DNA is the information that programs all the cell's activities. The DNA, however, is not directly involved in running the operations of the cell, any more than computer software by itself can read the bar code on a box of cereal. Just as a scanner is needed to read a bar code, proteins are required to implement genetic programs. The molecular hardware of the cell—the tools for biological functions—consists mostly of proteins. For example, the oxygen carrier in red blood cells is the protein hemoglobin that you saw earlier (see Figure 5.17), not the DNA that specifies its structure.

How does RNA, the other type of nucleic acid, fit into gene expression, the flow of genetic information from DNA to proteins? Each gene along a DNA molecule directs synthesis of a type of RNA called *messenger RNA* (*mRNA*). The mRNA molecule interacts with the cell's protein-synthesizing machinery to direct production of a polypeptide, which folds into all or part of a protein. We can summarize the flow of genetic information as DNA → RNA → protein (see Figure 5.23). The sites of protein synthesis are cellular structures called ribosomes. In a eukaryotic cell, ribosomes are in the region between the nucleus and the plasma membrane (the cytoplasm), but DNA resides in the nucleus. Messenger RNA conveys genetic instructions for building proteins from the nucleus to the cytoplasm. Prokaryotic cells lack nuclei but still use mRNA to convey a message from the DNA to ribosomes and other cellular equipment that translate the coded information into amino acid sequences.

The Components of Nucleic Acids

Nucleic acids are macromolecules that exist as polymers called **polynucleotides** (Figure 5.24a). As indicated by the name, each polynucleotide consists of monomers called **nucleotides**. A nucleotide, in general, is composed of three parts: a five-carbon sugar (a pentose), a nitrogen-containing (nitrogenous) base, and one or more phosphate groups (Figure 5.24b). In a polynucleotide, each monomer has only one phosphate group. The portion of a nucleotide without any phosphate groups is called a *nucleoside*.

To build a nucleotide, let's first consider the nitrogenous bases (Figure 5.24c). Each nitrogenous base has one or two rings that include nitrogen atoms. (They are called nitrogenous *bases* because the nitrogen atoms tend to take up

▼ Figure 5.24 **Components of nucleic acids. (a)** A polynucleotide has a sugar-phosphate backbone with variable appendages, the nitrogenous bases. **(b)** A nucleotide monomer includes a nitrogenous base, a sugar, and a phosphate group. Note that carbon numbers in the sugar include primes ('). **(c)** A nucleoside includes a nitrogenous base (purine or pyrimidine) and a five-carbon sugar (deoxyribose or ribose).

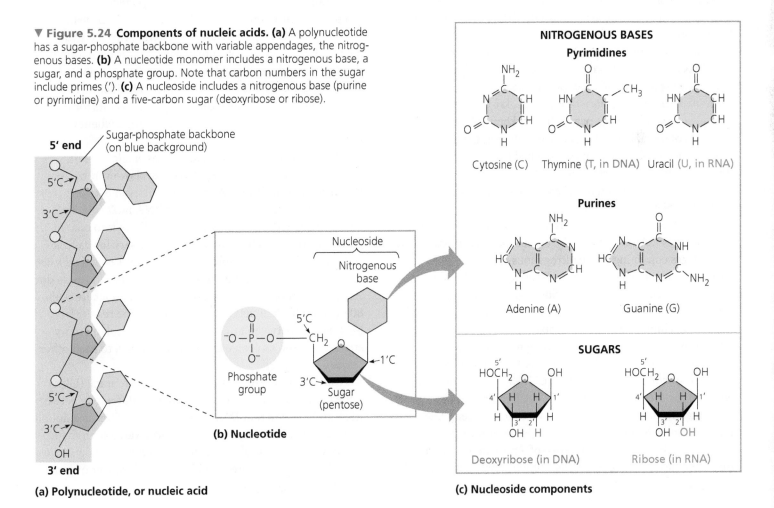

(a) Polynucleotide, or nucleic acid

(b) Nucleotide

(c) Nucleoside components

H⁺ from solution, thus acting as bases.) There are two families of nitrogenous bases: pyrimidines and purines. A **pyrimidine** has one six-membered ring of carbon and nitrogen atoms. The members of the pyrimidine family are cytosine (C), thymine (T), and uracil (U). **Purines** are larger, with a six-membered ring fused to a five-membered ring. The purines are adenine (A) and guanine (G). The specific pyrimidines and purines differ in the chemical groups attached to the rings. Adenine, guanine, and cytosine are found in both DNA and RNA; thymine is found only in DNA and uracil only in RNA.

Now let's add the sugar to which the nitrogenous base is attached. In DNA the sugar is **deoxyribose**; in RNA it is **ribose** (see Figure 5.24c). The only difference between these two sugars is that deoxyribose lacks an oxygen atom on the second carbon in the ring; hence the name *deoxy*ribose.

So far, we have built a nucleoside (nitrogenous base plus sugar). To complete the construction of a nucleotide, we attach a phosphate group to the 5′ carbon of the sugar (see Figure 5.24b). The molecule is now a nucleoside monophosphate, more often called a nucleotide.

Nucleotide Polymers

The linkage of nucleotides into a polynucleotide involves a dehydration reaction. (You will learn the details in Chapter 16). In the polynucleotide, adjacent nucleotides are joined by a phosphodiester linkage, which consists of a phosphate group that links the sugars of two nucleotides. This bonding results in a repeating pattern of sugar-phosphate units called the *sugar-phosphate backbone* (see Figure 5.24a). (Note that the nitrogenous bases are not part of the backbone.) The two free ends of the polymer are distinctly different from each other. One end has a phosphate attached to a 5′ carbon, and the other end has a hydroxyl group on a 3′ carbon; we refer to these as the *5′ end* and the *3′ end*, respectively. We can say that a polynucleotide has a built-in directionality along its sugar-phosphate backbone, from 5′ to 3′, somewhat like a one-way street. All along this sugar-phosphate backbone are appendages consisting of the nitrogenous bases.

The sequence of bases along a DNA (or mRNA) polymer is unique for each gene and provides very specific information to the cell. Because genes are hundreds to thousands of nucleotides long, the number of possible base sequences is effectively limitless. A gene's meaning to the cell is encoded in its specific sequence of the four DNA bases. For example, the sequence 5′-AGGTAACTT-3′ means one thing, whereas the sequence 5′-CGCTTTAAC-3′ has a different meaning. (Entire genes, of course, are much longer.) The linear order of bases in a gene specifies the amino acid sequence—the primary structure—of a protein, which in turn specifies that protein's three-dimensional structure and its function in the cell.

The Structures of DNA and RNA Molecules

DNA molecules have two polynucleotides, or "strands," that wind around an imaginary axis, forming a **double helix** (Figure 5.25a). The two sugar-phosphate backbones run in opposite 5′ → 3′ directions from each other; this arrangement is referred to as **antiparallel**, somewhat like a divided highway. The sugar-phosphate backbones are on the outside of the helix, and the nitrogenous bases are paired in the interior of the helix. The two strands are held together by hydrogen bonds between the paired bases (see Figure 5.25a). Most DNA molecules are very long, with thousands or even millions of base pairs. For example, the one long DNA double helix in a eukaryotic chromosome includes many genes, each one a particular segment of the molecule.

In base pairing, only certain bases in the double helix are compatible with each other. Adenine (A) in one strand always pairs with thymine (T) in the other, and guanine (G) always pairs with cytosine (C). Reading the sequence of bases along one strand of the double helix would tell us the sequence of bases along the other strand. If a stretch of one strand has the base sequence 5′-AGGTCCG-3′, then the base-pairing rules tell us that the same stretch of the other strand must have the sequence 3′-TCCAGGC-5′. The two strands of the double helix are *complementary*, each the predictable counterpart of the other. It is this feature of DNA that makes it possible to generate two identical copies of each DNA molecule in a cell that is preparing to divide. When the cell divides, the copies are distributed to the daughter cells, making them genetically identical to the parent cell. Thus, the structure of DNA accounts for its function of transmitting genetic information whenever a cell reproduces.

RNA molecules, by contrast, exist as single strands. Complementary base pairing can occur, however, between regions of two RNA molecules or even between two stretches of nucleotides in the *same* RNA molecule. In fact, base pairing within an RNA molecule allows it to take on the particular three-dimensional shape necessary for its function. Consider, for example, the type of RNA called *transfer RNA (tRNA)*, which brings amino acids to the ribosome during the synthesis of a polypeptide. A tRNA molecule is about 80 nucleotides in length. Its functional shape results from base pairing between nucleotides where complementary stretches of the molecule can run antiparallel to each other (Figure 5.25b).

Note that in RNA, adenine (A) pairs with uracil (U); thymine (T) is not present in RNA. Another difference between RNA and DNA is that DNA almost always exists as a double helix, whereas RNA molecules are more variable in shape. RNAs are very versatile molecules, and many biologists believe RNA may have preceded DNA as the carrier of genetic information in early forms of life.

► **Figure 5.25 The structures of DNA and tRNA molecules. (a)** The DNA molecule is usually a double helix, with the sugar-phosphate backbones of the antiparallel poly-nucleotide strands (symbolized here by blue ribbons) on the outside of the helix. Hydrogen bonds between pairs of nitrogenous bases hold the two strands together. As illustrated here with symbolic shapes for the bases, adenine (A) can pair only with thymine (T), and guanine (G) can pair only with cytosine (C). Each DNA strand in this figure is the structural equivalent of the polynucleotide diagrammed in Figure 5.24a. **(b)** A tRNA molecule has a roughly L-shaped structure, with complementary base pairing of antiparallel stretches of RNA. In RNA, A pairs with U.

Sugar-phosphate backbones

Hydrogen bonds

Base pair joined by hydrogen bonding

Base pair joined by hydrogen bonding

(a) DNA

(b) Transfer RNA

CONCEPT CHECK 5.5

1. **DRAW IT** Go to Figure 5.24a and, for the top three nucleotides, number all the carbons in the sugars, circle the nitrogenous bases, and star the phosphates.

2. **DRAW IT** In a DNA double helix, a region along one DNA strand has this sequence of nitrogenous bases: 5'-TAGGCCT-3'. Copy this sequence, and write down its complementary strand, clearly indicating the 5' and 3' ends of the complementary strand.

CONCEPT 5.6

Genomics and proteomics have transformed biological inquiry and applications

Experimental work in the first half of the 20th century established the role of DNA as the bearer of genetic information, passed from generation to generation, that specified the functioning of living cells and organisms. Once the structure of the DNA molecule was described in 1953, and the linear sequence of nucleotide bases was understood to specify the amino acid sequence of proteins, biologists sought to "decode" genes by learning their base sequences.

The first chemical techniques for *DNA sequencing*, or determining the sequence of nucleotides along a DNA strand, one by one, were developed in the 1970s. Researchers began to study gene sequences, gene by gene, and the more they learned, the more questions they had: How was expression of genes regulated? Genes and their protein products clearly interacted with each other, but how? What was the function, if any, of the DNA that is not part of genes? To fully understand the genetic functioning of a living organism, the entire sequence of the full complement of DNA, the organism's

genome, would be most enlightening. In spite of the apparent impracticality of this idea, in the late 1980s several prominent biologists put forth an audacious proposal to launch a project that would sequence the entire human genome—all 3 billion bases of it! This endeavor began in 1990 and was effectively completed in the early 2000s.

An unplanned but profound side benefit of this project—the Human Genome Project—was the rapid development of faster and less expensive methods of sequencing. This trend has continued apace: The cost for sequencing 1 million bases in 2001, well over $5,000, has decreased to less than $0.10 in 2012. And a human genome, the first of which took over 10 years to sequence, could be completed at today's pace in just a few days. The number of genomes that have been fully sequenced has burgeoned, generating reams of data and prompting development of *bioinformatics*, the use of computer software and other computational tools that can handle and analyze these large data sets.

The reverberations of these developments have transformed the study of biology and related fields. Biologists often look at problems by analyzing large sets of genes or even comparing whole genomes of different species, an approach called **genomics**. A similar analysis of large sets of proteins, including their sequences, is called **proteomics**. (Protein sequences can be determined either by using biochemical techniques or by translating the DNA sequences that code for them.) These approaches permeate all fields of biology, some examples of which are shown in **Figure 5.26**.

Perhaps the most significant impact of genomics and proteomics on the field of biology as a whole has been their contributions to our understanding of evolution. In addition to confirming evidence for evolution from the study of fossils and characteristics of currently existing species, genomics has helped us tease out relationships among different groups of organisms that had not been resolved by previous types of evidence, and thus infer evolutionary history.

MAKE CONNECTIONS

Contributions of Genomics and Proteomics to Biology

Nucleotide sequencing and the analysis of large sets of genes and proteins can be done rapidly and inexpensively due to advances in technology and information processing. Taken together, genomics and proteomics have advanced our understanding of biology across many different fields.

Paleontology

New DNA sequencing techniques have allowed decoding of minute quantities of DNA found in ancient tissues from our extinct relatives, the Neanderthals (*Homo neanderthalensis*). Sequencing the Neanderthal genome has informed our understanding of their physical appearance as well as their relationship with modern humans.

Medical Science

Identifying the genetic basis for human diseases like cancer helps researchers focus their search for potential future treatments. Currently, sequencing the sets of genes expressed in an individual's tumor can allow a more targeted approach to treating the cancer, a type of "personalized medicine." *See Figure 12.20.*

Evolution

A major aim of evolutionary biology is to understand the relationships among species, both living and extinct. For example, genome sequence comparisons have identified the hippopotamus as the land mammal sharing the most recent common ancestor with whales.

Hippopotamus

Short-finned pilot whale

Conservation Biology

The tools of molecular genetics and genomics are increasingly used by ecologists to identify which species of animals and plants are killed illegally. In one case, genomic sequences of DNA from illegal shipments of elephant tusks were used to track down poachers and pinpoint the territory where they were operating.

Species Interactions

Over 90% of all plant species exist in a mutually beneficial partnership with fungi that are associated with the plants' roots. Genome sequencing and analysis of gene expression in several plant-fungal pairs promise major advances in our understanding of such interactions and may have implications for agricultural practices.

MAKE CONNECTIONS *Considering the examples provided here, describe how the approaches of genomics and proteomics help us to address a variety of biological questions.*

DNA and Proteins as Tape Measures of Evolution

EVOLUTION We are accustomed to thinking of shared traits, such as hair and milk production in mammals, as evidence of shared ancestry. Because DNA carries heritable information in the form of genes, sequences of genes and their protein products document the hereditary background of an organism. The linear sequences of nucleotides in DNA molecules are passed from parents to offspring; these sequences determine the amino acid sequences of proteins. As a result, siblings have greater similarity in their DNA and proteins than do unrelated individuals of the same species.

Given our evolutionary view of life, we can extend this concept of "molecular genealogy" to relationships between species: We would expect two species that appear to be closely related based on anatomical evidence (and possibly fossil evidence) to also share a greater proportion of their DNA and protein sequences than do less closely related species. In fact, that is the case. An example is the comparison of the β polypeptide chain of human hemoglobin with the corresponding hemoglobin polypeptide in other vertebrates. In this chain of 146 amino acids, humans and gorillas differ in just 1 amino acid, while humans and frogs, more distantly related, differ in 67 amino acids. In the Scientific Skills Exercise, you can apply this sort of reasoning to additional species. And this conclusion holds true as well when comparing whole genomes: The human genome is 95–98% identical to that of the chimpanzee, but only roughly 85% identical to that of the mouse, a more distant evolutionary relative. Molecular biology has added a new tape measure to the toolkit biologists use to assess evolutionary kinship.

CONCEPT CHECK 5.6

1. How would sequencing the entire genome of an organism help scientists to understand how that organism functioned?

2. Given the function of DNA, why would you expect two species with very similar traits to also have very similar genomes?

SCIENTIFIC SKILLS EXERCISE

Analyzing Polypeptide Sequence Data

 ► Human

 ► Rhesus monkey

 ► Gibbon

Are Rhesus Monkeys or Gibbons More Closely Related to Humans? DNA and polypeptide sequences from closely related species are more similar to each other than are sequences from more distantly related species. In this exercise, you will look at amino acid sequence data for the β polypeptide chain of hemoglobin, often called β-globin. You will then interpret the data to hypothesize whether the monkey or the gibbon is more closely related to humans.

How Such Experiments Are Done Researchers can isolate the polypeptide of interest from an organism and then determine the amino acid sequence. More frequently, the DNA of the relevant gene is sequenced, and the amino acid sequence of the polypeptide is deduced from the DNA sequence of its gene.

Data from the Experiments In the data below, the letters give the sequence of the 146 amino acids in β-globin from humans, rhesus monkeys, and gibbons. Because a complete sequence would not fit on one line here, the sequences are broken into three segments. The sequences for the three different species are aligned so that you can compare them easily. For example, you can see that for all three species, the first amino acid is V (valine) and the 146th amino acid is H (histidine).

Interpret the Data

1. Scan the monkey and gibbon sequences, letter by letter, circling any amino acids that do not match the human sequence. (a) How many amino acids differ between the monkey and the human sequences? (b) Between the gibbon and human?

2. For each nonhuman species, what percent of its amino acids are identical to the human sequence of β-globin?

3. Based on these data alone, state a hypothesis for which of these two species is more closely related to humans. What is your reasoning?

4. What other evidence could you use to support your hypothesis?

MB A version of this Scientific Skills Exercise can be assigned in MasteringBiology.

Data from Human: http://www.ncbi.nlm.nih.gov/protein/AAA21113.1; rhesus monkey: http://www.ncbi.nlm.nih.gov/protein/122634; gibbon: http://www.ncbi.nlm.nih.gov/protein/122616

Species	Alignment of Amino Acid Sequences of β-globin
Human	1 VHLTPEEKSA VTALWGKVNV DEVGGEALGR LLVVYPWTQR FFESFGDLST
Monkey	1 VHLTPEEKNA VTTLWGKVNV DEVGGEALGR LLLVYPWTQR FFESFGDLSS
Gibbon	1 VHLTPEEKSA VTALWGKVNV DEVGGEALGR LLVVYPWTQR FFESFGDLST
Human	51 PDAVMGNPKV KAHGKKVLGA FSDGLAHLDN LKGTFATLSE LHCDKLHVDP
Monkey	51 PDAVMGNPKV KAHGKKVLGA FSDGLNHLDN LKGTFAQLSE LHCDKLHVDP
Gibbon	51 PDAVMGNPKV KAHGKKVLGA FSDGLAHLDN LKGTFAQLSE LHCDKLHVDP
Human	101 ENFRLLGNVL VCVLAHHFGK EFTPPVQAAY QKVVAGVANA LAHKYH
Monkey	101 ENFKLLGNVL VCVLAHHFGK EFTPQVQAAY QKVVAGVANA LAHKYH
Gibbon	101 ENFRLLGNVL VCVLAHHFGK EFTPQVQAAY QKVVAGVANA LAHKYH

5 Chapter Review

SUMMARY OF KEY CONCEPTS

CONCEPT 5.1

Macromolecules are polymers, built from monomers (pp. 67–68)

- Large carbohydrates (polysaccharides), proteins, and nucleic acids are **polymers**, which are chains of **monomers**. The

components of lipids vary. Monomers form larger molecules by **dehydration reactions**, in which water molecules are released. Polymers can disassemble by the reverse process, **hydrolysis**. An immense variety of polymers can be built from a small set of monomers.

? *What is the fundamental basis for the differences between large carbohydrates, proteins, and nucleic acids?*

Large Biological Molecules	Components	Examples	Functions
CONCEPT 5.2 **Carbohydrates serve as fuel and building material (pp. 68–72)** **?** *Compare the composition, structure, and function of starch and cellulose. What role do starch and cellulose play in the human body?*	Monosaccharide monomer	**Monosaccharides:** glucose, fructose	Fuel; carbon sources that can be converted to other molecules or combined into polymers
		Disaccharides: lactose, sucrose	
		Polysaccharides: • Cellulose (plants) • Starch (plants) • Glycogen (animals) • Chitin (animals and fungi)	• Strengthens plant cell walls • Stores glucose for energy • Stores glucose for energy • Strengthens exoskeletons and fungal cell walls
CONCEPT 5.3 **Lipids are a diverse group of hydrophobic molecules (pp. 72–75)** **?** *Why are lipids not considered to be polymers or macromolecules?*	Glycerol, 3 fatty acids	**Triacylglycerols** (fats or oils): glycerol + 3 fatty acids	Important energy source
	Head with P, 2 fatty acids	**Phospholipids:** glycerol + phosphate group + 2 fatty acids	Lipid bilayers of membranes Hydrophobic tails Hydrophilic heads
	Steroid backbone	**Steroids:** four fused rings with attached chemical groups	• Component of cell membranes (cholesterol) • Signaling molecules that travel through the body (hormones)
CONCEPT 5.4 **Proteins include a diversity of structures, resulting in a wide range of functions (pp. 75–84)** **?** *Explain the basis for the great diversity of proteins.*	Amino acid monomer (20 types)	• Enzymes • Structural proteins • Hormones • Receptor proteins • Motor proteins • Defensive proteins	• Catalyze chemical reactions • Provide structural support • Coordinate organismal responses • Receive signals from outside cell • Function in cell movement • Protect against disease
CONCEPT 5.5 **Nucleic acids store, transmit, and help express hereditary information (pp. 84–87)** **?** *What role does complementary base pairing play in the functions of nucleic acids?*	Nucleotide monomer	**DNA:** • Sugar = deoxyribose • Nitrogenous bases = C, G, A, T • Usually double-stranded	Stores hereditary information
		RNA: • Sugar = ribose • Nitrogenous bases = C, G, A, U • Usually single-stranded	Various functions in gene expression, including carrying instructions from DNA to ribosomes

CONCEPT 5.6

Genomics and proteomics have transformed biological inquiry and applications (pp. 87–89)

- Recent technological advances in DNA sequencing have given rise to **genomics**, an approach that analyzes large sets of genes or whole genomes, and **proteomics**, a similar approach for large sets of proteins. Bioinformatics is the use of computational tools and computer software to analyze these large data sets.
- The more closely two species are related evolutionarily, the more similar their DNA sequences are. DNA sequence data confirms models of evolution based on fossils and anatomical evidence.

? *Given the sequences of a particular gene in fruit flies, fish, mice, and humans, predict the relative similarity of the human sequence to that of each of the other species.*

TEST YOUR UNDERSTANDING

LEVEL 1: KNOWLEDGE/COMPREHENSION

1. Which of the following categories includes all others in the list?
   a. monosaccharide
   b. polysaccharide
   c. starch
   d. carbohydrate

2. The enzyme amylase can break glycosidic linkages between glucose monomers only if the monomers are in the α form. Which of the following could amylase break down?
   a. glycogen, starch, and amylopectin
   b. glycogen and cellulose
   c. cellulose and chitin
   d. starch, chitin, and cellulose

3. Which of the following is true of *unsaturated* fats?
   a. They are more common in animals than in plants.
   b. They have double bonds in the carbon chains of their fatty acids.
   c. They generally solidify at room temperature.
   d. They contain more hydrogen than do saturated fats having the same number of carbon atoms.

4. The structural level of a protein *least* affected by a disruption in hydrogen bonding is the
   a. primary level.
   b. secondary level.
   c. tertiary level.
   d. quaternary level.

5. Enzymes that break down DNA catalyze the hydrolysis of the covalent bonds that join nucleotides together. What would happen to DNA molecules treated with these enzymes?
   a. The two strands of the double helix would separate.
   b. The phosphodiester linkages of the polynucleotide backbone would be broken.
   c. The pyrimidines would be separated from the deoxyribose sugars.
   d. All bases would be separated from the deoxyribose sugars.

LEVEL 2: APPLICATION/ANALYSIS

6. The molecular formula for glucose is $C_6H_{12}O_6$. What would be the molecular formula for a polymer made by linking ten glucose molecules together by dehydration reactions?
   a. $C_{60}H_{120}O_{60}$
   b. $C_{60}H_{102}O_{51}$
   c. $C_{60}H_{100}O_{50}$
   d. $C_{60}H_{111}O_{51}$

7. Which of the following pairs of base sequences could form a short stretch of a normal double helix of DNA?
   a. 5'-AGCT-3' with 5'-TCGA-3'
   b. 5'-GCGC-3' with 5'-TATA-3'
   c. 5'-ATGC-3' with 5'-GCAT-3'
   d. All of these pairs are correct.

8. Construct a table that organizes the following terms, and label the columns and rows.

Monosaccharides	Polypeptides	Phosphodiester linkages
Fatty acids	Triacylglycerols	Peptide bonds
Amino acids	Polynucleotides	Glycosidic linkages
Nucleotides	Polysaccharides	Ester linkages

9. **DRAW IT** Copy the polynucleotide strand in Figure 5.24a and label the bases G, T, C, and T, starting from the 5' end. Assuming this is a DNA polynucleotide, now draw the complementary strand, using the same symbols for phosphates (circles), sugars (pentagons), and bases. Label the bases. Draw arrows showing the 5' → 3' direction of each strand. Use the arrows to make sure the second strand is antiparallel to the first. *Hint*: After you draw the first strand vertically, turn the paper upside down; it is easier to draw the second strand from the 5' toward the 3' direction as you go from top to bottom.

LEVEL 3: SYNTHESIS/EVALUATION

10. **EVOLUTION CONNECTION**
    Comparisons of amino acid sequences can shed light on the evolutionary divergence of related species. If you were comparing two living species, would you expect all proteins to show the same degree of divergence? Why or why not?

11. **SCIENTIFIC INQUIRY**
    Suppose you are a research assistant in a lab studying DNA-binding proteins. You have been given the amino acid sequences of all the proteins encoded by the genome of a certain species and have been asked to find candidate proteins that could bind DNA. What type of amino acids would you expect to see in the DNA-binding regions of such proteins? Why?

12. **WRITE ABOUT A THEME: ORGANIZATION**
    Proteins, which have diverse functions in a cell, are all polymers of the same kinds of monomers—amino acids. Write a short essay (100–150 words) that discusses how the structure of amino acids allows this one type of polymer to perform so many functions.

13. **SYNTHESIZE YOUR KNOWLEDGE**

Given that the function of egg yolk is to nourish and support the developing chick, explain why egg yolks are so high in fat, protein, and cholesterol.

MasteringBiology®

Students Go to **MasteringBiology** for assignments, the eText, and the Study Area with practice tests, animations, and activities.

Instructors Go to **MasteringBiology** for automatically graded tutorials and questions that you can assign to your students, plus Instructor Resources.

6

A Tour of the Cell

▲ Figure 6.1 How do your cells help you learn about biology?

The Fundamental Units of Life

Cells are as fundamental to the living systems of biology as the atom is to chemistry. Many different types of cells are working for you right now. The contraction of muscle cells moves your eyes as you read this sentence. **Figure 6.1** shows extensions from a nerve cell (orange) making contact with muscle cells (red). The words on the page are translated into signals that nerve cells carry to your brain, where they are passed on to other nerve cells. As you study, you are making cell connections like these that solidify memories and permit learning to occur.

All organisms are made of cells. In the hierarchy of biological organization, the cell is the simplest collection of matter that can be alive. Indeed, many forms of life exist as single-celled organisms. Larger, more complex organisms, including plants and animals, are multicellular; their bodies are cooperatives of many kinds of specialized cells that could not survive for long on their own. Even when cells are arranged into higher levels of organization, such as tissues and organs, the cell remains the organism's basic unit of structure and function.

All cells are related by their descent from earlier cells. During the long evolutionary history of life on Earth, cells have been modified in many different ways. But although cells can differ substantially from one another, they share common features. In this chapter, we'll first examine the tools and techniques that allow us to understand cells, then tour the cell and become acquainted with its components.

Biologists use microscopes and the tools of biochemistry to study cells

Dr. Haifan Lin, featured in the interview before this chapter, points out that studying the inner workings of cells is often the first step in making exciting biological discoveries. But how do we study cells, usually too small to be seen by the unaided eye?

Microscopy

The development of instruments that extend the human senses allowed the discovery and early study of cells. Microscopes were invented in 1590 and further refined during the 1600s. Cell walls were first seen by Robert Hooke in 1665 as he looked through a microscope at dead cells from the bark of an oak tree. But it took the wonderfully crafted lenses of Antoni van Leeuwenhoek to visualize living cells. Imagine Hooke's awe when he visited van Leeuwenhoek in 1674 and the world of microorganisms—what his host called "very little animalcules"—was revealed to him.

The microscopes first used by Renaissance scientists, as well as the microscopes you are likely to use in the laboratory, are all light microscopes. In a **light microscope (LM)**, visible light is passed through the specimen and then through glass lenses. The lenses refract (bend) the light in such a way that the image of the specimen is magnified as it is projected into the eye or into a camera.

Three important parameters in microscopy are magnification, resolution, and contrast. *Magnification* is the ratio of an object's image size to its real size. Light microscopes can magnify effectively to about 1,000 times the actual size of the specimen; at greater magnifications, additional details cannot be seen clearly. *Resolution* is a measure of the clarity of the image; it is the minimum distance two points can be separated and still be distinguished as separate points. For example, what appears to the unaided eye as one star in the sky may be resolved as twin stars with a telescope, which has a higher resolving ability than the eye. Similarly, using standard techniques, the light microscope cannot resolve detail finer than about 0.2 micrometer (μm), or 200 nanometers (nm), regardless of the magnification **(Figure 6.2)**. The third parameter, *contrast*, is the difference in brightness between the light and dark areas of an image. Methods for enhancing contrast include staining or labeling cell components to stand out visually. **Figure 6.3** shows some different types of microscopy; study this figure as you read this section.

Until recently, the resolution barrier prevented cell biologists from using standard light microscopy when studying **organelles**, the membrane-enclosed structures within eukaryotic cells. To see these structures in any detail required the development of a new instrument. In the 1950s, the electron microscope was introduced to biology. Rather than

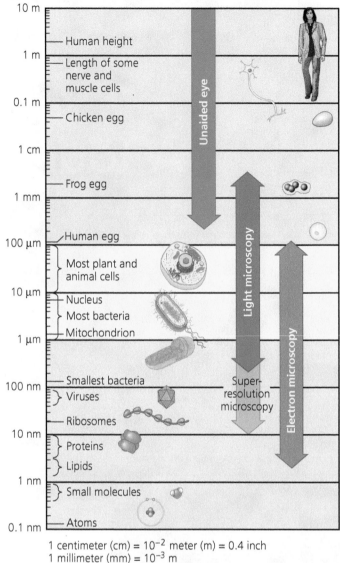

1 centimeter (cm) = 10^{-2} meter (m) = 0.4 inch
1 millimeter (mm) = 10^{-3} m
1 micrometer (μm) = 10^{-3} mm = 10^{-6} m
1 nanometer (nm) = 10^{-3} μm = 10^{-9} m

▲ **Figure 6.2 The size range of cells.** Most cells are between 1 and 100 μm in diameter (yellow region of chart) and their components are even smaller, as are viruses. Notice that the scale along the left side is logarithmic, to accommodate the range of sizes shown. Starting at the top of the scale with 10 m and going down, each reference measurement marks a tenfold decrease in diameter or length.

focusing light, the **electron microscope (EM)** focuses a beam of electrons through the specimen or onto its surface. Resolution is inversely related to the wavelength of the light (or electrons) a microscope uses for imaging, and electron beams have much shorter wavelengths than visible light. Modern electron microscopes can theoretically achieve a resolution of about 0.002 nm, though in practice they usually cannot resolve structures smaller than about 2 nm across. Still, this is a 100-fold improvement over the standard light microscope.

The **scanning electron microscope (SEM)** is especially useful for detailed study of the topography of a specimen

▼ Figure 6.3

Exploring Microscopy

Light Microscopy (LM)

Brightfield (unstained specimen). Light passes directly through the specimen. Unless the cell is naturally pigmented or artificially stained, the image has little contrast. (The first four light micrographs show human cheek epithelial cells; the scale bar pertains to all four micrographs.)

Brightfield (stained specimen). Staining with various dyes enhances contrast. Most staining procedures require that cells be fixed (preserved), thereby killing them.

Phase-contrast. Variations in density within the specimen are amplified to enhance contrast in unstained cells; this is especially useful for examining living, unpigmented cells.

Differential-interference-contrast (Nomarski). As in phase-contrast microscopy, optical modifications are used to exaggerate differences in density; the image appears almost 3-D.

Fluorescence. The locations of specific molecules in the cell can be revealed by labeling the molecules with fluorescent dyes or antibodies; some cells have molecules that fluoresce on their own. Fluorescent substances absorb ultraviolet radiation and emit visible light. In this fluorescently labeled uterine cell, nuclear material is blue, organelles called mitochondria are orange, and the cell's "skeleton" is green.

50 μm

10 μm

Confocal. The top image is a standard fluorescence micrograph of fluorescently labeled nervous tissue (nerve cells are green, support cells are orange, and regions of overlap are yellow); below it is a confocal image of the same tissue. Using a laser, this "optical sectioning" technique eliminates out-of-focus light from a thick sample, creating a single plane of fluorescence in the image. By capturing sharp images at many different planes, a 3-D reconstruction can be created. The standard image is blurry because out-of-focus light is not excluded.

50 μm

Deconvolution. The top of this split image is a compilation of standard fluorescence micrographs through the depth of a white blood cell. Below is an image of the same cell reconstructed from many blurry images at different planes, each of which was processed using deconvolution software. This process digitally removes out-of-focus light and reassigns it to its source, creating a much sharper 3-D image.

10 μm

Super-resolution. On the top is a confocal image of part of a nerve cell, using a fluorescent label that binds to a molecule clustered in small sacs in the cell (vesicles) that are 40 nm in diameter. The greenish-yellow spots are blurry because 40 nm is below the 200-nm limit of resolution for standard light microscopy. Below is an image of the same part of the cell, seen using a new super-resolution technique. Sophisticated equipment is used to light up individual fluorescent molecules and record their position. Combining information from many molecules in different places "breaks" the limit of resolution, resulting in the sharp greenish-yellow dots seen here. (Each dot is a 40-nm vesicle.)

1 μm

Electron Microscopy (EM)

Scanning electron microscopy (SEM). Micrographs taken with a scanning electron microscope show a 3-D image of the surface of a specimen. This SEM shows the surface of a cell from a trachea (windpipe) covered with cilia. Beating of the cilia helps move inhaled debris upward toward the throat. Electron micrographs are black and white, but are often artificially colorized to highlight particular structures, as has been done with both micrographs (SEM and TEM) shown here.

Abbreviations used in figure legends in this book:
LM = Light Micrograph
SEM = Scanning Electron Micrograph
TEM = Transmission Electron Micrograph

Cilia

Longitudinal section of cilium   Cross section of cilium

2 μm

2 μm

Transmission electron microscopy (TEM). A transmission electron microscope profiles a thin section of a specimen. Here we see a section through a tracheal cell, revealing its internal structure. In preparing the specimen, some cilia were cut along their lengths, creating longitudinal sections, while other cilia were cut straight across, creating cross sections.

(see Figure 6.3). The electron beam scans the surface of the sample, usually coated with a thin film of gold. The beam excites electrons on the surface, and these secondary electrons are detected by a device that translates the pattern of electrons into an electronic signal sent to a video screen. The result is an image of the specimen's surface that appears three-dimensional.

The **transmission electron microscope (TEM)** is used to study the internal structure of cells (see Figure 6.3). The TEM aims an electron beam through a very thin section of the specimen, much as a light microscope aims light through a sample on a slide. For the TEM, the specimen has been stained with atoms of heavy metals, which attach to certain cellular structures, thus enhancing the electron density of some parts of the cell more than others. The electrons passing through the specimen are scattered more in the denser regions, so fewer are transmitted. The image displays the pattern of transmitted electrons. Instead of using glass lenses, both the SEM and TEM use electromagnets as lenses to bend the paths of the electrons, ultimately focusing the image onto a monitor for viewing.

Electron microscopes have revealed many subcellular structures that were impossible to resolve with the light microscope. But the light microscope offers advantages, especially in studying living cells. A disadvantage of electron microscopy is that the methods used to prepare the specimen kill the cells. Specimen preparation for any type of microscopy can introduce artifacts, structural features seen in micrographs that do not exist in the living cell.

In the past several decades, light microscopy has been revitalized by major technical advances (see Figure 6.3). Labeling individual cellular molecules or structures with fluorescent markers has made it possible to see such structures with increasing detail. In addition, both confocal and deconvolution microscopy have produced sharper images of three-dimensional tissues and cells. Finally, a group of new techniques and labeling molecules developed in recent years have allowed researchers to "break" the resolution barrier and distinguish subcellular structures as small as 10–20 nm across. As this *super-resolution microscopy* becomes more widespread, the images we see of living cells are proving as awe-inspiring to us as van Leeuwenhoek's were to Robert Hooke 350 years ago.

Microscopes are the most important tools of *cytology*, the study of cell structure. Understanding the function of each structure, however, required the integration of cytology and *biochemistry*, the study of the chemical processes (metabolism) of cells.

Cell Fractionation

A useful technique for studying cell structure and function is **cell fractionation (Figure 6.4)**, which takes cells apart

▼ Figure 6.4

Research Method

Cell Fractionation

Application Cell fractionation is used to isolate (fractionate) cell components based on size and density.

Technique Cells are homogenized in a blender to break them up. The resulting mixture (homogenate) is centrifuged. The supernatant (liquid) is poured into another tube and centrifuged at a higher speed for a longer period. This process is repeated several times. This "differential centrifugation" results in a series of pellets, each containing different cell components.

Tissue cells

Homogenization

Homogenate

Centrifuged at 1,000 *g* (1,000 times the force of gravity) for 10 min

Centrifugation

Supernatant poured into next tube

Differential centrifugation

20,000 *g* 20 min

80,000 *g* 60 min

150,000 *g* 3 hr

Pellet rich in nuclei and cellular debris

Pellet rich in mitochondria (and chloroplasts if cells are from a plant)

Pellet rich in "microsomes" (pieces of plasma membranes and cells' internal membranes)

Pellet rich in ribosomes

Results In early experiments, researchers used microscopy to identify the organelles in each pellet and biochemical methods to determine their metabolic functions. These identifications established a baseline for this method, enabling today's researchers to know which cell fraction they should collect in order to isolate and study particular organelles.

and separates major organelles and other subcellular structures from one another. The piece of equipment that is used for this task is the centrifuge, which spins test tubes holding mixtures of disrupted cells at a series of increasing speeds. At each speed, the resulting force causes a subset of the cell components to settle to the bottom of the tube, forming a pellet. At lower speeds, the pellet consists of larger components, and higher speeds result in a pellet with smaller components.

Cell fractionation enables researchers to prepare specific cell components in bulk and identify their functions, a task not usually possible with intact cells. For example, on one of the cell fractions, biochemical tests showed the presence of enzymes involved in cellular respiration, while electron microscopy revealed large numbers of the organelles called mitochondria. Together, these data helped biologists determine that mitochondria are the sites of cellular respiration. Biochemistry and cytology thus complement each other in correlating cell function with structure.

CONCEPT CHECK 6.1

1. How do stains used for light microscopy compare with those used for electron microscopy?
2. **WHAT IF?** Which type of microscope would you use to study (a) the changes in shape of a living white blood cell and (b) the details of surface texture of a hair?

Eukaryotic cells have internal membranes that compartmentalize their functions

Cells—the basic structural and functional units of every organism—are of two distinct types: prokaryotic and eukaryotic. Organisms of the domains Bacteria and Archaea consist of prokaryotic cells. Protists, fungi, animals, and plants all consist of eukaryotic cells. ("Protist" is an informal term referring to a group of mostly unicellular eukaryotes.)

Comparing Prokaryotic and Eukaryotic Cells

All cells share certain basic features: They are all bounded by a selective barrier, called the *plasma membrane*. Inside all cells is a semifluid, jellylike substance called **cytosol**, in which subcellular components are suspended. All cells contain *chromosomes*, which carry genes in the form of DNA. And all cells have *ribosomes*, tiny complexes that make proteins according to instructions from the genes.

A major difference between prokaryotic and eukaryotic cells is the location of their DNA. In a **eukaryotic cell**, most of the DNA is in an organelle called the *nucleus*, which is bounded by a double membrane (see Figure 6.8). In a **prokaryotic cell**, the DNA is concentrated in a region that is not membrane-enclosed, called the **nucleoid** (Figure 6.5).

Fimbriae: attachment structures on the surface of some prokaryotes

Nucleoid: region where the cell's DNA is located (not enclosed by a membrane)

Ribosomes: complexes that synthesize proteins

Plasma membrane: membrane enclosing the cytoplasm

Cell wall: rigid structure outside the plasma membrane

Capsule: jellylike outer coating of many prokaryotes

Bacterial chromosome

Flagella: locomotion organelles of some bacteria

0.5 μm

(a) A typical rod-shaped bacterium

(b) A thin section through the bacterium *Bacillus coagulans* (TEM)

▲ **Figure 6.5 A prokaryotic cell.** Lacking a true nucleus and the other membrane-enclosed organelles of the eukaryotic cell, the prokaryotic cell appears much simpler in internal structure. Prokaryotes include bacteria and archaea; the general cell structure of the two domains is quite similar.

Eukaryotic means "true nucleus" (from the Greek *eu*, true, and *karyon*, kernel, referring to the nucleus), and *prokaryotic* means "before nucleus" (from the Greek *pro*, before), reflecting the earlier evolution of prokaryotic cells.

The interior of either type of cell is called the **cytoplasm**; in eukaryotic cells, this term refers only to the region between the nucleus and the plasma membrane. Within the cytoplasm of a eukaryotic cell, suspended in cytosol, are a variety of organelles of specialized form and function. These membrane-bounded structures are absent in prokaryotic cells, another distinction between prokaryotic and eukaryotic cells. However, in spite of the absence of organelles, the prokaryotic cytoplasm is not a formless soup of cytoplasm, but appears to be organized into different regions.

Eukaryotic cells are generally much larger than prokaryotic cells (see Figure 6.2). Size is a general feature of cell structure that relates to function. The logistics of carrying out cellular metabolism sets limits on cell size. At the lower limit, the smallest cells known are bacteria called mycoplasmas, which have diameters between 0.1 and 1.0 μm. These are perhaps the smallest packages with enough DNA to program metabolism and enough enzymes and other cellular equipment to carry out the activities necessary for a cell to sustain itself and reproduce. Typical bacteria are 1–5 μm in diameter, about ten times the size of mycoplasmas. Eukaryotic cells are typically 10–100 μm in diameter.

Metabolic requirements also impose theoretical upper limits on the size that is practical for a single cell. At the boundary of every cell, the **plasma membrane** functions as a selective barrier that allows passage of enough oxygen, nutrients, and wastes to service the entire cell **(Figure 6.6)**. For each square micrometer of membrane, only a limited amount of a particular substance can cross per second, so the ratio of surface area to volume is critical. As a cell (or any other object) increases in size, its surface area grows proportionately less than its volume. (Area is proportional to a linear dimension squared, whereas volume is proportional to the linear dimension cubed.) Thus, a smaller object has a greater ratio of surface area to volume **(Figure 6.7)**. The Scientific Skills Exercise gives you a chance to calculate the volumes and surface areas of two actual cells—a mature yeast cell and a cell budding from it.

The need for a surface area sufficiently large to accommodate the volume helps explain the microscopic size of most cells and the narrow, elongated shapes of others, such as nerve cells. Larger organisms do not generally have *larger* cells than smaller organisms—they simply have *more* cells (see Figure 6.7). A sufficiently high ratio of surface area to volume is especially important in cells that exchange a lot of material with their surroundings, such as intestinal cells. Such cells may have many long, thin projections from their surface called *microvilli*, which increase surface area without an appreciable increase in volume.

Outside of cell

Inside of cell ⊢ 0.1 μm

(a) TEM of a plasma membrane. The plasma membrane, here in a red blood cell, appears as a pair of dark bands separated by a light band.

Carbohydrate side chains

Hydrophilic region

Hydrophobic region

Hydrophilic region

Phospholipid   Proteins

(b) Structure of the plasma membrane

© Pearson Education, Inc.

▲ **Figure 6.6 The plasma membrane.** The plasma membrane and the membranes of organelles consist of a double layer (bilayer) of phospholipids with various proteins attached to or embedded in it. The hydrophobic parts of phospholipids and membrane proteins are found in the interior of the membrane, while the hydrophilic parts are in contact with aqueous solutions on either side. Carbohydrate side chains may be attached to proteins or lipids on the outer surface of the plasma membrane.

MAKE CONNECTIONS *Review Figure 5.11 and describe the characteristics of phospholipids that allow them to function as the major components of the plasma membrane.*

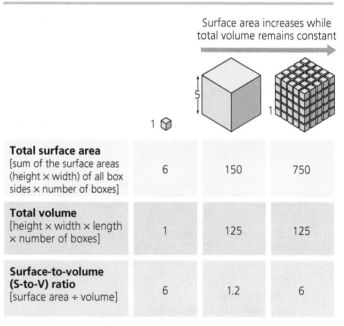

Surface area increases while total volume remains constant

5

1

1

Total surface area [sum of the surface areas (height × width) of all box sides × number of boxes]	6	150	750
Total volume [height × width × length × number of boxes]	1	125	125
Surface-to-volume (S-to-V) ratio [surface area ÷ volume]	6	1.2	6

▲ **Figure 6.7 Geometric relationships between surface area and volume.** In this diagram, cells are represented as boxes. Using arbitrary units of length, we can calculate the cell's surface area (in square units, or units²), volume (in cubic units, or units³), and ratio of surface area to volume. A high surface-to-volume ratio facilitates the exchange of materials between a cell and its environment.

Using a Scale Bar to Calculate Volume and Surface Area of a Cell

How Much New Cytoplasm and Plasma Membrane Are Made by a Growing Yeast Cell? The unicellular yeast *Saccharomyces cerevisiae* divides by budding off a small new cell that then grows to full size (see the yeast cells at the bottom of Figure 6.8). During its growth, the new cell synthesizes new cytoplasm, which increases its volume, and new plasma membrane, which increases its surface area. In this exercise, you will use a scale bar to determine the sizes of a mature parent yeast cell and a cell budding from it. You will then calculate the volume and surface area of each cell. You will use your calculations to determine how much cytoplasm and plasma membrane the new cell needs to synthesize to grow to full size.

How the Experiment Was Done Yeast cells were grown under conditions that promoted division by budding. The cells were then viewed with a differential interference contrast light microscope and photographed.

Data from the Experiment This light micrograph shows a budding yeast cell about to be released from the mature parent cell:

Budding cell

Mature parent cell

1 µm

Interpret the Data

1. Examine the micrograph of the yeast cells. The scale bar under the photo is labeled 1 µm. The scale bar works in the same way as a scale on a map, where, for example, 1 inch equals 1 mile. In this case the bar represents one thousandth of a millimeter. Using the scale bar as a basic unit, determine the diameter of the mature parent cell and the

new cell. Start by measuring the scale bar and then the diameter of each cell. The units you use are irrelevant, but working in millimeters is convenient. Divide each diameter by the length of the scale bar and then multiply by the scale bar's length value to give you the diameter in micrometers.

2. The shape of a yeast cell can be approximated by a sphere. (a) Calculate the volume of each cell using the formula for the volume of a sphere:

$$V = \frac{4}{3}\pi r^3$$

Note that π (the Greek letter pi) is a constant with an approximate value of 3.14, *d* stands for diameter, and *r* stands for radius, which is half the diameter. (b) How much new cytoplasm will the new cell have to synthesize as it matures? To determine this, calculate the difference between the volume of the full-sized cell and the volume of the new cell.

3. As the new cell grows, its plasma membrane needs to expand to contain the increased volume of the cell. (a) Calculate the surface area of each cell using the formula for the surface area of a sphere: $A = 4\pi r^2$. (b) How much area of new plasma membrane will the new cell have to synthesize as it matures?

4. When the new cell matures, it will be approximately how many times greater in volume and how many times greater in surface area than its current size?

Micrograph from Kelly Tatchell, using yeast cells grown for experiments described in L. Kozubowski et al., Role of the septin ring in the asymmetric localization of proteins at the mother-bud neck in *Saccharomyces cerevisiae*, *Molecular Biology of the Cell* 16:3455–3466 (2005).

(MB) A version of this Scientific Skills Exercise can be assigned in MasteringBiology.

The evolutionary relationships between prokaryotic and eukaryotic cells will be discussed later in this chapter. Most of the discussion of cell structure that follows in this chapter applies to eukaryotic cells.

A Panoramic View of the Eukaryotic Cell

In addition to the plasma membrane at its outer surface, a eukaryotic cell has extensive, elaborately arranged internal membranes that divide the cell into compartments—the organelles mentioned earlier. The cell's compartments provide different local environments that support specific metabolic functions, so incompatible processes can occur simultaneously in a single cell. The plasma membrane and organelle membranes also participate directly in the cell's metabolism, because many enzymes are built right into the membranes.

The basic fabric of most biological membranes is a double layer of phospholipids and other lipids. Embedded in this lipid bilayer or attached to its surfaces are diverse proteins (see Figure 6.6). However, each type of membrane has a unique composition of lipids and proteins suited to that membrane's specific functions. For example, enzymes embedded in the membranes of the organelles called mitochondria function in cellular respiration. Because membranes are so fundamental to the organization of the cell, Chapter 7 will discuss them in detail.

Before continuing with this chapter, examine the eukaryotic cells in **Figure 6.8**, on the next two pages. The generalized diagrams of an animal cell and a plant cell introduce the various organelles and show the key differences between animal and plant cells. The micrographs at the bottom of the figure give you a glimpse of cells from different types of eukaryotic organisms.

Exploring Eukaryotic Cells

Animal Cell (cutaway view of generalized cell)

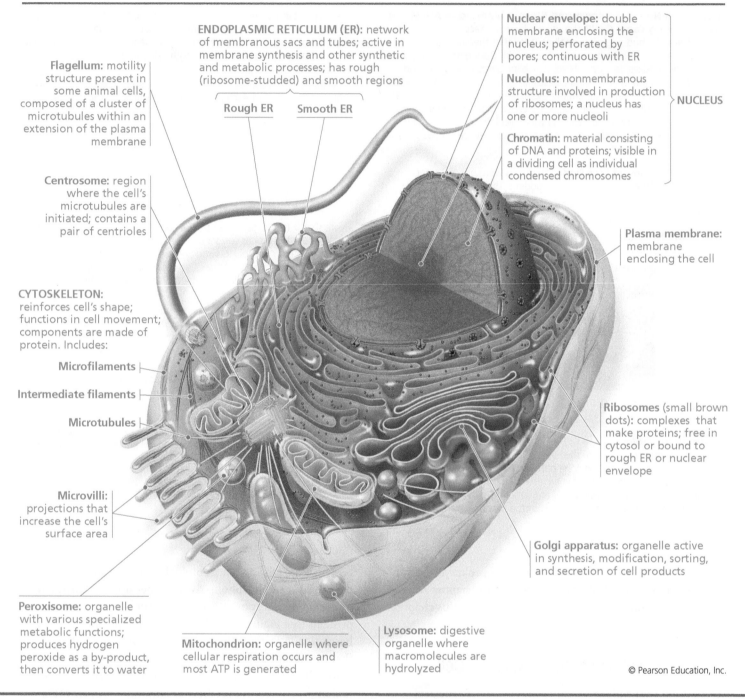

Flagellum: motility structure present in some animal cells, composed of a cluster of microtubules within an extension of the plasma membrane

ENDOPLASMIC RETICULUM (ER): network of membranous sacs and tubes; active in membrane synthesis and other synthetic and metabolic processes; has rough (ribosome-studded) and smooth regions

Rough ER   Smooth ER

Nuclear envelope: double membrane enclosing the nucleus; perforated by pores; continuous with ER

Nucleolus: nonmembranous structure involved in production of ribosomes; a nucleus has one or more nucleoli

Chromatin: material consisting of DNA and proteins; visible in a dividing cell as individual condensed chromosomes

NUCLEUS

Centrosome: region where the cell's microtubules are initiated; contains a pair of centrioles

Plasma membrane: membrane enclosing the cell

CYTOSKELETON: reinforces cell's shape; functions in cell movement; components are made of protein. Includes:

Microfilaments

Intermediate filaments

Microtubules

Ribosomes (small brown dots): complexes that make proteins; free in cytosol or bound to rough ER or nuclear envelope

Microvilli: projections that increase the cell's surface area

Golgi apparatus: organelle active in synthesis, modification, sorting, and secretion of cell products

Peroxisome: organelle with various specialized metabolic functions; produces hydrogen peroxide as a by-product, then converts it to water

Mitochondrion: organelle where cellular respiration occurs and most ATP is generated

Lysosome: digestive organelle where macromolecules are hydrolyzed

© Pearson Education, Inc.

Animal Cells

Cell

Nucleus

Nucleolus

10 µm

Human cells from lining of uterus (colorized TEM)

Fungal Cells

Parent cell

Buds

5 µm

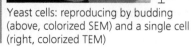

Yeast cells: reproducing by budding (above, colorized SEM) and a single cell (right, colorized TEM)

1 µm

Cell wall

Vacuole

Nucleus

Mitochondrion

▲ **Surface of nuclear envelope (TEM)**. This specimen was prepared by a technique known as freeze-fracture.

Nucleus

Nucleolus

Chromatin

Nuclear envelope:
Inner membrane
Outer membrane

Nuclear pore

Nucleus

Rough ER

Pore complex

Ribosome

▲ **Pore complexes (TEM).** Each pore is ringed by protein particles.

◀ **Close-up of nuclear envelope**

▲ **Chromatin.** This segment of a chromosome from a non-dividing cell shows two states of coiling of the DNA (blue) and protein (purple) complex. The thicker form is sometimes also organized into long loops.

◀ **Nuclear lamina (TEM).** The netlike lamina lines the inner surface of the nuclear envelope.

© Pearson Education, Inc.

▲ **Figure 6.9 The nucleus and its envelope.** Within the nucleus are the chromosomes, which appear as a mass of chromatin (DNA and associated proteins) and one or more nucleoli (singular, *nucleolus*), which function in ribosome synthesis. The nuclear envelope, which consists of two membranes separated by a narrow space, is perforated with pores and lined by the nuclear lamina.

MAKE CONNECTIONS *Since the chromosomes contain the genetic material and reside in the nucleus, how does the rest of the cell get access to the information they carry? (See Figure 5.23.)*

Ribosomes

ER

Free ribosomes in cytosol

Endoplasmic reticulum (ER)

Ribosomes bound to ER

Large subunit

Small subunit

TEM showing ER and ribosomes

Diagram of a ribosome

Computer model of a ribosome

▲ **Figure 6.10 Ribosomes.** This electron micrograph of a pancreas cell shows both free and bound ribosomes. The simplified diagram and computer model show the two subunits of a ribosome.

Ribosomes build proteins in two cytoplasmic locales. At any given time, *free ribosomes* are suspended in the cytosol, while *bound ribosomes* are attached to the outside of the endoplasmic reticulum or nuclear envelope (see Figure 6.10). Bound and free ribosomes are structurally identical, and ribosomes can alternate between the two roles. Most of the proteins made on free ribosomes function within the cytosol; examples are enzymes that catalyze the first steps of sugar breakdown. Bound ribosomes generally make proteins that are destined for insertion into membranes, for packaging within certain organelles such as lysosomes (see Figure 6.8), or for export from the cell (secretion). Cells that specialize in protein secretion—for instance, the cells of the pancreas that secrete digestive enzymes—frequently have a high proportion of bound ribosomes. (You will learn more about ribosome structure and function in Chapter 17.)

CONCEPT CHECK 6.3

1. What role do ribosomes play in carrying out genetic instructions?
2. Describe the molecular composition of nucleoli and explain their function.
3. **WHAT IF?** As a cell begins the process of dividing, its chromosomes become shorter, thicker, and individually visible in an LM. Explain what is happening at the molecular level.

CONCEPT 6.4

The endomembrane system regulates protein traffic and performs metabolic functions in the cell

Many of the different membranes of the eukaryotic cell are part of the **endomembrane system**, which includes the nuclear envelope, the endoplasmic reticulum, the Golgi apparatus, lysosomes, various kinds of vesicles and vacuoles, and the plasma membrane. This system carries out a variety of tasks in the cell, including synthesis of proteins, transport of proteins into membranes and organelles or out of the cell, metabolism and movement of lipids, and detoxification of poisons. The membranes of this system are related either through direct physical continuity or by the transfer of membrane segments as tiny **vesicles** (sacs made of membrane). Despite these relationships, the various membranes are not identical in structure and function. Moreover, the thickness, molecular composition, and types of chemical reactions carried out in a given membrane are not fixed, but may be modified several times during the membrane's life. Having already discussed the nuclear envelope, we will now

focus on the endoplasmic reticulum and the other endomembranes to which the endoplasmic reticulum gives rise.

The Endoplasmic Reticulum: Biosynthetic Factory

The **endoplasmic reticulum (ER)** is such an extensive network of membranes that it accounts for more than half the total membrane in many eukaryotic cells. (The word *endoplasmic* means "within the cytoplasm," and *reticulum* is Latin for "little net.") The ER consists of a network of membranous tubules and sacs called cisternae (from the Latin *cisterna*, a reservoir for a liquid). The ER membrane separates the internal compartment of the ER, called the *ER lumen* (cavity) or cisternal space, from the cytosol. And because the ER membrane is continuous with the nuclear envelope, the space between the two membranes of the envelope is continuous with the lumen of the ER **(Figure 6.11)**.

There are two distinct, though connected, regions of the ER that differ in structure and function: smooth ER and rough ER. **Smooth ER** is so named because its outer surface lacks ribosomes. **Rough ER** is studded with ribosomes on the outer surface of the membrane and thus appears rough through the electron microscope. As already mentioned, ribosomes are also attached to the cytoplasmic side of the nuclear envelope's outer membrane, which is continuous with rough ER.

Functions of Smooth ER

The smooth ER functions in diverse metabolic processes, which vary with cell type. These processes include synthesis of lipids, metabolism of carbohydrates, detoxification of drugs and poisons, and storage of calcium ions.

Enzymes of the smooth ER are important in the synthesis of lipids, including oils, steroids, and new membrane phospholipids. Among the steroids produced by the smooth ER in animal cells are the sex hormones of vertebrates and the various steroid hormones secreted by the adrenal glands. The cells that synthesize and secrete these hormones—in the testes and ovaries, for example—are rich in smooth ER, a structural feature that fits the function of these cells.

Other enzymes of the smooth ER help detoxify drugs and poisons, especially in liver cells. Detoxification usually involves adding hydroxyl groups to drug molecules, making them more soluble and easier to flush from the body. The sedative phenobarbital and other barbiturates are examples of drugs metabolized in this manner by smooth ER in liver cells. In fact, barbiturates, alcohol, and many other drugs induce the proliferation of smooth ER and its associated detoxification enzymes, thus increasing the rate of detoxification. This, in turn, increases tolerance to the drugs, meaning that higher doses are required to achieve a particular effect, such as sedation. Also, because some of the detoxification enzymes have relatively broad action, the proliferation of smooth ER in response to one drug can increase the need for higher dosages of other drugs as well. Barbiturate abuse, for example, can decrease the effectiveness of certain antibiotics and other useful drugs.

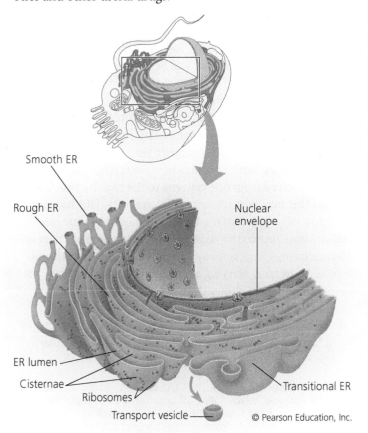

Smooth ER

Rough ER

Nuclear envelope

ER lumen

Cisternae

Ribosomes

Transitional ER

Transport vesicle

© Pearson Education, Inc.

Smooth ER

Rough ER

0.20 μm

▲ **Figure 6.11 Endoplasmic reticulum (ER).** A membranous system of interconnected tubules and flattened sacs called cisternae, the ER is also continuous with the nuclear envelope, as shown in the cutaway diagram at the top. The membrane of the ER encloses a continuous compartment called the ER lumen (or cisternal space). Rough ER, which is studded on its outer surface with ribosomes, can be distinguished from smooth ER in the electron micrograph (TEM). Transport vesicles bud off from a region of the rough ER called transitional ER and travel to the Golgi apparatus and other destinations.

The smooth ER also stores calcium ions. In muscle cells, for example, the smooth ER membrane pumps calcium ions from the cytosol into the ER lumen. When a muscle cell is stimulated by a nerve impulse, calcium ions rush back across the ER membrane into the cytosol and trigger contraction of the muscle cell. In other cell types, calcium ion release from the smooth ER triggers different responses, such as secretion of vesicles carrying newly synthesized proteins.

Functions of Rough ER

Many cells secrete proteins that are produced by ribosomes attached to rough ER. For example, certain pancreatic cells synthesize the protein insulin in the ER and secrete this hormone into the bloodstream. As a polypeptide chain grows from a bound ribosome, the chain is threaded into the ER lumen through a pore formed by a protein complex in the ER membrane. The new polypeptide folds into its functional shape as it enters the ER lumen. Most secretory proteins are **glycoproteins**, proteins with carbohydrates covalently bonded to them. The carbohydrates are attached to the proteins in the ER lumen by enzymes built into the ER membrane.

After secretory proteins are formed, the ER membrane keeps them separate from proteins that are produced by free ribosomes and that will remain in the cytosol. Secretory proteins depart from the ER wrapped in the membranes of vesicles that bud like bubbles from a specialized region called transitional ER (see Figure 6.11). Vesicles in transit from one part of the cell to another are called **transport vesicles**; we will discuss their fate shortly.

In addition to making secretory proteins, rough ER is a membrane factory for the cell; it grows in place by adding membrane proteins and phospholipids to its own membrane. As polypeptides destined to be membrane proteins grow from the ribosomes, they are inserted into the ER membrane itself and anchored there by their hydrophobic portions. Like the smooth ER, the rough ER also makes membrane phospholipids; enzymes built into the ER membrane assemble phospholipids from precursors in the cytosol. The ER membrane expands, and portions of it are transferred in the form of transport vesicles to other components of the endomembrane system.

The Golgi Apparatus: Shipping and Receiving Center

After leaving the ER, many transport vesicles travel to the **Golgi apparatus**. We can think of the Golgi as a warehouse for receiving, sorting, shipping, and even some manufacturing. Here, products of the ER, such as proteins, are modified and stored and then sent to other destinations. Not surprisingly, the Golgi apparatus is especially extensive in cells specialized for secretion.

The Golgi apparatus consists of flattened membranous sacs—cisternae—looking like a stack of pita bread (Figure 6.12). A cell may have many, even hundreds, of these stacks. The membrane of each cisterna in a stack separates its internal space from the cytosol. Vesicles concentrated in the vicinity of the Golgi apparatus are engaged in the transfer of material between parts of the Golgi and other structures.

A Golgi stack has a distinct structural directionality, with the membranes of cisternae on opposite sides of the stack differing in thickness and molecular composition. The two sides of a Golgi stack are referred to as the *cis* face and the *trans* face; these act, respectively, as the receiving and shipping departments of the Golgi apparatus. The term *cis* means "on the same side," and the *cis* face is usually located near the ER. Transport vesicles move material from the ER to the Golgi apparatus. A vesicle that buds from the ER can add its membrane and the contents of its lumen to the *cis* face by fusing with a Golgi membrane. The *trans* face ("on the opposite side") gives rise to vesicles that pinch off and travel to other sites.

Products of the endoplasmic reticulum are usually modified during their transit from the *cis* region to the *trans* region of the Golgi apparatus. For example, glycoproteins formed in the ER have their carbohydrates modified, first in the ER itself, then as they pass through the Golgi. The Golgi removes some sugar monomers and substitutes others, producing a large variety of carbohydrates. Membrane phospholipids may also be altered in the Golgi.

In addition to its finishing work, the Golgi apparatus also manufactures some macromolecules. Many polysaccharides secreted by cells are Golgi products. For example, pectins and certain other noncellulose polysaccharides are made in the Golgi of plant cells and then incorporated along with cellulose into their cell walls. Like secretory proteins, nonprotein Golgi products that will be secreted depart from the *trans* face of the Golgi inside transport vesicles that eventually fuse with the plasma membrane.

The Golgi manufactures and refines its products in stages, with different cisternae containing unique teams of enzymes. Until recently, biologists viewed the Golgi as a static structure, with products in various stages of processing transferred from one cisterna to the next by vesicles. While this may occur, research from several labs has given rise to a new model of the Golgi as a more dynamic structure. According to the *cisternal maturation model*, the cisternae of the Golgi actually progress forward from the *cis* to the *trans* face, carrying and modifying their cargo as they move. Figure 6.12 shows the details of this model.

Before a Golgi stack dispatches its products by budding vesicles from the *trans* face, it sorts these products and targets them for various parts of the cell. Molecular

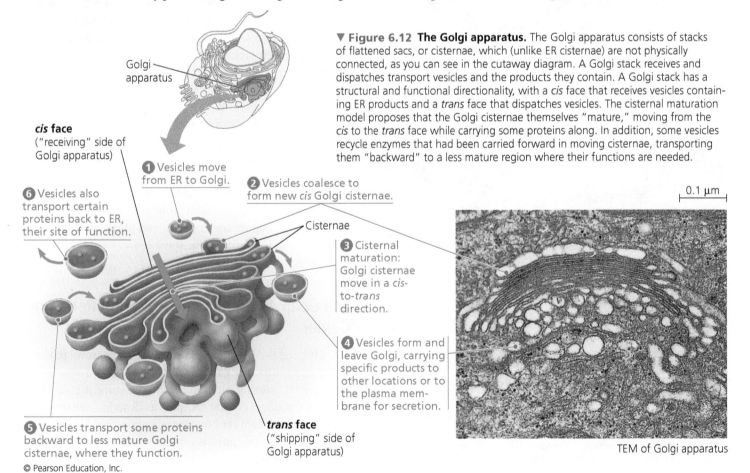

▼ **Figure 6.12 The Golgi apparatus.** The Golgi apparatus consists of stacks of flattened sacs, or cisternae, which (unlike ER cisternae) are not physically connected, as you can see in the cutaway diagram. A Golgi stack receives and dispatches transport vesicles and the products they contain. A Golgi stack has a structural and functional directionality, with a *cis* face that receives vesicles containing ER products and a *trans* face that dispatches vesicles. The cisternal maturation model proposes that the Golgi cisternae themselves "mature," moving from the *cis* to the *trans* face while carrying some proteins along. In addition, some vesicles recycle enzymes that had been carried forward in moving cisternae, transporting them "backward" to a less mature region where their functions are needed.

Golgi apparatus

***cis* face** ("receiving" side of Golgi apparatus)

6 Vesicles also transport certain proteins back to ER, their site of function.

1 Vesicles move from ER to Golgi.

2 Vesicles coalesce to form new *cis* Golgi cisternae.

Cisternae

3 Cisternal maturation: Golgi cisternae move in a *cis*-to-*trans* direction.

4 Vesicles form and leave Golgi, carrying specific products to other locations or to the plasma membrane for secretion.

5 Vesicles transport some proteins backward to less mature Golgi cisternae, where they function.

***trans* face** ("shipping" side of Golgi apparatus)

0.1 μm

TEM of Golgi apparatus

© Pearson Education, Inc.

identification tags, such as phosphate groups added to the Golgi products, aid in sorting by acting like zip codes on mailing labels. Finally, transport vesicles budded from the Golgi may have external molecules on their membranes that recognize "docking sites" on the surface of specific organelles or on the plasma membrane, thus targeting the vesicles appropriately.

Lysosomes: Digestive Compartments

A **lysosome** is a membranous sac of hydrolytic enzymes that many eukaryotic cells use to digest (hydrolyze) macromolecules. Lysosomal enzymes work best in the acidic environment found in lysosomes. If a lysosome breaks open or leaks its contents, the released enzymes are not very active because the cytosol has a near-neutral pH. However, excessive leakage from a large number of lysosomes can destroy a cell by self-digestion.

Hydrolytic enzymes and lysosomal membrane are made by rough ER and then transferred to the Golgi apparatus for further processing. At least some lysosomes probably arise by budding from the *trans* face of the Golgi apparatus (see Figure 6.12). How are the proteins of the inner surface of the lysosomal membrane and the digestive enzymes themselves spared from destruction? Apparently, the three-dimensional shapes of these proteins protect vulnerable bonds from enzymatic attack.

Lysosomes carry out intracellular digestion in a variety of circumstances. Amoebas and many other unicellular eukaryotes eat by engulfing smaller organisms or food particles, a process called **phagocytosis** (from the Greek *phagein*, to eat, and *kytos*, vessel, referring here to the cell). The *food vacuole* formed in this way then fuses with a lysosome, whose enzymes digest the food (**Figure 6.13a**, bottom). Digestion products, including simple sugars, amino acids, and other monomers, pass into the cytosol and become nutrients for the cell. Some human cells also carry out phagocytosis. Among them are macrophages, a type of white blood cell that helps defend the body by engulfing and destroying bacteria and other invaders (see Figure 6.13a, top, and Figure 6.31).

(a) Phagocytosis: lysosome digesting food

① Lysosome contains active hydrolytic enzymes.

② Lysosome fuses with food vacuole.

③ Hydrolytic enzymes digest food particles.

Nucleus

1 μm

Lysosome

Digestive enzymes

Lysosome

Plasma membrane

Food vacuole

Digestion

(b) Autophagy: lysosome breaking down damaged organelles

① Lysosome fuses with vesicle containing damaged organelles.

② Hydrolytic enzymes digest organelle components.

Vesicle containing two damaged organelles

1 μm

Mitochondrion fragment

Peroxisome fragment

Lysosome

Peroxisome

Vesicle

Mitochondrion

Digestion

▲ **Figure 6.13 Lysosomes.** Lysosomes digest (hydrolyze) materials taken into the cell and recycle intracellular materials. **(a)** *Top*: In this macrophage (a type of white blood cell) from a rat, the lysosomes are very dark because of a stain that reacts with one of the products of digestion inside the lysosome (TEM).

Macrophages ingest bacteria and viruses and destroy them using lysosomes. *Bottom*: This diagram shows a lysosome fusing with a food vacuole during the process of phagocytosis by a unicellular eukaryote. **(b)** *Top*: In the cytoplasm of this rat liver cell is a vesicle containing two disabled organelles (TEM). The vesicle will fuse

with a lysosome in the process of autophagy. *Bottom*: This diagram shows fusion of such a vesicle with a lysosome. This type of vesicle has a double membrane of unknown origin. The outer membrane fuses with the lysosome, and the inner membrane is degraded along with the damaged organelles.

Lysosomes also use their hydrolytic enzymes to recycle the cell's own organic material, a process called *autophagy*. During autophagy, a damaged organelle or small amount of cytosol becomes surrounded by a double membrane (of unknown origin), and a lysosome fuses with the outer membrane of this vesicle (**Figure 6.13b**). The lysosomal enzymes dismantle the enclosed material, and the resulting small organic compounds are released to the cytosol for reuse. With the help of lysosomes, the cell continually renews itself. A human liver cell, for example, recycles half of its macromolecules each week.

The cells of people with inherited lysosomal storage diseases lack a functioning hydrolytic enzyme normally present in lysosomes. The lysosomes become engorged with indigestible material, which begins to interfere with other cellular activities. In Tay-Sachs disease, for example, a lipid-digesting enzyme is missing or inactive, and the brain becomes impaired by an accumulation of lipids in the cells. Fortunately, lysosomal storage diseases are rare in the general population.

Vacuoles: Diverse Maintenance Compartments

Vacuoles are large vesicles derived from the endoplasmic reticulum and Golgi apparatus. Thus, vacuoles are an integral part of a cell's endomembrane system. Like all cellular membranes, the vacuolar membrane is selective in transporting solutes; as a result, the solution inside a vacuole differs in composition from the cytosol.

Vacuoles perform a variety of functions in different kinds of cells. **Food vacuoles**, formed by phagocytosis, have already been mentioned (see Figure 6.13a). Many unicellular eukaryotes living in fresh water have **contractile vacuoles** that pump excess water out of the cell, thereby maintaining a suitable concentration of ions and molecules inside the cell (see Figure 7.13). In plants and fungi, certain vacuoles carry out enzymatic hydrolysis, a function shared by lysosomes in animal cells. (In fact, some biologists consider these hydrolytic vacuoles to be a type of lysosome.) In plants, small vacuoles can hold reserves of important organic compounds, such as the proteins stockpiled in the storage cells in seeds. Vacuoles may also help protect the plant against herbivores by storing compounds that are poisonous or unpalatable to animals. Some plant vacuoles contain pigments, such as the red and blue pigments of petals that help attract pollinating insects to flowers.

Mature plant cells generally contain a large **central vacuole** (**Figure 6.14**), which develops by the coalescence of smaller vacuoles. The solution inside the central vacuole, called cell sap, is the plant cell's main repository of inorganic ions, including potassium and chloride. The central vacuole plays a major role in the growth of plant cells, which enlarge

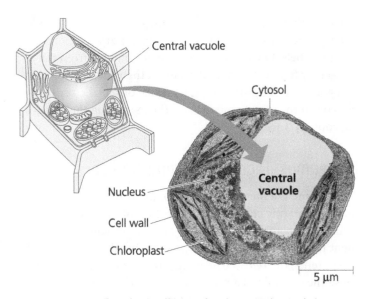

▲ **Figure 6.14 The plant cell vacuole.** The central vacuole is usually the largest compartment in a plant cell; the rest of the cytoplasm is often confined to a narrow zone between the vacuolar membrane and the plasma membrane (TEM).

as the vacuole absorbs water, enabling the cell to become larger with a minimal investment in new cytoplasm. The cytosol often occupies only a thin layer between the central vacuole and the plasma membrane, so the ratio of plasma membrane surface to cytosolic volume is sufficient, even for a large plant cell.

The Endomembrane System: *A Review*

Figure 6.15 reviews the endomembrane system, showing the flow of membrane lipids and proteins through the various organelles. As the membrane moves from the ER to the Golgi and then elsewhere, its molecular composition and metabolic functions are modified, along with those of its contents. The endomembrane system is a complex and dynamic player in the cell's compartmental organization.

We'll continue our tour of the cell with some organelles that are not closely related to the endomembrane system but play crucial roles in the energy transformations carried out by cells.

CONCEPT CHECK 6.4

1. Describe the structural and functional distinctions between rough and smooth ER.

2. Describe how transport vesicles integrate the endomembrane system.

3. **WHAT IF?** Imagine a protein that functions in the ER but requires modification in the Golgi apparatus before it can achieve that function. Describe the protein's path through the cell, starting with the mRNA molecule that specifies the protein.

① Nuclear envelope is connected to rough ER, which is also continuous with smooth ER.

② Membranes and proteins produced by the ER flow in the form of transport vesicles to the Golgi.

③ Golgi pinches off transport vesicles and other vesicles that give rise to lysosomes, other types of specialized vesicles, and vacuoles.

Nucleus

Rough ER

Smooth ER

cis Golgi

trans Golgi

Plasma membrane

④ Lysosome is available for fusion with another vesicle for digestion.

⑤ Transport vesicle carries proteins to plasma membrane for secretion.

⑥ Plasma membrane expands by fusion of vesicles; proteins are secreted from cell.

© Pearson Education, Inc.

▲ **Figure 6.15 Review: relationships among organelles of the endomembrane system.** The red arrows show some of the migration pathways for membranes and the materials they enclose.

Mitochondria and chloroplasts change energy from one form to another

Organisms transform the energy they acquire from their surroundings. In eukaryotic cells, mitochondria and chloroplasts are the organelles that convert energy to forms that cells can use for work. **Mitochondria** (singular, *mitochondrion*) are the sites of cellular respiration, the metabolic process that uses oxygen to drive the generation of ATP by extracting energy from sugars, fats, and other fuels. **Chloroplasts**, found in plants and algae, are the sites of photosynthesis. This process in chloroplasts converts solar energy to chemical energy by absorbing sunlight and using it to drive the synthesis of organic compounds such as sugars from carbon dioxide and water.

In addition to having related functions, mitochondria and chloroplasts share similar evolutionary origins, which we'll discuss briefly before describing their structures. In this section, we will also consider the peroxisome, an oxidative organelle. The evolutionary origin of the peroxisome, as well as its relation to other organelles, is still a matter of some debate.

The Evolutionary Origins of Mitochondria and Chloroplasts

EVOLUTION Mitochondria and chloroplasts display similarities with bacteria that led to the **endosymbiont theory**, illustrated in **Figure 6.16**. This theory states that an early ancestor of eukaryotic cells engulfed an oxygen-using nonphotosynthetic prokaryotic cell. Eventually, the engulfed cell formed a relationship with the host cell in which it was enclosed, becoming an *endosymbiont* (a cell living within another cell). Indeed, over the course of evolution, the host cell and its endosymbiont merged into a single organism, a eukaryotic cell with a mitochondrion. At least one of these cells may have then taken up a photosynthetic prokaryote, becoming the ancestor of eukaryotic cells that contain chloroplasts.

This is a widely accepted theory, which is consistent with many structural features of mitochondria and chloroplasts. First, rather than being bounded by a single membrane like organelles of the endomembrane system, mitochondria and typical chloroplasts have two membranes surrounding them. (Chloroplasts also have an internal system of membranous sacs.) There is evidence that the ancestral engulfed prokaryotes had two outer

Ancestor of eukaryotic cells (host cell)

Endoplasmic reticulum

Nucleus

Nuclear envelope

Engulfing of oxygen-using nonphotosynthetic prokaryote, which, over many generations of cells, becomes a mitochondrion

Mitochondrion

Nonphotosynthetic eukaryote

Engulfing of photosynthetic prokaryote

Chloroplast

Mitochondrion

At least one cell

Photosynthetic eukaryote

▲ **Figure 6.16 The endosymbiont theory of the origins of mitochondria and chloroplasts in eukaryotic cells.** According to this theory, the proposed ancestors of mitochondria were oxygen-using nonphotosynthetic prokaryotes, while the proposed ancestors of chloroplasts were photosynthetic prokaryotes. The large arrows represent change over evolutionary time; the small arrows inside the cells show the process of the endosymbiont becoming an organelle, also over long periods of time.

membranes, which became the double membranes of mitochondria and chloroplasts. Second, like prokaryotes, mitochondria and chloroplasts contain ribosomes, as well as multiple circular DNA molecules associated with their inner membranes. The DNA in these organelles programs the synthesis of some organelle proteins on ribosomes that have been synthesized and assembled there as well. Third, also consistent with their probable evolutionary origins as cells, mitochondria and chloroplasts are autonomous (somewhat independent) organelles that grow and reproduce within the cell.

Next, we focus on the structures of mitochondria and chloroplasts, while providing an overview of their structures and functions. (In Chapters 10 and 11, we will examine their roles as energy transformers.)

Mitochondria: Chemical Energy Conversion

Mitochondria are found in nearly all eukaryotic cells, including those of plants, animals, fungi, and most unicellular eukaryotes. Some cells have a single large mitochondrion, but more often a cell has hundreds or even thousands of mitochondria; the number correlates with the cell's level of metabolic activity. For example, cells that move or contract have proportionally more mitochondria per volume than less active cells.

Each of the two membranes enclosing the mitochondrion is a phospholipid bilayer with a unique collection of embedded proteins **(Figure 6.17)**. The outer membrane is smooth, but the inner membrane is convoluted, with infoldings called **cristae**. The inner membrane divides the mitochondrion into two internal compartments. The first is the intermembrane space, the narrow region between the inner and outer membranes. The second compartment, the **mitochondrial matrix**, is enclosed by the inner membrane. The matrix contains many different enzymes as well as the mitochondrial DNA and ribosomes. Enzymes in the matrix catalyze some of the steps of cellular respiration. Other proteins that function in respiration, including the enzyme that makes ATP, are built into the inner membrane. As highly folded surfaces, the cristae give the inner mitochondrial membrane a large surface area, thus enhancing the productivity of cellular respiration. This is another example of structure fitting function.

Mitochondria are generally in the range of 1–10 μm long. Time-lapse films of living cells reveal mitochondria moving around, changing their shapes, and fusing or dividing in two, unlike the static structures seen in electron micrographs of dead cells. These observations helped cell biologists understand that mitochondria in a living cell form a branched tubular network, seen in a whole cell in Figure 6.17b, that is in a dynamic state of flux.

Chloroplasts: Capture of Light Energy

Chloroplasts contain the green pigment chlorophyll, along with enzymes and other molecules that function in the photosynthetic production of sugar. These lens-shaped organelles, about 3–6 μm in length, are found in leaves and other green organs of plants and in algae **(Figure 6.18**; see also Figure 6.26c).

The contents of a chloroplast are partitioned from the cytosol by an envelope consisting of two membranes separated by a very narrow intermembrane space. Inside the chloroplast is another membranous system in the form of flattened, interconnected sacs called **thylakoids**. In some regions, thylakoids are stacked like poker chips; each stack is called a **granum** (plural, *grana*). The fluid outside the thylakoids is the **stroma**, which contains the chloroplast DNA and ribosomes as well as many enzymes. The membranes of the chloroplast divide the chloroplast space into three compartments: the intermembrane space, the stroma, and the thylakoid space. This compartmental organization enables the chloroplast to convert light energy to chemical energy

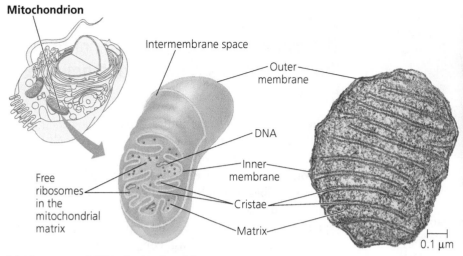

Mitochondrion

Intermembrane space

Outer membrane

DNA

Inner membrane

Cristae

Matrix

Free ribosomes in the mitochondrial matrix

0.1 μm

(a) Diagram and TEM of mitochondrion

10 μm

Mitochondria

Mitochondrial DNA

Nuclear DNA

(b) Network of mitochondria in *Euglena* (LM)

▲ **Figure 6.17 The mitochondrion, site of cellular respiration. (a)** The inner and outer membranes of the mitochondrion are evident in the drawing and electron micrograph (TEM). The cristae are infoldings of the inner membrane, which increase its surface area. The cutaway drawing shows the two compartments bounded by the membranes: the intermembrane space and the mitochondrial matrix. Many respiratory enzymes are found in the inner membrane and the matrix. Free ribosomes are also present in the matrix. The DNA molecules are usually circular and they are associated with the inner mitochondrial membrane. **(b)** The light micrograph shows an entire unicellular eukaryote (*Euglena gracilis*) at a much lower magnification than the TEM. The mitochondrial matrix has been stained green. The mitochondria form a branched tubular network. The nuclear DNA is stained red; molecules of mitochondrial DNA appear as bright yellow spots.

during photosynthesis. (You will learn more about photosynthesis in Chapter 11.)

As with mitochondria, the static and rigid appearance of chloroplasts in micrographs or schematic diagrams is not true to their dynamic behavior in the living cell. Their shape is changeable, and they grow and occasionally pinch in two, reproducing themselves. They are mobile and, with mitochondria and other organelles, move around the cell along tracks of the cytoskeleton, a structural network we will consider later in this chapter.

The chloroplast is a specialized member of a family of closely related plant organelles called **plastids**. One type of plastid, the *amyloplast*, is a colorless organelle that stores starch (amylose), particularly in roots and tubers. Another is the *chromoplast*, which has pigments that give fruits and flowers their orange and yellow hues.

▼ **Figure 6.18 The chloroplast, site of photosynthesis. (a)** Many plants have lens-shaped chloroplasts, as shown here. A typical chloroplast has three compartments: the intermembrane space, the stroma, and the thylakoid space. Free ribosomes are present in the stroma, as are copies of chloroplast DNA molecules. **(b)** This fluorescence micrograph shows a whole cell of the green alga *Spirogyra crassa*, which is named for its spiral chloroplasts. Under natural light the chloroplasts appear green, but under ultraviolet light they naturally fluoresce red, as shown here.

Chloroplast

Ribosomes

Stroma

Inner and outer membranes

Granum

DNA

Thylakoid

Intermembrane space

1 μm

(a) Diagram and TEM of chloroplast

50 μm

Chloroplasts (red)

(b) Chloroplasts in an algal cell

► **Figure 6.19**
A peroxisome. Peroxisomes are roughly spherical and often have a granular or crystalline core that is thought to be a dense collection of enzyme molecules. Chloroplasts and mitochondria cooperate with peroxisomes in certain metabolic functions (TEM).

Peroxisomes: Oxidation

The **peroxisome** is a specialized metabolic compartment bounded by a single membrane (**Figure 6.19**). Peroxisomes contain enzymes that remove hydrogen atoms from various substrates and transfer them to oxygen (O_2), producing hydrogen peroxide (H_2O_2) as a by-product (from which the organelle derives its name). These reactions have many different functions. Some peroxisomes use oxygen to break fatty acids down into smaller molecules that are transported to mitochondria and used as fuel for cellular respiration. Peroxisomes in the liver detoxify alcohol and other harmful compounds by transferring hydrogen from the poisons to oxygen. The H_2O_2 formed by peroxisomes is itself toxic, but the organelle also contains an enzyme that converts H_2O_2 to water. This is an excellent example of how the cell's compartmental structure is crucial to its functions: The enzymes that produce H_2O_2 and those that dispose of this toxic compound are sequestered away from other cellular components that could be damaged.

Specialized peroxisomes called *glyoxysomes* are found in the fat-storing tissues of plant seeds. These organelles contain enzymes that initiate the conversion of fatty acids to sugar, which the emerging seedling uses as a source of energy and carbon until it can produce its own sugar by photosynthesis.

How peroxisomes are related to other organelles is still an open question. They grow larger by incorporating proteins made in the cytosol and ER, as well as lipids made in the ER and within the peroxisome itself. Peroxisomes may increase in number by splitting in two when they reach a certain size, sparking the suggestion of an endosymbiotic evolutionary origin, but others argue against this scenario. Discussion of this issue is ongoing.

CONCEPT CHECK 6.5

1. Describe two common characteristics of chloroplasts and mitochondria. Consider both function and membrane structure.

2. Do plant cells have mitochondria? Explain.

3. **WHAT IF?** A classmate proposes that mitochondria and chloroplasts should be classified in the endomembrane system. Argue against the proposal.

CONCEPT 6.6

The cytoskeleton is a network of fibers that organizes structures and activities in the cell

In the early days of electron microscopy, biologists thought that the organelles of a eukaryotic cell floated freely in the cytosol. But improvements in both light microscopy and electron microscopy have revealed the **cytoskeleton**, a network of fibers extending throughout the cytoplasm (**Figure 6.20**). Bacterial cells also have fibers that form a type of cytoskeleton, constructed of proteins similar to eukaryotic ones, but here we will concentrate on eukaryotes. The eukaryotic cytoskeleton, which plays a major role in organizing the structures and activities of the cell, is composed of three types of molecular structures: microtubules, microfilaments, and intermediate filaments.

Roles of the Cytoskeleton: Support and Motility

The most obvious function of the cytoskeleton is to give mechanical support to the cell and maintain its shape. This is especially important for animal cells, which lack walls. The remarkable strength and resilience of the cytoskeleton as a whole are based on its architecture. Like a dome tent, the cytoskeleton is stabilized by a balance between opposing forces exerted by its elements. And just as the skeleton of an animal helps fix the positions of other body parts, the cytoskeleton provides anchorage for many organelles and even cytosolic enzyme molecules. The cytoskeleton is more dynamic than an animal skeleton, however. It can be quickly dismantled in one part of the cell and reassembled in a new location, changing the shape of the cell.

▲ **Figure 6.20 The cytoskeleton.** As shown in this fluorescence micrograph, the cytoskeleton extends throughout the cell. The cytoskeletal elements have been tagged with different fluorescent molecules: green for microtubules and reddish orange for microfilaments. A third component of the cytoskeleton, intermediate filaments, is not evident here. (The blue color tags the DNA in the nucleus.)

Some types of cell motility (movement) also involve the cytoskeleton. The term *cell motility* includes both changes in cell location and movements of cell parts. Cell motility generally requires interaction of the cytoskeleton with **motor proteins**. There are many such examples: Cytoskeletal elements and motor proteins work together with plasma membrane molecules to allow whole cells to move along fibers outside the cell. Inside the cell, vesicles and other organelles often use motor protein "feet" to "walk" to their destinations along a track provided by the cytoskeleton. For example, this is how vesicles containing neurotransmitter molecules migrate to the tips of axons, the long extensions of nerve cells that release these molecules as chemical signals to adjacent nerve cells **(Figure 6.21)**. The cytoskeleton also manipulates the plasma membrane, bending it inward to form food vacuoles or other phagocytic vesicles.

Components of the Cytoskeleton

Now let's look more closely at the three main types of fibers that make up the cytoskeleton: *Microtubules* are the thickest of the three types; *microfilaments* (also called actin filaments) are the thinnest; and *intermediate filaments* are fibers with diameters in a middle range **(Table 6.1)**.

(a) Motor proteins that attach to receptors on vesicles can "walk" the vesicles along microtubules or, in some cases, along microfilaments.

(b) In this SEM of a squid giant axon (a nerve cell extension), two vesicles containing neurotransmitters move toward the axon's tip.

▲ **Figure 6.21 Motor proteins and the cytoskeleton.**

Property	Microtubules (Tubulin Polymers)	Microfilaments (Actin Filaments)	Intermediate Filaments
Structure	Hollow tubes	Two intertwined strands of actin	Fibrous proteins coiled into cables
Diameter	25 nm with 15-nm lumen	7 nm	8–12 nm
Protein subunits	Tubulin, a dimer consisting of α-tubulin and β-tubulin	Actin	One of several different proteins (such as keratins)
Main functions	Maintenance of cell shape (compression-resisting "girders"); cell motility (as in cilia or flagella); chromosome movements in cell division; organelle movements	Maintenance of cell shape (tension-bearing elements); changes in cell shape; muscle contraction; cytoplasmic streaming in plant cells; cell motility (as in amoeboid movement); division of animal cells	Maintenance of cell shape (tension-bearing elements); anchorage of nucleus and certain other organelles; formation of nuclear lamina
Fluorescence micrographs of fibroblasts. Fibroblasts are a favorite cell type for cell biology studies. In each, the structure of interest has been tagged with fluorescent molecules. The DNA in the nucleus has also been tagged in the first micrograph (blue) and third micrograph (orange).	10 µm Column of tubulin dimers 25 nm α β Tubulin dimer	10 µm Actin subunit 7 nm	5 µm Keratin proteins Fibrous subunit (keratins coiled together) 8–12 nm

Table 6.1   The Structure and Function of the Cytoskeleton

Microtubules

All eukaryotic cells have **microtubules**, hollow rods constructed from a globular protein called tubulin. Each tubulin protein is a *dimer*, a molecule made up of two subunits. A tubulin dimer consists of two slightly different polypeptides, α-tubulin and β-tubulin. Microtubules grow in length by adding tubulin dimers; they can also be disassembled and their tubulin used to build microtubules elsewhere in the cell. Because of the orientation of tubulin dimers, the two ends of a microtubule are slightly different. One end can accumulate or release tubulin dimers at a much higher rate than the other, thus growing and shrinking significantly during cellular activities. (This is called the "plus end," not because it can only add tubulin proteins but because it's the end where both "on" and "off" rates are much higher.)

Microtubules shape and support the cell and also serve as tracks along which organelles equipped with motor proteins can move. In addition to the example in Figure 6.21, microtubules guide vesicles from the ER to the Golgi apparatus and from the Golgi to the plasma membrane. Microtubules are also involved in the separation of chromosomes during cell division, which will be discussed in Chapter 12.

Centrosomes and Centrioles In animal cells, microtubules grow out from a **centrosome**, a region that is often located near the nucleus. These microtubules function as compression-resisting girders of the cytoskeleton. Within the centrosome is a pair of **centrioles**, each composed of nine sets of triplet microtubules arranged in a ring (**Figure 6.22**). Although centrosomes with centrioles may help organize microtubule assembly in animal cells, many other eukaryotic cells lack centrosomes with centrioles and instead organize microtubules by other means.

Cilia and Flagella In eukaryotes, a specialized arrangement of microtubules is responsible for the beating of **flagella** (singular, *flagellum*) and **cilia** (singular, *cilium*), microtubule-containing extensions that project from some cells. (The bacterial flagellum, shown in Figure 6.5, has a completely different structure.) Many unicellular eukaryotes are propelled through water by cilia or flagella that act as locomotor appendages, and the sperm of animals, algae, and some plants have flagella. When cilia or flagella extend from cells that are held in place as part of a tissue layer, they can move fluid over the surface of the tissue. For example, the ciliated lining of the trachea (windpipe) sweeps mucus containing trapped debris out of the lungs (see the EMs in Figure 6.3). In a woman's reproductive tract, the cilia lining the oviducts help move an egg toward the uterus.

Motile cilia usually occur in large numbers on the cell surface. Flagella are usually limited to just one or a few per cell, and they are longer than cilia. Flagella and cilia differ in their beating patterns (**Figure 6.23**). A flagellum has an

Centrosome

Microtubule

Centrioles

0.25 μm

Longitudinal section of one centriole   Microtubules   Cross section of the other centriole

▲ **Figure 6.22 Centrosome containing a pair of centrioles.** Most animal cells have a centrosome, a region near the nucleus where the cell's microtubules are initiated. Within the centrosome is a pair of centrioles, each about 250 nm (0.25 μm) in diameter. The two centrioles are at right angles to each other, and each is made up of nine sets of three microtubules. The blue portions of the drawing represent nontubulin proteins that connect the microtubule triplets.

? *How many microtubules are in a centrosome? In the drawing, circle and label one microtubule and describe its structure. Circle and label a triplet.*

undulating motion like the tail of a fish. In contrast, cilia work more like oars, with alternating power and recovery strokes, much like the oars of a racing crew boat.

A cilium may also act as a signal-receiving "antenna" for the cell. Cilia that have this function are generally nonmotile, and there is only one per cell. (In fact, in vertebrate animals, it appears that almost all cells have such a cilium, which is called a *primary cilium*.) Membrane proteins on this kind of cilium transmit molecular signals from the cell's environment to its interior, triggering signaling pathways that may lead to changes in the cell's activities. Cilium-based

(a) Motion of flagella. A flagellum usually undulates, its snakelike motion driving a cell in the same direction as the axis of the flagellum. Propulsion of a human sperm cell is an example of flagellate locomotion (LM).

Direction of swimming

5 μm

(b) Motion of cilia. Cilia have a back-and-forth motion. The rapid power stroke moves the cell in a direction perpendicular to the axis of the cilium. Then, during the slower recovery stroke, the cilium bends and sweeps sideways, closer to the cell surface. A dense nap of cilia, beating at a rate of about 40 to 60 strokes a second, covers this *Colpidium*, a freshwater protist (colorized SEM).

Direction of organism's movement

Power stroke   Recovery stroke

15 μm

▲ **Figure 6.23 A comparison of the beating of flagella and motile cilia.**

signaling appears to be crucial to brain function and to embryonic development.

Though different in length, number per cell, and beating pattern, motile cilia and flagella share a common structure. Each motile cilium or flagellum has a group of microtubules sheathed in an extension of the plasma membrane **(Figure 6.24a)**. Nine doublets of microtubules are arranged in a ring, with two single microtubules in its center **(Figure 6.24b)**. This arrangement, referred to as the "9 + 2" pattern, is found in nearly all eukaryotic flagella and motile cilia. (Nonmotile primary cilia have a "9 + 0" pattern, lacking the central pair of microtubules.) The microtubule assembly of a cilium or flagellum is anchored in the cell by a **basal body**, which is structurally very similar to a centriole, with microtubule triplets in a "9 + 0" pattern **(Figure 6.24c)**. In fact, in many animals (including humans), the basal body of the fertilizing sperm's flagellum enters the egg and becomes a centriole.

How does the microtubule assembly produce the bending movements of flagella and motile cilia? Bending involves large motor proteins called **dyneins** (red in the diagram in Figure 6.24) that are attached along each outer microtubule doublet. A typical dynein protein has two "feet" that "walk" along the microtubule of the adjacent doublet, using ATP

for energy. One foot maintains contact, while the other releases and reattaches one step farther along the microtubule (see Figure 6.21). The outer doublets and two central microtubules are held together by flexible cross-linking proteins (blue in the diagram in Figure 6.24), and the walking movement is coordinated so that it happens on one side of the circle at a time. If the doublets were not held in place, the walking action would make them slide past each other. Instead, the movements of the dynein feet cause the microtubules—and the organelle as a whole—to bend.

Microfilaments (Actin Filaments)

Microfilaments are thin solid rods. They are also called actin filaments because they are built from molecules of **actin**, a globular protein. A microfilament is a twisted double chain of actin subunits (see Table 6.1). Besides occurring as linear filaments, microfilaments can form structural networks when certain proteins bind along the side of such a filament and allow a new filament to extend as a branch. Like microtubules, microfilaments seem to be present in all eukaryotic cells.

In contrast to the compression-resisting role of microtubules, the structural role of microfilaments in the cytoskeleton is to bear tension (pulling forces). A three-dimensional

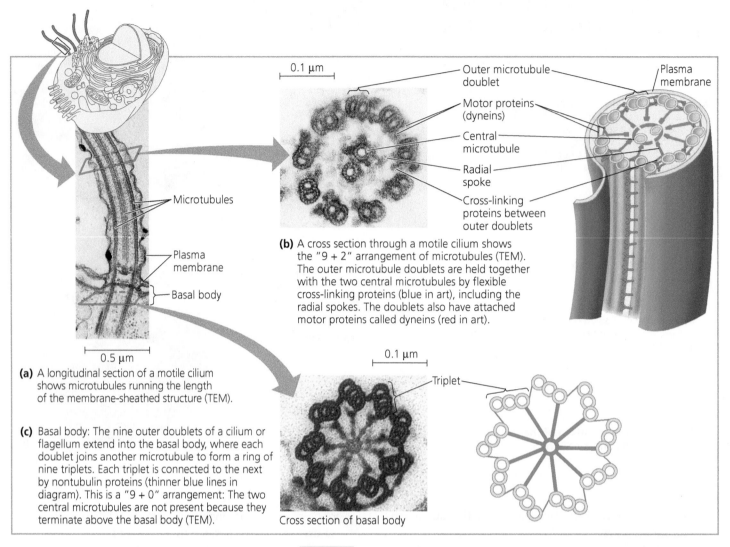

(b) A cross section through a motile cilium shows the "9 + 2" arrangement of microtubules (TEM). The outer microtubule doublets are held together with the two central microtubules by flexible cross-linking proteins (blue in art), including the radial spokes. The doublets also have attached motor proteins called dyneins (red in art).

(a) A longitudinal section of a motile cilium shows microtubules running the length of the membrane-sheathed structure (TEM).

(c) Basal body: The nine outer doublets of a cilium or flagellum extend into the basal body, where each doublet joins another microtubule to form a ring of nine triplets. Each triplet is connected to the next by nontubulin proteins (thinner blue lines in diagram). This is a "9 + 0" arrangement: The two central microtubules are not present because they terminate above the basal body (TEM).

Cross section of basal body

▲ **Figure 6.24 Structure of a flagellum or motile cilium.**

DRAW IT *In (a) and (b), circle the central pair of microtubules. In (a), show where they terminate, and explain why they aren't seen in the cross section of the basal body in (c).*

network formed by microfilaments just inside the plasma membrane (*cortical microfilaments*) helps support the cell's shape (see Figure 6.8). This network gives the outer cytoplasmic layer of a cell, called the **cortex**, the semi-solid consistency of a gel, in contrast with the more fluid state of the interior cytoplasm. In some kinds of animal cells, such as nutrient-absorbing intestinal cells, bundles of microfilaments make up the core of microvilli, delicate projections that increase the cell's surface area **(Figure 6.25)**.

Microfilaments are well known for their role in cell motility. Thousands of actin filaments and thicker filaments

▶ **Figure 6.25 A structural role of microfilaments.** The surface area of this nutrient-absorbing intestinal cell is increased by its many microvilli (singular, *microvillus*), cellular extensions reinforced by bundles of microfilaments. These actin filaments are anchored to a network of intermediate filaments (TEM).

made of a protein called **myosin** interact to cause contraction of muscle cells (**Figure 6.26a**). In the unicellular eukaryote *Amoeba* and some of our white blood cells, localized contractions brought about by actin and myosin are involved in the amoeboid (crawling) movement of the cells (**Figure 6.26b**). The cell crawls along a surface by extending cellular extensions called **pseudopodia** (from the Greek *pseudes*, false, and *pod*, foot) and moving toward them. In plant cells, both actin-myosin interactions contribute to **cytoplasmic streaming**, a circular flow of cytoplasm within cells (**Figure 6.26c**). This movement, which is especially common in large plant cells, speeds the distribution of materials within the cell.

Intermediate Filaments

Intermediate filaments are named for their diameter, which is larger than the diameter of microfilaments but smaller than that of microtubules (see Table 6.1). Unlike microtubules and microfilaments, which are found in all eukaryotic cells, intermediate filaments are only found in the cells of some animals, including vertebrates. Specialized for bearing tension (like microfilaments), intermediate filaments are a diverse class of cytoskeletal elements. Each type is constructed from a particular molecular subunit belonging to a family of proteins whose members include the keratins. Microtubules and microfilaments, in contrast, are consistent in diameter and composition in all eukaryotic cells.

Intermediate filaments are more permanent fixtures of cells than are microfilaments and microtubules, which are often disassembled and reassembled in various parts of a cell. Even after cells die, intermediate filament networks often persist; for example, the outer layer of our skin consists of dead skin cells full of keratin filaments. Chemical treatments that remove microfilaments and microtubules from the cytoplasm of living cells leave a web of intermediate filaments that retains its original shape. Such experiments suggest that intermediate filaments are especially sturdy and that they play an important role in reinforcing the shape of a cell and fixing the position of certain organelles. For instance, the nucleus typically sits within a cage made of intermediate filaments, fixed in location by branches of the filaments that extend into the cytoplasm. Other intermediate filaments make up the nuclear lamina, which lines the interior of the nuclear envelope (see Figure 6.9). By supporting a cell's shape, intermediate filaments help the cell carry out its specific function. For example, the network of intermediate filaments shown in Figure 6.25 anchor the microfilaments supporting the intestinal microvilli. Thus, the various kinds of intermediate filaments may function together as the permanent framework of the entire cell.

(a) Myosin motors in muscle cell contraction. The "walking" of myosin projections (the so-called heads) drives the parallel myosin and actin filaments past each other so that the actin filaments approach each other in the middle (red arrows). This shortens the muscle cell. Muscle contraction involves the shortening of many muscle cells at the same time (TEM).

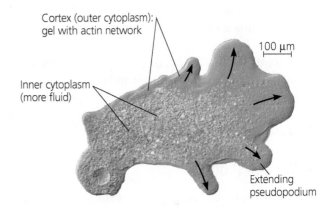

(b) Amoeboid movement. Interaction of actin filaments with myosin causes contraction of the cell, pulling the cell's trailing end (at left) forward (to the right) (LM).

(c) Cytoplasmic streaming in plant cells. A layer of cytoplasm cycles around the cell, moving over a carpet of parallel actin filaments. Myosin motors attached to organelles in the fluid cytosol may drive the streaming by interacting with the actin (LM).

▲ **Figure 6.26 Microfilaments and motility.** In these three examples, interactions between actin filaments and motor proteins bring about cell movement.

1. Describe shared features of microtubule-based motion of flagella and microfilament-based muscle contraction.

2. **WHAT IF?** Males afflicted with Kartagener's syndrome are sterile because of immotile sperm, and they tend to suffer from lung infections. This disorder has a genetic basis. Suggest what the underlying defect might be.

CONCEPT 6.7

Extracellular components and connections between cells help coordinate cellular activities

Having crisscrossed the cell to explore its interior components, we complete our tour of the cell by returning to the surface of this microscopic world, where there are additional structures with important functions. The plasma membrane is usually regarded as the boundary of the living cell, but most cells synthesize and secrete materials that are then extracellular, or external to the plasma membrane. Although these materials and the structures they form are outside the cell, their study is important to cell biology because they are involved in a great many important cellular functions.

Cell Walls of Plants

The **cell wall** is an extracellular structure of plant cells that distinguishes them from animal cells (see Figure 6.8). The wall protects the plant cell, maintains its shape, and prevents excessive uptake of water. On the level of the whole plant, the strong walls of specialized cells hold the plant up against the force of gravity. Prokaryotes, fungi, and some unicellular eukaryotes also have cell walls, as you saw in Figures 6.5 and 6.8, but we will postpone discussion of them until Unit Five.

Plant cell walls are much thicker than the plasma membrane, ranging from 0.1 μm to several micrometers. The exact chemical composition of the wall varies from species to species and even from one cell type to another in the same plant, but the basic design of the wall is consistent. Microfibrils made of the polysaccharide cellulose (see Figure 5.6) are synthesized by an enzyme called cellulose synthase and secreted to the extracellular space, where they become embedded in a matrix of other polysaccharides and proteins. This combination of materials, strong fibers in a "ground substance" (matrix), is the same basic architectural design found in steel-reinforced concrete and in fiberglass.

A young plant cell first secretes a relatively thin and flexible wall called the **primary cell wall** (Figure 6.27). Between primary walls of adjacent cells is the **middle lamella**, a thin layer rich in sticky polysaccharides called pectins. The

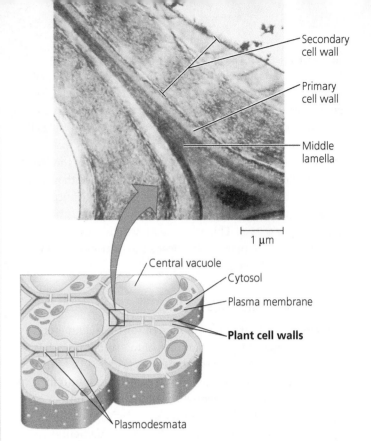

▲ **Figure 6.27 Plant cell walls.** The drawing shows several cells, each with a large vacuole, a nucleus, and several chloroplasts and mitochondria. The transmission electron micrograph shows the cell walls where two cells come together. The multilayered partition between plant cells consists of adjoining walls individually secreted by the cells.

middle lamella glues adjacent cells together. (Pectin is used in cooking as a thickening agent in jams and jellies.) When the cell matures and stops growing, it strengthens its wall. Some plant cells do this simply by secreting hardening substances into the primary wall. Other cells add a **secondary cell wall** between the plasma membrane and the primary wall. The secondary wall, often deposited in several laminated layers, has a strong and durable matrix that affords the cell protection and support. Wood, for example, consists mainly of secondary walls. Plant cell walls are usually perforated by channels between adjacent cells called plasmodesmata (see Figure 6.27), which will be discussed shortly.

The Extracellular Matrix (ECM) of Animal Cells

Although animal cells lack walls akin to those of plant cells, they do have an elaborate **extracellular matrix (ECM)**. The main ingredients of the ECM are glycoproteins and other carbohydrate-containing molecules secreted by the cells. (Recall that glycoproteins are proteins with covalently bonded carbohydrates, usually short chains of sugars.) The most abundant glycoprotein in the ECM of most animal cells is **collagen**, which forms strong fibers outside the cells (see Figure 5.18). In fact, collagen accounts for about 40% of the total protein in the human body. The collagen fibers are embedded in a network woven out of **proteoglycans**

Collagen fibers are embedded in a web of proteoglycan complexes.

Fibronectin attaches the ECM to integrins embedded in the plasma membrane.

Plasma membrane

EXTRACELLULAR FLUID

A **proteoglycan complex** consists of hundreds of proteoglycan molecules attached noncovalently to a single long polysaccharide molecule.

Integrins, membrane proteins with two subunits, bind to the ECM on the outside and to associated proteins attached to microfilaments on the inside. This linkage can transmit signals between the cell's external environment and its interior and can result in changes in cell behavior.

Micro-filaments

CYTOPLASM

Polysaccharide molecule

Carbo-hydrates

Core protein

Proteoglycan molecule

Proteoglycan complex

▲ **Figure 6.28 Extracellular matrix (ECM) of an animal cell.** The molecular composition and structure of the ECM vary from one cell type to another. In this example, three different types of ECM molecules are present: proteoglycans, collagen, and fibronectin.

secreted by cells (**Figure 6.28**). A proteoglycan molecule consists of a small core protein with many carbohydrate chains covalently attached, so that it may be up to 95% carbohydrate. Large proteoglycan complexes can form when hundreds of proteoglycan molecules become noncovalently attached to a single long polysaccharide molecule, as shown in Figure 6.28. Some cells are attached to the ECM by ECM glycoproteins such as **fibronectin**. Fibronectin and other ECM proteins bind to cell-surface receptor proteins called **integrins** that are built into the plasma membrane. Integrins span the membrane and bind on their cytoplasmic side to associated proteins attached to microfilaments of the cytoskeleton. The name *integrin* is based on the word *integrate*: Integrins are in a position to transmit signals between the ECM and the cytoskeleton and thus to integrate changes occurring outside and inside the cell.

Current research on fibronectin, other ECM molecules, and integrins is revealing the influential role of the ECM in the lives of cells. By communicating with a cell through integrins, the ECM can regulate a cell's behavior. For example, some cells in a developing embryo migrate along specific pathways by matching the orientation of their microfilaments to the "grain" of fibers in the extracellular matrix. Researchers have also learned that the extracellular matrix around a cell can influence the activity of genes in the nucleus. Information about the ECM probably reaches the nucleus by a combination of mechanical and chemical signaling pathways. Mechanical signaling involves fibronectin, integrins, and microfilaments of the cytoskeleton. Changes in the cytoskeleton may in turn trigger chemical signaling pathways inside the cell, leading to changes in the

set of proteins being made by the cell and therefore changes in the cell's function. In this way, the extracellular matrix of a particular tissue may help coordinate the behavior of all the cells of that tissue. Direct connections between cells also function in this coordination, as we discuss next.

Cell Junctions

Cells in an animal or plant are organized into tissues, organs, and organ systems. Neighboring cells often adhere, interact, and communicate via sites of direct physical contact.

Plasmodesmata in Plant Cells

It might seem that the nonliving cell walls of plants would isolate plant cells from one another. But in fact, as shown in **Figure 6.29**, cell walls are perforated with **plasmodesmata** (singular, *plasmodesma*; from the Greek *desma*, bond), channels that connect cells. Cytosol passing

Cell walls

Interior of cell

Interior of cell

0.5 μm

Plasmodesmata   Plasma membranes

▲ **Figure 6.29 Plasmodesmata between plant cells.** The cytoplasm of one plant cell is continuous with the cytoplasm of its neighbors via plasmodesmata, cytoplasmic channels through the cell walls (TEM).

through the plasmodesmata joins the internal chemical environments of adjacent cells. These connections unify most of the plant into one living continuum. The plasma membranes of adjacent cells line the channel of each plasmodesma and thus are continuous. Water and small solutes can pass freely from cell to cell, and several experiments have shown that in some circumstances, certain proteins and RNA molecules can do this as well. The macromolecules transported to neighboring cells appear to reach the plasmodesmata by moving along fibers of the cytoskeleton.

Tight Junctions, Desmosomes, and Gap Junctions in Animal Cells

In animals, there are three main types of cell junctions: *tight junctions*, *desmosomes*, and *gap junctions*. (Gap junctions are most like the plasmodesmata of plants, although gap junction pores are not lined with membrane.) All three types of cell junctions are especially common in epithelial tissue, which lines the external and internal surfaces of the body. **Figure 6.30** uses epithelial cells of the intestinal lining to illustrate these junctions.

▼ Figure 6.30

Exploring Cell Junctions in Animal Tissues

Tight junctions prevent fluid from moving across a layer of cells.

Tight junction

Intermediate filaments

Tight junction

Desmosome

Gap junction

Ions or small molecules

Plasma membranes of adjacent cells

Space between cells

Extracellular matrix

Tight Junctions

At **tight junctions**, the plasma membranes of neighboring cells are very tightly pressed against each other, bound together by specific proteins (purple). Forming continuous seals around the cells, tight junctions establish a barrier that prevents leakage of extracellular fluid across a layer of epithelial cells (see red dashed arrow). For example, tight junctions between skin cells make us watertight.

TEM   0.5 µm

Desmosomes

Desmosomes (also called *anchoring junctions*) function like rivets, fastening cells together into strong sheets. Intermediate filaments made of sturdy keratin proteins anchor desmosomes in the cytoplasm. Desmosomes attach muscle cells to each other in a muscle. Some "muscle tears" involve the rupture of desmosomes.

TEM   1 µm

Gap Junctions

Gap junctions (also called *communicating junctions*) provide cytoplasmic channels from one cell to an adjacent cell and in this way are similar in their function to the plasmodesmata in plants. Gap junctions consist of membrane proteins that surround a pore through which ions, sugars, amino acids, and other small molecules may pass. Gap junctions are necessary for communication between cells in many types of tissues, such as heart muscle, and in animal embryos.

TEM   0.1 µm

1. In what way are the cells of plants and animals structurally different from single-celled eukaryotes?
2. **WHAT IF?** If the plant cell wall or the animal extracellular matrix were impermeable, what effect would this have on cell function?
3. **MAKE CONNECTIONS** The polypeptide chain that makes up a tight junction weaves back and forth through the membrane four times, with two extracellular loops, and one loop plus short C-terminal and N-terminal tails in the cytoplasm. Looking at Figure 5.14, what would you predict about the amino acid sequence of the tight-junction protein?

5 µm

▲ **Figure 6.31 The emergence of cellular functions.** The ability of this macrophage (brown) to recognize, apprehend, and destroy bacteria (yellow) is a coordinated activity of the whole cell. Its cytoskeleton, lysosomes, and plasma membrane are among the components that function in phagocytosis (colorized SEM).

The Cell: A Living Unit Greater Than the Sum of Its Parts

From our panoramic view of the cell's compartmental organization to our close-up inspection of each organelle's architecture, this tour of the cell has provided many opportunities to correlate structure with function. (This would be a good time to review cell structure by returning to Figure 6.8.) But even as we dissect the cell, remember that none of its components works alone. As an example of cellular integration, consider the microscopic scene in **Figure 6.31**. The large cell is a macrophage (see Figure 6.13a). It helps defend the mammalian body against infections by ingesting bacteria (the smaller cells) into phagocytic vesicles. The macrophage crawls along a surface and reaches out to the bacteria with thin pseudopodia

(specifically, filopodia). Actin filaments interact with other elements of the cytoskeleton in these movements. After the macrophage engulfs the bacteria, they are destroyed by lysosomes. The elaborate endomembrane system produces the lysosomes. The digestive enzymes of the lysosomes and the proteins of the cytoskeleton are all made by ribosomes. And the synthesis of these proteins is programmed by genetic messages dispatched from the DNA in the nucleus. All these processes require energy, which mitochondria supply in the form of ATP. Cellular functions arise from cellular order: The cell is a living unit greater than the sum of its parts.

---

6 Chapter Review

SUMMARY OF KEY CONCEPTS

CONCEPT 6.1

Biologists use microscopes and the tools of biochemistry to study cells (pp. 94–97)

- Improvements in microscopy that affect the parameters of magnification, resolution, and contrast have catalyzed progress in the study of cell structure. **Light microscopy** (LM) and **electron microscopy** (EM), as well as other types, remain important tools.
- Cell biologists can obtain pellets enriched in particular cellular components by centrifuging disrupted cells at sequential speeds, a process known as **cell fractionation**. Larger cellular components are in the pellet after lower-speed centrifugation, and smaller components are in the pellet after higher-speed centrifugation.

? *How do microscopy and biochemistry complement each other to reveal cell structure and function?*

CONCEPT 6.2

Eukaryotic cells have internal membranes that compartmentalize their functions (pp. 97–102)

- All cells are bounded by a **plasma membrane**.
- **Prokaryotic cells** lack nuclei and other membrane-enclosed **organelles**, while **eukaryotic cells** have internal membranes that compartmentalize cellular functions.
- The surface-to-volume ratio is an important parameter affecting cell size and shape.
- Plant and animal cells have most of the same organelles: a nucleus, endoplasmic reticulum, Golgi apparatus, and mitochondria. Chloroplasts are present only in cells of photosynthetic eukaryotes.

? *Explain how the compartmental organization of a eukaryotic cell contributes to its biochemical functioning.*

	Cell Component	Structure	Function
CONCEPT 6.3 The eukaryotic cell's genetic instructions are housed in the nucleus and carried out by the ribosomes (pp. 102–104) ? *Describe the relationship between the nucleus and ribosomes.*	Nucleus (ER)	Surrounded by nuclear envelope (double membrane) perforated by nuclear pores; nuclear envelope continuous with endoplasmic reticulum (ER)	Houses chromosomes, which are made of chromatin (DNA and proteins); contains nucleoli, where ribosomal subunits are made; pores regulate entry and exit of materials
	Ribosome	Two subunits made of ribosomal RNA and proteins; can be free in cytosol or bound to ER	Protein synthesis
CONCEPT 6.4 The endomembrane system regulates protein traffic and performs metabolic functions in the cell (pp. 104–109) ? *Describe the key role played by transport vesicles in the endomembrane system.*	Endoplasmic reticulum (Nuclear envelope)	Extensive network of membrane-bounded tubules and sacs; membrane separates lumen from cytosol; continuous with nuclear envelope	Smooth ER: synthesis of lipids, metabolism of carbohydrates, Ca^{2+} storage, detoxification of drugs and poisons Rough ER: aids in synthesis of secretory and other proteins from bound ribosomes; adds carbohydrates to proteins to make glycoproteins; produces new membrane
	Golgi apparatus	Stacks of flattened membranous sacs; has polarity (*cis* and *trans* faces)	Modification of proteins, carbohydrates on proteins, and phospholipids; synthesis of many polysaccharides; sorting of Golgi products, which are then released in vesicles
	Lysosome	Membranous sac of hydrolytic enzymes (in animal cells)	Breakdown of ingested substances, cell macromolecules, and damaged organelles for recycling
	Vacuole	Large membrane-bounded vesicle	Digestion, storage, waste disposal, water balance, cell growth, and protection
CONCEPT 6.5 Mitochondria and chloroplasts change energy from one form to another (pp. 109–112) ? *What is the endosymbiont theory?*	Mitochondrion	Bounded by double membrane; inner membrane has infoldings (cristae)	Cellular respiration
	Chloroplast	Typically two membranes around fluid stroma, which contains thylakoids stacked into grana (in cells of photosynthetic eukaryotes, including plants)	Photosynthesis
	Peroxisome	Specialized metabolic compartment bounded by a single membrane	Contains enzymes that transfer hydrogen atoms from substrates to oxygen, producing hydrogen peroxide (H_2O_2) as a by-product; H_2O_2 is converted to water by another enzyme

CONCEPT 6.6

The cytoskeleton is a network of fibers that organizes structures and activities in the cell (pp. 112–118)

- The **cytoskeleton** functions in structural support for the cell and in motility and signal transmission.
- **Microtubules** shape the cell, guide organelle movement, and separate chromosomes in dividing cells. **Cilia** and **flagella** are motile appendages containing microtubules. Primary cilia also play sensory and signaling roles. **Microfilaments** are thin rods that function in muscle contraction, amoeboid movement, **cytoplasmic streaming**, and support of microvilli. **Intermediate filaments** support cell shape and fix organelles in place.

? *Describe the role of motor proteins inside the eukaryotic cell and in whole-cell movement.*

CONCEPT 6.7

Extracellular components and connections between cells help coordinate cellular activities (pp. 118–121)

- Plant **cell walls** are made of cellulose fibers embedded in other polysaccharides and proteins.
- Animal cells secrete glycoproteins and proteoglycans that form the **extracellular matrix (ECM)**, which functions in support, adhesion, movement, and regulation.
- Cell junctions connect neighboring cells. Plants have **plasmodesmata** that pass through adjoining cell walls. Animal cells have **tight junctions**, **desmosomes**, and **gap junctions**.

? *Compare the structure and functions of a plant cell wall and the extracellular matrix of an animal cell.*

TEST YOUR UNDERSTANDING

LEVEL 1: KNOWLEDGE/COMPREHENSION

1. Which structure is *not* part of the endomembrane system?
   a. nuclear envelope
   b. chloroplast
   c. Golgi apparatus
   d. plasma membrane

2. Which structure is common to plant *and* animal cells?
   a. chloroplast
   b. central vacuole
   c. mitochondrion
   d. centriole

3. Which of the following is present in a prokaryotic cell?
   a. mitochondrion
   b. ribosome
   c. nuclear envelope
   d. chloroplast

4. Which structure-function pair is *mismatched*?
   a. microtubule; muscle contraction
   b. ribosome; protein synthesis
   c. Golgi; protein trafficking
   d. nucleolus; production of ribosomal subunits

LEVEL 2: APPLICATION/ANALYSIS

5. Cyanide binds to at least one molecule involved in producing ATP. If a cell is exposed to cyanide, most of the cyanide will be found within the
   a. mitochondria.
   b. ribosomes.
   c. peroxisomes.
   d. lysosomes.

6. What is the most likely pathway taken by a newly synthesized protein that will be secreted by a cell?
   a. Golgi → ER → lysosome
   b. nucleus → ER → Golgi
   c. ER → Golgi → vesicles that fuse with plasma membrane
   d. ER → lysosomes → vesicles that fuse with plasma membrane

7. Which cell would be best for studying lysosomes?
   a. muscle cell
   b. nerve cell
   c. phagocytic white blood cell
   d. bacterial cell

8. **DRAW IT** From memory, draw two eukaryotic cells, labeling the structures listed here and showing any physical connections between the internal structures of each cell: nucleus, rough ER, smooth ER, mitochondrion, centrosome, chloroplast, vacuole, lysosome, microtubule, cell wall, ECM, microfilament, Golgi apparatus, intermediate filament, plasma membrane, peroxisome, ribosome, nucleolus, nuclear pore, vesicle, flagellum, microvilli, plasmodesma.

LEVEL 3: SYNTHESIS/EVALUATION

9. **EVOLUTION CONNECTION**
   Which aspects of cell structure best reveal evolutionary unity? What are some examples of specialized modifications?

10. **SCIENTIFIC INQUIRY**
    Imagine protein X, destined to span the plasma membrane. Assume that the mRNA carrying the genetic message for protein X has already been translated by ribosomes in a cell culture. If you fractionate the cells (see Figure 6.4), in which fraction would you find protein X? Explain by describing its transit through the cell.

11. **WRITE ABOUT A THEME: ORGANIZATION**
    Considering some of the characteristics that define life and drawing on your knowledge of cellular structures and functions, write a short essay (100–150 words) that discusses this statement: Life is an emergent property that appears at the level of the cell. (See Concept 1.1.)

12. **SYNTHESIZE YOUR KNOWLEDGE**

Epithelial cell

The cells in the SEM are epithelial cells from the small intestine. Discuss how aspects of their structure contribute to their specialized functions of nutrient absorption and as a barrier between the intestinal contents and the blood supply on the other side of the sheet of epithelial cells.

MasteringBiology®

Students Go to **MasteringBiology** for assignments, the eText, and the Study Area with practice tests, animations, and activities.

Instructors Go to **MasteringBiology** for automatically graded tutorials and questions that you can assign to your students, plus Instructor Resources.

7

Membrane Structure and Function

▲ Figure 7.1 How do cell membrane proteins help regulate chemical traffic?

Life at the Edge

The plasma membrane is the edge of life, the boundary that separates the living cell from its surroundings and controls traffic into and out of the cell it surrounds. Like all biological membranes, the plasma membrane exhibits **selective permeability**; that is, it allows some substances to cross it more easily than others. The ability of the cell to discriminate in its chemical exchanges with its environment is fundamental to life, and it is the plasma membrane and its component molecules that make this selectivity possible.

In this chapter, you will learn how cellular membranes control the passage of substances. The image in **Figure 7.1** shows a computer model of water molecules (red and gray) passing through a short section of membrane. The blue ribbons within the lipid bilayer (green) represent helical regions of a membrane protein called an aquaporin. One molecule of this protein enables billions of water molecules to pass through the membrane every second, many more than could cross on their own. Found in many cells, aquaporins are but one example of how the plasma membrane and its proteins enable cells to survive and function. To understand how membranes work, we'll begin by examining their structure. Then, in the rest of the chapter, we'll describe in some detail how plasma membranes control transport into and out of cells, sometimes through proteins like the ion channel to the left.

Cellular membranes are fluid mosaics of lipids and proteins

Lipids and proteins are the staple ingredients of membranes, although carbohydrates are also important. The most abundant lipids in most membranes are phospholipids. The ability of phospholipids to form membranes is inherent in their molecular structure. A phospholipid is an **amphipathic** molecule, meaning it has both a hydrophilic region and a hydrophobic region (see Figure 5.11). Other types of membrane lipids are also amphipathic. A phospholipid bilayer can exist as a stable boundary between two aqueous compartments because the molecular arrangement shelters the hydrophobic tails of the phospholipids from water while exposing the hydrophilic heads to water (Figure 7.2).

Like membrane lipids, most membrane proteins are amphipathic. Such proteins can reside in the phospholipid bilayer with their hydrophilic regions protruding. This molecular orientation maximizes contact of hydrophilic regions of proteins with water in the cytosol and extracellular fluid, while providing their hydrophobic

parts with a nonaqueous environment. **Figure 7.3** shows the currently accepted model of the arrangement of molecules in the plasma membrane. In this **fluid mosaic model**, the membrane is a mosaic of protein molecules bobbing in a fluid bilayer of phospholipids.

▼ **Figure 7.2** Phospholipid bilayer (cross section).

Hydrophilic head

Hydrophobic tail

WATER

WATER

MAKE CONNECTIONS *Consulting Figure 5.11, circle the hydrophilic and hydrophobic portions of the enlarged phospholipids on the right. Explain what each portion contacts when the phospholipids are in the plasma membrane.*

Fibers of extra-cellular matrix (ECM)

Glyco-protein

Carbohydrate

Glycolipid

EXTRACELLULAR SIDE OF MEMBRANE

Cholesterol

Microfilaments of cytoskeleton

Peripheral proteins

Integral protein

CYTOPLASMIC SIDE OF MEMBRANE

▲ **Figure 7.3 Updated model of an animal cell's plasma membrane (cutaway view).**

The proteins are not randomly distributed in the membrane, however. Groups of proteins are often associated in long-lasting, specialized patches, where they carry out common functions. The lipids themselves appear to form defined regions as well. Also, in some regions the membrane may be much more packed with proteins than shown in Figure 7.3. Like all models, the fluid mosaic model is continually being refined as new research reveals more about membrane structure.

The Fluidity of Membranes

Membranes are not static sheets of molecules locked rigidly in place. A membrane is held together primarily by hydrophobic interactions, which are much weaker than covalent bonds (see Figure 5.18). Most of the lipids and some of the proteins can shift about laterally—that is, in the plane of the membrane, like partygoers elbowing their way through a crowded room. Very rarely, also, a lipid may flip-flop across the membrane, switching from one phospholipid layer to the other.

The lateral movement of phospholipids within the membrane is rapid. Adjacent phospholipids switch positions about 10^7 times per second, which means that a phospholipid can travel about 2 μm—the length of many bacterial cells—in 1 second. Proteins are much larger than lipids and move more slowly, but some membrane proteins do drift, as shown in a classic experiment described in **Figure 7.4**. Some membrane proteins seem to move in a highly directed manner, perhaps driven along cytoskeletal fibers in the cell by motor proteins connected to the membrane proteins' cytoplasmic regions. However, many other membrane proteins seem to be held immobile by their attachment to the cytoskeleton or to the extracellular matrix (see Figure 7.3).

A membrane remains fluid as temperature decreases until the phospholipids settle into a closely packed arrangement and the membrane solidifies, much as bacon grease forms lard when it cools. The temperature at which a membrane solidifies depends on the types of lipids it is made of. The membrane remains fluid to a lower temperature if it is rich in phospholipids with unsaturated hydrocarbon tails (see Figures 5.10 and 5.11). Because of kinks in the tails where double bonds are located, unsaturated hydrocarbon tails cannot pack together as closely as saturated hydrocarbon tails, making the membrane more fluid (**Figure 7.5a**).

The steroid cholesterol, which is wedged between phospholipid molecules in the plasma membranes of animal cells, has different effects on membrane fluidity at different temperatures (**Figure 7.5b**). At relatively high temperatures—at 37°C, the body temperature of humans, for example—cholesterol makes the membrane less fluid by restraining phospholipid movement. However, because cholesterol also hinders the close packing of phospholipids, it lowers the temperature required for the membrane to solidify. Thus, cholesterol can be thought of as a "fluidity buffer" for the membrane, resisting changes in membrane fluidity that can be caused by changes in temperature.

▼ **Figure 7.4** | Inquiry

Do membrane proteins move?

Experiment Larry Frye and Michael Edidin, at Johns Hopkins University, labeled the plasma membrane proteins of a mouse cell and a human cell with two different markers and fused the cells. Using a microscope, they observed the markers on the hybrid cell.

Results

Membrane proteins

Mouse cell + Human cell → Hybrid cell → Mixed proteins after 1 hour

Conclusion The mixing of the mouse and human membrane proteins indicates that at least some membrane proteins move sideways within the plane of the plasma membrane.

Source: L. D. Frye and M. Edidin, The rapid intermixing of cell surface antigens after formation of mouse-human heterokaryons, *Journal of Cell Science* 7:319 (1970).

WHAT IF? *Suppose the proteins did not mix in the hybrid cell, even many hours after fusion. Would you be able to conclude that proteins don't move within the membrane? What other explanation could there be?*

▼ **Figure 7.5 Factors that affect membrane fluidity.**

(a) Unsaturated versus saturated hydrocarbon tails.

Fluid

Viscous

Unsaturated hydrocarbon tails (kinked) prevent packing, enhancing membrane fluidity.

Saturated hydrocarbon tails pack together, increasing membrane viscosity.

(b) Cholesterol within the animal cell membrane.

Cholesterol reduces membrane fluidity at moderate temperatures by reducing phospholipid movement, but at low temperatures it hinders solidification by disrupting the regular packing of phospholipids.

Cholesterol

Membranes must be fluid to work properly; the fluidity of a membrane affects both its permeability and the ability of membrane proteins to move to where their function is needed. Usually, membranes are about as fluid as salad oil. When a membrane solidifies, its permeability changes, and enzymatic proteins in the membrane may become inactive if their activity requires movement within the membrane. However, membranes that are too fluid cannot support protein function either. Therefore, extreme environments pose a challenge for life, resulting in evolutionary adaptations that include differences in membrane lipid composition.

Evolution of Differences in Membrane Lipid Composition

EVOLUTION Variations in the cell membrane lipid compositions of many species appear to be evolutionary adaptations that maintain the appropriate membrane fluidity under specific environmental conditions. For instance, fishes that live in extreme cold have membranes with a high proportion of unsaturated hydrocarbon tails, enabling their membranes to remain fluid (see Figure 7.5a). At the other extreme, some bacteria and archaea thrive at temperatures greater than 90°C (194°F) in thermal hot springs and geysers. Their membranes include unusual lipids that may prevent excessive fluidity at such high temperatures.

The ability to change the lipid composition of cell membranes in response to changing temperatures has evolved in organisms that live where temperatures vary. In many plants that tolerate extreme cold, such as winter wheat, the percentage of unsaturated phospholipids increases in autumn, an adjustment that keeps the membranes from solidifying during winter. Certain bacteria and archaea can also change the proportion of unsaturated phospholipids in their cell membranes, depending on the temperature at which they are growing. Overall, natural selection has apparently favored organisms whose mix of membrane lipids ensures an appropriate level of membrane fluidity for their environment.

Membrane Proteins and Their Functions

Now we come to the *mosaic* aspect of the fluid mosaic model. Somewhat like a tile mosaic, a membrane is a collage of different proteins, often clustered together in groups, embedded in the fluid matrix of the lipid bilayer (see Figure 7.3). In the plasma membrane of red blood cells alone, for example, more than 50 kinds of proteins have been found so far. Phospholipids form the main fabric of the membrane, but proteins determine most of the membrane's functions. Different types of cells contain different sets of membrane proteins, and the various membranes within a cell each have a unique collection of proteins.

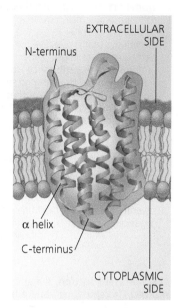

▶ **Figure 7.6 The structure of a transmembrane protein.** Bacteriorhodopsin (a bacterial transport protein) has a distinct orientation in the membrane, with its N-terminus outside the cell and its C-terminus inside. This ribbon model highlights the α-helical secondary structure of the hydrophobic parts, which lie mostly within the hydrophobic interior of the membrane. The protein includes seven transmembrane helices. The nonhelical hydrophilic segments are in contact with the aqueous solutions on the extracellular and cytoplasmic sides of the membrane. Although shown as simple purple shapes in many figures in this book, each protein has its own unique structure.

EXTRACELLULAR SIDE

N-terminus

α helix

C-terminus

CYTOPLASMIC SIDE

Notice in Figure 7.3 that there are two major populations of membrane proteins: integral proteins and peripheral proteins. **Integral proteins** penetrate the hydrophobic interior of the lipid bilayer. The majority are *transmembrane proteins*, which span the membrane; other integral proteins extend only partway into the hydrophobic interior. The hydrophobic regions of an integral protein consist of one or more stretches of nonpolar amino acids (see Figure 5.14), usually coiled into α helices **(Figure 7.6)**. The hydrophilic parts of the molecule are exposed to the aqueous solutions on either side of the membrane. Some proteins also have one or more hydrophilic channels that allow passage through the membrane of hydrophilic substances (even of water itself; see Figure 7.1). **Peripheral proteins** are not embedded in the lipid bilayer at all; they are appendages loosely bound to the surface of the membrane, often to exposed parts of integral proteins (see Figure 7.3).

On the cytoplasmic side of the plasma membrane, some membrane proteins are held in place by attachment to the cytoskeleton. And on the extracellular side, certain membrane proteins are attached to fibers of the extracellular matrix (see Figure 6.28; *integrins* are one type of integral, transmembrane protein). These attachments combine to give animal cells a stronger framework than the plasma membrane alone could provide.

A single cell may have cell surface membrane proteins that carry out several different functions, such as transport through the cell membrane, enzymatic activity, or attaching a cell to either a neighboring cell or the extracellular matrix. Furthermore, a single membrane protein may itself carry out multiple functions. Thus, the membrane is not only a structural mosaic, but also a functional mosaic. **Figure 7.7** illustrates six major functions performed by proteins of the plasma membrane.

(a) Transport. *Left:* A protein that spans the membrane may provide a hydrophilic channel across the membrane that is selective for a particular solute. *Right:* Other transport proteins shuttle a substance from one side to the other by changing shape (see Figure 7.14b). Some of these proteins hydrolyze ATP as an energy source to actively pump substances across the membrane.

(b) Enzymatic activity. A protein built into the membrane may be an enzyme with its active site exposed to substances in the adjacent solution. In some cases, several enzymes in a membrane are organized as a team that carries out sequential steps of a metabolic pathway.

(c) Signal transduction. A membrane protein (receptor) may have a binding site with a specific shape that fits the shape of a chemical messenger, such as a hormone. The external messenger (signaling molecule) may cause the protein to change shape, allowing it to relay the message to the inside of the cell, usually by binding to a cytoplasmic protein (see Figure 11.6).

(d) Cell-cell recognition. Some glycoproteins serve as identification tags that are specifically recognized by membrane proteins of other cells. This type of cell-cell binding is usually short-lived compared to that shown in (e).

(e) Intercellular joining. Membrane proteins of adjacent cells may hook together in various kinds of junctions, such as gap junctions or tight junctions (see Figure 6.30). This type of binding is more long-lasting than that shown in (d).

(f) Attachment to the cytoskeleton and extracellular matrix (ECM). Microfilaments or other elements of the cytoskeleton may be noncovalently bound to membrane proteins, a function that helps maintain cell shape and stabilizes the location of certain membrane proteins. Proteins that can bind to ECM molecules can coordinate extracellular and intracellular changes (see Figure 6.28).

▲ **Figure 7.7 Some functions of membrane proteins.** In many cases, a single protein performs multiple tasks.

? *Some transmembrane proteins can bind to a particular ECM molecule and, when bound, transmit a signal into the cell. Use the proteins shown in (c) and (f) to explain how this might occur.*

Proteins on a cell's surface are important in the medical field. For example, a protein called CD4 on the surface of immune cells helps the human immunodeficiency virus (HIV) infect these cells, leading to acquired immune deficiency syndrome (AIDS). Despite multiple exposures to HIV, however, a small number of people do not develop AIDS and show no evidence of HIV-infected cells. Comparing their genes with the genes of infected individuals, researchers learned that resistant people have an unusual form of a gene that codes for an immune cell-surface protein called CCR5. Further work showed although CD4 is the main HIV receptor, HIV must also bind to CCR5 as a "co-receptor" to infect most cells **(Figure 7.8a).** An absence of CCR5 on the cells of resistant individuals, due to the gene alteration, prevents the virus from entering the cells **(Figure 7.8b).**

This information has been key to developing a treatment for HIV infection. Interfering with CD4 could cause dangerous side effects because it performs many important functions in cells. Discovery of the CCR5 co-receptor provided a safer target for development of drugs that mask this protein and block HIV entry. One such drug, maraviroc (brand name Selzentry), was approved for treatment of HIV in 2007 and is still being used today. A clinical trial began in 2012 to test whether this drug might also work to prevent HIV infection in uninfected, at-risk patients.

The Role of Membrane Carbohydrates in Cell-Cell Recognition

Cell-cell recognition, a cell's ability to distinguish one type of neighboring cell from another, is crucial to the functioning of an organism. It is important, for example, in the sorting of cells into tissues and organs in an animal embryo. It is also the basis for the rejection of foreign cells by the immune

▲ **Figure 7.8 The genetic basis for HIV resistance. (a)** HIV can infect a cell with CCR5 on its surface, as in most people. **(b)** HIV cannot infect a cell lacking CCR5 on its surface, as in resistant individuals.

MAKE CONNECTIONS *Study Figures 2.16 and 5.17, both of which show pairs of molecules binding to each other. What would you predict about CCR5 that would allow HIV to bind to it? How could a drug molecule interfere with this binding?*

system, an important line of defense in vertebrate animals Cells recognize other cells by binding to molecules, often containing carbohydrates, on the extracellular surface of the plasma membrane (see Figure 7.7d).

Membrane carbohydrates are usually short, branched chains of fewer than 15 sugar units. Some are covalently bonded to lipids, forming molecules called **glycolipids**. (Recall that *glyco* refers to the presence of carbohydrate.) However, most are covalently bonded to proteins, which are thereby **glycoproteins** (see Figure 7.3).

The carbohydrates on the extracellular side of the plasma membrane vary from species to species, among individuals of the same species, and even from one cell type to another in a single individual. The diversity of the molecules and their location on the cell's surface enable membrane carbohydrates to function as markers that distinguish one cell from another. For example, the four human blood types designated A, B, AB, and O reflect variation in the carbohydrate part of glycoproteins on the surface of red blood cells.

Synthesis and Sidedness of Membranes

Membranes have distinct inside and outside faces. The two lipid layers may differ in lipid composition, and each protein has directional orientation in the membrane (see Figure 7.6). **Figure 7.9** shows how membrane sidedness arises: The asymmetrical arrangement of proteins, lipids, and their

associated carbohydrates in the plasma membrane is determined as the membrane is being built by the endoplasmic reticulum (ER) and Golgi apparatus, components of the endomembrane system (see Figure 6.15).

CONCEPT CHECK 7.1

1. Plasma membrane proteins have carbohydrates attached to them in the ER and Golgi apparatus, then are transported in vesicles to the cell surface. On which side of the vesicle membrane are the carbohydrates?

2. **WHAT IF?** How would the membrane lipid composition of a native grass found in very warm soil around hot springs compare with that of a native grass found in cooler soil? Explain.

CONCEPT 7.2

Membrane structure results in selective permeability

The biological membrane is an exquisite example of a supramolecular structure—many molecules ordered into a higher level of organization—with emergent properties beyond those of the individual molecules. The remainder of this chapter focuses on one of those properties: the ability to regulate transport across cellular boundaries, a function

▼ **Figure 7.9 Synthesis of membrane components and their orientation in the membrane.** The cytoplasmic (orange) face of the plasma membrane differs from the extracellular (aqua) face. The latter arises from the inside face of ER, Golgi, and vesicle membranes.

1 Membrane proteins and lipids are synthesized in the endoplasmic reticulum (ER). Carbohydrates (green) are added to the transmembrane proteins (purple dumbbells), making them glycoproteins. The carbohydrate portions may then be modified.

2 Inside the Golgi apparatus, the glycoproteins undergo further carbohydrate modification, and lipids acquire carbohydrates, becoming glycolipids.

3 The glycoproteins, glycolipids, and secretory proteins (purple spheres) are transported in vesicles to the plasma membrane.

4 As vesicles fuse with the plasma membrane, the outside face of the vesicle becomes continuous with the inside (cytoplasmic) face of the plasma membrane. This releases the secretory proteins from the cell, a process called *exocytosis*, and positions the carbohydrates of membrane glycoproteins and glycolipids on the outside (extracellular) face of the plasma membrane.

DRAW IT *Draw an integral membrane protein extending from partway through the ER membrane into the ER lumen. Next, draw the protein where it would be located in a series of numbered steps ending at the plasma membrane. Would the protein contact the cytoplasm or the extracellular fluid? Explain.*

essential to the cell's existence. We will see once again that form fits function: The fluid mosaic model helps explain how membranes regulate the cell's molecular traffic.

A steady traffic of small molecules and ions moves across the plasma membrane in both directions. Consider the chemical exchanges between a muscle cell and the extracellular fluid that bathes it. Sugars, amino acids, and other nutrients enter the cell, and metabolic waste products leave it. The cell takes in O_2 for use in cellular respiration and expels CO_2. Also, the cell regulates its concentrations of inorganic ions, such as Na^+, K^+, Ca^{2+}, and Cl^-, by shuttling them one way or the other across the plasma membrane. Although the heavy traffic through them may seem to suggest otherwise, cell membranes are selectively permeable, and substances do not cross the barrier indiscriminately. The cell is able to take up some small molecules and ions and exclude others.

The Permeability of the Lipid Bilayer

Nonpolar molecules, such as hydrocarbons, CO_2, and O_2, are hydrophobic. They can therefore dissolve in the lipid bilayer of the membrane and cross it easily, without the aid of membrane proteins. However, the hydrophobic interior of the membrane impedes direct passage through the membrane of ions and polar molecules, which are hydrophilic. Polar molecules such as glucose and other sugars pass only slowly through a lipid bilayer, and even water, a very small polar molecule, does not cross rapidly. A charged atom or molecule and its surrounding shell of water (see Figure 3.7) are even less likely to penetrate the hydrophobic interior of the membrane. Furthermore, the lipid bilayer is only one aspect of the gatekeeper system responsible for a cell's selective permeability. Proteins built into the membrane play key roles in regulating transport.

Transport Proteins

Specific ions and a variety of polar molecules can't move through cell membranes on their own. However, these hydrophilic substances can avoid contact with the lipid bilayer by passing through **transport proteins** that span the membrane.

Some transport proteins, called *channel proteins*, function by having a hydrophilic channel that certain molecules or atomic ions use as a tunnel through the membrane (see Figure 7.7a, left). For example, the passage of water molecules through the membrane in certain cells is greatly facilitated by channel proteins known as **aquaporins** (see Figure 7.1). Each aquaporin allows entry of up to *3 billion* (3×10^9) water molecules per second, passing single file through its central channel, which fits ten at a time. Without aquaporins, only a tiny fraction of these water molecules would pass through the same area of the cell membrane in a second, so the channel protein brings about a tremendous increase in rate. Other transport proteins, called *carrier proteins*, hold

onto their passengers and change shape in a way that shuttles them across the membrane (see Figure 7.7a, right).

A transport protein is specific for the substance it translocates (moves), allowing only a certain substance (or a small group of related substances) to cross the membrane. For example, a specific carrier protein in the plasma membrane of red blood cells transports glucose across the membrane 50,000 times faster than glucose can pass through on its own. This "glucose transporter" is so selective that it even rejects fructose, a structural isomer of glucose.

Thus, the selective permeability of a membrane depends on both the discriminating barrier of the lipid bilayer and the specific transport proteins built into the membrane. But what establishes the *direction* of traffic across a membrane? At a given time, what determines whether a particular substance will enter the cell or leave the cell? And what mechanisms actually drive molecules across membranes? We will address these questions next as we explore two modes of membrane traffic: passive transport and active transport.

CONCEPT CHECK 7.2

1. What property allows O_2 and CO_2 to cross a lipid bilayer without the help of membrane proteins?

2. Why is a transport protein needed to move many water molecules rapidly across a membrane?

3. MAKE CONNECTIONS Aquaporins exclude passage of hydronium ions (H_3O^+), but some aquaporins allow passage of glycerol, a three-carbon alcohol (see Figure 5.9), as well as H_2O. Since H_3O^+ is closer in size to water than glycerol is, yet cannot pass through, what might be the basis of this selectivity?

CONCEPT 7.3

Passive transport is diffusion of a substance across a membrane with no energy investment

Molecules have a type of energy called thermal energy, due to their constant motion (see Concept 3.2). One result of this motion is **diffusion**, the movement of particles of any substance so that they spread out into the available space. Each molecule moves randomly, yet diffusion of a *population* of molecules may be directional. To understand this process, let's imagine a synthetic membrane separating pure water from a solution of a dye in water. Study **Figure 7.10a** carefully to appreciate how diffusion would result in both solutions having equal concentrations of the dye molecules. Once that point is reached, there will be a dynamic equilibrium, with roughly as many dye molecules crossing the membrane each second in one direction as in the other.

Molecules of dye — Membrane (cross section)

WATER

Net diffusion   Net diffusion   Equilibrium

(a) Diffusion of one solute. The membrane has pores large enough for molecules of dye to pass through. Random movement of dye molecules will cause some to pass through the pores; this will happen more often on the side with more dye molecules. The dye diffuses from where it is more concentrated to where it is less concentrated (called diffusing down a concentration gradient). This leads to a dynamic equilibrium: The solute molecules continue to cross the membrane, but at roughly equal rates in both directions.

Net diffusion   Net diffusion   Equilibrium
Net diffusion   Net diffusion   Equilibrium

(b) Diffusion of two solutes. Solutions of two different dyes are separated by a membrane that is permeable to both. Each dye diffuses down its own concentration gradient. There will be a net diffusion of the purple dye toward the left, even though the *total* solute concentration was initially greater on the left side.

▲ **Figure 7.10 The diffusion of solutes across a synthetic membrane.** Each of the large arrows under the diagrams shows the net diffusion of the dye molecules of that color.

We can now state a simple rule of diffusion: In the absence of other forces, a substance will diffuse from where it is more concentrated to where it is less concentrated. Put another way, any substance will diffuse down its **concentration gradient**, the region along which the density of a chemical substance increases or decreases (in this case, decreases). No work must be done to make this happen; diffusion is a spontaneous process, needing no input of energy. Note that each substance diffuses down its *own* concentration gradient, unaffected by the concentration gradients of other substances **(Figure 7.10b)**.

Much of the traffic across cell membranes occurs by diffusion. When a substance is more concentrated on one side of a membrane than on the other, there is a tendency for the substance to diffuse across the membrane down its concentration gradient (assuming that the membrane is permeable to that substance). One important example is the uptake of oxygen by a cell performing cellular respiration. Dissolved oxygen diffuses into the cell across the plasma membrane. As long as cellular respiration consumes the O_2 as it enters, diffusion into the cell will continue because the concentration gradient favors movement in that direction.

The diffusion of a substance across a biological membrane is called **passive transport** because the cell does not have to expend energy to make it happen. The concentration gradient itself represents potential energy (see Concept 2.2 and Figure 9.5b) and drives diffusion. Remember, however, that membranes are selectively permeable and therefore have different effects on the rates of diffusion of various molecules. In the case of water, aquaporins allow water to diffuse very rapidly across the membranes of certain cells. As we'll see next, the movement of water across the plasma membrane has important consequences for cells.

Effects of Osmosis on Water Balance

To see how two solutions with different solute concentrations interact, picture a U-shaped glass tube with a selectively permeable artificial membrane separating two sugar solutions **(Figure 7.11)**. Pores in this synthetic membrane

Lower concentration of solute (sugar)   Higher concentration of solute   More similar concentrations of solute

Sugar molecule

H_2O

Selectively permeable membrane

Water molecules can pass through pores, but sugar molecules cannot.

Water molecules cluster around sugar molecules.

This side has fewer solute molecules, more free water molecules.

This side has more solute molecules, fewer free water molecules.

Osmosis

Water moves from an area of higher to lower free water concentration (lower to higher solute concentration).

▲ **Figure 7.11 Osmosis.** Two sugar solutions of different concentrations are separated by a membrane that the solvent (water) can pass through but the solute (sugar) cannot. Water molecules move randomly and may cross in either direction, but overall, water diffuses from the solution with less concentrated solute to that with more concentrated solute. This passive transport of water, or osmosis, makes the sugar concentrations on both sides more nearly equal. (The concentrations are prevented from being exactly equal due to the effect of water pressure on the higher side, which is not discussed here for simplicity.)

WHAT IF? *If an orange dye capable of passing through the membrane was added to the left side of the tube above, how would it be distributed at the end of the experiment? (See Figure 7.10.) Would the final solution levels in the tube be affected?*

are too small for sugar molecules to pass through but large enough for water molecules. However, tight clustering of water molecules around the hydrophilic solute molecules makes some of the water unavailable to cross the membrane. As a result, the solution with a higher solute concentration has a lower *free* water concentration. Water diffuses across the membrane from the region of higher free water concentration (lower solute concentration) to that of lower free water concentration (higher solute concentration) until the solute concentrations on both sides of the membrane are more nearly equal. The diffusion of free water across a selectively permeable membrane, whether artificial or cellular, is called **osmosis**. The movement of water across cell membranes and the balance of water between the cell and its environment are crucial to organisms. Let's now apply what we've learned in this system to living cells.

Water Balance of Cells Without Cell Walls

To explain the behavior of a cell in a solution, we must consider both solute concentration and membrane permeability. Both factors are taken into account in the concept of **tonicity**, the ability of a surrounding solution to cause a cell to gain or lose water. The tonicity of a solution depends in part on its concentration of solutes that cannot cross the membrane (nonpenetrating solutes) relative to that inside the cell. If there is a higher concentration of nonpenetrating solutes in the surrounding solution, water will tend to leave the cell, and vice versa.

If a cell without a cell wall, such as an animal cell, is immersed in an environment that is **isotonic** to the cell (*iso* means "same"), there will be no *net* movement of water across the plasma membrane. Water diffuses across the membrane, but at the same rate in both directions. In an isotonic environment, the volume of an animal cell is stable **(Figure 7.12a)**.

Let's transfer the cell to a solution that is **hypertonic** to the cell (*hyper* means "more," in this case referring to nonpenetrating solutes). The cell will lose water, shrivel, and probably die. This is why an increase in the salinity (saltiness) of a lake can kill the animals there; if the lake water becomes hypertonic to the animals' cells, they might shrivel and die. However, taking up too much water can be just as hazardous as losing water. If we place the cell in a solution that is **hypotonic** to the cell (*hypo* means "less"), water will enter the cell faster than it leaves, and the cell will swell and lyse (burst) like an overfilled water balloon.

A cell without rigid cell walls can tolerate neither excessive uptake nor excessive loss of water. This problem of water balance is automatically solved if such a cell lives in isotonic surroundings. Seawater is isotonic to many marine invertebrates. The cells of most terrestrial (land-dwelling) animals are bathed in an extracellular fluid that is isotonic to the cells. In hypertonic or hypotonic environments, however, organisms that lack rigid cell walls must have other adaptations for **osmoregulation**, the control of solute concentrations and water balance. For example, the unicellular protist *Paramecium caudatum* lives in pond water, which is hypotonic to the cell. *P. caudatum* has a plasma membrane that is much less permeable to water than the membranes of most other cells, but this only slows the uptake of water, which continually enters the cell. The *P. caudatum* cell doesn't burst because it is also equipped with a contractile vacuole, an organelle that functions as a bilge pump to force water out of the cell as fast as it enters by osmosis **(Figure 7.13)**.

Water Balance of Cells with Cell Walls

The cells of plants, prokaryotes, fungi, and some protists are surrounded by cell walls (see Figure 6.27). When such a cell is immersed in a hypotonic solution—bathed in rainwater, for example—the cell wall helps maintain the cell's water balance. Consider a plant cell. Like an animal cell, the plant cell swells as water enters by osmosis **(Figure 7.12b)**. However, the relatively inelastic cell wall will expand only so much before it exerts a back pressure on the cell, called *turgor pressure*, that opposes further water uptake. At this point, the cell is **turgid** (very firm), which is the healthy state for most plant cells. Plants that are not woody, such as

(a) Animal cell. An animal cell fares best in an isotonic environment unless it has special adaptations that offset the osmotic uptake or loss of water.

(b) Plant cell. Plant cells are turgid (firm) and generally healthiest in a hypotonic environment, where the uptake of water is eventually balanced by the wall pushing back on the cell.

Hypotonic solution	Isotonic solution	Hypertonic solution
Lysed	Normal	Shriveled
Turgid (normal)	Flaccid	Plasmolyzed

▲ **Figure 7.12 The water balance of living cells.** How living cells react to changes in the solute concentration of their environment depends on whether or not they have cell walls. **(a)** Animal cells, such as this red blood cell, do not have cell walls. **(b)** Plant cells do. (Arrows indicate net water movement after the cells were first placed in these solutions.)

Contractile vacuole

50 μm

▲ **Figure 7.13 The contractile vacuole of *Paramecium caudatum*.** The vacuole collects fluid from a system of canals in the cytoplasm. When full, the vacuole and canals contract, expelling fluid from the cell (LM).

most houseplants, depend for mechanical support on cells kept turgid by a surrounding hypotonic solution. If a plant's cells and their surroundings are isotonic, there is no net tendency for water to enter, and the cells become **flaccid** (limp).

However, a cell wall is of no advantage if the cell is immersed in a hypertonic environment. In this case, a plant cell, like an animal cell, will lose water to its surroundings and shrink. As the plant cell shrivels, its plasma membrane pulls away from the cell wall at multiple places. This phenomenon, called **plasmolysis**, causes the plant to wilt and can lead to plant death. The walled cells of bacteria and fungi also plasmolyze in hypertonic environments.

Facilitated Diffusion: Passive Transport Aided by Proteins

Let's look more closely at how water and certain hydrophilic solutes cross a membrane. As mentioned earlier, many polar molecules and ions impeded by the lipid bilayer of the membrane diffuse passively with the help of transport proteins that span the membrane. This phenomenon is called **facilitated diffusion**. Cell biologists are still trying to learn exactly how various transport proteins facilitate diffusion. Most transport proteins are very specific: They transport some substances but not others.

As mentioned earlier, the two types of transport proteins are channel proteins and carrier proteins. Channel proteins simply provide corridors that allow specific molecules or ions to cross the membrane **(Figure 7.14a)**. The hydrophilic passageways provided by these proteins can allow water molecules or small ions to diffuse very quickly from one side of the membrane to the other. Aquaporins, the water channel proteins, facilitate the massive amounts of diffusion that occur in plant cells and in animal cells such as red blood cells (see Figure 7.12). Certain kidney cells also have a high number of aquaporins, allowing them to reclaim water from urine before it is excreted. If the kidneys did not perform

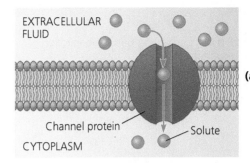

Channel protein
Solute
EXTRACELLULAR FLUID
CYTOPLASM

(a) A channel protein (purple) has a channel through which water molecules or a specific solute can pass.

Carrier protein
Solute

(b) A carrier protein alternates between two shapes, moving a solute across the membrane during the shape change.

▲ **Figure 7.14 Two types of transport proteins that carry out facilitated diffusion.** In both cases, the protein can transport the solute in either direction, but the net movement is down the concentration gradient of the solute.

this function, you would excrete about 180 L of urine per day—and have to drink an equal volume of water!

Channel proteins that transport ions are called **ion channels**. Many ion channels function as **gated channels**, which open or close in response to a stimulus. For some gated channels, the stimulus is electrical. In a nerve cell, for example, an ion channel opens in response to an electrical stimulus, allowing a stream of potassium ions to leave the cell. (See the orange ion in the center of the ion channel shown at the bottom left of the chapter-opening page.) This restores the cell's ability to fire again. Other gated channels open or close when a specific substance other than the one to be transported binds to the channel. These are also important in the functioning of the nervous system.

Carrier proteins, such as the glucose transporter mentioned earlier, seem to undergo a subtle change in shape that somehow translocates the solute-binding site across the membrane **(Figure 7.14b)**. Such a change in shape may be triggered by the binding and release of the transported molecule. Like ion channels, carrier proteins involved in facilitated diffusion result in the net movement of a substance down its concentration gradient. No energy input is thus required: This is passive transport. The Scientific Skills Exercise gives you an opportunity to work with data from an experiment related to glucose transport.

CONCEPT CHECK 7.3

1. How do you think a cell performing cellular respiration rids itself of the resulting CO_2?

2. **WHAT IF?** If a *Paramecium caudatum* swims from a hypotonic to an isotonic environment, will its contractile vacuole become more active or less? Why?

CONCEPT 7.4

Active transport uses energy to move solutes against their gradients

Despite the help of transport proteins, facilitated diffusion is considered passive transport because the solute is moving down its concentration gradient, a process that requires no energy. Facilitated diffusion speeds transport of a solute by providing efficient passage through the membrane, but it does not alter the direction of transport. Some other transport proteins, however, can move solutes against their concentration gradients, across the plasma membrane from the side where they are less concentrated (whether inside or outside) to the side where they are more concentrated.

The Need for Energy in Active Transport

To pump a solute across a membrane against its gradient requires work; the cell must expend energy. Therefore, this type of membrane traffic is called **active transport**. The transport proteins that move solutes against their concentration gradients are all carrier proteins rather than channel proteins. This makes sense because when channel proteins are open, they merely allow solutes to diffuse down their concentration gradients rather than picking them up and transporting them against their gradients.

Active transport enables a cell to maintain internal concentrations of small solutes that differ from concentrations in its environment. For example, compared with its surroundings, an animal cell has a much higher concentration of potassium ions (K^+) and a much lower concentration of sodium ions (Na^+). The plasma membrane helps maintain these steep gradients by pumping Na^+ out of the cell and K^+ into the cell.

As in other types of cellular work, ATP supplies the energy for most active transport. One way ATP can power active transport is by transferring its terminal phosphate group directly to the transport protein. This can induce the protein to change its shape in a manner that translocates a solute

---

SCIENTIFIC SKILLS EXERCISE

Interpreting a Scatter Plot with Two Sets of Data

Is Glucose Uptake into Cells Affected by Age? Glucose, an important energy source for animals, is transported into cells by facilitated diffusion using protein carriers. In this exercise, you will interpret a graph with two sets of data from an experiment that examined glucose uptake over time in red blood cells from guinea pigs of different ages. You will determine if the age of the guinea pigs affected their cells' rate of glucose uptake.

How the Experiment Was Done Researchers incubated guinea pig red blood cells in a 300 m*M* (millimolar) radioactive glucose solution at pH 7.4 at 25°C. Every 10 or 15 minutes, they removed a sample of cells and measured the concentration of radioactive glucose inside those cells. The cells came from either a 15-day-old or 1-month-old guinea pig.

Data from the Experiment When you have multiple sets of data, it can be useful to plot them on the same graph for comparison. In the graph here, each set of dots (of the same color) forms a *scatter plot*, in which every data point represents two numerical values, one for each variable. For each data set, a curve that best fits the points has been drawn to make it easier to see the trends.

Interpret the Data

1. First make sure you understand the parts of the graph. (a) Which variable is the independent variable—the variable controlled by the researchers? (b) Which variable is the dependent variable—the variable that depended on the treatment and was measured by the researchers? (c) What do the red dots represent? (d) the blue dots?

2. From the data points on the graph, construct a table of the data. Put "Incubation Time (min)" in the left column of the table.

Glucose Uptake Over Time in Guinea Pig Red Blood Cells

3. What does the graph show? Compare and contrast glucose uptake in red blood cells from 15-day-old and 1-month-old guinea pigs.

4. Develop a hypothesis to explain the difference between glucose uptake in red blood cells from 15-day-old and 1-month-old guinea pigs. (Think about how glucose gets into cells.)

5. Design an experiment to test your hypothesis.

MB A version of this Scientific Skills Exercise can be assigned in MasteringBiology.

Data from T. Kondo and E. Beutler, Developmental changes in glucose transport of guinea pig erythrocytes, *Journal of Clinical Investigation* 65:1–4 (1980).

► **Figure 7.15 The sodium-potassium pump: a specific case of active transport.** This transport system pumps ions against steep concentration gradients: Sodium ion concentration ([Na$^+$]) is high outside the cell and low inside, while potassium ion concentration ([K$^+$]) is low outside the cell and high inside. The pump oscillates between two shapes in a cycle that moves 3 Na$^+$ out of the cell for every 2 K$^+$ pumped into the cell. The two shapes have different affinities for Na$^+$ and K$^+$. ATP powers the shape change by transferring a phosphate group to the transport protein (phosphorylating the protein).

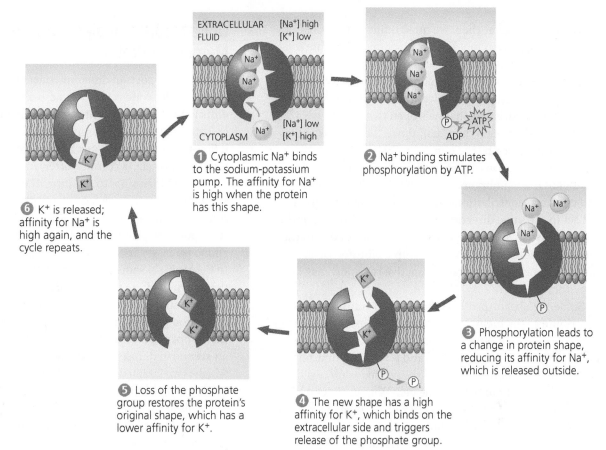

EXTRACELLULAR FLUID — [Na$^+$] high, [K$^+$] low

CYTOPLASM — [Na$^+$] low, [K$^+$] high

1 Cytoplasmic Na$^+$ binds to the sodium-potassium pump. The affinity for Na$^+$ is high when the protein has this shape.

2 Na$^+$ binding stimulates phosphorylation by ATP.

3 Phosphorylation leads to a change in protein shape, reducing its affinity for Na$^+$, which is released outside.

4 The new shape has a high affinity for K$^+$, which binds on the extracellular side and triggers release of the phosphate group.

5 Loss of the phosphate group restores the protein's original shape, which has a lower affinity for K$^+$.

6 K$^+$ is released; affinity for Na$^+$ is high again, and the cycle repeats.

bound to the protein across the membrane. One transport system that works this way is the **sodium-potassium pump**, which exchanges Na$^+$ for K$^+$ across the plasma membrane of animal cells **(Figure 7.15)**. The distinction between passive transport and active transport is reviewed in **Figure 7.16**.

How Ion Pumps Maintain Membrane Potential

All cells have voltages across their plasma membranes. Voltage is electrical potential energy—a separation of opposite charges. The cytoplasmic side of the membrane is negative in charge relative to the extracellular side because of an unequal distribution of anions and cations on the two sides. The voltage across a membrane, called a **membrane potential**, ranges from about −50 to −200 millivolts (mV). (The minus sign indicates that the inside of the cell is negative relative to the outside.)

The membrane potential acts like a battery, an energy source that affects the traffic of all charged substances across the membrane. Because the inside of the cell is negative compared with the outside, the membrane potential favors the passive transport of cations into the cell and anions out of the cell. Thus, *two* forces drive the diffusion of ions across a membrane: a chemical force (the ion's concentration gradient) and an electrical force (the effect of the membrane potential on the ion's movement). This combination of forces acting on an ion is called the **electrochemical gradient**.

▼ **Figure 7.16 Review: passive and active transport.**

Passive transport. Substances diffuse spontaneously down their concentration gradients, crossing a membrane with no expenditure of energy by the cell. The rate of diffusion can be greatly increased by transport proteins in the membrane.

Diffusion. Hydrophobic molecules and (at a slow rate) very small uncharged polar molecules can diffuse through the lipid bilayer.

Facilitated diffusion. Many hydrophilic substances diffuse through membranes with the assistance of transport proteins, either channel proteins (left) or carrier proteins (right).

Active transport. Some transport proteins act as pumps, moving substances across a membrane against their concentration (or electrochemical) gradients. Energy for this work is usually supplied by ATP.

? For each solute in the right panel, describe its direction of movement, and state whether it is going with or against its concentration gradient.

In the case of ions, then, we must refine our concept of passive transport: An ion diffuses not simply down its *concentration* gradient but, more exactly, down its *electrochemical* gradient. For example, the concentration of Na^+ inside a resting nerve cell is much lower than outside it. When the cell is stimulated, gated channels open that facilitate Na^+ diffusion. Sodium ions then "fall" down their electrochemical gradient, driven by the concentration gradient of Na^+ and by the attraction of these cations to the negative side (inside) of the membrane. In this example, both electrical and chemical contributions to the electrochemical gradient act in the same direction across the membrane, but this is not always so. In cases where electrical forces due to the membrane potential oppose the simple diffusion of an ion down its concentration gradient, active transport may be necessary.

Some membrane proteins that actively transport ions contribute to the membrane potential. An example is the sodium-potassium pump. Notice in Figure 7.15 that the pump does not translocate Na^+ and K^+ one for one, but pumps three sodium ions out of the cell for every two potassium ions it pumps into the cell. With each "crank" of the pump, there is a net transfer of one positive charge from the cytoplasm to the extracellular fluid, a process that stores energy as voltage. A transport protein that generates voltage across a membrane is called an **electrogenic pump**. The sodium-potassium pump appears to be the major electrogenic pump of animal cells. The main electrogenic pump of plants, fungi, and bacteria is a **proton pump**, which actively transports protons (hydrogen ions, H^+) out of the cell. The pumping of H^+ transfers positive charge from the cytoplasm to the extracellular solution (Figure 7.17). By generating voltage across membranes, electrogenic pumps help store energy that can be tapped for cellular work. One important use of proton gradients in the cell is for ATP synthesis during cellular respiration, as you will see in Chapter 10. Another is a type of membrane traffic called cotransport.

Cotransport: Coupled Transport by a Membrane Protein

A solute that exists in different concentrations across a membrane can do work as it moves across that membrane by diffusion down its concentration gradient. This is analogous to water that has been pumped uphill and performs work as it flows back down. In a mechanism called **cotransport**, a transport protein (a cotransporter) can couple the "downhill" diffusion of the solute to the "uphill" transport of a second substance against its own concentration gradient. For instance, a plant cell uses the gradient of H^+ generated by its ATP-powered proton pumps to drive the active transport of amino acids, sugars, and several other nutrients into the cell. In the example shown in **Figure 7.18,** a cotransporter couples the return of H^+ to the transport of sucrose into the cell. This protein can translocate sucrose into the cell against its concentration gradient, but only if the sucrose molecule travels in the company of an H^+. The H^+ uses the transport protein as an avenue to diffuse down its own electrochemical gradient, which is maintained by the proton pump. Plants use sucrose-H^+ cotransport to load sucrose produced by photosynthesis into cells in the veins of leaves. The vascular tissue of the plant can then distribute the sugar to nonphotosynthetic organs, such as roots.

What we know about cotransport proteins in animal cells has helped us find more effective treatments for diarrhea, a serious problem in developing countries. Normally, sodium in waste is reabsorbed in the colon, maintaining constant levels in the body, but diarrhea expels waste so rapidly that

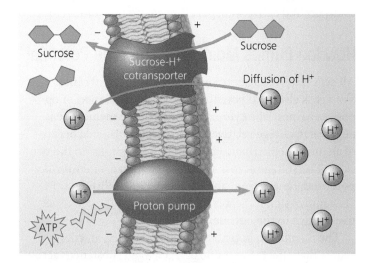

▲ **Figure 7.18 Cotransport: active transport driven by a concentration gradient.** A carrier protein, such as this sucrose-H^+ cotransporter in a plant cell (top), is able to use the diffusion of H^+ down its electrochemical gradient into the cell to drive the uptake of sucrose. (The cell wall is not shown.) Although not technically part of the cotransport process, an ATP-driven proton pump is shown here (bottom), which concentrates H^+ outside the cell. The resulting H^+ gradient represents potential energy that can be used for active transport—of sucrose, in this case. Thus, ATP indirectly provides the energy necessary for cotransport.

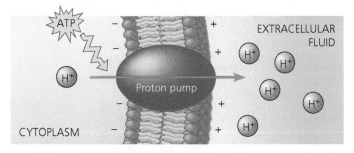

▲ **Figure 7.17 A proton pump.** Proton pumps are electrogenic pumps that store energy by generating voltage (charge separation) across membranes. A proton pump translocates positive charge in the form of hydrogen ions. The voltage and H^+ concentration gradient represent a dual energy source that can drive other processes, such as the uptake of nutrients. Most proton pumps are powered by ATP.

reabsorption is not possible, and sodium levels fall precipitously. To treat this life-threatening condition, patients are given a solution to drink containing high concentrations of salt (NaCl) and glucose. The solutes are taken up by sodium-glucose cotransporters on the surface of intestinal cells and passed through the cells into the blood. This simple treatment has lowered infant mortality worldwide.

CONCEPT CHECK 7.4

1. Sodium-potassium pumps help nerve cells establish a voltage across their plasma membranes. Do these pumps use ATP or produce ATP? Explain.

2. Explain why the sodium-potassium pump in Figure 7.15 would not be considered a cotransporter.

3. **MAKE CONNECTIONS** Review the characteristics of the lysosome in Concept 6.4. Given the internal environment of a lysosome, what transport protein might you expect to see in its membrane?

CONCEPT 7.5

Bulk transport across the plasma membrane occurs by exocytosis and endocytosis

Water and small solutes enter and leave the cell by diffusing through the lipid bilayer of the plasma membrane or by being pumped or moved across the membrane by transport proteins. However, large molecules—such as proteins and polysaccharides, as well as larger particles—generally cross the membrane in bulk, packaged in vesicles. Like active transport, these processes require energy.

Exocytosis

As seen in Chapter 6, the cell secretes certain molecules by the fusion of vesicles with the plasma membrane; this process is called **exocytosis**. A transport vesicle that has budded from the Golgi apparatus moves along microtubules of the cytoskeleton to the plasma membrane. When the vesicle membrane and plasma membrane come into contact, specific proteins rearrange the lipid molecules of the two bilayers so that the two membranes fuse. The contents of the vesicle spill out of the cell, and the vesicle membrane becomes part of the plasma membrane (see Figure 7.9, step 4).

Many secretory cells use exocytosis to export products. For example, cells in the pancreas that make insulin secrete it into the extracellular fluid by exocytosis. In another example, nerve cells use exocytosis to release neurotransmitters that signal other neurons or muscle cells. When plant cells are making cell walls, exocytosis delivers proteins and carbohydrates from Golgi vesicles to the outside of the cell.

Endocytosis

In **endocytosis**, the cell takes in molecules and particulate matter by forming new vesicles from the plasma membrane. Although the proteins involved in the processes are different, the events of endocytosis look like the reverse of exocytosis. First, a small area of the plasma membrane sinks inward to form a pocket. Then, as the pocket deepens, it pinches in, forming a vesicle containing material that had been outside the cell. Study **Figure 7.19** carefully to understand the three types of endocytosis: phagocytosis ("cellular eating"), pinocytosis ("cellular drinking"), and receptor-mediated endocytosis (which is considered a form of pinocytosis).

Human cells use receptor-mediated endocytosis to take in cholesterol for membrane synthesis and the synthesis of other steroids. Cholesterol travels in the blood in particles called low-density lipoproteins (LDLs), each a complex of lipids and a protein. LDLs bind to LDL receptors on plasma membranes and then enter the cells by endocytosis. (LDLs thus act as **ligands**, a term for any molecule that binds specifically to a receptor site on another molecule.) In the inherited disease familial hypercholesterolemia, characterized by a very high level of cholesterol in the blood, LDLs cannot enter cells because the LDL receptor proteins are defective or missing. Consequently, cholesterol accumulates in the blood, where it contributes to early atherosclerosis, the buildup of lipid deposits within the walls of blood vessels. This buildup narrows the space in the vessels and impedes blood flow, and can result in heart damage and stroke.

Vesicles not only transport substances to be released from the cell but also provide a mechanism for rejuvenating or remodeling the plasma membrane. Endocytosis and exocytosis occur continually in most eukaryotic cells, yet the amount of plasma membrane in a nongrowing cell remains fairly constant. The addition of membrane by one process appears to offset the loss of membrane by the other.

Energy and cellular work have figured prominently in our study of membranes. We have seen, for example, that active transport is powered by ATP. In the next three chapters, you will learn more about how cells acquire chemical energy to do the work of life.

CONCEPT CHECK 7.5

1. As a cell grows, its plasma membrane expands. Does this involve endocytosis or exocytosis? Explain.

2. **DRAW IT** Return to Figure 7.9, and circle a patch of plasma membrane that is coming from a vesicle involved in exocytosis.

3. **MAKE CONNECTIONS** In Concept 6.7, you learned that animal cells make an extracellular matrix (ECM). Describe the cellular pathway of synthesis and deposition of an ECM glycoprotein.

Phagocytosis

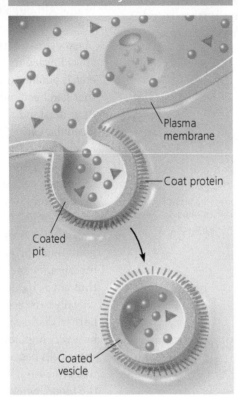

EXTRACELLULAR FLUID

Solutes

Pseudopodium

"Food" or other particle

Food vacuole

CYTOPLASM

In **phagocytosis**, a cell engulfs a particle by extending pseudopodia (singular, *pseudopodium*) around it and packaging it within a membranous sac called a food vacuole. The particle will be digested after the food vacuole fuses with a lysosome (see Figure 6.13a).

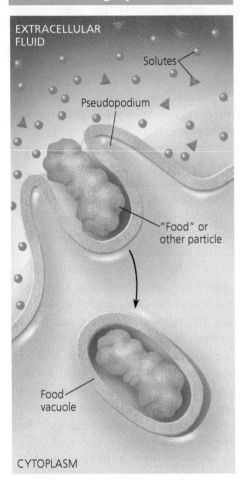

Pseudopodium of amoeba

Bacterium

Food vacuole

1 μm

An amoeba engulfing a bacterium via phago-cytosis (TEM).

Pinocytosis

Plasma membrane

Coat protein

Coated pit

Coated vesicle

In **pinocytosis**, a cell continually "gulps" droplets of extracellular fluid into tiny vesicles, formed by infoldings of the plasma membrane. In this way, the cell obtains molecules dissolved in the droplets. Because any and all solutes are taken into the cell, pinocytosis as shown here is nonspecific for the substances it transports. In many cases, as above, the parts of the plasma membrane that form vesicles are lined on their cytoplasmic side by a fuzzy layer of coat protein; the "pits" and resulting vesicles are said to be "coated."

0.25 μm

Pinocytotic vesicles forming (TEMs).

Receptor-Mediated Endocytosis

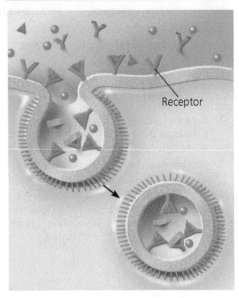

Receptor

Receptor-mediated endocytosis is a specialized type of pinocytosis that enables the cell to acquire bulk quantities of specific substances, even though those substances may not be very concentrated in the extracellular fluid. Embedded in the plasma membrane are proteins with receptor sites exposed to the extracellular fluid. Specific solutes bind to the sites. The receptor proteins then cluster in coated pits, and each coated pit forms a vesicle containing the bound molecules. Notice that there are relatively more bound molecules (purple triangles) inside the vesicle, but other molecules (green balls) are also present. After the ingested material is liberated from the vesicle, the emptied receptors are recycled to the plasma membrane by the same vesicle (not shown).

Plasma membrane

Coat protein

0.25 μm

Top: A coated pit. *Bottom*: A coated vesicle forming during receptor-mediated endocytosis (TEMs).

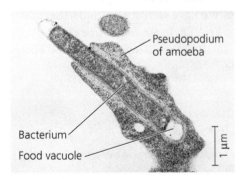

CONCEPT 7.1

Cellular membranes are fluid mosaics of lipids and proteins (pp. 125–129)

- In the **fluid mosaic model**, **amphipathic** proteins are embedded in the phospholipid bilayer. Proteins with related functions often cluster in patches.
- Phospholipids and some proteins move laterally within the membrane. The unsaturated hydrocarbon tails of some phospholipids keep membranes fluid at lower temperatures, while cholesterol helps membranes resist changes in fluidity caused by temperature changes. Differences in membrane lipid composition, as well as the ability to change lipid composition, are evolutionary adaptations that ensure membrane fluidity.
- **Integral proteins** are embedded in the lipid bilayer; **peripheral proteins** are attached to the membrane surface. The functions of membrane proteins include transport, enzymatic activity, signal transduction, cell-cell recognition, intercellular joining, and attachment to the cytoskeleton and extracellular matrix. Short chains of sugars linked to proteins (in **glycoproteins**) and lipids (in **glycolipids**) on the exterior side of the plasma membrane interact with surface molecules of other cells.
- Membrane proteins and lipids are synthesized in the ER and modified in the ER and Golgi apparatus. The inside and outside faces of membranes differ in molecular composition.

> [?] *In what ways are membranes crucial to life?*

CONCEPT 7.2

Membrane structure results in selective permeability (pp. 129–130)

- A cell must exchange molecules and ions with its surroundings, a process controlled by the **selective permeability** of the plasma membrane. Hydrophobic substances are soluble in lipids and pass through membranes rapidly, whereas polar molecules and ions generally require specific **transport proteins** to cross the membrane.

> [?] *How do **aquaporins** affect the permeability of a membrane?*

CONCEPT 7.3

Passive transport is diffusion of a substance across a membrane with no energy investment (pp. 130–134)

- **Diffusion** is the spontaneous movement of a substance down its **concentration gradient**. Water diffuses out through the permeable membrane of a cell (**osmosis**) if the solution outside has a higher solute concentration (**hypertonic**) than the cytosol; water enters the cell if the solution has a lower solute concentration (**hypotonic**). If the concentrations are equal (**isotonic**), no net osmosis occurs. Cell survival depends on balancing water uptake and loss. Cells lacking cell walls (as in animals and some protists) are isotonic with their environments or have adaptations for **osmoregulation**. Plants, prokaryotes, fungi, and some protists have relatively inelastic cell walls, so the cells don't burst in a hypotonic environment.

- In a type of **passive transport** called **facilitated diffusion**, a transport protein speeds the movement of water or a solute across a membrane down its concentration gradient. **Ion channels**, some of which are **gated channels**, facilitate the diffusion of ions across a membrane. Carrier proteins can undergo changes in shape that translocate bound solutes across the membrane.

Passive transport: Facilitated diffusion

Channel protein

Carrier protein

> [?] *What happens to a cell placed in a hypertonic solution? Describe the free water concentration inside and out.*

CONCEPT 7.4

Active transport uses energy to move solutes against their gradients (pp. 134–137)

- Specific membrane proteins use energy, usually in the form of ATP, to do the work of **active transport**. One example of such a protein is the **sodium-potassium pump**.
- Ions can have both a concentration (chemical) gradient and an electrical gradient (voltage). These gradients combine in the **electrochemical gradient**, which determines the net direction of ionic diffusion. **Electrogenic pumps**, such as the sodium-potassium pump and **proton pumps**, are transport proteins that contribute to electrochemical gradients.
- **Cotransport** of two solutes occurs when a membrane protein enables the "downhill" diffusion of one solute to drive the "uphill" transport of the other.

Active transport

ATP

> [?] *ATP is not directly involved in the functioning of a cotransporter. Why, then, is cotransport considered active transport?*

CONCEPT 7.5

Bulk transport across the plasma membrane occurs by exocytosis and endocytosis (pp. 137–138)

- In **exocytosis**, transport vesicles migrate to the plasma membrane, fuse with it, and release their contents. In **endocytosis**, molecules enter cells within vesicles that pinch inward from the plasma membrane. The three types of endocytosis are **phagocytosis**, **pinocytosis**, and **receptor-mediated endocytosis**.

> [?] *Which type of endocytosis involves ligands? What does this type of transport enable a cell to do?*

LEVEL 1: KNOWLEDGE/COMPREHENSION

1. In what way do the membranes of a eukaryotic cell vary?
   a. Phospholipids are found only in certain membranes.
   b. Certain proteins are unique to each membrane.
   c. Only certain membranes of the cell are selectively permeable.
   d. Only certain membranes are constructed from amphipathic molecules.

2. According to the fluid mosaic model of membrane structure, proteins of the membrane are mostly
   a. spread in a continuous layer over the inner and outer surfaces of the membrane.
   b. confined to the hydrophobic interior of the membrane.
   c. embedded in a lipid bilayer.
   d. randomly oriented in the membrane, with no fixed inside-outside polarity.

3. Which of the following factors would tend to increase membrane fluidity?
   a. a greater proportion of unsaturated phospholipids
   b. a greater proportion of saturated phospholipids
   c. a lower temperature
   d. a relatively high protein content in the membrane

LEVEL 2: APPLICATION/ANALYSIS

4. Which of the following processes includes all the others?
   a. osmosis
   b. diffusion of a solute across a membrane
   c. passive transport
   d. transport of an ion down its electrochemical gradient

5. Based on Figure 7.18, which of these experimental treatments would increase the rate of sucrose transport into a plant cell?
   a. decreasing extracellular sucrose concentration
   b. decreasing extracellular pH
   c. decreasing cytoplasmic pH
   d. adding a substance that makes the membrane more permeable to hydrogen ions

6. **DRAW IT** An artificial "cell" consisting of an aqueous solution enclosed in a selectively permeable membrane is immersed in a beaker containing a different solution, the "environment," as shown below. The membrane is permeable to water and to the simple sugars glucose and fructose but impermeable to the disaccharide sucrose.
   a. Draw solid arrows to indicate the net movement of solutes into and/or out of the cell.
   b. Is the solution outside the cell isotonic, hypotonic, or hypertonic?
   c. Draw a dashed arrow to show the net osmosis, if any.
   d. Will the artificial cell become more flaccid, more turgid, or stay the same?
   e. Eventually, will the two solutions have the same or different solute concentrations?

"Cell"
0.03 M sucrose
0.02 M glucose

"Environment"
0.01 M sucrose
0.01 M glucose
0.01 M fructose

LEVEL 3: SYNTHESIS/EVALUATION

7. **EVOLUTION CONNECTION**
   Paramecium and other protists that live in hypotonic environments have cell membranes that limit water uptake, while those living in isotonic environments have membranes that are more permeable to water. What adaptations might have evolved in protists in hypertonic habitats such as the Great Salt Lake? In habitats with changing salt concentration?

8. **SCIENTIFIC INQUIRY**
   An experiment is designed to study the mechanism of sucrose uptake by plant cells. Cells are immersed in a sucrose solution, and the pH of the solution is monitored. Samples of the cells are taken at intervals, and their sucrose concentration is measured. After a decrease in the pH of the solution to a steady, slightly acidic level, sucrose uptake begins. Propose a hypothesis for these results. What do you think would happen if an inhibitor of ATP regeneration by the cell were added to the beaker once the pH was at a steady level? Explain.

9. **SCIENCE, TECHNOLOGY, AND SOCIETY**
   Extensive irrigation in arid regions causes salts to accumulate in the soil. (When water evaporates, salts that were dissolved in the water are left behind in the soil.) Based on what you learned about water balance in plant cells, explain why increased soil salinity (saltiness) might be harmful to crops.

10. **WRITE ABOUT A THEME: INTERACTIONS**
    A human pancreatic cell obtains O_2, and necessary molecules such as glucose, amino acids, and cholesterol, from its environment, and it releases CO_2 as a waste product. In response to hormonal signals, the cell secretes digestive enzymes. It also regulates its ion concentrations by exchange with its environment. Based on what you have just learned about the structure and function of cellular membranes, write a short essay (100–150 words) that describes how such a cell accomplishes these interactions with its environment.

11. SYNTHESIZE YOUR KNOWLEDGE

In the supermarket, lettuce and other produce is often sprayed with water. Explain why this makes vegetables crisp.

MasteringBiology®

Students Go to **MasteringBiology** for assignments, the eText, and the Study Area with practice tests, animations, and activities.

Instructors Go to **MasteringBiology** for automatically graded tutorials and questions that you can assign to your students, plus Instructor Resources.

8

Cell Communication

KEY CONCEPTS

8.1 External signals are converted to responses within the cell

8.2 Reception: A signaling molecule binds to a receptor protein, causing it to change shape

8.3 Transduction: Cascades of molecular interactions relay signals from receptors to target molecules in the cell

8.4 Response: Cell signaling leads to regulation of transcription or cytoplasmic activities

8.5 Apoptosis integrates multiple cell-signaling pathways

▲ **Figure 8.1 How does cell signaling trigger the desperate flight of this impala?**

Cellular Messaging

The impala in **Figure 8.1** flees for its life, racing to escape the predatory cheetah nipping at its heels. The impala is breathing rapidly, its heart pounding and its legs pumping furiously. These physiological functions are all part of the impala's "fight-or-flight" response, driven by hormones released from its adrenal glands at times of stress—in this case, upon sensing the cheetah. What systems of cell-to-cell communication allow the trillions of cells in the impala to "talk" to each other, coordinating their activities?

Cells can signal to each other and interpret the signals they receive from other cells and the environment. The signals may include light and touch, but are most often chemicals. The flight response shown here is triggered by a signaling molecule called epinephrine (also called adrenaline; see the model to the left). Studying cell communication, biologists have discovered ample evidence for the evolutionary relatedness of all life. The same small set of cell-signaling mechanisms shows up again and again in diverse species, in processes ranging from bacterial signaling to embryonic development to cancer. In this chapter, we focus on the main mechanisms by which cells receive, process, and respond to chemical signals sent from other cells. We will also consider *apoptosis*, a type of programmed cell death that integrates input from multiple signaling pathways.

▶ **Epinephrine**

External signals are converted to responses within the cell

What does a "talking" cell say to a "listening" cell, and how does the latter cell respond to the message? Let's approach these questions by first looking at communication among microorganisms.

Evolution of Cell Signaling

EVOLUTION One topic of cell "conversation" is sex. Cells of the yeast *Saccharomyces cerevisiae*—which are used to make bread, wine, and beer—identify their mates by chemical signaling. There are two sexes, or mating types, called **a** and **α** (Figure 8.2). Each type secretes a specific factor that binds to receptors only on the other type of cell. When exposed to each other's mating factors, a pair of cells of opposite type change shape, grow toward each other, and fuse (mate). The new **a/α** cell contains all the genes of both original cells, a combination of genetic resources that provides advantages to the cell's descendants, which arise by subsequent cell divisions.

Once received by the yeast cell surface receptor, a mating signal is changed, or *transduced*, into a form that brings

about the cellular response of mating. This occurs in a series of steps called a *signal transduction pathway*. Many such pathways exist in both yeast and animal cells. In fact, the molecular details of signal transduction in yeasts and mammals are strikingly similar, even though their last common ancestor lived over a billion years ago. This suggests that early versions of cell-signaling mechanisms evolved well before the first multicellular creatures appeared on Earth.

Scientists think that signaling mechanisms first evolved in ancient prokaryotes and single-celled eukaryotes and then were adopted for new uses by their multicellular descendants. Cell signaling is critical in the microbial world (Figure 8.3). Bacterial cells secrete molecules that can be detected by other bacterial cells. Sensing the concentration of such signaling molecules allows bacteria to monitor the local density of cells, a phenomenon called *quorum sensing*. Quorum sensing allows bacterial populations to coordinate their behaviors in activities that require a given number

① **Exchange of mating factors.** Each cell type secretes a mating factor that binds to receptors on the other cell type.

Receptor

α factor

a

α

Yeast cell, mating type **a**

a factor

Yeast cell, mating type **α**

② **Mating.** Binding of the factors to receptors induces changes in the cells that lead to their fusion.

a

α

③ **New a/α cell.** The nucleus of the fused cell includes all the genes from the **a** and **α** cells.

a/α

▲ **Figure 8.2 Communication between mating yeast cells.** *Saccharomyces cerevisiae* cells use chemical signaling to identify cells of opposite mating type and initiate the mating process. The two mating types and their corresponding chemical signaling molecules, or mating factors, are called **a** and **α**.

① Individual rod-shaped cells

0.5 mm

② Aggregation in progress

2.5 mm

③ Spore-forming structure (fruiting body)

Fruiting bodies

▲ **Figure 8.3 Communication among bacteria.** Soil-dwelling bacteria called myxobacteria ("slime bacteria") use chemical signals to share information about nutrient availability. When food is scarce, starving cells secrete a molecule that stimulates neighboring cells to aggregate. The cells form a structure, called a fruiting body, that produces thick-walled spores capable of surviving until the environment improves. The bacteria shown here are *Myxococcus xanthus* (steps 1–3, SEMs; lower photo, LM).

of cells acting synchronously. One example is formation of a *biofilm*, an aggregation of bacterial cells adhered to a surface. The cells in the biofilm generally derive nutrition from the surface they are on. You have probably encountered biofilms many times, perhaps without realizing it. The slimy coating on a fallen log or on leaves lying on a forest path, and even the film on your teeth each morning, are examples of bacterial biofilms. (In fact, tooth-brushing disrupts biofilms that would otherwise cause cavities.) The formation of biofilms requires a sophisticated communication system, the basis of which is cell signaling.

Local and Long-Distance Signaling

Like bacteria or yeast cells, cells in a multicellular organism usually communicate via signaling molecules targeted for cells that may or may not be immediately adjacent. As we saw in Chapters 6 and 7, eukaryotic cells may communicate by direct contact, one type of local signaling (Figure 8.4). Both animals and plants have cell junctions that, where present, directly connect the cytoplasms of adjacent cells (Figure 8.4a). In these cases, signaling substances dissolved in the cytosol can pass freely between adjacent cells. Moreover, animal cells may communicate via direct contact between membrane-bound cell-surface molecules in a process called cell-cell recognition (Figure 8.4b). This sort of local signaling is especially important in embryonic development and the immune response.

In many other cases of local signaling, messenger molecules are secreted by the signaling cell. Some of these travel only short distances; such local regulators influence cells in the vicinity. One class of local regulators in animals, *growth factors*, are compounds that stimulate nearby target cells to grow and divide. Numerous cells can simultaneously receive and respond to the molecules of growth factor produced by a single cell in their vicinity. This type of local signaling in animals is called *paracrine signaling* (Figure 8.5a).

Another, more specialized type of local signaling called *synaptic signaling* occurs in the animal nervous system (Figure 8.5b). An electrical signal along a nerve cell triggers the secretion of neurotransmitter molecules. These molecules act as chemical signals, diffusing across the synapse—the narrow space between the nerve cell and its target cell—triggering a response in the target cell.

Beyond communication through plasmodesmata (plant cell junctions), local signaling in plants is not as well understood. Because of their cell walls, plants use mechanisms different from those operating locally in animals.

Both animals and plants use chemicals called **hormones** for long-distance signaling. In hormonal signaling in animals, also known as *endocrine signaling*, specialized cells release hormone molecules, which travel via the circulatory system to other parts of the body, where they reach target cells that can recognize and respond to the hormones (Figure 8.5c). Plant hormones (often called *plant growth regulators*) sometimes travel in vessels but more often reach their targets by moving through cells or by diffusing through the air as a gas. Hormones vary widely in size and type, as do local regulators. For instance, the plant hormone ethylene, a gas that promotes fruit ripening and helps regulate growth, is a hydrocarbon of only six atoms (C_2H_4), small enough to pass through cell walls. In contrast, the mammalian hormone insulin, which regulates sugar levels in the blood, is a protein with thousands of atoms.

What happens when a cell encounters a secreted signaling molecule? The ability of a cell to respond is determined by whether it has a specific receptor molecule that can bind to the signaling molecule. The information conveyed by this binding, the signal, must then be changed into another form—transduced—inside the cell before the cell can respond. The remainder of the chapter discusses this process, primarily as it occurs in animal cells.

Plasma membranes — Cell wall

Gap junctions between animal cells

Plasmodesmata between plant cells

(a) Cell junctions. Both animals and plants have cell junctions that allow molecules to pass readily between adjacent cells without crossing plasma membranes.

(b) Cell-cell recognition. Two cells in an animal may communicate by interaction between molecules protruding from their surfaces.

▲ **Figure 8.4 Communication by direct contact between cells.**

The Three Stages of Cell Signaling: *A Preview*

Our current understanding of how chemical messengers act via signal transduction pathways had its origins in the pioneering work of Earl W. Sutherland, whose research led to a Nobel Prize in 1971. Sutherland and his colleagues at Vanderbilt University were investigating how the animal hormone epinephrine (adrenaline) stimulates the breakdown of the storage polysaccharide glycogen within liver cells and skeletal muscle cells. Glycogen breakdown releases the sugar glucose 1-phosphate, which the cell converts

Local signaling

Target cells

Secreting cell

Secretory vesicles

Local regulator

(a) Paracrine signaling. A secreting cell acts on nearby target cells by secreting molecules of a local regulator (a growth factor, for example).

Electrical signal triggers release of neurotransmitter.

Neurotransmitter diffuses across synapse.

Target cell

(b) Synaptic signaling. A nerve cell releases neurotransmitter molecules into a synapse, stimulating the target cell, such as a muscle or nerve cell.

Long-distance signaling

Endocrine cell

Target cell specifically binds hormone.

Hormone travels in bloodstream.

Blood vessel

(c) Endocrine (hormonal) signaling. Specialized endocrine cells secrete hormones into body fluids, often blood. Hormones reach virtually all body cells, but are bound only by some cells.

▲ **Figure 8.5 Local and long-distance cell signaling by secreted molecules in animals.** In both local and long-distance signaling, only specific target cells that can recognize a given signaling molecule will respond to it.

to glucose 6-phosphate. The liver or muscle cell can then use this compound, an early intermediate in glycolysis, for energy production. Alternatively, the compound can be stripped of phosphate and released from the cell into the blood as glucose, which can fuel cells throughout the body. Thus, one effect of epinephrine is the mobilization of fuel reserves, which can be used by the animal to either defend itself (fight) or escape whatever elicited a scare (flight). (The impala in Figure 8.1 is obviously engaged in the latter.)

Sutherland's research team discovered that epinephrine stimulates glycogen breakdown by somehow activating a cytosolic enzyme, glycogen phosphorylase. However, when epinephrine was added to a test-tube mixture containing the enzyme and its substrate, glycogen, no breakdown occurred. Glycogen phosphorylase could be activated by epinephrine only when the hormone was added to *intact* cells

in a solution. This result told Sutherland two things. First, epinephrine does not interact directly with the enzyme responsible for glycogen breakdown; an intermediate step or series of steps must be occurring inside the cell. Second, the plasma membrane itself is necessary for transmission of the signal to take place.

Sutherland's early work suggested that the process going on at the receiving end of a cellular conversation can be dissected into three stages: reception, transduction, and response **(Figure 8.6)**:

❶ **Reception.** Reception is the target cell's detection of a signaling molecule coming from outside the cell. A chemical signal is "detected" when the signaling molecule binds to a receptor protein located at the cell's surface (or inside the cell, to be discussed later).

▶ **Figure 8.6 Overview of cell signaling.** From the perspective of the cell receiving the message, cell signaling can be divided into three stages: signal reception, signal transduction, and cellular response. When reception occurs at the plasma membrane, as shown here, the transduction stage is usually a pathway of several steps, with each specific relay molecule in the pathway bringing about a change in the next molecule. The final molecule in the pathway triggers the cell's response.

? *How does the epinephrine in Sutherland's experiment fit into this diagram of cell signaling?*

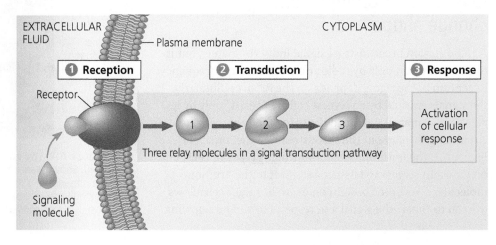

EXTRACELLULAR FLUID

CYTOPLASM

Plasma membrane

❶ **Reception**

❷ **Transduction**

❸ **Response**

Receptor

1 → 2 → 3

Three relay molecules in a signal transduction pathway

Activation of cellular response

Signaling molecule

② Transduction. The binding of the signaling molecule changes the receptor protein in some way, initiating the process of transduction. The transduction stage converts the signal to a form that can bring about a specific cellular response. In Sutherland's system, the binding of epinephrine to a receptor protein in a liver cell's plasma membrane leads to activation of glycogen phosphorylase. Transduction sometimes occurs in a single step but more often requires a sequence of changes in a series of different molecules—a **signal transduction pathway**. The molecules in the pathway are often called relay molecules.

③ Response. In the third stage of cell signaling, the transduced signal finally triggers a specific cellular response. The response may be almost any imaginable cellular activity—such as catalysis by an enzyme (for example, glycogen phosphorylase), rearrangement of the cytoskeleton, or activation of specific genes in the nucleus. The cell-signaling process helps ensure that crucial activities like these occur in the right cells, at the right time, and in proper coordination with the activities of other cells of the organism. We'll now explore the mechanisms of cell signaling in more detail, including a discussion of regulation and termination of the process.

CONCEPT CHECK 8.1

1. Explain how signaling is involved in ensuring that yeast cells fuse only with cells of the opposite mating type.

2. In liver cells, glycogen phosphorylase acts in which of the three stages of the signaling pathway associated with an epinephrine-initiated signal?

3. **WHAT IF?** When epinephrine is mixed with glycogen phosphorylase and glycogen in a test tube, is glucose 1-phosphate generated? Why or why not?

CONCEPT 8.2

Reception: A signaling molecule binds to a receptor protein, causing it to change shape

A radio station broadcasts its signal indiscriminately, but it can be picked up only by radios tuned to the right frequency: Reception of the signal depends on the receiver. Similarly, the signals emitted by an **a** yeast cell are "heard" only by its prospective mates, **α** cells. In the case of the epinephrine circulating throughout the bloodstream of the impala in Figure 8.1, the hormone encounters many types of cells, but only certain target cells detect and react to the hormone molecule. A receptor protein on or in the target cell allows the cell to "hear" the signal and respond to it. The signaling

molecule is complementary in shape to a specific site on the receptor and attaches there, like a key in a lock. The signaling molecule acts as a **ligand**, the term for a molecule that specifically binds to another molecule, often a larger one. Ligand binding generally causes a receptor protein to undergo a change in shape. For many receptors, this shape change directly activates the receptor, enabling it to interact with other cellular molecules. For other kinds of receptors, the immediate effect of ligand binding is to cause the aggregation of two or more receptor molecules, which leads to further molecular events inside the cell. Most signal receptors are plasma membrane proteins, but others are located inside the cell. We discuss both of these types next.

Receptors in the Plasma Membrane

Cell-surface receptor proteins play crucial roles in the biological systems of animals. The largest family of human cell surface receptors are the nearly 1,000 G protein-coupled receptors (GPCRs); an example is shown in **(Figure 8.7)**.

Most water-soluble signaling molecules bind to specific sites on transmembrane receptor proteins that transmit information from the extracellular environment to the inside of the cell. We can see how cell-surface transmembrane receptors work by looking at three major types: G protein-coupled receptors (GPCRs), receptor tyrosine kinases, and ion channel receptors. These receptors are discussed and illustrated in **Figure 8.8**; study this figure before going on.

Given the many important functions of cell-surface receptors, it is not surprising that their malfunctions are associated with many human diseases, including cancer, heart disease, and asthma. To better understand and treat these conditions, a major focus of both university research teams and the pharmaceutical industry has been to analyze the structure of these receptors.

▲ **Figure 8.7 The structure of a G protein-coupled receptor (GPCR).** Shown here is a model of the human β₂-adrenergic receptor in the presence of a molecule mimicking the natural ligand (green in the model) and cholesterol (orange). Two receptor molecules (blue) are shown as ribbon models in a side view within the plasma membrane.

Exploring Cell-Surface Transmembrane Receptors

G Protein-Coupled Receptors

Signaling molecule binding site

Segment that interacts with G proteins

G protein-coupled receptor

A **G protein-coupled receptor** (GPCR) is a cell-surface transmembrane receptor that works with the help of a **G protein**, a protein that binds the energy-rich molecule GTP. Many different signaling molecules—including yeast mating factors, epinephrine (adrenaline) and many other hormones, as well as neurotransmitters—use GPCRs. These receptors vary in the binding sites for their signaling molecules (often referred to as their ligands) and also for different types of G proteins inside the cell. Nevertheless, GPCR proteins are all remarkably similar in structure. In fact, they make up a large family of eukaryotic receptor proteins with a secondary structure in which the single polypeptide, represented here in a ribbon model, has seven transmembrane α helices, outlined with cylinders and depicted in a row for clarity. Specific loops between the helices (here, the loops on the right) form binding sites for signaling molecules (outside the cell) and G proteins (on the cytoplasmic side).

GPCR-based signaling systems are extremely widespread and diverse in their functions, including roles in embryonic development and sensory reception. In humans, for example, vision, smell, and taste depend on GPCRs. Similarities in structure in G proteins and GPCRs in diverse organisms suggest that G proteins and their associated receptors evolved very early among eukaryotes.

Malfunctions of the associated G proteins themselves are involved in many human diseases, including bacterial infections. The bacteria that cause cholera, pertussis (whooping cough), and botulism, among others, make their victims ill by producing toxins that interfere with G protein function. Pharmacologists now realize that up to 60% of all medicines used today exert their effects by influencing G protein pathways.

1 Loosely attached to the cytoplasmic side of the membrane, the G protein functions as a molecular switch that is either on or off, depending on which of two guanine nucleotides is attached, GDP or GTP—hence the term *G protein*. (GTP, or guanosine triphosphate, is similar to ATP.) When GDP is bound to the G protein, as shown above, the G protein is inactive. The receptor and G protein work together with another protein, usually an enzyme.

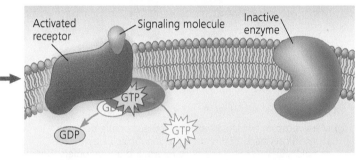

2 When the appropriate signaling molecule binds to the extracellular side of the receptor, the receptor is activated and changes shape. Its cytoplasmic side then binds an inactive G protein, causing a GTP to displace the GDP. This activates the G protein.

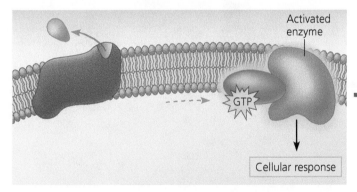

3 The activated G protein dissociates from the receptor, diffuses along the membrane, and then binds to an enzyme, altering the enzyme's shape and activity. Once activated, the enzyme can trigger the next step leading to a cellular response. Binding of signaling molecules is reversible: Like other ligands, they bind and dissociate many times. The ligand concentration outside the cell determines how often a ligand is bound and causes signaling.

4 The changes in the enzyme and G protein are only temporary because the G protein also functions as a GTPase enzyme—in other words, it then hydrolyzes its bound GTP to GDP and P_i. Now inactive again, the G protein leaves the enzyme, which returns to its original state. The G protein is now available for reuse. The GTPase function of the G protein allows the pathway to shut down rapidly when the signaling molecule is no longer present.

Continued on next page

Exploring Cell-Surface Transmembrane Receptors

Receptor Tyrosine Kinases

Receptor tyrosine kinases (RTKs) belong to a major class of plasma membrane receptors characterized by having enzymatic activity. A kinase is any enzyme that catalyzes the transfer of phosphate groups. The part of the receptor protein extending into the cytoplasm functions more specifically as a tyrosine kinase, an enzyme that catalyzes the transfer of a phosphate group from ATP to the amino acid tyrosine on a substrate protein. Thus, RTKs are membrane receptors that attach phosphates to tyrosines.

One RTK may activate ten or more different transduction pathways and cellular responses. Often, more than one signal transduction pathway can be triggered at once, helping the cell regulate and coordinate many aspects of cell growth and cell reproduction. The ability of a single ligand-binding event to trigger so many pathways is a key difference between RTKs and GPCRs, which activate a single transduction pathway. Abnormal RTKs that function even in the absence of signaling molecules are associated with many kinds of cancer.

① Many receptor tyrosine kinases have the structure depicted schematically here. Before the signaling molecule binds, the receptors exist as individual units referred to as monomers. Notice that each has an extracellular ligand-binding site, an α helix spanning the membrane, and an intracellular tail containing multiple tyrosines.

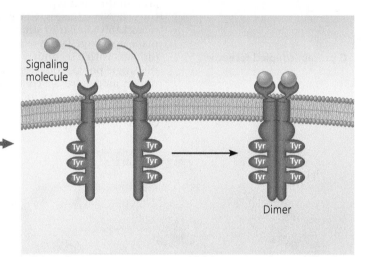

② The binding of a signaling molecule (such as a growth factor) causes two receptor monomers to associate closely with each other, forming a complex known as a dimer in a process called dimerization (In some cases, larger clusters form. The details of monomer association are a focus of current research.)

③ Dimerization activates the tyrosine kinase region of each monomer; each tyrosine kinase adds a phosphate from an ATP molecule to a tyrosine on the tail of the other monomer.

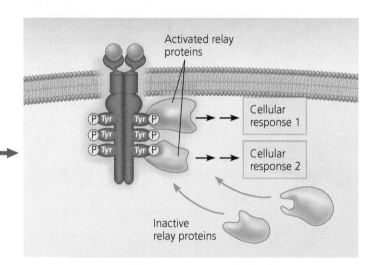

④ Now that the receptor is fully activated, it is recognized by specific relay proteins inside the cell. Each such protein binds to a specific phosphorylated tyrosine, undergoing a resulting structural change that activates the bound protein. Each activated protein triggers a transduction pathway, leading to a cellular response.

Ion Channel Receptors

A **ligand-gated ion channel** is a type of membrane receptor containing a region that can act as a "gate" when the receptor changes shape. When a signaling molecule binds as a ligand to the receptor protein, the gate opens or closes, allowing or blocking the flow of specific ions, such as Na^+ or Ca^{2+}, through a channel in the receptor. Like the other receptors we have discussed, these proteins bind the ligand at a specific site on their extracellular sides.

1 Here we show a ligand-gated ion channel receptor in which the gate remains closed until a ligand binds to the receptor.

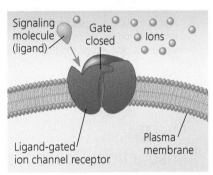

2 When the ligand binds to the receptor and the gate opens, specific ions can flow through the channel and rapidly change the concentration of that particular ion inside the cell. This change may directly affect the activity of the cell in some way.

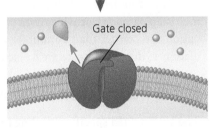

3 When the ligand dissociates from this receptor, the gate closes and ions no longer enter the cell.

Ligand-gated ion channels are very important in the nervous system. For example, the neurotransmitter molecules released at a synapse between two nerve cells (see Figure 10.5b) bind as ligands to ion channels on the receiving cell, causing the channels to open. Ions flow in (or, in some cases, out), triggering an electrical signal that propagates down the length of the receiving cell. Some gated ion channels are controlled by electrical signals instead of ligands; these voltage-gated ion channels are also crucial to the functioning of the nervous system. Some ion channels are present on membranes of organelles, such as the ER.

MAKE CONNECTIONS *Is the flow of ions through a ligand-gated channel an example of active or passive transport? (Review Concepts 7.3 and 7.4.)*

Although cell-surface receptors represent 30% of all human proteins, determining their structures has proved challenging: They make up only 1% of the proteins whose structures have been determined by X-ray crystallography (see Figure 5.22). For one thing, cell-surface receptors tend to be flexible and inherently unstable, thus difficult to crystallize. It took years of persistent efforts for researchers to determine the first few of these structures, such as the GPCR shown in Figure 8.7. In that case, the β-adrenergic receptor was stable enough to be crystallized while it was among membrane molecules, in the presence of its ligand.

Abnormal functioning of receptor tyrosine kinases (RTKs) is associated with many types of cancers. For example, breast cancer patients have a poor prognosis if their tumor cells harbor excessive levels of a receptor tyrosine kinase called HER2 (see Concept 12.3). Using molecular biological techniques, researchers have developed a protein called Herceptin that binds to HER2 on cells and inhibits cell division, thus thwarting further tumor development. In some clinical studies, treatment with Herceptin improved patient survival rates by more than one-third. One goal of ongoing research into these cell-surface receptors and other cell-signaling proteins is development of additional successful treatments.

Intracellular Receptors

Intracellular receptor proteins are found in either the cytoplasm or nucleus of target cells. To reach such a receptor, a signaling molecule passes through the target cell's plasma membrane. A number of important signaling molecules can do this because they are either hydrophobic enough or small enough to cross the hydrophobic interior of the membrane. These hydrophobic chemical messengers include the steroid hormones and thyroid hormones of animals. Another chemical signaling molecule with an intracellular receptor is nitric oxide (NO), a gas; its very small molecules readily pass between the membrane phospholipids.

Once a hormone has entered a cell, it may bind to an intracellular receptor in the cytoplasm or the nucleus. The binding changes the receptor into a hormone-receptor complex that is able to cause a response—in many cases, the turning on or off of particular genes.

The behavior of aldosterone is a representative example of how steroid hormones work. This hormone is secreted by cells of the adrenal gland, a gland that sits above the kidney. Aldosterone then travels through the blood and enters cells all over the body. However, a response occurs only in kidney cells, which contain receptor molecules for this hormone. In these cells, the hormone binds to the receptor protein, activating it. With aldosterone attached, the active form of the receptor protein then enters the nucleus and turns on specific genes that control water and sodium flow in kidney cells, ultimately affecting blood volume (Figure 8.9).

How does the activated hormone-receptor complex turn on genes? Recall that the genes in a cell's DNA function by being transcribed and processed into messenger RNA (mRNA), which leaves the nucleus and is translated into a specific protein by ribosomes in the cytoplasm (see Figure 5.23). Special proteins called *transcription factors* control which genes are turned on—that is, which genes are transcribed into mRNA—in a particular cell at a particular time. When the aldosterone receptor is activated, it acts as a transcription factor that turns on specific genes. (You'll learn more about transcription factors in Chapter 17.)

By acting as a transcription factor, the aldosterone receptor itself carries out the transduction part of the signaling pathway. Most other intracellular receptors function in the same way, although many of them, such as the thyroid hormone receptor, are already in the nucleus before the signaling molecule reaches them. Interestingly, many of these intracellular receptor proteins are structurally similar, suggesting an evolutionary kinship.

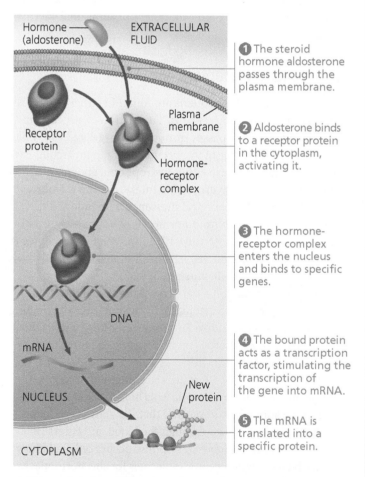

▲ **Figure 8.9 Steroid hormone interacting with an intracellular receptor.**

? *Why is a cell-surface receptor protein not required for this steroid hormone to enter the cell?*

In figure:

Hormone (aldosterone)

EXTRACELLULAR FLUID

Plasma membrane

Receptor protein

Hormone-receptor complex

DNA

mRNA

New protein

NUCLEUS

CYTOPLASM

1 The steroid hormone aldosterone passes through the plasma membrane.

2 Aldosterone binds to a receptor protein in the cytoplasm, activating it.

3 The hormone-receptor complex enters the nucleus and binds to specific genes.

4 The bound protein acts as a transcription factor, stimulating the transcription of the gene into mRNA.

5 The mRNA is translated into a specific protein.

CONCEPT CHECK 8.2

1. Nerve growth factor (NGF) is a water-soluble signaling molecule. Would you expect the receptor for NGF to be intracellular or in the plasma membrane? Why?

2. **WHAT IF?** What would the effect be if a cell made defective receptor tyrosine kinase proteins that were unable to dimerize?

3. **MAKE CONNECTIONS** How is ligand binding similar to the process of allosteric regulation of enzymes? See Figure 8.20.

4. **WHAT IF?** The model shown in Figure 8.7 represents the receptor in an inactive state, not bound to a G protein. Can you suggest an approach for crystallizing the protein that would reveal the structure of the receptor while it is actively signaling?

CONCEPT 8.3

Transduction: Cascades of molecular interactions relay signals from receptors to target molecules in the cell

When receptors for signaling molecules are plasma membrane proteins, like most of those we have discussed, the transduction stage of cell signaling is usually a multistep pathway involving many molecules. Steps often include activation of proteins by addition or removal of phosphate groups or release of other small molecules or ions that act as messengers. One benefit of multiple steps is the possibility of greatly amplifying a signal. If each molecule in a pathway transmits the signal to numerous molecules at the next step in the series, the result is a geometric increase in the number of activated molecules by the end of the pathway. Moreover, multistep pathways provide more opportunities for coordination and control than do simpler systems. This allows regulation of the response, as we'll discuss later in the chapter.

Signal Transduction Pathways

The binding of a specific signaling molecule to a receptor in the plasma membrane triggers the first step in the chain of molecular interactions—the signal transduction pathway—that leads to a particular response within the cell. Like falling dominoes, the signal-activated receptor activates another molecule, which activates yet another molecule, and so on, until the protein that produces the final cellular response is activated. The molecules that relay a signal from receptor to response, which we call relay molecules in this book, are often proteins. The interaction of proteins is a major theme of cell signaling. Indeed, protein interaction is a unifying theme of all cellular activities.

Keep in mind that the original signaling molecule is not physically passed along a signaling pathway; in most cases, it never even enters the cell. When we say that the signal is relayed along a pathway, we mean that certain information is passed on. At each step, the signal is transduced into a different form, commonly a shape change in the next protein. Very often, the shape change is brought about by phosphorylation.

Protein Phosphorylation and Dephosphorylation

Previous chapters introduced the concept of activating a protein by adding one or more phosphate groups to it (see Figure 9.11a). In Figure 8.8, you have already seen how phosphorylation is involved in the activation of receptor tyrosine kinases. In fact, the phosphorylation and dephosphorylation of proteins is a widespread cellular mechanism for regulating protein activity. An enzyme that transfers phosphate groups from ATP to a protein is generally known as a **protein kinase**. Recall that a receptor tyrosine kinase is a specific kind of protein kinase that phosphorylates tyrosines on the other receptor tyrosine kinase in a dimer. Most cytoplasmic protein kinases, however, act on proteins different from themselves. Another distinction is that most cytoplasmic protein kinases phosphorylate either of two other amino acids, serine or threonine, rather than tyrosine. Serine/threonine kinases are widely involved in signaling pathways in animals, plants, and fungi.

Many of the relay molecules in signal transduction pathways are protein kinases, and they often act on other protein kinases in the pathway. **Figure 8.10** depicts a hypothetical pathway containing three different protein kinases that create a **phosphorylation cascade**. The sequence of steps

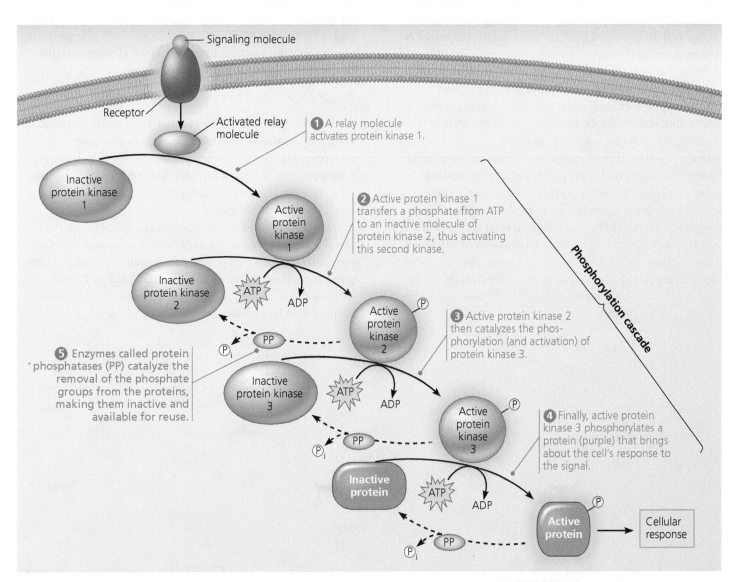

▲ Figure 8.10 **A phosphorylation cascade.** In a phosphorylation cascade, a series of different proteins in a pathway are phosphorylated in turn, each protein adding a phosphate group to the next one in line. Here, phosphorylation activates each protein, and dephosphorylation returns it to its inactive form. The active and inactive forms of each protein are represented by different shapes to remind you that activation is usually associated with a change in molecular shape.

WHAT IF? *What would happen if a mutation in protein kinase 3 made it incapable of being phosphorylated?*

shown in the figure is similar to many known pathways, including those triggered in yeast by mating factors and in animal cells by many growth factors. The signal is transmitted by a cascade of protein phosphorylations, each causing a shape change because of the interaction of the newly added phosphate groups with charged or polar amino acids on the protein being phosphorylated (see Figure 5.14). The change in shape alters the function of the protein, most often activating it. In some cases, though, phosphorylation *decreases* the activity of the protein.

The importance of protein kinases can hardly be overstated. About 2% of our own genes are thought to code for protein kinases. A single cell may have hundreds of different kinds, each specific for a different substrate protein. Together, they probably regulate the activity of a large proportion of the thousands of proteins in a cell. Among these are most of the proteins that, in turn, regulate cell division. Abnormal activity of such a kinase can cause abnormal cell division and contribute to the development of cancer.

Equally important in the phosphorylation cascade are the **protein phosphatases**, enzymes that can rapidly remove phosphate groups from proteins, a process called dephosphorylation. By dephosphorylating and thus inactivating protein kinases, phosphatases provide the mechanism for turning off the signal transduction pathway when the initial signal is no longer present. Phosphatases also make the protein kinases available for reuse, enabling the cell to respond again to an extracellular signal. The phosphorylation-dephosphorylation system acts as a molecular switch in the cell, turning activities on or off, or up or down, as required. At any given moment, the activity of a protein regulated by phosphorylation depends on the balance in the cell between active kinase molecules and active phosphatase molecules.

Small Molecules and Ions as Second Messengers

Not all components of signal transduction pathways are proteins. Many signaling pathways also involve small, non-protein, water-soluble molecules or ions called **second messengers**. (This term is used because the pathway's "first messenger" is considered to be the extracellular signaling molecule—the ligand—that binds to the membrane receptor.) Because second messengers are small and also water-soluble, they can readily spread throughout the cell by diffusion. For example, as we'll see shortly, a second messenger called cyclic AMP carries the signal initiated by epinephrine from the plasma membrane of a liver or muscle cell into the cell's interior, where the signal eventually brings about glycogen breakdown. Second messengers participate in pathways that are initiated by both G protein-coupled receptors and receptor tyrosine kinases. The two most widely used second messengers are cyclic AMP and calcium ions, Ca^{2+}. A large variety of relay proteins are sensitive to the cytosolic concentration of one or the other of these second messengers.

Cyclic AMP

As discussed previously, Earl Sutherland established that epinephrine somehow causes glycogen breakdown without passing through the plasma membrane. This discovery prompted him to search for a second messenger that transmits the signal from the plasma membrane to the metabolic machinery in the cytoplasm.

Sutherland found that the binding of epinephrine to the plasma membrane of a liver cell elevates the cytosolic concentration of a compound called cyclic adenosine monophosphate, abbreviated as either **cyclic AMP** or **cAMP** **(Figure 8.11)**. An enzyme embedded in the plasma membrane, **adenylyl cyclase**, converts ATP to cAMP in response

▲ **Figure 8.11 Cyclic AMP.** The second messenger cyclic AMP (cAMP) is made from ATP by adenylyl cyclase, an enzyme embedded in the plasma membrane. Note that the phosphate group in cAMP is attached to both the 5′ and the 3′ carbons; this cyclic arrangement is the basis for the molecule's name. Cyclic AMP is inactivated by phosphodiesterase, an enzyme that converts it to AMP.

WHAT IF? *What would happen if a molecule that inactivated phosphodiesterase were introduced into the cell?*

to an extracellular signal—in this case, provided by epinephrine. But epinephrine doesn't stimulate adenylyl cyclase directly. When epinephrine outside the cell binds to a specific receptor protein, the protein activates adenylyl cyclase, which in turn can catalyze the synthesis of many molecules of cAMP. In this way, the normal cellular concentration of cAMP can be boosted 20-fold in a matter of seconds. The cAMP broadcasts the signal to the cytoplasm. It does not persist for long in the absence of the hormone because another enzyme, called phosphodiesterase, converts cAMP to AMP. Another surge of epinephrine is needed to boost the cytosolic concentration of cAMP again.

Subsequent research has revealed that epinephrine is only one of many hormones and other signaling molecules that trigger the formation of cAMP. It has also brought to light the other components of cAMP pathways, including G proteins, G protein-coupled receptors, and protein kinases **(Figure 8.12)**. The immediate effect of an elevation in cAMP levels is usually the activation of a serine/threonine kinase called *protein kinase A*. The activated protein kinase A then phosphorylates various other proteins, depending on the cell type. (The complete pathway for epinephrine's stimulation of glycogen breakdown is shown later, in Figure 8.16.)

Further regulation of cell metabolism is provided by other G protein systems that *inhibit* adenylyl cyclase. In these systems, a different signaling molecule activates a different receptor, which in turn activates an *inhibitory* G protein that blocks activation of adenylyl cyclase.

Now that we know about the role of cAMP in G protein signaling pathways, we can explain in molecular detail how certain microbes cause disease. Consider cholera, a disease that is frequently epidemic in places where the water supply is contaminated with human feces. People acquire the cholera bacterium, *Vibrio cholerae*, by drinking contaminated water. The bacteria form a biofilm on the lining of the small intestine and produce a toxin. The cholera toxin is an enzyme that chemically modifies a G protein involved in regulating salt and water secretion. Because the modified G protein is unable to hydrolyze GTP to GDP, it remains stuck in its active form, continuously stimulating adenylyl cyclase to make cAMP. The resulting high concentration of cAMP causes the intestinal cells to secrete large amounts of salts into the intestines, with water following by osmosis. An infected person quickly develops profuse diarrhea and if left untreated can soon die from the loss of water and salts.

Our understanding of signaling pathways involving cyclic AMP or related messengers has allowed us to develop treatments for certain conditions in humans. In one pathway, *cyclic GMP*, or *cGMP*, acts as a signaling molecule whose effects include relaxation of smooth muscle cells in artery walls. A compound that inhibits the hydrolysis of cGMP to GMP, thus prolonging the signal, was originally prescribed for chest pains because it increased blood flow to the heart muscle. Under the trade name Viagra, this compound is now widely used as a treatment for erectile dysfunction in human males. Because Viagra leads to dilation of blood vessels, it also allows increased blood flow to the penis, optimizing physiological conditions for penile erections.

Calcium Ions and Inositol Trisphosphate (IP₃)

Many of the signaling molecules that function in animals—including neurotransmitters, growth factors, and some hormones—induce responses in their target cells via signal transduction pathways that increase the cytosolic concentration of calcium ions (Ca^{2+}). Calcium is even more widely used than cAMP as a second messenger. Increasing the cytosolic concentration of Ca^{2+} causes many responses in animal cells, including muscle cell contraction, secretion of certain substances, and cell division. In plant cells, a wide range of hormonal and environmental stimuli can cause brief increases in cytosolic Ca^{2+} concentration, triggering various signaling pathways, such as the pathway for greening in response to light. Cells use Ca^{2+} as a second messenger in pathways triggered by both G protein-coupled receptors and receptor tyrosine kinases.

Although cells always contain some Ca^{2+}, this ion can function as a second messenger because its concentration in the cytosol is normally much lower than the concentration

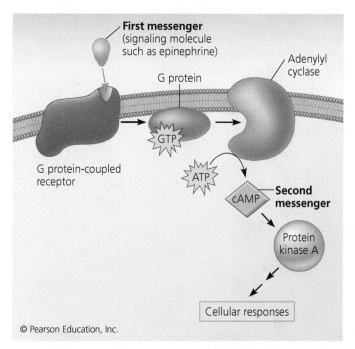

© Pearson Education, Inc.

▲ **Figure 8.12 cAMP as a second messenger in a G protein signaling pathway.** The first messenger activates a G protein coupled receptor, which activates a specific G protein. In turn, the G protein activates adenylyl cyclase, which catalyzes the conversion of ATP to cAMP. The cAMP then acts as a second messenger and activates another protein, usually protein kinase A, leading to cellular responses.

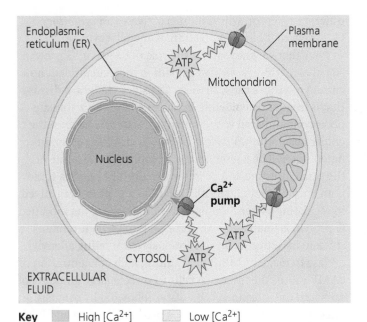

Key ☐ High [Ca²⁺] ☐ Low [Ca²⁺]

Key ■ High [Ca^{2+}]   ■ Low [Ca^{2+}]

▲ **Figure 8.13 The maintenance of calcium ion concentrations in an animal cell.** The Ca^{2+} concentration in the cytosol is usually much lower (beige) than in the extracellular fluid and ER (blue). Protein pumps in the plasma membrane and the ER membrane, driven by ATP, move Ca^{2+} from the cytosol into the extracellular fluid and into the lumen of the ER. Mitochondrial pumps, driven by chemiosmosis (see Concept 8.4), move Ca^{2+} into mitochondria when the calcium level in the cytosol rises significantly.

outside the cell (**Figure 8.13**). In fact, the level of Ca^{2+} in the blood and extracellular fluid of an animal is often more than 10,000 times higher than that in the cytosol. Calcium ions are actively transported out of the cell and are actively imported from the cytosol into the endoplasmic reticulum (and, under some conditions, into mitochondria and chloroplasts) by various protein pumps. As a result, the calcium concentration in the ER is usually much higher than that in the cytosol. Because the cytosolic calcium level is low, a small change in absolute numbers of ions represents a relatively large percentage change in calcium concentration.

In response to a signal relayed by a signal transduction pathway, the cytosolic calcium level may rise, usually by a mechanism that releases Ca^{2+} from the cell's ER. The pathways leading to calcium release involve two other second messengers, **inositol trisphosphate (IP₃)** and **diacylglycerol (DAG)**. These two

messengers are produced by cleavage of a certain kind of phospholipid in the plasma membrane. **Figure 8.14** shows the complete picture of how a signal causes IP₃ to stimulate the release of calcium from the ER. Because IP₃ acts before calcium in these pathways, calcium could be considered a "*third* messenger." However, scientists use the term *second messenger* for all small, nonprotein components of signal transduction pathways.

CONCEPT CHECK 8.3

1. What is a protein kinase, and what is its role in a signal transduction pathway?

2. When a signal transduction pathway involves a phosphorylation cascade, how does the cell's response get turned off?

3. What is the actual "signal" that is being transduced in any signal transduction pathway, such as those shown in Figures 8.6 and 8.10? In what way is this information being passed from the exterior to the interior of the cell?

4. **WHAT IF?** Upon activation of phospholipase C by the binding of a ligand to a receptor, what effect does the IP₃-gated calcium channel have on Ca^{2+} concentration in the cytosol?

---

① A signaling molecule binds to a receptor, leading to activation of phospholipase C.

② Phospholipase C cleaves a plasma membrane phospholipid called PIP₂ into DAG and IP₃.

③ DAG functions as a second messenger in other pathways.

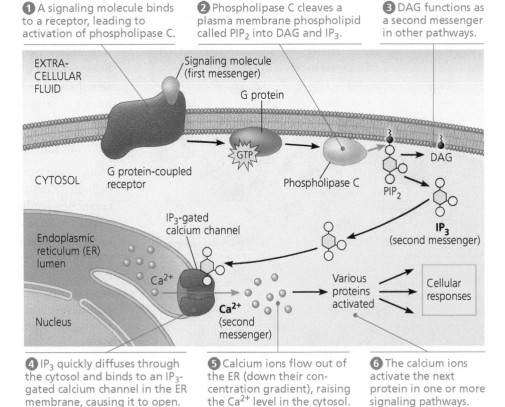

④ IP₃ quickly diffuses through the cytosol and binds to an IP₃-gated calcium channel in the ER membrane, causing it to open.

⑤ Calcium ions flow out of the ER (down their concentration gradient), raising the Ca^{2+} level in the cytosol.

⑥ The calcium ions activate the next protein in one or more signaling pathways.

▲ **Figure 8.14 Calcium and IP₃ in signaling pathways.** Calcium ions (Ca^{2+}) and inositol trisphosphate (IP₃) function as second messengers in many signal transduction pathways. In this figure, the process is initiated by the binding of a signaling molecule to a G protein-coupled receptor. A receptor tyrosine kinase could also initiate this pathway by activating phospholipase C.

Response: Cell signaling leads to regulation of transcription or cytoplasmic activities

We now take a closer look at the cell's subsequent response to an extracellular signal—what some researchers call the "output response." What is the nature of the final step in a signaling pathway?

Nuclear and Cytoplasmic Responses

Ultimately, a signal transduction pathway leads to the regulation of one or more cellular activities. The response at the end of the pathway may occur in the nucleus of the cell or in the cytoplasm.

Many signaling pathways ultimately regulate protein synthesis, usually by turning specific genes on or off in the nucleus. Like an activated steroid receptor (see Figure 8.9), the final activated molecule in a signaling pathway may function as a transcription factor. **Figure 8.15** shows an example in which a signaling pathway activates a transcription factor that turns a gene on: The response to this growth factor signal is transcription, the synthesis of one or more specific mRNAs, which will be translated in the cytoplasm into specific proteins. In other cases, the transcription factor might regulate a gene by turning it off. Often a transcription factor regulates several different genes.

Sometimes a signaling pathway may regulate the *activity* of proteins rather than causing their *synthesis* by activating gene expression. This directly affects proteins that function outside the nucleus. For example, a signal may cause the opening or closing of an ion channel in the plasma membrane or a change in cell metabolism. As we have seen, the response of liver cells to the hormone epinephrine helps regulate cellular energy metabolism by affecting the activity of an enzyme. The final step in the signaling pathway that begins with epinephrine binding activates the enzyme that catalyzes the breakdown of glycogen. **Figure 8.16** shows the complete pathway leading to the release of glucose 1-phosphate molecules from glycogen. Notice that as each molecule is activated, the response is amplified, a subject we'll return to shortly.

Signal receptors, relay molecules, and second messengers participate in a variety of pathways, leading to both nuclear and cytoplasmic responses. Some of these pathways lead to cell division. The molecular messengers that initiate cell division pathways include growth factors and certain plant and animal hormones. Malfunctioning of growth factor pathways like the one in Figure 8.15 can contribute to the development of cancer.

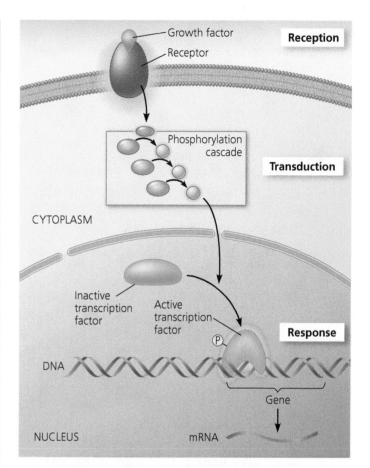

▲ **Figure 8.15 Nuclear responses to a signal: the activation of a specific gene by a growth factor.** This diagram is a simplified representation of a typical signaling pathway that leads to regulation of gene activity in the cell nucleus. The initial signaling molecule, a growth factor, triggers a phosphorylation cascade, as in Figure 8.10. (The ATP molecules and phosphate groups are not shown here.) Once phosphorylated, the last kinase in the sequence enters the nucleus and activates a gene-regulating protein, a transcription factor. This protein stimulates transcription of a specific gene (or genes). The resulting mRNAs then direct the synthesis of a particular protein in the cytoplasm.

Regulation of the Response

Whether the response occurs in the nucleus or in the cytoplasm, it is not simply turned "on" or "off." Rather, the extent and specificity of the response are regulated in multiple ways. Here we'll consider four aspects of this regulation. First, as mentioned earlier, signaling pathways generally amplify the cell's response to a single signaling event. The degree of amplification depends on the function of the specific molecules in the pathway. Second, the many steps in a multistep pathway provide control points at which the cell's response can be further regulated, contributing to the specificity of the response and allowing coordination with other signaling pathways. Third, the overall efficiency of the response is enhanced by the presence of proteins known as scaffolding proteins. Finally, a crucial point in regulating the response is the termination of the signal.

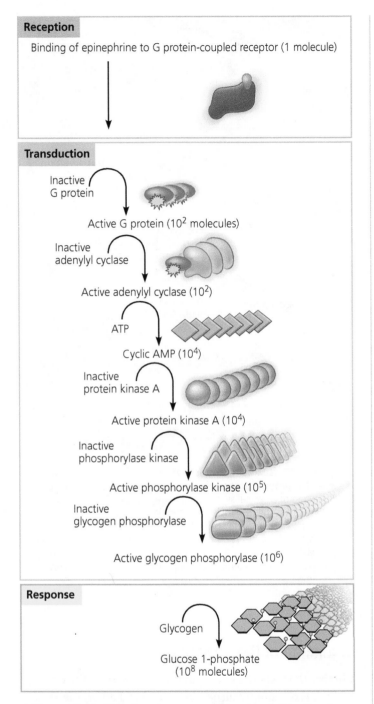

Reception

Binding of epinephrine to G protein-coupled receptor (1 molecule)

Transduction

Inactive G protein

Active G protein (10^2 molecules)

Inactive adenylyl cyclase

Active adenylyl cyclase (10^2)

ATP

Cyclic AMP (10^4)

Inactive protein kinase A

Active protein kinase A (10^4)

Inactive phosphorylase kinase

Active phosphorylase kinase (10^5)

Inactive glycogen phosphorylase

Active glycogen phosphorylase (10^6)

Response

Glycogen

Glucose 1-phosphate (10^8 molecules)

▲ **Figure 8.16 Cytoplasmic response to a signal: the stimulation of glycogen breakdown by epinephrine (adrenaline).** In this signaling system, the hormone epinephrine acts through a G protein-coupled receptor to activate a succession of relay molecules, including cAMP and two protein kinases (see also Figure 8.12). The final protein activated is the enzyme glycogen phosphorylase, which uses inorganic phosphate to release glucose monomers from glycogen in the form of glucose 1-phosphate molecules. This pathway amplifies the hormonal signal: One receptor protein can activate approximately 100 molecules of G protein, and each enzyme in the pathway, once activated, can act on many molecules of its substrate, the next molecule in the cascade. The number of activated molecules given for each step is approximate.

? *In the figure, how many glucose molecules are released in response to one signaling molecule? Calculate the factor by which the response is amplified in going from each step to the next.*

Signal Amplification

Elaborate enzyme cascades amplify the cell's response to a signal. At each catalytic step in the cascade, the number of activated products can be much greater than in the preceding step. For example, in the epinephrine-triggered pathway in Figure 8.16, each adenylyl cyclase molecule catalyzes the formation of 100 or so cAMP molecules, each molecule of protein kinase A phosphorylates about 10 molecules of the next kinase in the pathway, and so on. The amplification effect stems from the fact that these proteins persist in the active form long enough to process multiple molecules of substrate before they become inactive again. As a result of the signal's amplification, a small number of epinephrine molecules binding to receptors on the surface of a liver cell or muscle cell can lead to the release of hundreds of millions of glucose molecules from glycogen.

The Specificity of Cell Signaling and Coordination of the Response

Consider two different cells in your body—a liver cell and a heart muscle cell, for example. Both are in contact with your bloodstream and are therefore constantly exposed to many different hormone molecules, as well as to local regulators secreted by nearby cells. Yet the liver cell responds to some signals but ignores others, and the same is true for the heart cell. And some kinds of signals trigger responses in both cells—but different responses. For instance, epinephrine stimulates the liver cell to break down glycogen, but the main response of the heart cell to epinephrine is contraction, leading to a more rapid heartbeat. How do we account for this difference?

The explanation for the specificity exhibited in cellular responses to signals is the same as the basic explanation for virtually all differences between cells: Because different kinds of cells turn on different sets of genes, *different kinds of cells have different collections of proteins* **(Figure 8.17).** The response of a particular cell to a signal depends on its particular collection of signal receptor proteins, relay proteins, and proteins needed to carry out the response. A liver cell, for example, is poised to respond appropriately to epinephrine by having the proteins listed in Figure 8.16 as well as those needed to manufacture glycogen.

Thus, two cells that respond differently to the same signal differ in one or more of the proteins that handle and respond to the signal. Notice in Figure 8.17 that different pathways may have some molecules in common. For example, cells A, B, and C all use the same receptor protein for the red signaling molecule; differences in other proteins account for their differing responses. In cell D, a different receptor protein is used for the same signaling molecule, leading to yet another response. In cell B, a pathway that is triggered by a single kind of signal diverges to produce two

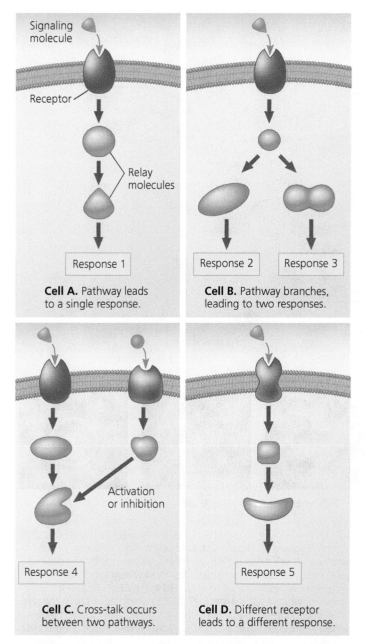

Cell A. Pathway leads to a single response.

Cell B. Pathway branches, leading to two responses.

Cell C. Cross-talk occurs between two pathways.

Cell D. Different receptor leads to a different response.

▲ **Figure 8.17 The specificity of cell signaling.** The particular proteins a cell possesses determine what signaling molecules it responds to and the nature of the response. The four cells in these diagrams respond to the same signaling molecule (red) in different ways because each has a different set of proteins (purple and teal). Note, however, that the same kinds of molecules can participate in more than one pathway.

MAKE CONNECTIONS *Study the signaling pathway shown in Figure 8.14, and explain how the situation pictured for cell B above could apply to that pathway.*

responses; such branched pathways often involve receptor tyrosine kinases (which can activate multiple relay proteins) or second messengers (which can regulate numerous proteins). In cell C, two pathways triggered by separate signals converge to modulate a single response. Branching of pathways and "cross-talk" (interaction) between pathways are

important in regulating and coordinating a cell's responses to information coming in from different sources in the body. (You'll learn more about this coordination in Concept 8.5.) Moreover, the use of some of the same proteins in more than one pathway allows the cell to economize on the number of different proteins it must make.

An example of a signal that leads to a complex, coordinated cellular response can be found in the processes leading to the mating of yeast cells described earlier (see Figure 8.2). In the Scientific Skills Exercise, you can work with data from experiments investigating the cellular response of a yeast cell to the signal initiated by a mating factor from a cell of the opposite mating type.

Signaling Efficiency: Scaffolding Proteins and Signaling Complexes

The illustrations of signaling pathways in Figure 8.17 (as well as diagrams of other pathways in this chapter) are greatly simplified. The diagrams show only a few relay molecules and, for clarity's sake, display these molecules spread out in the cytosol. If this were true in the cell, signaling pathways would operate very inefficiently because most relay molecules are proteins, and proteins are too large to diffuse quickly through the viscous cytosol. How does a particular protein kinase, for instance, find its substrate?

In many cases, the efficiency of signal transduction is apparently increased by the presence of **scaffolding proteins**, large relay proteins to which several other relay proteins are simultaneously attached. For example, one scaffolding protein isolated from mouse brain cells holds three protein kinases and carries these kinases with it when it binds to an appropriately activated membrane receptor; it thus facilitates a specific phosphorylation cascade (**Figure 8.18**). Researchers have found scaffolding proteins in brain cells that *permanently* hold together networks of signaling pathway proteins at synapses. This hardwiring enhances the speed and accuracy of signal transfer between cells, because the

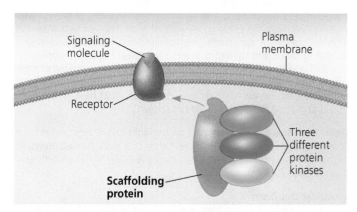

▲ **Figure 8.18 A scaffolding protein.** The scaffolding protein shown here simultaneously binds to a specific activated membrane receptor and three different protein kinases. This physical arrangement facilitates signal transduction by these molecules.

Using Experiments to Test a Model

1 Mating factor activates receptor.

Mating factor

G protein-coupled receptor

2 G protein binds GTP and becomes activated.

GDP

GTP

Phosphoryl-ation cascade

Fus3

Fus3

P

3 Phosphorylation cascade activates Fus3, which moves to plasma membrane.

Shmoo projection forming

Formin

P

Fus3

P

Formin

Formin

P

4 Fus3 phos-phorylates formin, activating it.

Actin subunit

Microfilament

5 Formin initiates growth of microfilaments that form the shmoo projections.

Are Both Fus3 Kinase and Formin Required for Directional Cell Growth During Mating in Yeast? When a yeast cell binds mating factor molecules from a cell of the opposite mating type, a signaling pathway causes it to grow a projection toward the potential mate. The cell with the projection is called a "shmoo" (because it resembles a 1950s cartoon character by that name). Researchers sought to determine how mating factor signaling leads to growth of this cell projection on one side of the cell—in other words, to asymmetric cell growth. Previous work had shown that activation of Fus3, one of the kinases in the signaling cascade, caused it to move to the membrane near where the mating factor bound its receptor. The researchers' first experiment identified one of the phosphorylation targets of Fus3 kinase as formin, a protein directing microfilament construction. Based on this information, the researchers developed the working model shown here for the signaling pathway that leads to the formation of shmoo projections in yeast cells.

How the Experiment Was Done To determine if Fus3 and formin were required for shmoo formation, the researchers generated two mutant yeast strains: one that lacked the gene for making Fus3 kinase (a strain called ΔFus3) and one that lacked the gene for making formin (Δformin). To observe the effects of these mutations on schmoo formation after cells' exposure to mating factor, the symmetry of growth was investigated. First, the existing cell walls of each strain were stained with a green fluorescent dye. These green-stained cells were then exposed to mating factor and stained with a red fluorescent dye that labels only new cell wall growth. Growth of the cell on all sides (symmetric growth) is indicated by a uniform yellow color, resulting from merged green and red stains. (This occurs normally in wild-type cells that have not been exposed to mating factor, which are not shown.)

Data from the Experiment The micrographs above, right, were taken of wild-type, ΔFus3, and Δformin cells after they were stained green, exposed to mating factor, and then stained red. The wild-type cells expressed both Fus3 and formin.

Interpret the Data

1. A model helps scientists form a testable hypothesis. The diagram shows the working model of shmoo formation developed by the researchers. (a) What hypothesis from the model was being tested with the ΔFus3 strain? (b) With the Δformin strain? (c) What is the purpose of including wild-type yeast cells in the experiment?

Wild type   ΔFus3   Δformin

2. When designing an experiment, scientists make predictions about what results will occur if their hypothesis is correct. (a) If the hypothesis about the role of Fus3 kinase activity in shmoo production is correct, what result should be observed in the ΔFus3 strain? If it is incorrect, what result is expected? (b) If the hypothesis about the role of formin in shmoo production is correct, what result should be observed in the Δformin strain? If it is incorrect, what result is expected?

3. For each micrograph, describe the shape of the cells and the pattern of cell wall staining. Explain the significance of your observations. Which strain(s) of yeast cells formed shmoos?

4. (a) Do the data support the hypothesis about the role of Fus3 kinase in shmoo production? (b) Do the data support the hypothesis about the role of formin in shmoo production? (c) Do the data support the working model (the working hypothesis) in the diagram?

5. Fus3 kinase and formin proteins are generally distributed evenly throughout a yeast cell. Based on the model in the diagram, explain why the projection would emerge on the same side of the cell that bound the mating factor.

6. What do you predict would happen if the yeast had a mutation that prevented the G protein from binding GTP?

(**MB**) A version of this Scientific Skills Exercise can be assigned in MasteringBiology.

Data from D. Matheos et al., Pheromone-induced polarization is dependent on the Fus3p MAPK acting through the formin Bni1p, *Journal of Cell Biology* 165:99–109 (2004).

rate of protein-protein interaction is not limited by diffusion. Furthermore, in some cases the scaffolding proteins themselves may directly activate relay proteins.

When signaling pathways were first discovered, they were thought to be linear, independent pathways. Our understanding of cellular communication has benefited from the realization that signaling pathway components interact with each other in various ways. As seen in Figure 8.17, some proteins may participate in more than one pathway, either in different cell types or in the same cell at different times or under different conditions. These observations underscore the importance of transient—or, in some cases, permanent—protein complexes in the process of cell signaling.

The importance of the relay proteins that serve as points of branching or intersection in signaling pathways is highlighted by the problems arising when these proteins are defective or missing. For instance, in an inherited disorder called Wiskott-Aldrich syndrome (WAS), the absence of a single relay protein leads to such diverse effects as abnormal bleeding, eczema, and a predisposition to infections and leukemia. These symptoms are thought to arise primarily from the absence of the protein in cells of the immune system. By studying normal cells, scientists found that the WAS protein is located just beneath the immune cell surface. The protein interacts both with microfilaments of the cytoskeleton and with several different components of signaling pathways that relay information from the cell surface, including pathways regulating immune cell proliferation. This multifunctional relay protein is thus both a branch point and an important intersection point in a complex signal transduction network that controls immune cell behavior. When the WAS protein is absent, the cytoskeleton is not properly organized and signaling pathways are disrupted, leading to the WAS symptoms.

Termination of the Signal

To keep Figure 8.17 simple, we did not indicate the *inactivation* mechanisms that are an essential aspect of any cell-signaling pathway. For a cell of a multicellular organism to remain capable of responding to incoming signals, each molecular change in its signaling pathways must last only a short time. As we saw in the cholera example, if a signaling pathway component becomes locked into one state, whether active or inactive, consequences for the organism can be dire.

The ability of a cell to receive new signals depends on reversibility of the changes produced by prior signals. The binding of signaling molecules to receptors is reversible. As the external concentration of signaling molecules falls, fewer receptors are bound at any given moment, and the unbound receptors revert to their inactive form. The cellular response occurs only when the concentration of receptors with bound signaling molecules is above a certain threshold. When the number of active receptors falls below that threshold, the cellular response ceases. Then, by a variety of means, the relay molecules return to their inactive forms: The GTPase activity intrinsic to a G protein hydrolyzes its bound GTP; the enzyme phosphodiesterase converts cAMP to AMP; protein phosphatases inactivate phosphorylated kinases and other proteins; and so forth. As a result, the cell is soon ready to respond to a fresh signal.

In this section, we explored the complexity of signaling initiation and termination in a single pathway, and we saw the potential for pathways to intersect with each other. In the next section, we'll consider one especially important network of interacting pathways in the cell.

CONCEPT 8.5

Apoptosis integrates multiple cell-signaling pathways

To be or not to be? One of the most elaborate networks of signaling pathways in the cell seems to ask and answer this question, originally posed by Hamlet. Cells that are infected, are damaged, or have reached the end of their functional life span often undergo "programmed cell death" **(Figure 8.19)**.

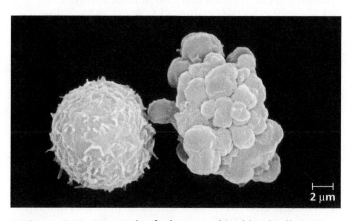

▲ **Figure 8.19 Apoptosis of a human white blood cell.** On the left is a normal white blood cell, while on the right is a white blood cell undergoing apoptosis. The apoptotic cell is shrinking and forming lobes ("blebs"), which eventually are shed as membrane-bounded cell fragments (colorized SEMs).

The best-understood type of this controlled cell suicide is **apoptosis** (from the Greek, meaning "falling off," and used in a classic Greek poem to refer to leaves falling from a tree). During this process, cellular agents chop up the DNA and fragment the organelles and other cytoplasmic components. The cell shrinks and becomes lobed (a change called "blebbing"), and the cell's parts are packaged up in vesicles that are engulfed and digested by specialized scavenger cells, leaving no trace. Apoptosis protects neighboring cells from damage that they would otherwise suffer if a dying cell merely leaked out all its contents, including its many digestive enzymes.

The signal that triggers apoptosis can come from either outside or inside the cell. Outside the cell, signaling molecules released from other cells can initiate a signal transduction pathway that activates the genes and proteins responsible for carrying out cell death. Within a cell whose DNA has been irretrievably damaged, a series of protein-protein interactions can pass along a signal that similarly triggers cell death. Considering some examples of apoptosis can help us to see how signaling pathways are integrated in cells.

Apoptosis in the Soil Worm *Caenorhabditis elegans*

The molecular mechanisms of apoptosis were worked out by researchers studying embryonic development of a small soil worm, a nematode called *Caenorhabditis elegans*. Because the adult worm has only about 1,000 cells, the researchers were able to work out the entire ancestry of each cell. The timely suicide of cells occurs exactly 131 times during normal development of *C. elegans*, at precisely the same points in the cell lineage of each worm. In worms and other species, apoptosis is triggered by signals that activate a cascade of "suicide" proteins in the cells destined to die.

Genetic research on *C. elegans* initially revealed two key apoptosis genes, called *ced-3* and *ced-4* (*ced* stands for "cell death"), which encode proteins essential for apoptosis. The proteins are called Ced-3 and Ced-4, respectively. These and most other proteins involved in apoptosis are continually present in cells, but in inactive form; thus, regulation in this case occurs at the level of protein activity rather than through gene activity and protein synthesis. In *C. elegans*, a protein in the outer mitochondrial membrane, called Ced-9 (the product of the *ced-9* gene), serves as a master regulator of apoptosis, acting as a brake in the absence of a signal promoting apoptosis **(Figure 8.20)**. When a death signal is received by the cell, signal transduction involves a change in Ced-9 that disables the brake, and the apoptotic pathway activates proteases and nucleases, enzymes that cut up the proteins and DNA of the cell. The main proteases of apoptosis are called *caspases*; in the nematode, the chief caspase is the Ced-3 protein.

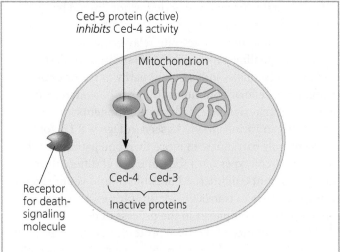

(a) No death signal. As long as Ced-9, located in the outer mitochondrial membrane, is active, apoptosis is inhibited, and the cell remains alive.

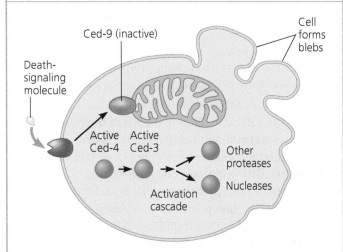

(b) Death signal. When a cell receives a death signal, Ced-9 is inactivated, relieving its inhibition of Ced-3 and Ced-4. Active Ced-3, a protease, triggers a cascade of reactions leading to activation of nucleases and other proteases. The action of these enzymes causes the changes seen in apoptotic cells and eventual cell death.

▲ **Figure 8.20 Molecular basis of apoptosis in *C. elegans*.** Three proteins, Ced-3, Ced-4, and Ced-9, are critical to apoptosis and its regulation in the nematode. Apoptosis is more complicated in mammals but involves proteins similar to those in the nematode.

Apoptotic Pathways and the Signals That Trigger Them

In humans and other mammals, several different pathways, involving about 15 different caspases, can carry out apoptosis. The pathway that is used depends on the type of cell and on the particular signal that initiates apoptosis. One major pathway involves certain mitochondrial proteins that are triggered to form molecular pores in the mitochondrial outer membrane, causing it to leak and release other proteins that promote apoptosis. Perhaps surprisingly, these latter include cytochrome *c*, which functions in mitochondrial electron transport in healthy cells (see Figure 10.15) but acts as a cell death factor when released from mitochondria. The process of mitochondrial apoptosis in mammals uses proteins similar to the nematode proteins Ced-3, Ced-4, and Ced-9. These can be thought of as relay proteins capable of transducing the apoptotic signal.

At key gateways into the apoptotic program, relay proteins integrate signals from several different sources and can send a cell down an apoptotic pathway. Often, the signal originates outside the cell, like the death-signaling molecule depicted in Figure 8.20b, which presumably was released by a neighboring cell. When a death-signaling ligand occupies a cell-surface receptor, this binding leads to activation of caspases and other enzymes that carry out apoptosis, without involving the mitochondrial pathway. This process of signal reception, transduction, and response is similar to what we have discussed throughout this chapter. In a twist on the classic scenario, two other types of alarm signals that can lead to apoptosis originate from *inside* the cell rather than from a cell-surface receptor. One signal comes from the nucleus, generated when the DNA has suffered irreparable damage, and a second comes from the endoplasmic reticulum when excessive protein misfolding occurs. Mammalian cells make life-or-death "decisions" by somehow integrating the death signals and life signals they receive from these external and internal sources.

A built-in cell suicide mechanism is essential to development and maintenance in all animals. The similarities between apoptosis genes in nematodes and those in mammals, as well as the observation that apoptosis occurs in multicellular fungi and even in single-celled yeasts, indicate that the basic mechanism evolved early in the evolution of eukaryotes. In vertebrates, apoptosis is essential for normal development of the nervous system, for normal operation of the immune system, and for normal morphogenesis of hands and feet in humans and paws in other mammals (**Figure 8.21**). The level of apoptosis between the developing digits is lower in the webbed feet of ducks and other water birds than in the nonwebbed feet of land birds, such as chickens. In the case of humans, the failure of appropriate apoptosis can result in webbed fingers and toes.

Significant evidence points to the involvement of apoptosis in certain degenerative diseases of the nervous system, such as Parkinson's disease and Alzheimer's disease. In Alzheimer's disease, an accumulation of aggregated proteins in neuronal cells activates an enzyme that triggers apoptosis, resulting in the loss of brain function seen in these patients. Furthermore, cancer can result from a failure of cell suicide; some cases of human melanoma, for example, have been linked to faulty forms of the human version of the *C. elegans* Ced-4 protein. It is not surprising, therefore, that the signaling pathways feeding into apoptosis are quite elaborate. After all, the life-or-death question is the most fundamental one imaginable for a cell.

This chapter has introduced you to many of the general mechanisms of cell communication, such as ligand binding, protein-protein interactions and shape changes, cascades of interactions, and protein phosphorylation. Throughout your study of biology, you will encounter numerous examples of cell signaling.

CONCEPT CHECK **8.5**

1. Give an example of apoptosis during embryonic development, and explain its function in the developing embryo.
2. **WHAT IF?** What types of protein defects could result in apoptosis occurring when it should not? What types could result in apoptosis not occurring when it should?

▲ **Figure 8.21 Effect of apoptosis during paw development in the mouse.** In mice, humans, other mammals, and land birds, the embryonic region that develops into feet or hands initially has a solid, platelike structure.

Apoptosis eliminates the cells in the interdigital regions, thus forming the digits. The embryonic mouse paws shown in these fluorescence light micrographs are stained so that cells undergoing apoptosis appear a bright yellowish green.

Apoptosis of cells begins at the margin of each interdigital region (left), peaks as the tissue in these regions is reduced (middle), and is no longer visible when the interdigital tissue has been eliminated (right).

CONCEPT 8.1

External signals are converted to responses within the cell (pp. 143–146)

- **Signal transduction pathways** are crucial for many processes. Signaling during yeast cell mating has much in common with processes in multicellular organisms, suggesting an early evolutionary origin of signaling mechanisms. Bacterial cells can sense the local density of bacterial cells (quorum sensing).
- Local signaling by animal cells involves direct contact or the secretion of local regulators. For long-distance signaling, animal and plant cells use **hormones**; animals also pass signals electrically.
- Like other hormones that bind to membrane receptors, epinephrine triggers a three-stage cell-signaling pathway:

? *What determines whether a cell responds to a hormone such as epinephrine? What determines how a cell responds to such a hormone?*

CONCEPT 8.2

Reception: A signaling molecule binds to a receptor protein, causing it to change shape (pp. 146–150)

- The binding between signaling molecule (**ligand**) and receptor is highly specific. A specific shape change in a receptor is often the initial transduction of the signal.
- There are three major types of cell-surface transmembrane receptors: (1) **G protein-coupled receptors (GPCRs)** work with cytoplasmic **G proteins**. Ligand binding activates the receptor, which then activates a specific G protein, which activates yet another protein, thus propagating the signal. (2) **Receptor tyrosine kinases (RTKs)** react to the binding of signaling molecules by forming dimers and then adding phosphate groups to tyrosines on the cytoplasmic part of the other monomer making up the dimer. Relay proteins in the cell can then be activated by binding to different phosphorylated tyrosines, allowing this receptor to trigger several pathways at once. (3) **Ligand-gated ion channels** open or close in response to binding by specific signaling molecules, regulating the flow of specific ions across the membrane.
- The activity of all three types of receptors is crucial; abnormal GPCRs and RTKs are associated with many human diseases.
- Intracellular receptors are cytoplasmic or nuclear proteins. Signaling molecules that are hydrophobic or small enough to cross the plasma membrane bind to these receptors inside the cell.

? *How are the structures of a GPCR and an RTK similar? How does initiation of signal transduction differ for these two types of receptors?*

CONCEPT 8.3

Transduction: Cascades of molecular interactions relay signals from receptors to target molecules in the cell (pp. 150–154)

- At each step in a signal transduction pathway, the signal is transduced into a different form, which commonly involves a shape change in a protein. Many signal transduction pathways include **phosphorylation cascades**, in which a series of **protein kinases** each add a phosphate group to the next one in line, activating it. Enzymes called **protein phosphatases** remove the phosphate groups. The balance between phosphorylation and dephosphorylation regulates the activity of proteins involved in the sequential steps of a signal transduction pathway.
- **Second messengers**, such as the small molecule **cyclic AMP (cAMP)** and the ion Ca^{2+}, diffuse readily through the cytosol and thus help broadcast signals quickly. Many G proteins activate **adenylyl cyclase**, which makes cAMP from ATP. Cells use Ca^{2+} as a second messenger in both GPCR and RTK pathways. The tyrosine kinase pathways can also involve two other second messengers, **diacylglycerol (DAG)** and **inositol trisphosphate (IP_3)**. IP_3 can trigger a subsequent increase in Ca^{2+} levels.

? *What is the difference between a protein kinase and a second messenger? Can both operate in the same signal transduction pathway?*

CONCEPT 8.4

Response: Cell signaling leads to regulation of transcription or cytoplasmic activities (pp. 155–159)

- Some pathways lead to a nuclear response: Specific genes are turned on or off by activated transcription factors. In others, the response involves cytoplasmic regulation.
- Cellular responses are not simply on or off; they are regulated at many steps. Each protein in a signaling pathway amplifies the signal by activating multiple copies of the next component; for long pathways, the total amplification may be over a millionfold. The combination of proteins in a cell confers specificity in the signals it detects and the responses it carries out. **Scaffolding proteins** increase signaling efficiency. Pathway branching further helps the cell coordinate signals and responses. Signal response is terminated quickly by the reversal of ligand binding.

? *What mechanisms in the cell terminate its response to a signal and maintain its ability to respond to new signals?*

CONCEPT 8.5

Apoptosis integrates multiple cell-signaling pathways (pp. 159–161)

- **Apoptosis** is a type of programmed cell death in which cell components are disposed of in an orderly fashion. Studies of the soil worm *Caenorhabditis elegans* clarified molecular details of the relevant signaling pathways. A death signal leads to activation of caspases and nucleases, the main enzymes involved in apoptosis.
- Several apoptotic signaling pathways exist in the cells of humans and other mammals, triggered in different ways. Signals eliciting apoptosis can originate from outside or inside the cell.

? *What is an explanation for the similarities between genes in yeasts, nematodes, and mammals that control apoptosis?*

LEVEL 1: KNOWLEDGE/COMPREHENSION

1. Binding of a signaling molecule to which type of receptor leads directly to a change in the distribution of ions on opposite sides of the membrane?
   a. intracellular receptor
   b. G protein-coupled receptor
   c. phosphorylated receptor tyrosine kinase dimer
   d. ligand-gated ion channel

2. The activation of receptor tyrosine kinases is characterized by
   a. dimerization and phosphorylation.
   b. dimerization and IP_3 binding.
   c. a phosphorylation cascade.
   d. GTP hydrolysis.

3. Lipid-soluble signaling molecules, such as aldosterone, cross the membranes of all cells but affect only target cells because
   a. only target cells retain the appropriate DNA segments.
   b. intracellular receptors are present only in target cells.
   c. only target cells have enzymes that break down aldosterone.
   d. only in target cells is aldosterone able to initiate the phosphorylation cascade that turns genes on.

4. Consider this pathway: epinephrine → G protein-coupled receptor → G protein → adenylyl cyclase → cAMP. Identify the second messenger.
   a. cAMP   c. GTP
   b. G protein   d. adenylyl cyclase

5. Apoptosis involves all but which of the following?
   a. fragmentation of the DNA
   b. cell-signaling pathways
   c. lysis of the cell
   d. digestion of cellular contents by scavenger cells

LEVEL 2: APPLICATION/ANALYSIS

6. Which observation suggested to Sutherland the involvement of a second messenger in epinephrine's effect on liver cells?
   a. Enzymatic activity was proportional to the amount of calcium added to a cell-free extract.
   b. Receptor studies indicated that epinephrine was a ligand.
   c. Glycogen breakdown was observed only when epinephrine was administered to intact cells.
   d. Glycogen breakdown was observed when epinephrine and glycogen phosphorylase were combined.

7. Protein phosphorylation is commonly involved with all of the following *except*
   a. activation of receptor tyrosine kinases.
   b. activation of protein kinase molecules.
   c. activation of G protein-coupled receptors.
   d. regulation of transcription by signaling molecules.

LEVEL 3: SYNTHESIS/EVALUATION

8. **DRAW IT** Draw the following apoptotic pathway, which operates in human immune cells. A death signal is received when a molecule called Fas binds its cell-surface receptor. The binding of many Fas molecules to receptors causes receptor clustering. The intracellular regions of the receptors, when together, bind proteins called adaptor proteins. These in turn bind to inactive molecules of caspase-8, which become activated and then activate caspase-3. Once activated, caspase-3 initiates apoptosis.

9. **EVOLUTION CONNECTION**
   What evolutionary mechanisms might account for the origin and persistence of cell-to-cell signaling systems in prokaryotes?

10. **SCIENTIFIC INQUIRY**
    Epinephrine initiates a signal transduction pathway that produces cyclic AMP (cAMP) and leads to the breakdown of glycogen to glucose, a major energy source for cells. But glycogen breakdown is only part of the fight-or-flight response that epinephrine brings about; the overall effect on the body includes an increase in heart rate and alertness, as well as a burst of energy. Given that caffeine blocks the activity of cAMP phosphodiesterase, propose a mechanism by which caffeine ingestion leads to heightened alertness and sleeplessness.

11. **SCIENCE, TECHNOLOGY, AND SOCIETY**
    The aging process is thought to be initiated at the cellular level. Among the changes that can occur after a certain number of cell divisions is the loss of a cell's ability to respond to growth factors and other signals. Much research into aging is aimed at understanding such losses, with the ultimate goal of extending the human life span. Not everyone, however, agrees that this is a desirable goal. If life expectancy were greatly increased, what might be the social and ecological consequences?

12. **WRITE ABOUT A THEME: ORGANIZATION**
    The properties of life emerge at the biological level of the cell. The highly regulated process of apoptosis is not simply the destruction of a cell; it is also an emergent property. Write a short essay (about 100–150 words) that briefly explains the role of apoptosis in the development and proper functioning of an animal, and describe how this form of programmed cell death is a process that emerges from the orderly integration of signaling pathways.

13. **SYNTHESIZE YOUR KNOWLEDGE**

There are five basic tastes—sour, salty, sweet, bitter, and "umami." Salt is detected when the concentration of salt outside of a taste bud cell is higher than that inside of it, and ion channels allow the passive leakage of Na^+ into the cell. The resulting change in membrane potential (see Concept 7.4) sends the "salty" signal to the brain. Umami is a savory taste generated by glutamate (glutamic acid, found in monosodium glutamate, or MSG), which is used as a flavor enhancer in foods such as taco-flavored tortilla chips. The glutamate receptor is a GPCR, which, when bound, initiates a signaling pathway that ends with a cellular response, perceived by you as "taste." If you eat a regular potato chip and then rinse your mouth, you will no longer taste salt. But if you eat a flavored tortilla chip and then rinse, the taste persists. (Try it!) Propose a possible explanation for this difference.

9

An Introduction to Metabolism

▲ **Figure 9.1 What causes these breaking waves to glow?**

The Energy of Life

The living cell is a chemical factory in miniature, where thousands of reactions occur within a microscopic space. Sugars can be converted to amino acids that are linked together into proteins when needed. Conversely, when food is digested, proteins are dismantled into amino acids that can be converted to sugars. In multicellular organisms, many cells export chemical products that are used in other parts of the organism. The process called cellular respiration drives this cellular economy by extracting the energy stored in sugars and other fuels. Cells apply this energy to perform various types of work, such as the transport of solutes across the plasma membrane, which we discussed in Chapter 7.

In a more exotic example, the ocean waves shown in **Figure 9.1** are brightly illuminated from within by free-floating, single-celled marine organisms called dinoflagellates. These dinoflagellates convert the energy stored in certain organic molecules to light, a process called bioluminescence. Most bioluminescent organisms are found in the oceans, but some exist on land, such as the bioluminescent fungus seen at the lower left. Bioluminescence and other metabolic activities carried out by a cell are precisely coordinated and controlled. In its complexity, its efficiency, and its responsiveness to subtle changes, the cell is peerless as a chemical factory. The concepts of metabolism that you learn in this chapter will help you understand how matter and energy flow during life's processes and how that flow is regulated.

165

An organism's metabolism transforms matter and energy, subject to the laws of thermodynamics

The totality of an organism's chemical reactions is called **metabolism** (from the Greek *metabole*, change). Metabolism is an emergent property of life that arises from orderly interactions between molecules.

Organization of the Chemistry of Life into Metabolic Pathways

We can picture a cell's metabolism as an elaborate road map of the thousands of chemical reactions that occur in a cell, arranged as intersecting metabolic pathways. A **metabolic pathway** begins with a specific molecule, which is then altered in a series of defined steps, resulting in a certain product. Each step of the pathway is catalyzed by a specific enzyme:

Analogous to the red, yellow, and green stoplights that control the flow of automobile traffic, mechanisms that regulate enzymes balance metabolic supply and demand.

Metabolism as a whole manages the material and energy resources of the cell. Some metabolic pathways release energy by breaking down complex molecules to simpler compounds. These degradative processes are called **catabolic pathways**, or breakdown pathways. A major pathway of catabolism is cellular respiration, in which the sugar glucose and other organic fuels are broken down in the presence of oxygen to carbon dioxide and water. (Pathways can have more than one starting molecule and/or product.) Energy that was stored in the organic molecules becomes available to do the work of the cell, such as ciliary beating or membrane transport. **Anabolic pathways**, in contrast, consume energy to build complicated molecules from simpler ones; they are sometimes called biosynthetic pathways. Examples of anabolism are the synthesis of an amino acid from simpler molecules and the synthesis of a protein from amino acids. Catabolic and anabolic pathways are the "downhill" and "uphill" avenues of the metabolic landscape. Energy released from the downhill reactions of catabolic pathways can be stored and then used to drive the uphill reactions of anabolic pathways.

In this chapter, we will focus on mechanisms common to metabolic pathways. Because energy is fundamental to all metabolic processes, a basic knowledge of energy is necessary to understand how the living cell works. Although we will use some nonliving examples to study energy, the concepts demonstrated by these examples also apply to **bioenergetics**, the study of how energy flows through living organisms.

Forms of Energy

Energy is the capacity to cause change. In everyday life, energy is important because some forms of energy can be used to do work—that is, to move matter against opposing forces, such as gravity and friction. Put another way, energy is the ability to rearrange a collection of matter. For example, you expend energy to turn the pages of this book, and your cells expend energy in transporting certain substances across membranes. Energy exists in various forms, and the work of life depends on the ability of cells to transform energy from one form to another.

Energy can be associated with the relative motion of objects; this energy is called **kinetic energy**. Moving objects can perform work by imparting motion to other matter: A pool player uses the motion of the cue stick to push the cue ball, which in turn moves the other balls; water gushing through a dam turns turbines; and the contraction of leg muscles pushes bicycle pedals. **Thermal energy** is kinetic energy associated with the random movement of atoms or molecules; thermal energy in transfer from one object to another is called **heat**. Light is also a type of energy that can be harnessed to perform work, such as powering photosynthesis in green plants.

An object not presently moving may still possess energy. Energy that is not kinetic is called **potential energy**; it is energy that matter possesses because of its location or structure. Water behind a dam, for instance, possesses energy because of its altitude above sea level. Molecules possess energy because of the arrangement of electrons in the bonds between their atoms. **Chemical energy** is a term used by biologists to refer to the potential energy available for release in a chemical reaction. Recall that catabolic pathways release energy by breaking down complex molecules. Biologists say that these complex molecules, such as glucose, are high in chemical energy. During a catabolic reaction, some bonds are broken and others formed, releasing energy and resulting in lower-energy breakdown products. This transformation also occurs in the engine of a car when the hydrocarbons of gasoline react explosively with oxygen, releasing the energy that pushes the pistons and producing exhaust. Although less explosive, a similar reaction of food molecules with oxygen provides chemical energy in biological systems, producing carbon dioxide and water as waste products. Biochemical pathways, carried out in the context of cellular structures, enable cells to release chemical energy from food molecules and use the energy to power life processes.

A diver has more potential energy on the platform than in the water.

Diving converts potential energy to kinetic energy.

Climbing up converts the kinetic energy of muscle movement to potential energy.

A diver has less potential energy in the water than on the platform.

▲ Figure 9.2 **Transformations between potential and kinetic energy.**

How is energy converted from one form to another? Consider **Figure 9.2**. The young woman climbing the ladder to the diving platform is releasing chemical energy from the food she ate for lunch and using some of that energy to perform the work of climbing. The kinetic energy of muscle movement is thus being transformed into potential energy due to her increasing height above the water. The young man diving is converting his potential energy to kinetic energy, which is then transferred to the water as he enters it. A small amount of energy is lost as heat due to friction.

Now let's consider the original source of the organic food molecules that provided the necessary chemical energy for the diver to climb the steps. This chemical energy was itself derived from light energy by plants during photosynthesis. Organisms are energy transformers.

The Laws of Energy Transformation

The study of the energy transformations that occur in a collection of matter is called **thermodynamics**. Scientists use the word *system* to denote the matter under study; they refer to the rest of the universe—everything outside the system—as the *surroundings*. An *isolated system*, such as that approximated by liquid in a thermos bottle, is unable to exchange either energy or matter with its surroundings outside the thermos. In an *open system*, energy and matter can be transferred between the system and its surroundings. Organisms are open systems. They absorb energy—for instance, light energy or chemical energy in the form of organic molecules—and release heat and metabolic waste products, such as carbon dioxide, to the surroundings. Two laws of thermodynamics govern energy transformations in organisms and all other collections of matter.

The First Law of Thermodynamics

According to the **first law of thermodynamics**, the energy of the universe is constant: *Energy can be transferred and transformed, but it cannot be created or destroyed.* The first law is also known as the *principle of conservation of energy*. The electric company does not make energy, but merely converts it to a form that is convenient for us to use. By converting sunlight to chemical energy, a plant acts as an energy transformer, not an energy producer.

The brown bear in **Figure 9.3a** will convert the chemical energy of the organic molecules in its food to kinetic and other forms of energy as it carries out biological processes.

Chemical energy

Heat

CO_2 + H_2O

(a) **First law of thermodynamics:** Energy can be transferred or transformed but neither created nor destroyed. For example, chemical reactions in this brown bear will convert the chemical (potential) energy in the fish into the kinetic energy of running.

(b) **Second law of thermodynamics:** Every energy transfer or transformation increases the disorder (entropy) of the universe. For example, as it runs, disorder is increased around the bear by the release of heat and small molecules that are the by-products of metabolism. A brown bear can run at speeds up to 35 miles per hour (56 km/hr)—as fast as a racehorse.

▲ Figure 9.3 **The two laws of thermodynamics.**

What happens to this energy after it has performed work? The second law of thermodynamics helps to answer this question.

The Second Law of Thermodynamics

If energy cannot be destroyed, why can't organisms simply recycle their energy over and over again? It turns out that during every energy transfer or transformation, some energy becomes unavailable to do work. In most energy transformations, more usable forms of energy are at least partly converted to thermal energy and released as heat. Only a small fraction of the chemical energy from the food in Figure 9.3a is transformed into the motion of the brown bear shown in **Figure 9.3b**; most is lost as heat, which dissipates rapidly through the surroundings.

In the process of carrying out chemical reactions that perform various kinds of work, living cells unavoidably convert other forms of energy to heat. A system can put this energy to work only when there is a temperature difference that results in thermal energy flowing as heat from a warmer location to a cooler one. If temperature is uniform, as it is in a living cell, then the heat generated during a chemical reaction will simply warm a body of matter, such as the organism. (This can make a room crowded with people uncomfortably warm, as each person is carrying out a multitude of chemical reactions!)

A logical consequence of the loss of usable energy as heat to the surroundings is that each energy transfer or transformation makes the universe more disordered. Scientists use a quantity called **entropy** as a measure of disorder, or randomness. The more randomly arranged a collection of matter is, the greater its entropy. We can now state the **second law of thermodynamics**: *Every energy transfer or transformation increases the entropy of the universe.* Although order can increase locally, there is an unstoppable trend toward randomization of the universe as a whole.

In many cases, increased entropy is evident in the physical disintegration of a system's organized structure. For example, you can observe increasing entropy in the gradual decay of an unmaintained building. Much of the increasing entropy of the universe is less obvious, however, because it takes the form of increasing amounts of heat and less ordered forms of matter. As the bear in Figure 9.3b converts chemical energy to kinetic energy, it is also increasing the disorder of its surroundings by producing heat and small molecules, such as the CO_2 it exhales, that are the breakdown products of food.

The concept of entropy helps us understand why certain processes are energetically favorable and occur on their own. It turns out that if a given process, by itself, leads to an increase in entropy, that process can proceed without requiring an input of energy. Such a process is called a **spontaneous process**. Note that as we're using it here, the word *spontaneous* does not imply that the process would occur quickly; rather, the word signifies that it is energetically favorable. (In fact, it may be helpful for you to think of the phrase "energetically favorable" when you read the formal term "spontaneous.") Some spontaneous processes, such as an explosion, may be virtually instantaneous, while others, such as the rusting of an old car over time, are much slower.

A process that, considered on its own, leads to a decrease in entropy is said to be nonspontaneous: It will happen only if energy is supplied. We know from experience that certain events occur spontaneously and others do not. For instance, we know that water flows downhill spontaneously but moves uphill only with an input of energy, such as when a machine pumps the water against gravity. Some energy is inevitably lost as heat, increasing entropy in the surroundings, so usage of energy ensures that a nonspontaneous process also leads to an increase in the entropy of the universe as a whole.

Biological Order and Disorder

Living systems increase the entropy of their surroundings, as predicted by thermodynamic law. It is true that cells create ordered structures from less organized starting materials. For example, simpler molecules are ordered into the more complex structure of an amino acid, and amino acids are ordered into polypeptide chains. At the organismal level as well, complex and beautifully ordered structures result from biological processes that use simpler starting materials (Figure 9.4). However, an organism also takes in organized forms of matter and energy from the surroundings and replaces them with less ordered forms. For example, an animal obtains starch, proteins, and other complex molecules from the food it eats. As catabolic pathways break these molecules down, the animal releases carbon

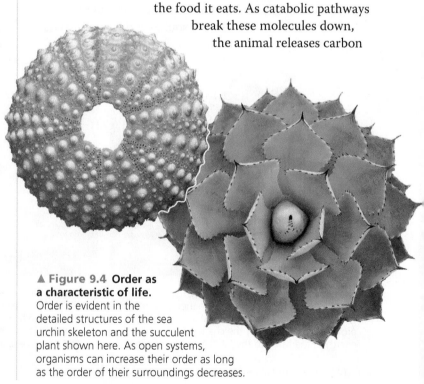

▲ **Figure 9.4 Order as a characteristic of life.** Order is evident in the detailed structures of the sea urchin skeleton and the succulent plant shown here. As open systems, organisms can increase their order as long as the order of their surroundings decreases.

dioxide and water—small molecules that possess less chemical energy than the food did (see Figure 9.3b). The depletion of chemical energy is accounted for by heat generated during metabolism. On a larger scale, energy flows into most ecosystems in the form of light and exits in the form of heat (see Figure 1.10).

During the early history of life, complex organisms evolved from simpler ancestors. For instance, we can trace the ancestry of the plant kingdom from much simpler organisms called green algae to more complex flowering plants. However, this increase in organization over time in no way violates the second law. The entropy of a particular system, such as an organism, may actually decrease as long as the total entropy of the *universe*—the system plus its surroundings—increases. Thus, organisms are islands of low entropy in an increasingly random universe. The evolution of biological order is perfectly consistent with the laws of thermodynamics.

CONCEPT CHECK 9.1

1. **MAKE CONNECTIONS** How does the second law of thermodynamics help explain the diffusion of a substance across a membrane? (See Figure 7.10.)

2. Describe the forms of energy found in an apple as it grows on a tree, then falls, then is digested by someone who eats it.

3. **WHAT IF?** If you place a teaspoon of sugar in the bottom of a glass of water, it will dissolve completely over time. Left longer, eventually the water will disappear and the sugar crystals will reappear. Explain these observations in terms of entropy.

CONCEPT 9.2

The free-energy change of a reaction tells us whether or not the reaction occurs spontaneously

The laws of thermodynamics that we've just discussed apply to the universe as a whole. As biologists, we want to understand the chemical reactions of life—for example, which reactions occur spontaneously and which ones require some input of energy from outside. But how can we know this without assessing the energy and entropy changes in the entire universe for each separate reaction?

Free-Energy Change, ΔG

Recall that the universe is really equivalent to "the system" plus "the surroundings." In 1878, J. Willard Gibbs, a professor at Yale, defined a very useful function called the Gibbs free energy of a system (without considering its surroundings), symbolized by the letter G. We'll refer to the Gibbs free energy simply as free energy. **Free energy** is the portion of a system's energy that can perform work when temperature and pressure are uniform throughout the system, as in a living cell. Let's consider how we determine the free-energy change that occurs when a system changes—for example, during a chemical reaction.

The change in free energy, ΔG, can be calculated for a chemical reaction by applying the following equation:

$$\Delta G = \Delta H - T\Delta S$$

This equation uses only properties of the system (the reaction) itself: ΔH symbolizes the change in the system's *enthalpy* (in biological systems, equivalent to total energy); ΔS is the change in the system's entropy; and T is the absolute temperature in Kelvin (K) units (K = °C + 273).

Once we know the value of ΔG for a process, we can use it to predict whether the process will be spontaneous (that is, whether it is energetically favorable and will occur without an input of energy). More than a century of experiments has shown that only processes with a negative ΔG are spontaneous. For ΔG to be negative, ΔH must be negative (the system gives up enthalpy and H decreases) or $T\Delta S$ must be positive (the system gives up order and S increases), or both: When ΔH and $T\Delta S$ are tallied, ΔG has a negative value ($\Delta G < 0$) for all spontaneous processes. In other words, every spontaneous process decreases the system's free energy, and processes that have a positive or zero ΔG are never spontaneous.

This information is immensely interesting to biologists, for it gives us the power to predict which kinds of change can happen without an input of energy. Such spontaneous changes can be harnessed to perform work. This principle is very important in the study of metabolism, where a major goal is to determine which reactions can supply energy for cellular work.

Free Energy, Stability, and Equilibrium

As we saw in the previous section, when a process occurs spontaneously in a system, we can be sure that ΔG is negative. Another way to think of ΔG is to realize that it represents the difference between the free energy of the final state and the free energy of the initial state:

$$\Delta G = G_{\text{final state}} - G_{\text{initial state}}$$

Thus, ΔG can be negative only when the process involves a loss of free energy during the change from initial state to final state. Because it has less free energy, the system in its final state is less likely to change and is therefore more stable than it was previously.

We can think of free energy as a measure of a system's instability—its tendency to change to a more stable state. Unstable systems (higher G) tend to change in such a way that they become more stable (lower G). For example, a diver on top of a platform is less stable (more likely to fall) than when floating in the water; a drop of concentrated dye is less stable (more likely to disperse) than when the dye is spread randomly through the liquid; and a glucose molecule is less stable (more likely to break down) than the simpler molecules into which it can be split (Figure 9.5). Unless something prevents it, each of these systems will move toward greater stability: The diver falls, the solution becomes uniformly colored, and the glucose molecule is broken down into smaller molecules.

Another term that describes a state of maximum stability is *equilibrium*, which you learned about in Chapter 2 in connection with chemical reactions. There is an important relationship between free energy and equilibrium, including chemical equilibrium. Recall that most chemical reactions are reversible and proceed to a point at which the forward and backward reactions occur at the same rate. The reaction is then said to be at chemical equilibrium, and there is no further net change in the relative concentration of products and reactants.

As a reaction proceeds toward equilibrium, the free energy of the mixture of reactants and products decreases. Free energy increases when a reaction is somehow pushed away from equilibrium, perhaps by removing some of the products (and thus changing their concentration relative to that of the reactants). For a system at equilibrium, G is at its lowest possible value in that system. We can think of the equilibrium state as a free-energy valley. Any change from the equilibrium position will have a positive ΔG and will not be spontaneous. For this reason, systems never spontaneously move away from equilibrium. Because a system at equilibrium cannot spontaneously change, it can do no work. *A process is spontaneous and can perform work only when it is moving toward equilibrium.*

Free Energy and Metabolism

We can now apply the free-energy concept more specifically to the chemistry of life's processes.

Exergonic and Endergonic Reactions in Metabolism

Based on their free-energy changes, chemical reactions can be classified as either exergonic ("energy outward") or endergonic ("energy inward"). An **exergonic reaction** proceeds

- More free energy (higher G)
- Less stable
- Greater work capacity

In a **spontaneous change**
- The free energy of the system decreases ($\Delta G < 0$)
- The system becomes more stable
- The released free energy can be harnessed to do work

- Less free energy (lower G)
- More stable
- Less work capacity

(a) Gravitational motion. Objects move spontaneously from a higher altitude to a lower one.

(b) Diffusion. Molecules in a drop of dye diffuse until they are randomly dispersed.

(c) Chemical reaction. In a cell, a glucose molecule is broken down into simpler molecules.

▲ **Figure 9.5 The relationship of free energy to stability, work capacity, and spontaneous change.** Unstable systems (top) are rich in free energy, G. They have a tendency to change spontaneously to a more stable state (bottom), and it is possible to harness this "downhill" change to perform work.

MAKE CONNECTIONS *Compare the redistribution of molecules shown in (b) to the transport of hydrogen ions (H^+) across a membrane by a proton pump, creating a concentration gradient, as shown in Figure 7.17. Which process(es) result(s) in higher free energy? Which system(s) can do work?*

(a) Exergonic reaction: energy released, spontaneous

(b) Endergonic reaction: energy required, nonspontaneous

with a net release of free energy **(Figure 9.6a)**. Because the chemical mixture loses free energy (G decreases), ΔG is negative for an exergonic reaction. Using ΔG as a standard for spontaneity, exergonic reactions are those that occur spontaneously. (Remember, the word *spontaneous* implies that it is energetically favorable, not that it will occur rapidly.) The magnitude of ΔG for an exergonic reaction represents the maximum amount of work the reaction can perform.* The greater the decrease in free energy, the greater the amount of work that can be done.

We can use the overall reaction for cellular respiration as an example:

$$C_6H_{12}O_6 + 6\,O_2 \rightarrow 6\,CO_2 + 6\,H_2O$$
$$\Delta G = -686 \text{ kcal/mol } (-2{,}870 \text{ kJ/mol})$$

For each mole (180 g) of glucose broken down by respiration under what are called "standard conditions" (1 M of each

---

*The word *maximum* qualifies this statement, because some of the free energy is released as heat and cannot do work. Therefore, ΔG represents a theoretical upper limit of available energy.

reactant and product, 25°C, pH 7), 686 kcal (2,870 kJ) of energy are made available for work. Because energy must be conserved, the chemical products of respiration store 686 kcal less free energy per mole than the reactants. The products are, in a sense, the spent exhaust of a process that tapped the free energy stored in the bonds of the sugar molecules.

It is important to realize that the breaking of bonds does not release energy; on the contrary, as you will soon see, it requires energy. The phrase "energy stored in bonds" is shorthand for the potential energy that can be released when new bonds are formed after the original bonds break, as long as the products are of lower free energy than the reactants.

An **endergonic reaction** is one that absorbs free energy from its surroundings **(Figure 9.6b)**. Because this kind of reaction essentially *stores* free energy in molecules (G increases), ΔG is positive. Such reactions are nonspontaneous, and the magnitude of ΔG is the quantity of energy required to drive the reaction. If a chemical process is exergonic (downhill), releasing energy in one direction, then the reverse process must be endergonic (uphill), using energy. A reversible process cannot be downhill in both directions. If $\Delta G = -686$ kcal/mol for respiration, which converts glucose and oxygen to carbon dioxide and water, then the reverse process—the conversion of carbon dioxide and water to glucose and oxygen—must be strongly endergonic, with $\Delta G = +686$ kcal/mol. Such a reaction would never happen by itself.

How, then, do plants make the sugar that organisms use for energy? Plants get the required energy—686 kcal to make a mole of glucose—from the environment by capturing light and converting its energy to chemical energy. Next, in a long series of exergonic steps, they gradually spend that chemical energy to assemble glucose molecules.

Equilibrium and Metabolism

Reactions in an isolated system eventually reach equilibrium and can then do no work, as illustrated by the isolated hydroelectric system in **Figure 9.7**. The chemical reactions of metabolism are reversible, and they, too, would reach

▲ **Figure 9.7 Equilibrium and work in an isolated hydroelectric system.** Water flowing downhill turns a turbine that drives a generator providing electricity to a lightbulb, but only until the system reaches equilibrium.

equilibrium if they occurred in the isolation of a test tube. Because systems at equilibrium are at a minimum of G and can do no work, a cell that has reached metabolic equilibrium is dead! The fact that metabolism as a whole is never at equilibrium is one of the defining features of life.

Like most systems, a living cell is not in equilibrium. The constant flow of materials in and out of the cell keeps the metabolic pathways from ever reaching equilibrium, and the cell continues to do work throughout its life. This principle is illustrated by the open (and more realistic) hydroelectric system in **Figure 9.8a**. However, unlike this simple system in which water flowing downhill turns a single turbine, a catabolic pathway in a cell releases free energy in a series of reactions. An example is cellular respiration, illustrated by analogy in **Figure 9.8b**. Some of the reversible reactions of respiration are constantly "pulled" in one direction—that is, they are kept out of equilibrium. The key to maintaining this lack of equilibrium is that the product of a reaction does not accumulate but instead becomes a reactant in the next step; finally, waste products are expelled from the cell. The overall sequence of reactions is kept going by the huge free-energy difference between glucose and oxygen at the top of the energy "hill" and carbon dioxide and water at the "downhill" end. As long as our cells have a steady supply of glucose or other fuels and oxygen and are able to expel waste products to the surroundings, their metabolic pathways never reach equilibrium and can continue to do the work of life.

Stepping back to look at the big picture, we can see once again how important it is to think of organisms as open systems. Sunlight provides a daily source of free energy for an ecosystem's plants and other photosynthetic organisms. Animals and other nonphotosynthetic organisms in an ecosystem must have a source of free energy in the form of the organic products of photosynthesis. Now that we have applied the free-energy concept to metabolism, we are ready to see how a cell actually performs the work of life.

CONCEPT 9.3

ATP powers cellular work by coupling exergonic reactions to endergonic reactions

A cell does three main kinds of work:

- *Chemical work*, the pushing of endergonic reactions that would not occur spontaneously, such as the synthesis of polymers from monomers (chemical work will be discussed further here and in Chapters 8 and 9)
- *Transport work*, the pumping of substances across membranes against the direction of spontaneous movement (see Chapter 7)
- *Mechanical work*, such as the beating of cilia (see Chapter 6), the contraction of muscle cells, and the movement of chromosomes during cellular reproduction

A key feature in the way cells manage their energy resources to do this work is **energy coupling**, the use of an exergonic process to drive an endergonic one. ATP is responsible for mediating most energy coupling in cells, and in most cases it acts as the immediate source of energy that powers cellular work.

(a) An open hydroelectric system. Water flowing through a turbine keeps driving the generator because intake and outflow of water keep the system from reaching equilibrium.

(b) A multistep open hydroelectric system. Cellular respiration is analogous to this system: Glucose is broken down in a series of exergonic reactions that power the work of the cell. The product of each reaction is used as the reactant for the next, so no reaction reaches equilibrium.

▲ **Figure 9.8 Equilibrium and work in open systems.**

The Structure and Hydrolysis of ATP

ATP (adenosine triphosphate) was introduced when we discussed the phosphate group as a functional group (see Concept 4.3). ATP contains the sugar ribose, with the nitrogenous base adenine and a chain of three phosphate groups (the triphosphate group) bonded to it **(Figure 9.9a)**. In addition to its role in energy coupling, ATP is also one of the nucleoside triphosphates used to make RNA (see Figure 5.24).

The bonds between the phosphate groups of ATP can be broken by hydrolysis. When the terminal phosphate bond is broken by addition of a water molecule, a molecule of inorganic phosphate ($HOPO_3^{2-}$, abbreviated ⓟ$_i$ throughout this book) leaves the ATP, which becomes adenosine diphosphate, or ADP **(Figure 9.9b)**. The reaction is exergonic and releases 7.3 kcal of energy per mole of ATP hydrolyzed:

$$ATP + H_2O \rightarrow ADP + ⓟ_i$$
$$\Delta G = -7.3 \text{ kcal/mol } (-30.5 \text{ kJ/mol})$$

This is the free-energy change measured under standard conditions. In the cell, conditions do not conform to standard conditions, primarily because reactant and product concentrations differ from 1 M. For example, when ATP hydrolysis occurs under cellular conditions, the actual ΔG is about −13 kcal/mol, 78% greater than the energy released by ATP hydrolysis under standard conditions.

Because their hydrolysis releases energy, the phosphate bonds of ATP are sometimes referred to as high-energy phosphate bonds, but the term is misleading. The phosphate bonds of ATP are not unusually strong bonds, as "high-energy" may imply; rather, the reactants (ATP and water) themselves have high energy relative to the energy of the products (ADP and ⓟ$_i$). The release of energy during the hydrolysis of ATP comes from the chemical change of the system to a state of lower free energy, not from the phosphate bonds themselves.

ATP is useful to the cell because the energy it releases on losing a phosphate group is somewhat greater than the energy most other molecules could deliver. But why does this hydrolysis release so much energy? If we reexamine the ATP molecule in Figure 9.9a, we can see that all three phosphate groups are negatively charged. These like charges are crowded together, and their mutual repulsion contributes to the instability of this region of the ATP molecule. The triphosphate tail of ATP is the chemical equivalent of a compressed spring.

How the Hydrolysis of ATP Performs Work

When ATP is hydrolyzed in a test tube, the release of free energy merely heats the surrounding water. In an organism, this same generation of heat can sometimes be beneficial. For instance, the process of shivering uses ATP hydrolysis during muscle contraction to warm the body. In most cases

(a) The structure of ATP. In the cell, most hydroxyl groups of phosphates are ionized (—O⁻).

(b) The hydrolysis of ATP. The reaction of ATP and water yields inorganic phosphate (ⓟ$_i$) and ADP and releases energy.

▲ **Figure 9.9 The structure and hydrolysis of adenosine triphosphate (ATP).** Throughout this book, the chemical structure of the triphosphate group seen in (a) will be represented by the three joined yellow circles shown in (b).

in the cell, however, the generation of heat alone would be an inefficient (and potentially dangerous) use of a valuable energy resource. Instead, the cell's proteins harness the energy released during ATP hydrolysis in several ways to perform the three types of cellular work—chemical, transport, and mechanical.

For example, with the help of specific enzymes, the cell is able to use the energy released by ATP hydrolysis directly to drive chemical reactions that, by themselves, are endergonic. If the ΔG of an endergonic reaction is less than the amount of energy released by ATP hydrolysis, then the two reactions can be coupled so that, overall, the coupled reactions are exergonic. This usually involves phosphorylation, the transfer of a phosphate group from ATP to some other molecule, such as the reactant. The recipient molecule with the phosphate group covalently bonded to it is then called a **phosphorylated intermediate**. The key to coupling exergonic and endergonic reactions is the formation of this phosphorylated intermediate, which is more reactive

(a) Glutamic acid conversion to glutamine. Glutamine synthesis from glutamic acid (Glu) by itself is endergonic (ΔG is positive), so it is not spontaneous.

(b) Conversion reaction coupled with ATP hydrolysis. In the cell, glutamine synthesis occurs in two steps, coupled by a phosphorylated intermediate. **1** ATP phosphorylates glutamic acid, making it less stable. **2** Ammonia displaces the phosphate group, forming glutamine.

(c) Free-energy change for coupled reaction. ΔG for the glutamic acid conversion to glutamine (+3.4 kcal/mol) plus ΔG for ATP hydrolysis (–7.3 kcal/mol) gives the free-energy change for the overall reaction (–3.9 kcal/mol). Because the overall process is exergonic (net ΔG is negative), it occurs spontaneously.

▲ **Figure 9.10 How ATP drives chemical work: Energy coupling using ATP hydrolysis.** In this example, the exergonic process of ATP hydrolysis is used to drive an endergonic process— the cellular synthesis of the amino acid glutamine from glutamic acid and ammonia.

MAKE CONNECTIONS *Referring to Figure 5.14, explain why glutamine (Gln) is diagrammed as a glutamic acid (Glu) with an amino group attached.*

(less stable) than the original unphosphorylated molecule (**Figure 9.10**).

Transport and mechanical work in the cell are also nearly always powered by the hydrolysis of ATP. In these cases, ATP hydrolysis leads to a change in a protein's shape and often its ability to bind another molecule. Sometimes this occurs via a phosphorylated intermediate, as seen for the transport protein in **Figure 9.11a**. In most instances of mechanical work involving motor proteins "walking" along cytoskeletal elements (**Figure 9.11b**), a cycle occurs in which ATP is first bound noncovalently to the motor protein. Next, ATP is hydrolyzed, releasing ADP and Ⓟᵢ. Another ATP molecule can then bind. At each stage, the motor protein changes its shape and ability to bind the cytoskeleton, resulting in movement of the protein along the cytoskeletal track. Phosphorylation and dephosphorylation promote crucial protein shape changes during many other important cellular processes as well.

(a) Transport work: ATP phosphorylates transport proteins.

(b) Mechanical work: ATP binds noncovalently to motor proteins and then is hydrolyzed.

▲ **Figure 9.11 How ATP drives transport and mechanical work.** ATP hydrolysis causes changes in the shapes and binding affinities of proteins. This can occur either **(a)** directly, by phosphorylation, as shown for a membrane protein carrying out active transport of a solute (see also Figure 7.15), or **(b)** indirectly, via noncovalent binding of ATP and its hydrolytic products, as is the case for motor proteins that move vesicles (and other organelles) along cytoskeletal "tracks" in the cell (see also Figure 6.21).

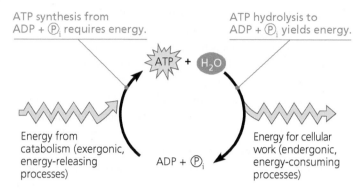

ATP synthesis from ADP + Ⓟ$_i$ requires energy.

ATP hydrolysis to ADP + Ⓟ$_i$ yields energy.

ATP + H$_2$O

Energy from catabolism (exergonic, energy-releasing processes)

Energy for cellular work (endergonic, energy-consuming processes)

ADP + Ⓟ$_i$

▲ **Figure 9.12 The ATP cycle.** Energy released by breakdown reactions (catabolism) in the cell is used to phosphorylate ADP, regenerating ATP. Chemical potential energy stored in ATP drives most cellular work.

The Regeneration of ATP

An organism at work uses ATP continuously, but ATP is a renewable resource that can be regenerated by the addition of phosphate to ADP **(Figure 9.12)**. The free energy required to phosphorylate ADP comes from exergonic breakdown reactions (catabolism) in the cell. This shuttling of inorganic phosphate and energy is called the ATP cycle, and it couples the cell's energy-yielding (exergonic) processes to the energy-consuming (endergonic) ones. The ATP cycle proceeds at an astonishing pace. For example, a working muscle cell recycles its entire pool of ATP in less than a minute. That turnover represents 10 million molecules of ATP consumed and regenerated per second per cell. If ATP could not be regenerated by the phosphorylation of ADP, humans would use up nearly their body weight in ATP each day.

Because both directions of a reversible process cannot be downhill, the regeneration of ATP is necessarily endergonic:

$$ADP + Ⓟ_i \rightarrow ATP + H_2O$$
$$\Delta G = +7.3 \text{ kcal/mol} (+30.5 \text{ kJ/mol}) \text{ (standard conditions)}$$

Since ATP formation from ADP and Ⓟ$_i$ is not spontaneous, free energy must be spent to make it occur. Catabolic (exergonic) pathways, especially cellular respiration, provide the energy for the endergonic process of making ATP. Plants also use light energy to produce ATP. Thus, the ATP cycle is a revolving door through which energy passes during its transfer from catabolic to anabolic pathways.

CONCEPT CHECK 9.3

1. How does ATP typically transfer energy from exergonic to endergonic reactions in the cell?

2. Which of the following has more free energy: glutamic acid + ammonia + ATP OR glutamine + ADP + Ⓟ$_i$? Explain your answer.

3. **MAKE CONNECTIONS** Does Figure 9.11a show passive or active transport? Explain. (See Concepts 7.3 and 7.4.)

CONCEPT 9.4

Enzymes speed up metabolic reactions by lowering energy barriers

The laws of thermodynamics tell us what will and will not happen under given conditions but say nothing about the rate of these processes. A spontaneous chemical reaction occurs without any requirement for outside energy, but it may occur so slowly that it is imperceptible. For example, even though the hydrolysis of sucrose (table sugar) to glucose and fructose is exergonic, occurring spontaneously with a release of free energy ($\Delta G = -7$ kcal/mol), a solution of sucrose dissolved in sterile water will sit for years at room temperature with no appreciable hydrolysis. However, if we add a small amount of the enzyme sucrase to the solution, then all the sucrose may be hydrolyzed within seconds, as shown below:

Sucrase

+ H$_2$O

Sucrose (C$_{12}$H$_{22}$O$_{11}$)   Glucose (C$_6$H$_{12}$O$_6$)   Fructose (C$_6$H$_{12}$O$_6$)

How does the enzyme do this?

An **enzyme** is a macromolecule that acts as a **catalyst**, a chemical agent that speeds up a reaction without being consumed by the reaction. In this chapter, we are focusing on enzymes that are proteins. (Some RNA molecules, called ribozymes, can function as enzymes; these will be discussed in Chapter 17.) Without regulation by enzymes, chemical traffic through the pathways of metabolism would become terribly congested because many chemical reactions would take such a long time. In the next two sections, we will see why spontaneous reactions can be slow and how an enzyme changes the situation.

The Activation Energy Barrier

Every chemical reaction between molecules involves both bond breaking and bond forming. For example, the hydrolysis of sucrose involves breaking the bond between glucose and fructose and one of the bonds of a water molecule and then forming two new bonds, as shown above. Changing one molecule into another generally involves contorting the starting molecule into a highly unstable state before the reaction can proceed. This contortion can be compared to the bending of a metal key ring when you pry it open to add a new key. The key ring is highly unstable in its opened form but returns to a stable state once the key is threaded all the way onto the ring. To reach the contorted state where bonds can change, reactant molecules must absorb energy from their surroundings. When the new bonds of the product molecules form, energy is released as heat, and the molecules return to stable shapes with lower energy than the contorted state.

The initial investment of energy for starting a reaction—the energy required to contort the reactant molecules so the bonds can break—is known as the *free energy of activation*, or **activation energy**, abbreviated E_A in this book. We can think of activation energy as the amount of energy needed to push the reactants to the top of an energy barrier, or uphill, so that the "downhill" part of the reaction can begin. Activation energy is often supplied by heat in the form of thermal energy that the reactant molecules absorb from the surroundings. The absorption of thermal energy accelerates the reactant molecules, so they collide more often and more forcefully. It also agitates the atoms within the molecules, making the breakage of bonds more likely. When the molecules have absorbed enough energy for the bonds to break, the reactants are in an unstable condition known as the *transition state*.

Figure 9.13 graphs the energy changes for a hypothetical exergonic reaction that swaps portions of two reactant molecules:

$$AB + CD \rightarrow AC + BD$$
$$\text{Reactants} \qquad \text{Products}$$

The reactants AB and CD must absorb enough energy from the surroundings to reach the unstable transition state, where bonds can break.

After bonds have broken, new bonds form, releasing energy to the surroundings.

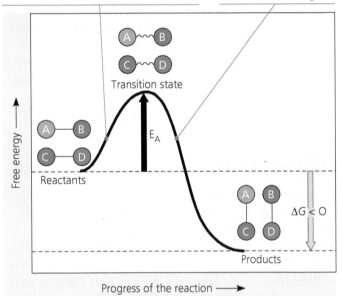

▲ Figure 9.13 Energy profile of an exergonic reaction. The "molecules" are hypothetical, with A, B, C, and D representing portions of the molecules. Thermodynamically, this is an exergonic reaction, with a negative ΔG, and the reaction occurs spontaneously. However, the activation energy (E_A) provides a barrier that determines the rate of the reaction.

DRAW IT *Graph the progress of an endergonic reaction in which EF and GH form products EG and FH, assuming that the reactants must pass through a transition state.*

The activation of the reactants is represented by the uphill portion of the graph, in which the free-energy content of the reactant molecules is increasing. At the summit, when energy equivalent to E_A has been absorbed, the reactants are in the transition state: They are activated, and their bonds can be broken. As the atoms then settle into their new, more stable bonding arrangements, energy is released to the surroundings. This corresponds to the downhill part of the curve, which shows the loss of free energy by the molecules. The overall decrease in free energy means that E_A is repaid with dividends, as the formation of new bonds releases more energy than was invested in the breaking of old bonds.

The reaction shown in Figure 9.13 is exergonic and occurs spontaneously ($\Delta G < 0$). However, the activation energy provides a barrier that determines the rate of the reaction. The reactants must absorb enough energy to reach the top of the activation energy barrier before the reaction can occur. For some reactions, E_A is modest enough that even at room temperature there is sufficient thermal energy for many of the reactant molecules to reach the transition state in a short time. In most cases, however, E_A is so high and the transition state is reached so rarely that the reaction will hardly proceed at all. In these cases, the reaction will occur at a noticeable rate only if energy is provided, usually by heat. For example, the reaction of gasoline and oxygen is exergonic and will occur spontaneously, but energy is required for the molecules to reach the transition state and react. Only when the spark plugs fire in an automobile engine can there be the explosive release of energy that pushes the pistons. Without a spark, a mixture of gasoline hydrocarbons and oxygen will not react because the E_A barrier is too high.

How Enzymes Speed Up Reactions

Proteins, DNA, and other complex cellular molecules are rich in free energy and have the potential to decompose spontaneously; that is, the laws of thermodynamics favor their breakdown. These molecules persist only because at temperatures typical for cells, few molecules can make it over the hump of activation energy. The barriers for selected reactions must occasionally be surmounted, however, for cells to carry out the processes needed for life. Heat can increase the rate of a reaction by allowing reactants to attain the transition state more often, but this would not work well in biological systems. First, high temperature denatures proteins and kills cells. Second, heat would speed up *all* reactions, not just those that are needed. Instead of heat, organisms use catalysis to speed up reactions.

An enzyme catalyzes a reaction by lowering the E_A barrier (Figure 9.14), enabling the reactant molecules to absorb enough energy to reach the transition state even at moderate temperatures, as we'll discuss shortly. An enzyme cannot change the ΔG for a reaction; it cannot make an endergonic

▲ **Figure 9.14 The effect of an enzyme on activation energy.** Without affecting the free-energy change (ΔG) for a reaction, an enzyme speeds the reaction by reducing its activation energy (E_A).

reaction exergonic. Enzymes can only hasten reactions that would eventually occur anyway, but this enables the cell to have a dynamic metabolism, routing chemicals smoothly through metabolic pathways. Also, enzymes are very specific for the reactions they catalyze, so they determine which chemical processes will be going on in the cell at any given time.

Substrate Specificity of Enzymes

The reactant an enzyme acts on is referred to as the enzyme's **substrate**. The enzyme binds to its substrate (or substrates, when there are two or more reactants), forming an **enzyme-substrate complex**. While enzyme and substrate are joined, the catalytic action of the enzyme converts the

substrate to the product (or products) of the reaction. The overall process can be summarized as follows:

$$\text{Enzyme + Substrate(s)} \rightleftharpoons \text{Enzyme-substrate complex} \rightleftharpoons \text{Enzyme + Product(s)}$$

For example, the enzyme sucrase (most enzyme names end in *-ase*) catalyzes the hydrolysis of the disaccharide sucrose into its two monosaccharides, glucose and fructose (see p. 175):

$$\text{Sucrase + Sucrose + } H_2O \rightleftharpoons \text{Sucrase-sucrose-}H_2O \text{ complex} \rightleftharpoons \text{Sucrase + Glucose + Fructose}$$

The reaction catalyzed by each enzyme is very specific; an enzyme can recognize its specific substrate even among closely related compounds. For instance, sucrase will act only on sucrose and will not bind to other disaccharides, such as maltose. What accounts for this molecular recognition? Recall that most enzymes are proteins, and proteins are macromolecules with unique three-dimensional configurations. The specificity of an enzyme results from its shape, which is a consequence of its amino acid sequence.

Only a restricted region of the enzyme molecule actually binds to the substrate. This region, called the **active site**, is typically a pocket or groove on the surface of the enzyme where catalysis occurs **(Figure 9.15a)**. Usually, the active site is formed by only a few of the enzyme's amino acids, with the rest of the protein molecule providing a framework that determines the shape of the active site. The specificity of an enzyme is attributed to a complementary fit between the shape of its active site and the shape of the substrate.

An enzyme is not a stiff structure locked into a given shape. In fact, recent work by biochemists has shown clearly that enzymes (and other proteins as well) seem to "dance" between subtly different shapes in a dynamic equilibrium, with slight differences in free energy for each "pose." The shape that best fits the substrate isn't necessarily the one with the lowest energy, but during the very short time the enzyme takes on this shape, its active site can bind to the substrate. It has been known for more than 50 years that the active site itself is also not a rigid receptacle for the substrate. As the substrate enters the active site, the enzyme changes shape slightly due to interactions between the substrate's chemical groups and chemical groups on the side chains of the amino acids that form the active site. This shape change makes the active site fit even more snugly around the substrate **(Figure 9.15b)**. The process is like

Substrate

Active site

Enzyme

Enzyme-substrate complex

(a) In this space-filling model of the enzyme hexokinase (blue), the active site forms a groove on the surface. The enzyme's substrate is glucose (red).

(b) When the substrate enters the active site, it forms weak bonds with the enzyme, inducing a change in the shape of the protein. This change allows additional weak bonds to form, causing the active site to enfold the substrate and hold it in place.

▲ **Figure 9.15 Induced fit between an enzyme and its substrate.**

a clasping handshake, with binding between enzyme and substrate becoming tighter after the initial contact. This so-called **induced fit** brings chemical groups of the active site into positions that enhance their ability to catalyze the chemical reaction.

Catalysis in the Enzyme's Active Site

In most enzymatic reactions, the substrate is held in the active site by so-called weak interactions, such as hydrogen bonds and ionic bonds. R groups of a few of the amino acids that make up the active site catalyze the conversion of substrate to product, and the product departs from the active site. The enzyme is then free to take another substrate molecule into its active site. The entire cycle happens so fast that a single enzyme molecule typically acts on about a thousand substrate molecules per second, and some enzymes are even faster. Enzymes, like other catalysts, emerge from the reaction in their original form. Therefore, very small amounts of enzyme can have a huge metabolic impact by functioning over and over again in catalytic cycles. **Figure 9.16** shows a catalytic cycle involving two substrates and two products.

Most metabolic reactions are reversible, and an enzyme can catalyze either the forward or the reverse reaction, depending on which direction has a negative ΔG. This in turn depends mainly on the relative concentrations of reactants and products. The net effect is always in the direction of equilibrium.

Enzymes use a variety of mechanisms that lower activation energy and speed up a reaction (see Figure 9.16, step ❸):

- When there are two or more reactants, the active site provides a template on which the substrates can come together in the proper orientation for a reaction to occur between them.
- As the active site of an enzyme clutches the bound substrates, the enzyme may stretch the substrate molecules toward their transition-state form, stressing and bending critical chemical bonds that must be broken during the reaction. Because E_A is proportional to the difficulty of breaking the bonds, distorting the substrate helps it approach the transition state and thus reduces the amount of free energy that must be absorbed to achieve that state.
- The active site may also provide a microenvironment that is more conducive to a particular type of reaction than the solution itself would be without the enzyme. For example, if the active site has amino acids with acidic R groups, the active site may be a pocket of low pH in an otherwise neutral cell. In such cases, an acidic amino acid may facilitate H^+ transfer to the substrate as a key step in catalyzing the reaction.
- Amino acids in the active site directly participate in the chemical reaction. Sometimes this process even involves

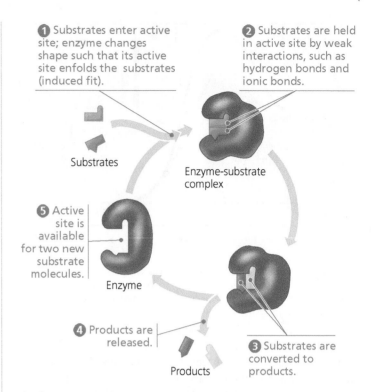

❶ Substrates enter active site; enzyme changes shape such that its active site enfolds the substrates (induced fit).

❷ Substrates are held in active site by weak interactions, such as hydrogen bonds and ionic bonds.

Substrates

Enzyme-substrate complex

❺ Active site is available for two new substrate molecules.

Enzyme

❹ Products are released.

Products

❸ Substrates are converted to products.

▲ **Figure 9.16 The active site and catalytic cycle of an enzyme.** An enzyme can convert one or more reactant molecules to one or more product molecules. The enzyme shown here converts two substrate molecules to two product molecules.

DRAW IT *The enzyme-substrate complex passes through a transition state (see Figure 9.13). Label the part of the cycle where the transition state occurs.*

brief covalent bonding between the substrate and the side chain of an amino acid of the enzyme. Subsequent steps of the reaction restore the side chains to their original states, so that the active site is the same after the reaction as it was before.

The rate at which a particular amount of enzyme converts substrate to product is partly a function of the initial concentration of the substrate: The more substrate molecules that are available, the more frequently they access the active sites of the enzyme molecules. However, there is a limit to how fast the reaction can be pushed by adding more substrate to a fixed concentration of enzyme. At some point, the concentration of substrate will be high enough that all enzyme molecules have their active sites engaged. As soon as the product exits an active site, another substrate molecule enters. At this substrate concentration, the enzyme is said to be *saturated*, and the rate of the reaction is determined by the speed at which the active site converts substrate to product. When an enzyme population is saturated, the only way to increase the rate of product formation is to add more enzyme. Cells often increase the rate of a reaction by producing more enzyme molecules. You can graph the overall progress of an enzymatic reaction in the Scientific Skills Exercise.

Making a Line Graph and Calculating a Slope

Does the Rate of Glucose 6-Phosphatase Activity Change over Time in Isolated Liver Cells? Glucose 6-phosphatase, which is found in mammalian liver cells, is a key enzyme in control of blood glucose levels. The enzyme catalyzes the breakdown of glucose 6-phosphate into glucose and inorganic phosphate (P_i). These products are transported out of liver cells into the blood, increasing blood glucose levels. In this exercise, you will graph data from a time-course experiment that measured P_i concentration in the buffer outside isolated liver cells, thus indirectly measuring glucose 6-phosphatase activity inside the cells.

How the Experiment Was Done Isolated rat liver cells were placed in a dish with buffer at physiological conditions (pH 7.4, 37°C). Glucose 6-phosphate (the substrate) was added to the dish, where it was taken up by the cells. Then a sample of buffer was removed every 5 minutes and the concentration of P_i determined.

Data from the Experiment

Time (min)	Concentration of P_i (μmol/mL)
0	0
5	10
10	90
15	180
20	270
25	330
30	355
35	355
40	355

Interpret the Data

1. To see patterns in the data from a time-course experiment like this, it is helpful to graph the data. First, determine which set of data goes on each axis. (a) What did the researchers intentionally vary in the experiment? This is the independent variable, which goes on the x-axis. (b) What are the units (abbreviated) for the independent variable? Explain in words what the abbreviation stands for. (c) What was measured by the researchers? This is the dependent variable, which goes on the y-axis. (d) What does the units abbreviation stand for? Label each axis, including the units.

2. Next, you'll want to mark off the axes with just enough evenly spaced tick marks to accommodate the full set of data. Determine the range of data values for each axis. (a) What is the largest value to go on the x-axis? What is a reasonable spacing for the tick marks, and what should be the highest one? (b) What is the largest value to go on the y-axis? What is a reasonable spacing for the tick marks, and what should be the highest one?

3. Plot the data points on your graph. Match each x-value with its partner y-value and place a point on the graph at that coordinate. Draw a line that connects the points.

4. Examine your graph and look for patterns in the data. (a) Does the concentration of P_i increase evenly through the course of the experiment? To answer this question, describe the pattern you see in the graph. (b) What part of the graph shows the highest rate of enzyme activity? Consider that the rate of enzyme activity is related to the slope of the line, $\Delta y / \Delta x$ (the "rise" over the "run"), in μmol/mL · min, with the steepest slope indicating the highest rate of enzyme activity. Calculate the rate of enzyme activity (slope) where the graph is steepest. (c) Can you think of a biological explanation for the pattern you see?

5. If your blood sugar level is low from skipping lunch, what reaction (discussed in this exercise) will occur in your liver cells? Write out the reaction and put the name of the enzyme over the reaction arrow. How will this reaction affect your blood sugar level?

MB A version of this Scientific Skills Exercise can be assigned in MasteringBiology.

Data from S. R. Commerford et al., Diets enriched in sucrose or fat increase gluconeogenesis and G-6-Pase but not basal glucose production in rats, *American Journal of Physiology—Endocrinology and Metabolism* 283:E545–E555 (2002).

Effects of Local Conditions on Enzyme Activity

The activity of an enzyme—how efficiently the enzyme functions—is affected by general environmental factors, such as temperature and pH. It can also be affected by chemicals that specifically influence that enzyme. In fact, researchers have learned much about enzyme function by employing such chemicals.

Effects of Temperature and pH

Recall from Chapter 5 that the three-dimensional structures of proteins are sensitive to their environment. As a consequence, each enzyme works better under some conditions than under other conditions, because these *optimal conditions* favor the most active shape for the enzyme.

Temperature and pH are environmental factors important in the activity of an enzyme. Up to a point, the rate of an enzymatic reaction increases with increasing temperature, partly because substrates collide with active sites more frequently when the molecules move rapidly. Above that temperature, however, the speed of the enzymatic reaction drops sharply. The thermal agitation of the enzyme molecule disrupts the hydrogen bonds, ionic bonds, and other weak interactions that stabilize the active shape of the enzyme, and the protein molecule eventually denatures. Each enzyme has an optimal temperature at which its reaction rate is greatest. Without denaturing the enzyme, this temperature allows the greatest number of molecular collisions and the fastest conversion of the reactants to product molecules. Most human enzymes have optimal temperatures of about 35–40°C (close to human body temperature). The thermophilic bacteria that live in hot springs contain enzymes with optimal temperatures of 70°C or higher **(Figure 9.17a)**.

(a) Optimal temperature for two enzymes

(b) Optimal pH for two enzymes

▲ **Figure 9.17 Environmental factors affecting enzyme activity.** Each enzyme has an optimal **(a)** temperature and **(b)** pH that favor the most active shape of the protein molecule.

DRAW IT *Given that a mature lysosome has an internal pH of around 4.5, draw a curve in (b) showing what you would predict for a lysosomal enzyme, labeling its optimal pH.*

Just as each enzyme has an optimal temperature, it also has a pH at which it is most active. The optimal pH values for most enzymes fall in the range of pH 6–8, but there are exceptions. For example, pepsin, a digestive enzyme in the human stomach, works best at pH 2. Such an acidic environment denatures most enzymes, but pepsin is adapted to maintain its functional three-dimensional structure in the acidic environment of the stomach. In contrast, trypsin, a digestive enzyme residing in the alkaline environment of the human intestine, has an optimal pH of 8 and would be denatured in the stomach **(Figure 9.17b)**.

Cofactors

Many enzymes require nonprotein helpers for catalytic activity. These adjuncts, called **cofactors**, may be bound tightly to the enzyme as permanent residents, or they may bind loosely and reversibly along with the substrate. The cofactors of some enzymes are inorganic, such as the metal atoms zinc, iron, and copper in ionic form. If the cofactor is an organic molecule, it is referred to, more specifically, as a **coenzyme**. Most vitamins are important in nutrition because they act as coenzymes or raw materials from which coenzymes are made.

Enzyme Inhibitors

Certain chemicals selectively inhibit the action of specific enzymes. Sometimes, the inhibitor attaches to the enzyme by covalent bonds, in which case the inhibition is usually irreversible. Many enzyme inhibitors, however, bind to the enzyme by weak interactions, and when this occurs the inhibition is reversible. Some reversible inhibitors resemble the normal substrate molecule and compete for admission into the active site **(Figure 9.18a** and **b)**. These mimics, called **competitive inhibitors**, reduce the productivity of enzymes by blocking substrates from entering active sites. This kind of inhibition can be overcome by increasing the concentration of substrate so that as active sites become available, more substrate molecules than inhibitor molecules are around to gain entry to the sites.

In contrast, **noncompetitive inhibitors** do not directly compete with the substrate to bind to the enzyme at the active site **(Figure 9.18c)**. Instead, they impede enzymatic reactions by binding to another part of the enzyme. This interaction causes the enzyme molecule to change its shape

▼ **Figure 9.18 Inhibition of enzyme activity.**

(a) Normal binding

A substrate can bind normally to the active site of an enzyme.

Substrate
Active site
Enzyme

(b) Competitive inhibition

A competitive inhibitor mimics the substrate, competing for the active site.

Competitive inhibitor

(c) Noncompetitive inhibition

A noncompetitive inhibitor binds to the enzyme away from the active site, altering the shape of the enzyme so that even if the substrate can bind, the active site functions less effectively, if it all.

Noncompetitive inhibitor

in such a way that the active site becomes less effective at catalyzing the conversion of substrate to product.

Toxins and poisons are often irreversible enzyme inhibitors. An example is sarin, a nerve gas. Sarin was released by terrorists in the Tokyo subway in 1995, causing the death of several people and injury to many others. This small molecule binds covalently to the R group on the amino acid serine, which is found in the active site of acetylcholinesterase, an enzyme important in the nervous system. Other examples include the pesticides DDT and parathion, inhibitors of key enzymes in the nervous system. Finally, many antibiotics are inhibitors of specific enzymes in bacteria. For instance, penicillin blocks the active site of an enzyme that many bacteria use to make their cell walls.

The Evolution of Enzymes

EVOLUTION Thus far, biochemists have discovered and named more than 4,000 different enzymes in various species, most likely a very small fraction of all enzymes. How did this grand profusion of enzymes arise? Recall that most enzymes are proteins, and proteins are encoded by genes. A permanent change in a gene, known as a *mutation*, can result in a protein with one or more changed amino acids. In the case of an enzyme, if the changed amino acids are in the active site or some other crucial region, the altered enzyme might have a novel activity or might bind to a different substrate. Under environmental conditions where the new function benefits the organism, natural selection would tend to favor the mutated form of the gene, causing it to persist in the population. This simplified model is generally accepted as the main way in which the multitude of different enzymes arose over the past few billion years of life's history.

Data supporting this model have been collected by researchers using a lab procedure that mimics evolution in natural populations. One group tested whether the function of an enzyme called β-galactosidase could change over time in populations of the bacterium *Escherichia coli* (*E. coli*). β-galactosidase breaks down the disaccharide lactose into the simple sugars glucose and galactose. Using molecular techniques, the researchers introduced random mutations into *E. coli* genes and then tested the bacteria for their ability to break down a slightly different disaccharide (one that has the sugar fucose in place of galactose). At the end of the experiment, the "evolved" enzyme bound the new substrate several hundred times more strongly, and broke it down 10 to 20 times more quickly, than did the original enzyme.

The researchers found that six amino acids had changed in the enzyme altered in this experiment. Two of these changed amino acids were in the active site, two were nearby, and two were on the surface of the protein **(Figure 9.19)**. This experiment and others like it strengthen the notion that a few changes can indeed alter enzyme function.

Two changed amino acids were found near the active site.

Active site

Two changed amino acids were found in the active site.

Two changed amino acids were found on the surface.

▲ **Figure 9.19 Mimicking evolution of an enzyme with a new function.** After seven rounds of mutation and selection in a lab, the enzyme β-galactosidase evolved into an enzyme specialized for breaking down a sugar different from lactose. This ribbon model shows one subunit of the altered enzyme; six amino acids were different.

CONCEPT CHECK **9.4**

1. Many spontaneous reactions occur very slowly. Why don't all spontaneous reactions occur instantly?

2. Why do enzymes act only on very specific substrates?

3. **WHAT IF?** Malonate is an inhibitor of the enzyme succinate dehydrogenase. How would you determine whether malonate is a competitive or noncompetitive inhibitor?

4. **MAKE CONNECTIONS** In nature, what conditions could lead to natural selection favoring bacteria with enzymes that could break down the fucose-containing disaccharide discussed above? See the discussion of natural selection in Concept 1.2.

CONCEPT 9.5

Regulation of enzyme activity helps control metabolism

Chemical chaos would result if all of a cell's metabolic pathways were operating simultaneously. Intrinsic to life's processes is a cell's ability to tightly regulate its metabolic pathways by controlling when and where its various enzymes are active. It does this either by switching on and off the genes that encode specific enzymes (as we will discuss in Unit Three) or, as we discuss here, by regulating the activity of enzymes once they are made.

Allosteric Regulation of Enzymes

In many cases, the molecules that naturally regulate enzyme activity in a cell behave something like reversible noncompetitive inhibitors (see Figure 9.18c): These regulatory molecules change an enzyme's shape and the functioning of its active site by binding to a site elsewhere on the molecule, via noncovalent interactions. **Allosteric regulation** is the term used to describe any case in which a protein's function at one site is affected by the binding of a regulatory molecule to a separate site. It may result in either inhibition or stimulation of an enzyme's activity.

Allosteric Activation and Inhibition

Most enzymes known to be allosterically regulated are constructed from two or more subunits, each composed of a polypeptide chain with its own active site. The entire complex oscillates between two different shapes, one catalytically active and the other inactive (**Figure 9.20a**). In the simplest kind of allosteric regulation, an activating or inhibiting regulatory molecule binds to a regulatory site (sometimes called an allosteric site), often located where subunits join. The binding of an *activator* to a regulatory site stabilizes the shape that has functional active sites, whereas the binding of an *inhibitor* stabilizes the inactive form of the enzyme. The subunits of an allosteric enzyme fit together in such a way that a shape change in one subunit is transmitted to all others. Through this interaction of subunits, a single activator or inhibitor molecule that binds to one regulatory site will affect the active sites of all subunits.

Fluctuating concentrations of regulators can cause a sophisticated pattern of response in the activity of cellular enzymes. The products of ATP hydrolysis (ADP and P_i), for example, play a complex role in balancing the flow of traffic between anabolic and catabolic pathways by their effects on key enzymes. ATP binds to several catabolic enzymes allosterically, lowering their affinity for substrate and thus inhibiting their activity. ADP, however, functions as an activator of the same enzymes. This is logical because catabolism functions in regenerating ATP. If ATP production lags behind its use, ADP accumulates and activates the enzymes that speed up catabolism, producing more ATP. If the supply of ATP exceeds demand, then catabolism slows down as ATP molecules accumulate and bind to the same enzymes, inhibiting them. (You'll see specific examples of this type of regulation when you learn about cellular respiration in the next chapter.) ATP, ADP, and other related molecules also affect key enzymes in anabolic pathways. In this way, allosteric enzymes control the rates of important reactions in both sorts of metabolic pathways.

In another kind of allosteric activation, a *substrate* molecule binding to one active site in a multisubunit enzyme triggers a shape change in all the subunits, thereby increasing catalytic activity at the other active sites (**Figure 9.20b**). Called **cooperativity**, this mechanism amplifies the response of enzymes to substrates: One substrate molecule primes an enzyme to act on additional substrate molecules more readily. Cooperativity is considered "allosteric" regulation

▼ **Figure 9.20 Allosteric regulation of enzyme activity.**

(a) Allosteric activators and inhibitors

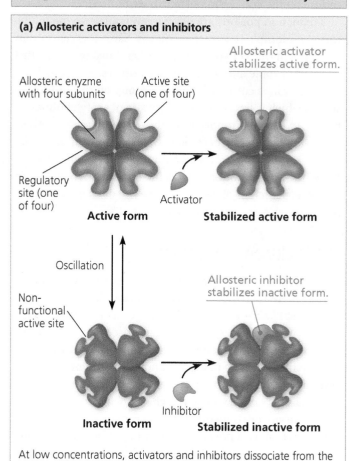

At low concentrations, activators and inhibitors dissociate from the enzyme. The enzyme can then oscillate again.

(b) Cooperativity: another type of allosteric activation

The inactive form shown on the left oscillates with the active form when the active form is not stabilized by substrate.

because binding of the substrate to one active site affects catalysis in another active site.

Although hemoglobin is not an enzyme (it carries O_2), classic studies on hemoglobin have elucidated the principle of cooperativity. Hemoglobin is made up of four subunits, each with an oxygen-binding site (see Figure 5.18). The binding of an oxygen molecule to one binding site increases the affinity for oxygen of the remaining binding sites. Thus, where oxygen is at high levels, such as in the lungs or gills, hemoglobin's affinity for oxygen increases as more binding sites are filled. In oxygen-deprived tissues, however, the release of each oxygen molecule decreases the oxygen affinity of the other binding sites, resulting in the release of oxygen where it is most needed. Cooperativity works similarly in multisubunit enzymes that have been studied.

Feedback Inhibition

When ATP allosterically inhibits an enzyme in an ATP-generating pathway, the result is feedback inhibition, a common mode of metabolic control. In **feedback inhibition**, a metabolic pathway is halted by the inhibitory binding of its end product to an enzyme that acts early in the pathway. **Figure 9.21** shows an example of feedback inhibition operating on an anabolic pathway. Some cells use this five-step pathway to synthesize the amino acid isoleucine from threonine, another amino acid. As isoleucine accumulates, it slows down its own synthesis by allosterically inhibiting the enzyme for the first step of the pathway. Feedback inhibition thereby prevents the cell from making more isoleucine than is necessary and thus wasting chemical resources.

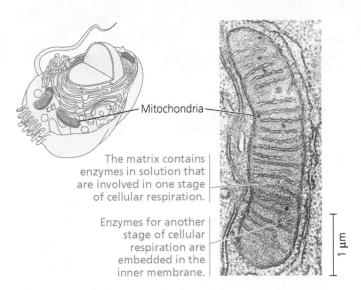

▲ **Figure 9.22 Organelles and structural order in metabolism.** Organelles such as the mitochondrion (TEM) contain enzymes that carry out specific functions, in this case cellular respiration.

Localization of Enzymes Within the Cell

The cell is not just a bag of chemicals with thousands of different kinds of enzymes and substrates in a random mix. The cell is compartmentalized, and cellular structures help bring order to metabolic pathways. In some cases, a team of enzymes for several steps of a metabolic pathway are assembled into a multienzyme complex. The arrangement facilitates the sequence of reactions, with the product from the first enzyme becoming the substrate for an adjacent enzyme in the complex, and so on, until the end product is released. Some enzymes and enzyme complexes have fixed locations within the cell and act as structural components of particular membranes. Others are in solution within particular membrane-enclosed eukaryotic organelles, each with its own internal chemical environment. For example, in eukaryotic cells, the enzymes for cellular respiration reside in specific locations within mitochondria **(Figure 9.22)**.

In this chapter, you have learned that metabolism, the intersecting set of chemical pathways characteristic of life, is a choreographed interplay of thousands of different kinds of cellular molecules. In the next chapter, we will explore cellular respiration, the major catabolic pathway that breaks down organic molecules, releasing energy that can be used for the crucial processes of life.

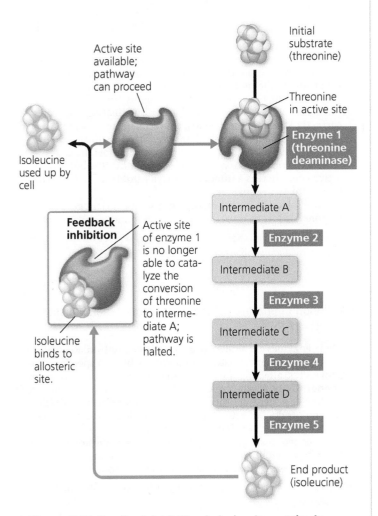

▲ **Figure 9.21 Feedback inhibition in isoleucine synthesis.**

CONCEPT CHECK 9.5

1. How do an activator and an inhibitor have different effects on an allosterically regulated enzyme?

2. Regulation of isoleucine synthesis is an example of feedback inhibition of an anabolic pathway. With that in mind, explain how ATP might be involved in feedback inhibition of a catabolic pathway.

SUMMARY OF KEY CONCEPTS

CONCEPT 9.1

An organism's metabolism transforms matter and energy, subject to the laws of thermodynamics (pp. 166–169)

- **Metabolism** is the collection of chemical reactions that occur in an organism. Enzymes catalyze reactions in intersecting **metabolic pathways**, which may be **catabolic** (breaking down molecules, releasing energy) or **anabolic** (building molecules, consuming energy).
- **Energy** is the capacity to cause change; some forms of energy do work by moving matter. **Kinetic energy** is associated with motion and includes **thermal energy** associated with random motion of atoms or molecules. **Heat** is thermal energy in transfer from one object to another. **Potential energy** is related to the location or structure of matter and includes **chemical energy** possessed by a molecule due to its structure.
- **The first law of thermodynamics**, conservation of energy, states that energy cannot be created or destroyed, only transferred or transformed. The **second law of thermodynamics** states that **spontaneous processes**, those requiring no outside input of energy, increase the **entropy** (disorder) of the universe.

? *Explain how the highly ordered structure of a cell does not conflict with the second law of thermodynamics.*

CONCEPT 9.2

The free-energy change of a reaction tells us whether or not the reaction occurs spontaneously (pp. 169–172)

- A living system's **free energy** is energy that can do work under cellular conditions. The change in free energy (ΔG) during a biological process is related directly to enthalpy change (ΔH) and to the change in entropy (ΔS): $\Delta G = \Delta H - T\Delta S$. Organisms live at the expense of free energy. A spontaneous process occurs with no energy input; during such a process, free energy decreases and the stability of a system increases. At maximum stability, the system is at equilibrium and can do no work.
- In an **exergonic** (spontaneous) chemical reaction, the products have less free energy than the reactants ($-\Delta G$). **Endergonic** (nonspontaneous) reactions require an input of energy ($+\Delta G$). The addition of starting materials and the removal of end products prevent metabolism from reaching equilibrium.

? *Explain the meaning of each component in the equation for the change in free energy of a spontaneous chemical reaction. Why are spontaneous reactions important in the metabolism of a cell?*

CONCEPT 9.3

ATP powers cellular work by coupling exergonic reactions to endergonic reactions (pp. 172–175)

- **ATP** is the cell's energy shuttle. Hydrolysis of its terminal phosphate yields ADP and ⓟᵢ and releases free energy.
- Through **energy coupling**, the exergonic process of ATP hydrolysis drives endergonic reactions by transfer of a phosphate group to specific reactants, forming a **phosphorylated intermediate** that is more reactive. ATP hydrolysis (sometimes with protein phosphorylation) also causes changes in the shape and binding affinities of transport and motor proteins.
- Catabolic pathways drive regeneration of ATP from ADP + ⓟᵢ.

? *Describe the ATP cycle: How is ATP used and regenerated in a cell?*

CONCEPT 9.4

Enzymes speed up metabolic reactions by lowering energy barriers (pp. 175–181)

- In a chemical reaction, the energy necessary to break the bonds of the reactants is the **activation energy**, E_A.
- **Enzymes** lower the E_A barrier:

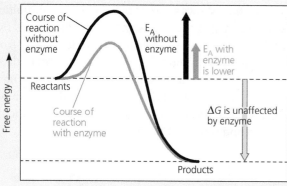

- Each enzyme has a unique **active site** that binds one or more **substrate(s)**, the reactants on which it acts. It then changes shape, binding the substrate(s) more tightly (**induced fit**).
- The active site can lower an E_A barrier by orienting substrates correctly, straining their bonds, providing a favorable microenvironment, or even covalently bonding with the substrate.
- Each enzyme has an optimal temperature and pH. Inhibitors reduce enzyme function. A **competitive inhibitor** binds to the active site, whereas a **noncompetitive inhibitor** binds to a different site on the enzyme.
- Natural selection, acting on organisms with variant enzymes, is responsible for the diversity of enzymes found in organisms.

? *How do both activation energy barriers and enzymes help maintain the structural and metabolic order of life?*

CONCEPT 9.5

Regulation of enzyme activity helps control metabolism (pp. 181–183)

- Many enzymes are subject to **allosteric regulation**: Regulatory molecules, either activators or inhibitors, bind to specific regulatory sites, affecting the shape and function of the enzyme. In **cooperativity**, binding of one substrate molecule can stimulate binding or activity at other active sites. In **feedback inhibition**, the end product of a metabolic pathway allosterically inhibits the enzyme for a previous step in the pathway.
- Some enzymes are grouped into complexes, some are incorporated into membranes, and some are contained inside organelles, increasing the efficiency of metabolic processes.

? *What roles do allosteric regulation and feedback inhibition play in the metabolism of a cell?*

LEVEL 1: KNOWLEDGE/COMPREHENSION

1. Choose the pair of terms that correctly completes this sentence: Catabolism is to anabolism as _____ is to
   _____.
   a. exergonic; spontaneous
   b. exergonic; endergonic
   c. free energy; entropy
   d. work; energy

2. Most cells cannot harness heat to perform work because
   a. heat does not involve a transfer of energy.
   b. cells do not have much thermal energy; they are relatively cool.
   c. temperature is usually uniform throughout a cell.
   d. heat can never be used to do work.

3. Which of the following metabolic processes can occur without a net influx of energy from some other process?
   a. $ADP + \textcircled{P}_i \rightarrow ATP + H_2O$
   b. $C_6H_{12}O_6 + 6\ O_2 \rightarrow 6\ CO_2 + 6\ H_2O$
   c. $6\ CO_2 + 6\ H_2O \rightarrow C_6H_{12}O_6 + 6\ O_2$
   d. Amino acids $\rightarrow$ Protein

4. If an enzyme in solution is saturated with substrate, the most effective way to obtain a faster yield of products is to
   a. add more of the enzyme.
   b. heat the solution to 90°C.
   c. add more substrate.
   d. add a noncompetitive inhibitor.

5. Some bacteria are metabolically active in hot springs because
   a. they are able to maintain a lower internal temperature.
   b. high temperatures make catalysis unnecessary.
   c. their enzymes have high optimal temperatures.
   d. their enzymes are completely insensitive to temperature.

LEVEL 2: APPLICATION/ANALYSIS

6. If an enzyme is added to a solution where its substrate and product are in equilibrium, what will occur?
   a. Additional substrate will be formed.
   b. The reaction will change from endergonic to exergonic.
   c. The free energy of the system will change.
   d. Nothing; the reaction will stay at equilibrium.

LEVEL 3: SYNTHESIS/EVALUATION

7. **DRAW IT** Using a series of arrows, draw the branched metabolic reaction pathway described by the following statements, and then answer the question at the end. Use red arrows and minus signs to indicate inhibition.

   L can form either M or N.

   M can form O.

   O can form either P or R.

   P can form Q.

   R can form S.

   O inhibits the reaction of L to form M.

   Q inhibits the reaction of O to form P.

   S inhibits the reaction of O to form R.

   Which reaction would prevail if both Q and S were present in the cell in high concentrations?
   a. $L \rightarrow M$
   b. $M \rightarrow O$
   c. $L \rightarrow N$
   d. $O \rightarrow P$

8. **EVOLUTION CONNECTION** A recent revival of the antievolutionary "intelligent design" argument holds that biochemical pathways are too complex to have evolved, because all intermediate steps in a given pathway must be present to produce the final product. Critique this argument. How could you use the diversity of metabolic pathways that produce the same or similar products to support your case?

9. **SCIENTIFIC INQUIRY**
   DRAW IT A researcher has developed an assay to measure the activity of an important enzyme present in liver cells growing in culture. She adds the enzyme's substrate to a dish of cells and then measures the appearance of reaction products. The results are graphed as the amount of product on the y-axis versus time on the x-axis. The researcher notes four sections of the graph. For a short period of time, no products appear (section A). Then (section B) the reaction rate is quite high (the slope of the line is steep). Next, the reaction gradually slows down (section C). Finally, the graph line becomes flat (section D). Draw and label the graph, and propose a model to explain the molecular events occurring at each stage of this reaction profile.

10. **WRITE ABOUT A THEME: ENERGY AND MATTER**
    Life requires energy. In a short essay (100–150 words), describe the basic principles of bioenergetics in an animal cell. How is the flow and transformation of energy different in a photosynthesizing cell? Include the role of ATP and enzymes in your discussion.

11. SYNTHESIZE YOUR KNOWLEDGE

Explain what is happening in this photo in terms of kinetic energy and potential energy. Include the energy conversions that occur when the penguins eat fish and climb back up on the glacier. Describe the role of ATP and enzymes in the underlying molecular processes, including what happens to the free energy of some of the molecules involved.

MasteringBiology®

Students Go to **MasteringBiology** for assignments, the eText, and the Study Area with practice tests, animations, and activities.

Instructors Go to **MasteringBiology** for automatically graded tutorials and questions that you can assign to your students, plus Instructor Resources.

10

Cellular Respiration and Fermentation

▲ Figure 10.1 **How do these leaves power the work of life for this giraffe?**

Life Is Work

Living cells require transfusions of energy from outside sources to perform their many tasks—for example, assembling polymers, pumping substances across membranes, moving, and reproducing. The giraffe in **Figure 10.1** is obtaining energy for its cells by eating the leaves of plants; some other animals obtain energy by feeding on other organisms that eat plants.

The energy stored in the organic molecules of food ultimately comes from the sun. Energy flows into an ecosystem as sunlight and exits as heat; in contrast, the chemical elements essential to life are recycled **(Figure 10.2)**. Photosynthesis generates oxygen and organic molecules that are used by the mitochondria of eukaryotes (including plants and algae) as fuel for cellular respiration. Respiration breaks this fuel down, generating ATP. The waste products of this type of respiration, carbon dioxide and water, are the raw materials for photosynthesis.

In this chapter, we consider how cells harvest the chemical energy stored in organic molecules and use it to generate ATP, the molecule that drives most cellular work. After presenting some basics about respiration, we'll focus on three key pathways of respiration: glycolysis, the citric acid cycle, and oxidative phosphorylation. We'll also consider fermentation, a somewhat simpler pathway coupled to glycolysis that has deep evolutionary roots.

Light energy

ECOSYSTEM

Photosynthesis
in chloroplasts

$CO_2 + H_2O$

Organic molecules $+ O_2$

Cellular respiration
in mitochondria

ATP

ATP powers most cellular work

Heat energy

▲ **Figure 10.2 Energy flow and chemical recycling in ecosystems.** Energy flows into an ecosystem as sunlight and ultimately leaves as heat, while the chemical elements essential to life are recycled.

CONCEPT 10.1

Catabolic pathways yield energy by oxidizing organic fuels

Metabolic pathways that release stored energy by breaking down complex molecules are called catabolic pathways (see Chapter 9). Electron transfer plays a major role in these pathways. In this section, we consider these processes, which are central to cellular respiration.

Catabolic Pathways and Production of ATP

Organic compounds possess potential energy as a result of the arrangement of electrons in the bonds between their atoms. Compounds that can participate in exergonic reactions can act as fuels. Through the activity of enzymes, a cell systematically degrades complex organic molecules that are rich in potential energy to simpler waste products that have less energy. Some of the energy taken out of chemical storage can be used to do work; the rest is dissipated as heat.

One catabolic process, **fermentation**, is a partial degradation of sugars or other organic fuel that occurs without the use of oxygen. However, the most efficient catabolic pathway is **aerobic respiration**, in which oxygen is consumed as a reactant along with the organic fuel (*aerobic* is from the Greek *aer*, air, and *bios*, life). The cells of most eukaryotic and many prokaryotic organisms can carry out aerobic respiration. Some prokaryotes use substances other than oxygen as reactants in a similar process that harvests chemical energy without oxygen; this process is called

anaerobic respiration (the prefix *an-* means "without"). Technically, the term **cellular respiration** includes both aerobic and anaerobic processes. However, it originated as a synonym for aerobic respiration because of the relationship of that process to organismal respiration, in which an animal breathes in oxygen. Thus, *cellular respiration* is often used to refer to the aerobic process, a practice we follow in most of this chapter.

Although very different in mechanism, aerobic respiration is in principle similar to the combustion of gasoline in an automobile engine after oxygen is mixed with the fuel (hydrocarbons). Food provides the fuel for respiration, and the exhaust is carbon dioxide and water. The overall process can be summarized as follows:

$$\text{Organic compounds} + \text{Oxygen} \rightarrow \text{Carbon dioxide} + \text{Water} + \text{Energy}$$

Carbohydrates, fats, and protein molecules from food can all be processed and consumed as fuel, as we will discuss later in the chapter. In animal diets, a major source of carbohydrates is starch, a storage polysaccharide that can be broken down into glucose ($C_6H_{12}O_6$) subunits. Here, we will learn the steps of cellular respiration by tracking the degradation of the sugar glucose:

$$C_6H_{12}O_6 + 6\ O_2 \rightarrow 6\ CO_2 + 6\ H_2O + \text{Energy (ATP + heat)}$$

This breakdown of glucose is exergonic, having a free-energy change of −686 kcal (2,870 kJ) per mole of glucose decomposed ($\Delta G = -686$ kcal/mol). Recall that a negative ΔG indicates that the products of the chemical process store less energy than the reactants and that the reaction can happen spontaneously—in other words, without an input of energy.

Catabolic pathways do not directly move flagella, pump solutes across membranes, polymerize monomers, or perform other cellular work. Catabolism is linked to work by a chemical drive shaft—ATP (see Chapter 11). To keep working, the cell must regenerate its supply of ATP from ADP and Ⓟ$_i$ (see Figure 11.12). To understand how cellular respiration accomplishes this, let's examine the fundamental chemical processes known as oxidation and reduction.

Redox Reactions: Oxidation and Reduction

How do the catabolic pathways that decompose glucose and other organic fuels yield energy? The answer is based on the transfer of electrons during the chemical reactions. The relocation of electrons releases energy stored in organic molecules, and this energy ultimately is used to synthesize ATP.

The Principle of Redox

In many chemical reactions, there is a transfer of one or more electrons (e^-) from one reactant to another. These electron transfers are called oxidation-reduction reactions, or **redox reactions** for short. In a redox reaction, the loss of electrons from one substance is called **oxidation**, and the addition of electrons to another substance is known as **reduction**. (Note that *adding* electrons is called *reduction*; adding negatively charged electrons to an atom *reduces* the amount of positive charge of that atom.) To take a simple, nonbiological example, consider the reaction between the elements sodium (Na) and chlorine (Cl) that forms table salt:

$$Na + Cl \longrightarrow Na^+ + Cl^-$$

becomes oxidized (loses electron)
becomes reduced (gains electron)

We could generalize a redox reaction this way:

$$Xe^- + Y \longrightarrow X + Ye^-$$

becomes oxidized
becomes reduced

In the generalized reaction, substance Xe^-, the electron donor, is called the **reducing agent**; it reduces Y, which accepts the donated electron. Substance Y, the electron acceptor, is the **oxidizing agent**; it oxidizes Xe^- by removing its electron. Because an electron transfer requires both an electron donor and an acceptor, oxidation and reduction always go hand in hand.

Not all redox reactions involve the complete transfer of electrons from one substance to another; some change the degree of electron sharing in covalent bonds. Methane combustion, shown in **Figure 10.3**, is an example. The covalent electrons in methane are shared nearly equally between the bonded atoms because carbon and hydrogen have about the same affinity for valence electrons; they are about equally electronegative (see Chapter 2). But when methane reacts with oxygen, forming carbon dioxide, electrons end up shared less equally between the carbon atom and its new covalent partners, the oxygen atoms, which are very electronegative. In effect, the carbon atom has partially "lost" its shared electrons; thus, methane has been oxidized.

Now let's examine the fate of the reactant O_2. The two atoms of the oxygen molecule (O_2) share their electrons equally. But when oxygen reacts with the hydrogen from methane, forming water, the electrons of the covalent bonds spend more time near the oxygen (see Figure 10.3). In effect, each oxygen atom has partially "gained" electrons, so the oxygen molecule has been reduced. Because oxygen is so electronegative, it is one of the most potent of all oxidizing agents.

Energy must be added to pull an electron away from an atom, just as energy is required to push a ball uphill. The more electronegative the atom (the stronger its pull on electrons), the more energy is required to take an electron away from it. An electron loses potential energy when it shifts from a less electronegative atom toward a more electronegative one, just as a ball loses potential energy when it rolls

▲ **Figure 10.3 Methane combustion as an energy-yielding redox reaction.** The reaction releases energy to the surroundings because the electrons lose potential energy when they end up being shared unequally, spending more time near electronegative atoms such as oxygen.

downhill. A redox reaction that moves electrons closer to oxygen, such as the burning (oxidation) of methane, therefore releases chemical energy that can be put to work.

Oxidation of Organic Fuel Molecules During Cellular Respiration

The oxidation of methane by oxygen is the main combustion reaction that occurs at the burner of a gas stove. The combustion of gasoline in an automobile engine is also a redox reaction; the energy released pushes the pistons. But the energy-yielding redox process of greatest interest to biologists is respiration: the oxidation of glucose and other molecules in food. Examine again the summary equation for cellular respiration, but this time think of it as a redox process:

$$C_6H_{12}O_6 + 6 O_2 \longrightarrow 6 CO_2 + 6 H_2O + Energy$$

becomes oxidized
becomes reduced

As in the combustion of methane or gasoline, the fuel (glucose) is oxidized and oxygen is reduced. The electrons lose potential energy along the way, and energy is released.

In general, organic molecules that have an abundance of hydrogen are excellent fuels because their bonds are a source of "hilltop" electrons, whose energy may be released as these electrons "fall" down an energy gradient when they are transferred to oxygen. The summary equation for respiration indicates that hydrogen is transferred from glucose to oxygen. But the important point, not visible in the summary equation, is that the energy state of the electron changes as hydrogen (with its electron) is transferred to oxygen. In respiration, the oxidation of glucose transfers electrons to a lower energy state, liberating energy that becomes available for ATP synthesis.

The main energy-yielding foods—carbohydrates and fats—are reservoirs of electrons associated with hydrogen.

Only the barrier of activation energy holds back the flood of electrons to a lower energy state (see Figure 9.13). Without this barrier, a food substance like glucose would combine almost instantaneously with O_2. If we supply the activation energy by igniting glucose, it burns in air, releasing 686 kcal (2,870 kJ) of heat per mole of glucose (about 180 g). Body temperature is not high enough to initiate burning, of course. Instead, if you swallow some glucose, enzymes in your cells will lower the barrier of activation energy, allowing the sugar to be oxidized in a series of steps.

Stepwise Energy Harvest via NAD⁺ and the Electron Transport Chain

If energy is released from a fuel all at once, it cannot be harnessed efficiently for constructive work. For example, if a gasoline tank explodes, it cannot drive a car very far. Cellular respiration does not oxidize glucose (or any other organic fuel) in a single explosive step either. Rather, glucose is broken down in a series of steps, each one catalyzed by an enzyme. At key steps, electrons are stripped from the glucose. As is often the case in oxidation reactions, each electron travels with a proton—thus, as a hydrogen atom. The hydrogen atoms are not transferred directly to oxygen, but instead are usually passed first to an electron carrier, a coenzyme called **NAD⁺** (nicotinamide adenine dinucleotide, a derivative of the vitamin niacin). NAD⁺ is well suited as an electron carrier because it can cycle easily between oxidized (NAD⁺) and reduced (NADH) states. As an electron acceptor, NAD⁺ functions as an oxidizing agent during respiration.

How does NAD⁺ trap electrons from glucose and the other organic molecules in food? Enzymes called dehydrogenases remove a pair of hydrogen atoms (2 electrons and 2 protons) from the substrate (glucose, in the above example),

thereby oxidizing it. The enzyme delivers the 2 electrons along with 1 proton to its coenzyme, NAD⁺ **(Figure 10.4)**. The other proton is released as a hydrogen ion (H⁺) into the surrounding solution:

$$H-\overset{|}{\underset{|}{C}}-OH + NAD^+ \xrightarrow{\text{Dehydrogenase}} \overset{|}{C}=O + NADH + H^+$$

By receiving 2 negatively charged electrons but only 1 positively charged proton, the nicotinamide portion of NAD⁺ has its charge neutralized when NAD⁺ is reduced to NADH. The name NADH shows the hydrogen that has been received in the reaction. NAD⁺ is the most versatile electron acceptor in cellular respiration and functions in several of the redox steps during the breakdown of glucose.

Electrons lose very little of their potential energy when they are transferred from glucose to NAD⁺. Each NADH molecule formed during respiration represents stored energy. This energy can be tapped to make ATP when the electrons complete their "fall" in a series of steps down an energy gradient from NADH to oxygen.

How do electrons that are extracted from glucose and stored as potential energy in NADH finally reach oxygen? It will help to compare the redox chemistry of cellular respiration to a much simpler reaction: the reaction between hydrogen and oxygen to form water **(Figure 10.5a)**. Mix H_2 and O_2, provide a spark for activation energy, and the gases combine explosively. In fact, combustion of liquid H_2 and O_2 was harnessed to help power the main engines of the Space Shuttle, boosting it into orbit. The explosion represents a release of energy as the electrons of hydrogen "fall" closer to the electronegative oxygen atoms. Cellular respiration also brings hydrogen and oxygen together to form water, but there are two important differences. First, in cellular respiration, the hydrogen that reacts with oxygen is derived from

▲ **Figure 10.4 NAD⁺ as an electron shuttle.** The full name for NAD⁺, nicotinamide adenine dinucleotide, describes its structure—the molecule consists of two nucleotides joined together at their phosphate groups (shown in yellow). (Nicotinamide is a nitrogenous base, although not one that is present in DNA or RNA; see Figure 5.24.) The enzymatic transfer of 2 electrons and 1 proton (H⁺) from an organic molecule in food to NAD⁺ reduces the NAD⁺ to NADH: Most of the electrons removed from food are transferred initially to NAD⁺, forming NADH.

? *Describe the structural differences between the oxidized form and the reduced form of nicotinamide.*

organic molecules rather than H_2. Second, instead of occurring in one explosive reaction, respiration uses an electron transport chain to break the fall of electrons to oxygen into several energy-releasing steps (**Figure 10.5b**). An **electron transport chain** consists of a number of molecules, mostly proteins, built into the inner membrane of the mitochondria of eukaryotic cells (and the plasma membrane of respiring prokaryotes). Electrons removed from glucose are shuttled by NADH to the "top," higher-energy end of the chain. At the "bottom," lower-energy end, O_2 captures these electrons along with hydrogen nuclei (H^+), forming water. (Anaerobically respiring prokaryotes have an electron acceptor at the end of the chain that is different from O_2.)

Electron transfer from NADH to oxygen is an exergonic reaction with a free-energy change of -53 kcal/mol (-222 kJ/mol). Instead of this energy being released and wasted in a single explosive step, electrons cascade down the chain from one carrier molecule to the next in a series of redox reactions, losing a small amount of energy with each step until they finally reach oxygen, the terminal electron acceptor, which has a very great affinity for electrons. Each "downhill" carrier is more electronegative than, and thus capable of oxidizing, its "uphill" neighbor, with oxygen at the bottom of the chain. Therefore, the electrons transferred from glucose to NAD^+, which is thus reduced to NADH, fall down an energy gradient in the electron transport chain to a far more stable location in the electronegative oxygen atom. Put another way, oxygen pulls electrons down the chain in an energy-yielding tumble analogous to gravity pulling objects downhill.

In summary, during cellular respiration, most electrons travel the following "downhill" route: glucose → NADH → electron transport chain → oxygen. Later in this chapter, you will learn more about how the cell uses the energy released from this exergonic electron fall to regenerate its supply of ATP. For now, having covered the basic redox mechanisms of cellular respiration, let's look at the entire process by which energy is harvested from organic fuels.

The Stages of Cellular Respiration: *A Preview*

The harvesting of energy from glucose by cellular respiration is a cumulative function of three metabolic stages. We list them here along with a color-coding scheme we will use throughout the chapter to help you keep track of the big picture:

1. GLYCOLYSIS (color-coded blue throughout the chapter)
2. PYRUVATE OXIDATION and the CITRIC ACID CYCLE (color-coded orange)
3. OXIDATIVE PHOSPHORYLATION: Electron transport and chemiosmosis (color-coded purple)

Biochemists usually reserve the term *cellular respiration* for stages 2 and 3 together. In this text, however, we include glycolysis as a part of cellular respiration because most respiring cells deriving energy from glucose use glycolysis to produce the starting material for the citric acid cycle.

As diagrammed in **Figure 10.6**, glycolysis and pyruvate oxidation followed by the citric acid cycle are the catabolic pathways that break down glucose and other organic fuels. **Glycolysis**, which occurs in the cytosol, begins the degradation process by breaking glucose into two molecules of a compound called pyruvate. In eukaryotes, pyruvate enters the mitochondrion and is oxidized to a compound called acetyl CoA, which enters the **citric acid cycle**. There, the breakdown of glucose to carbon dioxide is completed. (In prokaryotes, these processes take place in the cytosol.) Thus, the carbon dioxide produced by respiration represents fragments of oxidized organic molecules.

Some of the steps of glycolysis and the citric acid cycle are redox reactions in which dehydrogenases transfer electrons from substrates to NAD^+, forming NADH. In the third stage of respiration, the electron transport chain accepts electrons (most often via

(a) Uncontrolled reaction

(b) Cellular respiration

▲ **Figure 10.5 An introduction to electron transport chains. (a)** The one-step exergonic reaction of hydrogen with oxygen to form water releases a large amount of energy in the form of heat and light: an explosion. **(b)** In cellular respiration, the same reaction occurs in stages: An electron transport chain breaks the "fall" of electrons in this reaction into a series of smaller steps and stores some of the released energy in a form that can be used to make ATP. (The rest of the energy is released as heat.)

► **Figure 10.6 An overview of cellular respiration.** During glycolysis, each glucose molecule is broken down into two molecules of the compound pyruvate. In eukaryotic cells, as shown here, the pyruvate enters the mitochondrion. There it is oxidized to acetyl CoA, which is further oxidized to CO_2 in the citric acid cycle. NADH and a similar electron carrier, a coenzyme called $FADH_2$, transfer electrons derived from glucose to electron transport chains, which are built into the inner mitochondrial membrane. (In prokaryotes, the electron transport chains are located in the plasma membrane.) During oxidative phosphorylation, electron transport chains convert the chemical energy to a form used for ATP synthesis in the process called chemiosmosis.

 ANIMATION **BioFlix** Visit the Study Area in **MasteringBiology** for the BioFlix® 3-D Animation on Cellular Respiration. BioFlix Tutorials can also be assigned in MasteringBiology.

NADH) from the breakdown products of the first two stages and passes these electrons from one molecule to another. At the end of the chain, the electrons are combined with molecular oxygen and hydrogen ions (H^+), forming water (see Figure 10.5b). The energy released at each step of the chain is stored in a form the mitochondrion (or prokaryotic cell) can use to make ATP from ADP. This mode of ATP synthesis is called **oxidative phosphorylation** because it is powered by the redox reactions of the electron transport chain.

In eukaryotic cells, the inner membrane of the mitochondrion is the site of electron transport and chemiosmosis, the processes that together constitute oxidative phosphorylation. (In prokaryotes, these processes take place in the plasma membrane.) Oxidative phosphorylation accounts for almost 90% of the ATP generated by respiration. A smaller amount of ATP is formed directly in a few reactions of glycolysis and the citric acid cycle by a mechanism called **substrate-level phosphorylation** (Figure 10.7). This

mode of ATP synthesis occurs when an enzyme transfers a phosphate group from a substrate molecule to ADP, rather than adding an inorganic phosphate to ADP as in oxidative phosphorylation. "Substrate molecule" here refers to an organic molecule generated as an intermediate during the catabolism of glucose. You'll see examples of substrate-level phosphorylation later in the chapter, in both glycolysis and the citric acid cycle.

When you withdraw a relatively large sum of money from an ATM machine, it is not delivered to you in a single bill of larger denomination. Instead, a number of smaller denomination bills are dispensed that you can spend more easily. This is analogous to ATP production during cellular respiration. For each molecule of glucose degraded to carbon dioxide and water by respiration, the cell makes up to about 32 molecules of ATP, each with 7.3 kcal/mol of free energy. Respiration cashes in the large denomination of energy banked in a single molecule of glucose (686 kcal/mol) for the small change of many molecules of ATP, which is more practical for the cell to spend on its work.

This preview has introduced you to how glycolysis, the citric acid cycle, and oxidative phosphorylation fit into the process of cellular respiration. We are now ready to take a closer look at each of these three stages of respiration.

▲ **Figure 10.7 Substrate-level phosphorylation.** Some ATP is made by direct transfer of a phosphate group from an organic substrate to ADP by an enzyme. (For examples in glycolysis, see Figure 10.9, steps 7 and 10.)

MAKE CONNECTIONS *Review Figure 9.9. Do you think the potential energy is higher for the reactants or the products in the reaction shown above? Explain.*

CONCEPT CHECK 10.1

1. Compare and contrast aerobic and anaerobic respiration.

2. **WHAT IF?** If the following redox reaction occurred, which compound would be oxidized? Reduced?

$$C_4H_6O_5 + NAD^+ \rightarrow C_4H_4O_5 + NADH + H^+$$

Glycolysis harvests chemical energy by oxidizing glucose to pyruvate

The word *glycolysis* means "sugar splitting," and that is exactly what happens during this pathway. Glucose, a six-carbon sugar, is split into two three-carbon sugars. These smaller sugars are then oxidized and their remaining atoms rearranged to form two molecules of pyruvate. (Pyruvate is the ionized form of pyruvic acid.)

As summarized in **Figure 10.8**, glycolysis can be divided into two phases: the energy investment phase and the energy payoff phase. During the energy investment phase, the cell actually spends ATP. This investment is repaid with interest during the energy payoff phase, when ATP is produced by substrate-level phosphorylation and NAD^+ is reduced to NADH by electrons released from the oxidation of glucose. The net energy yield from glycolysis, per glucose molecule, is 2 ATP plus 2 NADH. The ten steps of the glycolytic pathway are shown in **Figure 10.9**.

All of the carbon originally present in glucose is accounted for in the two molecules of pyruvate; no carbon is released as CO_2 during glycolysis. Glycolysis occurs whether or not O_2 is present. However, if O_2 *is* present, the chemical energy stored in pyruvate and NADH can be extracted by pyruvate oxidation, the citric acid cycle, and oxidative phosphorylation.

Energy Investment Phase

Glucose

2 ATP used → 2 ADP + 2 Ⓟ

Energy Payoff Phase

4 ADP + 4 Ⓟ → 4 ATP formed

$2 NAD^+ + 4 e^- + 4 H^+$ → 2 NADH + 2 H^+

→ 2 Pyruvate + 2 H_2O

Net

Glucose → 2 Pyruvate + 2 H_2O

4 ATP formed – 2 ATP used → 2 ATP

$2 NAD^+ + 4 e^- + 4 H^+$ → 2 NADH + 2 H^+

▲ **Figure 10.8 The energy input and output of glycolysis.**

▼ **Figure 10.9 A closer look at glycolysis.** Note that glycolysis is a source of ATP and NADH.

GLYCOLYSIS: Energy Investment Phase

WHAT IF? *What would happen if you removed the dihydroxyacetone phosphate generated in step 4 as fast as it was produced?*

Glyceraldehyde 3-phosphate (G3P)

Glucose

Glucose 6-phosphate

Fructose 6-phosphate

Fructose 1,6-bisphosphate

ATP → ADP

Hexokinase ❶

Phosphogluco-isomerase ❷

ATP → ADP

Phospho-fructokinase ❸

Aldolase ❹

Isomerase ❺

Dihydroxyacetone phosphate (DHAP)

❶ Hexokinase transfers a phosphate group from ATP to glucose, making it more chemically reactive. The charge on the phosphate also traps the sugar in the cell.

❷ Glucose 6-phosphate is converted to fructose 6-phosphate.

❸ Phosphofructokinase transfers a phosphate group from ATP to the opposite end of the sugar, investing a second molecule of ATP. This is a key step for regulation of glycolysis.

❹ Aldolase cleaves the sugar molecule into two different three-carbon sugars.

❺ Conversion between DHAP and G3P: This reaction never reaches equilibrium; G3P is used in the next step as fast as it forms.

1. During the redox reaction in glycolysis (step 6 in Figure 10.9), which molecule acts as the oxidizing agent? The reducing agent?

CONCEPT 10.3

After pyruvate is oxidized, the citric acid cycle completes the energy-yielding oxidation of organic molecules

Glycolysis releases less than a quarter of the chemical energy in glucose that can be harvested by cells; most of the energy remains stockpiled in the two molecules of pyruvate. When O_2 is present, the pyruvate in eukaryotic cells enters a mitochondrion, where the oxidation of glucose is completed. In aerobically respiring prokaryotic cells, this process occurs in the cytosol. (Later in the chapter, we'll discuss what happens to pyruvate when O_2 is unavailable or in a prokaryote that is unable to use O_2.)

Oxidation of Pyruvate to Acetyl CoA

Upon entering the mitochondrion via active transport, pyruvate is first converted to a compound called acetyl coenzyme A, or **acetyl CoA (Figure 10.10)**. This step, linking glycolysis and the citric acid cycle, is carried out by a multienzyme

▲ **Figure 10.10 Oxidation of pyruvate to acetyl CoA, the step before the citric acid cycle.** Pyruvate is a charged molecule, so in eukaryotic cells it must enter the mitochondrion via active transport, with the help of a transport protein. Next, a complex of several enzymes (the pyruvate dehydrogenase complex) catalyzes the three numbered steps, which are described in the text. The acetyl group of acetyl CoA will enter the citric acid cycle. The CO_2 molecule will diffuse out of the cell. By convention, coenzyme A is abbreviated S-CoA when it is attached to a molecule, emphasizing the sulfur atom (S).

complex that catalyzes three reactions: ❶ Pyruvate's carboxyl group (—COO⁻), which is already fully oxidized and thus has little chemical energy, is removed and given off as a molecule of CO_2. This is the first step in which CO_2 is

The energy payoff phase occurs after glucose is split into two three-carbon sugars. Thus, the coefficient 2 precedes all molecules in this phase.

GLYCOLYSIS: Energy Payoff Phase

1,3-Bisphospho-glycerate

3-Phospho-glycerate

2-Phospho-glycerate

Phosphoenol-pyruvate (PEP)

Pyruvate

Two sequential reactions: (1) The sugar is oxidized by the transfer of electrons to NAD⁺, forming NADH. (2) Using energy from this exergonic redox reaction, a phosphate group is attached to the oxidized substrate, making a high-energy product.

The phosphate group is transferred to ADP (substrate-level phosphorylation) in an exergonic reaction. The carbonyl group of G3P has been oxidized to the carboxyl group (—COO⁻) of an organic acid (3-phosphoglycerate).

This enzyme relocates the remaining phosphate group.

Enolase causes a double bond to form in the substrate by extracting a water molecule, yielding phosphoenolpyruvate (PEP), a compound with a very high potential energy.

The phosphate group is transferred from PEP to ADP (a second example of substrate-level phosphorylation), forming pyruvate.

© Pearson Education, Inc.

released during respiration. ❷ The remaining two-carbon fragment is oxidized, forming acetate (CH_3COO^-, which is the ionized form of acetic acid). The extracted electrons are transferred to NAD^+, storing energy in the form of NADH. ❸ Finally, coenzyme A (CoA), a sulfur-containing compound derived from a B vitamin, is attached via its sulfur atom to the acetate, forming acetyl CoA, which has a high potential energy; in other words, the reaction of acetyl CoA to yield lower-energy products is highly exergonic. This molecule will now feed its acetyl group into the citric acid cycle for further oxidation.

The Citric Acid Cycle

The citric acid cycle functions as a metabolic furnace that oxidizes organic fuel derived from pyruvate. **Figure 10.11** summarizes the inputs and outputs as pyruvate is broken

▲ **Figure 10.11 An overview of pyruvate oxidation and the citric acid cycle.** The inputs and outputs per pyruvate molecule are shown. To calculate on a per-glucose basis, multiply by 2, because each glucose molecule is split during glycolysis into two pyruvate molecules.

down to three CO_2 molecules, including the molecule of CO_2 released during the conversion of pyruvate to acetyl CoA. The cycle generates 1 ATP per turn by substrate-level phosphorylation, but most of the chemical energy is transferred to NAD^+ and a related electron carrier, the coenzyme FAD (flavin adenine dinucleotide, derived from riboflavin, a B vitamin), during the redox reactions. The reduced coenzymes, NADH and $FADH_2$, shuttle their cargo of high-energy electrons into the electron transport chain. The citric acid cycle is also called the tricarboxylic acid cycle or the Krebs cycle, the latter honoring Hans Krebs, the German-British scientist who was largely responsible for working out the pathway in the 1930s.

Now let's look at the citric acid cycle in more detail. The cycle has eight steps, each catalyzed by a specific enzyme. You can see in **Figure 10.12** that for each turn of the citric acid cycle, two carbons (red) enter in the relatively reduced form of an acetyl group (step ❶), and two different carbons (blue) leave in the completely oxidized form of CO_2 molecules (steps ❸ and ❹). The acetyl group of acetyl CoA joins the cycle by combining with the compound oxaloacetate, forming citrate (step ❶). Citrate is the ionized form of citric acid, for which the cycle is named. The next seven steps decompose the citrate back to oxaloacetate. It is this regeneration of oxaloacetate that makes the process a *cycle*.

We can refer to Figure 10.12 in order to tally the energy-rich molecules produced by the citric acid cycle. For each acetyl group entering the cycle, 3 NAD^+ are reduced to NADH (steps ❸, ❹, and ❽). In step ❻, electrons are transferred not to NAD^+, but to FAD, which accepts 2 electrons and 2 protons to become $FADH_2$. In many animal tissue cells, the reaction in step ❺ produces a guanosine triphosphate (GTP) molecule by substrate-level phosphorylation. GTP is a molecule similar to ATP in its structure and cellular function. This GTP may be used to make an ATP molecule (as shown) or directly power work in the cell. In the cells of plants, bacteria, and some animal tissues, step ❺ forms an ATP molecule directly by substrate-level phosphorylation. The output from step ❺ represents the only ATP generated during the citric acid cycle. Recall that each glucose gives rise to two acetyl CoAs that enter the cycle. Because the numbers noted earlier are obtained from a single acetyl group entering the pathway, the total yield per glucose from the citric acid cycle turns out to be 6 NADHs, 2 $FADH_2$s, and the equivalent of 2 ATPs.

Most of the ATP produced by respiration results from oxidative phosphorylation, when the NADH and $FADH_2$ produced by the citric acid cycle relay the electrons extracted from food to the electron transport chain. In the process, they supply the necessary energy for the phosphorylation of ADP to ATP. We will explore this process in the next section.

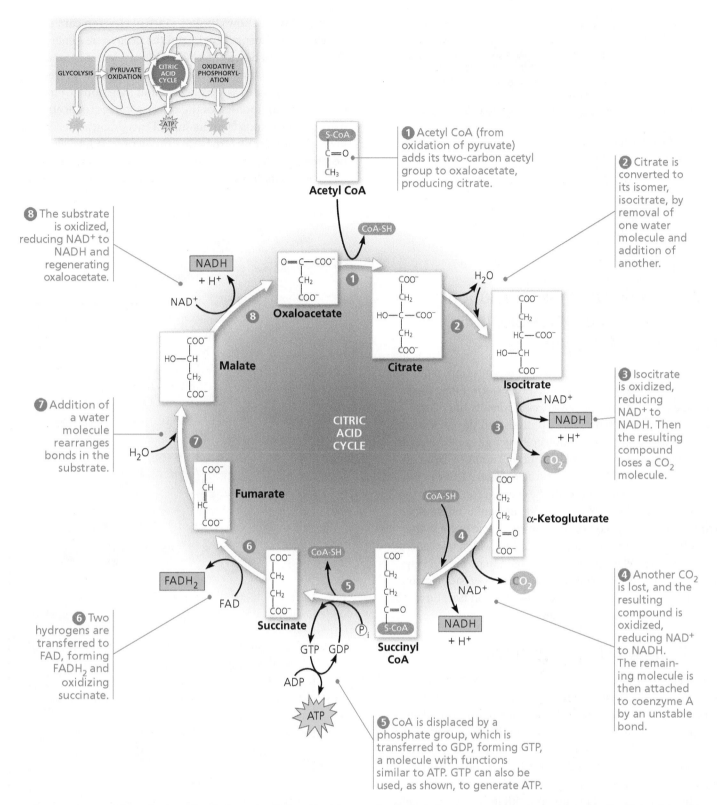

1 Acetyl CoA (from oxidation of pyruvate) adds its two-carbon acetyl group to oxaloacetate, producing citrate.

2 Citrate is converted to its isomer, isocitrate, by removal of one water molecule and addition of another.

3 Isocitrate is oxidized, reducing NAD^+ to NADH. Then the resulting compound loses a CO_2 molecule.

4 Another CO_2 is lost, and the resulting compound is oxidized, reducing NAD^+ to NADH. The remaining molecule is then attached to coenzyme A by an unstable bond.

5 CoA is displaced by a phosphate group, which is transferred to GDP, forming GTP, a molecule with functions similar to ATP. GTP can also be used, as shown, to generate ATP.

6 Two hydrogens are transferred to FAD, forming $FADH_2$ and oxidizing succinate.

7 Addition of a water molecule rearranges bonds in the substrate.

8 The substrate is oxidized, reducing NAD^+ to NADH and regenerating oxaloacetate.

Acetyl CoA
Oxaloacetate
Citrate
Isocitrate
α-Ketoglutarate
Malate
Fumarate
Succinate
Succinyl CoA

CITRIC ACID CYCLE

▲ **Figure 10.12 A closer look at the citric acid cycle.** In the chemical structures, red type traces the fate of the two carbon atoms that enter the cycle via acetyl CoA (step 1), and blue type indicates the two carbons that exit the cycle as CO_2 in steps 3 and 4. (The red type goes only through step 5 because the succinate molecule is symmetrical; the two ends cannot be distinguished from each other.) Notice that the carbon atoms that enter the cycle from acetyl CoA do not leave the cycle in the same turn. They remain in the cycle, occupying a different location in the molecules on their next turn, after another acetyl group is added. Therefore, the oxaloacetate regenerated at step 8 is made up of different carbon atoms each time around. In eukaryotic cells, all the citric acid cycle enzymes are located in the mitochondrial matrix except for the enzyme that catalyzes step 6, which resides in the inner mitochondrial membrane. Carboxylic acids are represented in their ionized forms, as —COO^-, because the ionized forms prevail at the pH within the mitochondrion.

1. Name the molecules that conserve most of the energy from the redox reactions of the citric acid cycle (see Figure 10.12). How is this energy converted to a form that can be used to make ATP?

2. What processes in your cells produce the CO_2 that you exhale?

3. **WHAT IF?** The conversions shown in Figure 10.10 and step 4 of Figure 10.12 are each catalyzed by a large multienzyme complex. What similarities are there in the reactions that occur in these two cases?

CONCEPT 10.4

During oxidative phosphorylation, chemiosmosis couples electron transport to ATP synthesis

Our main objective in this chapter is to learn how cells harvest the energy of glucose and other nutrients in food to make ATP. But the metabolic components of respiration we have dissected so far, glycolysis and the citric acid cycle, produce only 4 ATP molecules per glucose molecule, all by substrate-level phosphorylation: 2 net ATP from glycolysis and 2 ATP from the citric acid cycle. At this point, molecules of NADH (and $FADH_2$) account for most of the energy extracted from each glucose molecule. These electron escorts link glycolysis and the citric acid cycle to the machinery of oxidative phosphorylation, which uses energy released by the electron transport chain to power ATP synthesis. In this section, you will learn first how the electron transport chain works and then how electron flow down the chain is coupled to ATP synthesis.

The Pathway of Electron Transport

The electron transport chain is a collection of molecules embedded in the inner membrane of the mitochondrion in eukaryotic cells. (In prokaryotes, these molecules reside in the plasma membrane.) The folding of the inner membrane to form cristae increases its surface area, providing space for thousands of copies of the electron transport chain in each mitochondrion. Once again, we see that structure fits function—the infolded membrane with its placement of electron carrier molecules in a row, one after the other, is well-suited for the series of sequential redox reactions that take place along the electron transport chain. Most components of the chain are proteins, which exist in multiprotein complexes numbered I through IV. Tightly bound to these proteins are *prosthetic groups*, nonprotein components essential for the catalytic functions of certain enzymes.

Figure 10.13 shows the sequence of electron carriers in the electron transport chain and the drop in free energy as electrons travel down the chain. During electron transport along the chain, electron carriers alternate between reduced and oxidized states as they accept and then donate electrons. Each component of the chain becomes reduced when it accepts electrons from its "uphill" neighbor, which has a lower affinity for electrons (in other words, is less electronegative). It then returns to its oxidized form as it passes electrons to its "downhill," more electronegative neighbor.

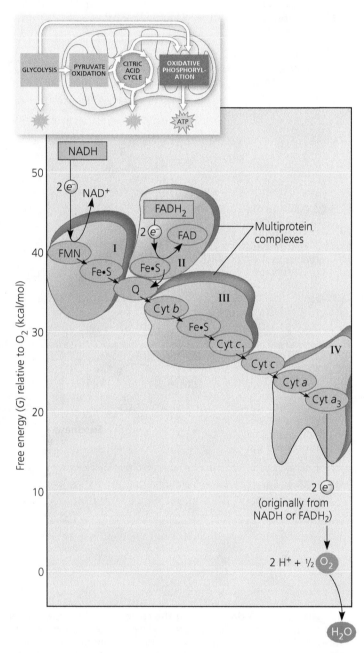

▲ **Figure 10.13 Free-energy change during electron transport.** The overall energy drop (ΔG) for electrons traveling from NADH to oxygen is 53 kcal/mol, but this "fall" is broken up into a series of smaller steps by the electron transport chain. (An oxygen atom is represented here as $\frac{1}{2}$ O_2 to emphasize that the electron transport chain reduces molecular oxygen, O_2, not individual oxygen atoms.)

Now let's take a closer look at the electron transport chain in Figure 10.13. We'll first describe the passage of electrons through complex I in some detail, as an illustration of the general principles involved in electron transport. Electrons acquired from glucose by NAD^+ during glycolysis and the citric acid cycle are transferred from NADH to the first molecule of the electron transport chain in complex I. This molecule is a flavoprotein, so named because it has a prosthetic group called flavin mononucleotide (FMN). In the next redox reaction, the flavoprotein returns to its oxidized form as it passes electrons to an iron-sulfur protein ($Fe \cdot S$ in complex I), one of a family of proteins with both iron and sulfur tightly bound. The iron-sulfur protein then passes the electrons to a compound called ubiquinone (Q in Figure 10.13). This electron carrier is a small hydrophobic molecule, the only member of the electron transport chain that is not a protein. Ubiquinone is individually mobile within the membrane rather than residing in a particular complex. (Another name for ubiquinone is coenzyme Q, or CoQ; you may have seen it sold as a nutritional supplement in health food stores.)

Most of the remaining electron carriers between ubiquinone and oxygen are proteins called **cytochromes**. Their prosthetic group, called a heme group, has an iron atom that accepts and donates electrons. (The heme group in the cytochromes is similar to the heme group in hemoglobin, the protein of red blood cells, except that the iron in hemoglobin carries oxygen, not electrons.) The electron transport chain has several types of cytochromes, each a different protein with a slightly different electron-carrying heme group. The last cytochrome of the chain, Cyt a_3, passes its electrons to oxygen, which is *very* electronegative. Each oxygen atom also picks up a pair of hydrogen ions (protons) from the aqueous solution, neutralizing the −2 charge of the added electrons and forming water.

Another source of electrons for the transport chain is $FADH_2$, the other reduced product of the citric acid cycle. Notice in Figure 10.13 that $FADH_2$ adds its electrons to the electron transport chain from within complex II, at a lower energy level than NADH does. Consequently, although NADH and $FADH_2$ each donate an equivalent number of electrons (2) for oxygen reduction, the electron transport chain provides about one-third less energy for ATP synthesis when the electron donor is $FADH_2$ rather than NADH. We'll see why in the next section.

The electron transport chain makes no ATP directly. Instead, it eases the fall of electrons from food to oxygen, breaking a large free-energy drop into a series of smaller steps that release energy in manageable amounts, step by step. How does the mitochondrion (or the plasma membrane, in the case of prokaryotes) couple this electron transport and energy release to ATP synthesis? The answer is a mechanism called chemiosmosis.

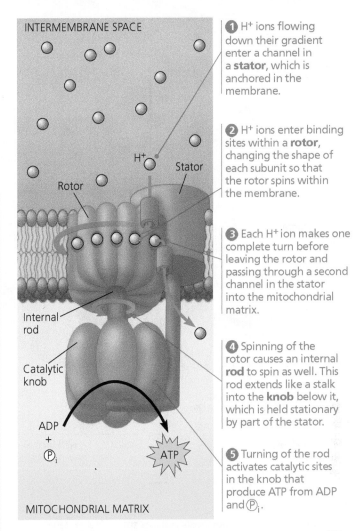

INTERMEMBRANE SPACE

① H^+ ions flowing down their gradient enter a channel in a **stator**, which is anchored in the membrane.

② H^+ ions enter binding sites within a **rotor**, changing the shape of each subunit so that the rotor spins within the membrane.

③ Each H^+ ion makes one complete turn before leaving the rotor and passing through a second channel in the stator into the mitochondrial matrix.

④ Spinning of the rotor causes an internal **rod** to spin as well. This rod extends like a stalk into the **knob** below it, which is held stationary by part of the stator.

⑤ Turning of the rod activates catalytic sites in the knob that produce ATP from ADP and $\textcircled{P}_i$.

H^+ Stator
Rotor
Internal rod
Catalytic knob
ADP + $\textcircled{P}_i$ ATP

MITOCHONDRIAL MATRIX

▲ **Figure 10.14 ATP synthase, a molecular mill.** The ATP synthase protein complex functions as a mill, powered by the flow of hydrogen ions. Multiple ATP synthases reside in eukaryotic mitochondrial and chloroplast membranes and in prokaryotic plasma membranes. Each part of the complex consists of a number of polypeptide subunits. ATP synthase is the smallest molecular rotary motor known in nature.

Chemiosmosis: The Energy-Coupling Mechanism

Populating the inner membrane of the mitochondrion or the prokaryotic plasma membrane are many copies of a protein complex called **ATP synthase**, the enzyme that makes ATP from ADP and inorganic phosphate (**Figure 10.14**). ATP synthase works like an ion pump running in reverse. Ion pumps usually use ATP as an energy source to transport ions against their gradients. Enzymes can catalyze a reaction in either direction, depending on the ΔG for the reaction, which is affected by the local concentrations of reactants and products (see Chapter 8). Rather than hydrolyzing ATP to pump protons against their concentration gradient, under the conditions of cellular respiration ATP synthase uses the energy of an existing ion gradient to power ATP synthesis. The power source for ATP synthase is a difference in the concentration of H^+ on opposite sides of the inner mitochondrial membrane.

▲ **Figure 10.15 Chemiosmosis couples the electron transport chain to ATP synthesis.** ❶ NADH and FADH₂ shuttle high-energy electrons extracted from food during glycolysis and the citric acid cycle into an electron transport chain built into the inner mitochondrial membrane. The gold arrows trace the transport of electrons, which are finally passed to a terminal acceptor (O₂, in the case of aerobic respiration) at the "downhill" end of the chain, forming water. Most of the electron carriers of the chain are grouped into four complexes (I–IV). Two mobile carriers, ubiquinone (Q) and cytochrome c (Cyt c), move rapidly, ferrying electrons between the large complexes. As the complexes shuttle electrons, they pump protons from the mitochondrial matrix into the intermembrane space. FADH₂ deposits its electrons via complex II—at a lower energy level than complex I, where NADH deposits its electrons—and so results in fewer protons being pumped into the intermembrane space than occurs with NADH. Chemical energy that was originally harvested from food is transformed into a proton-motive force, a gradient of H⁺ across the membrane. ❷ During chemiosmosis, the protons flow back down their gradient via ATP synthase, which is built into the membrane nearby. The ATP synthase harnesses the proton-motive force to phosphorylate ADP, forming ATP. Together, electron transport and chemiosmosis make up oxidative phosphorylation.

WHAT IF? *If complex IV were nonfunctional, could chemiosmosis produce any ATP, and if so, how would the rate of synthesis differ?*

This process, in which energy stored in the form of a hydrogen ion gradient across a membrane is used to drive cellular work such as the synthesis of ATP, is called **chemiosmosis** (from the Greek *osmos*, push). We have previously used the word *osmosis* in discussing water transport, but here it refers to the flow of H⁺ across a membrane.

From studying the structure of ATP synthase, scientists have learned how the flow of H⁺ through this large enzyme powers ATP generation. ATP synthase is a multisubunit complex with four main parts, each made up of multiple polypeptides. Protons move one by one into binding sites on one of the parts (the rotor), causing it to spin in a way that catalyzes ATP production from ADP and inorganic phosphate. The flow of protons thus behaves somewhat like a rushing stream that turns a waterwheel.

How does the inner mitochondrial membrane or the prokaryotic plasma membrane generate and maintain the H⁺ gradient that drives ATP synthesis by the ATP synthase protein complex? Establishing the H⁺ gradient is a major function of the electron transport chain, which is shown in its mitochondrial location in **Figure 10.15**. The chain is an energy converter that uses the exergonic flow of electrons from NADH and FADH₂ to pump H⁺ across the membrane, from the mitochondrial matrix into the intermembrane space. The H⁺ has a tendency to move back across the membrane, diffusing down its gradient. And the ATP synthases are the only sites that provide a route through the membrane for H⁺. As we described previously, the passage of H⁺ through ATP synthase uses the exergonic flow of H⁺ to drive the phosphorylation of ADP. Thus, the energy stored in an

H⁺ gradient across a membrane couples the redox reactions of the electron transport chain to ATP.

At this point, you may be wondering how the electron transport chain pumps hydrogen ions. Researchers have found that certain members of the electron transport chain accept and release protons (H^+) along with electrons. (The aqueous solutions inside and surrounding the cell are a ready source of H^+.) At certain steps along the chain, electron transfers cause H^+ to be taken up and released into the surrounding solution. In eukaryotic cells, the electron carriers are spatially arranged in the inner mitochondrial membrane in such a way that H^+ is accepted from the mitochondrial matrix and deposited in the intermembrane space (see Figure 10.15). The H^+ gradient that results is referred to as a **proton-motive force**, emphasizing the capacity of the gradient to perform work. The force drives H^+ back across the membrane through the H^+ channels provided by ATP synthases.

In general terms, *chemiosmosis is an energy-coupling mechanism that uses energy stored in the form of an H^+ gradient across a membrane to drive cellular work.* In mitochondria, the energy for gradient formation comes from exergonic redox reactions, and ATP synthesis is the work performed. But chemiosmosis also occurs elsewhere and in other variations. Chloroplasts use chemiosmosis to generate ATP during photosynthesis; in these organelles, light (rather than chemical energy) drives both electron flow down an electron transport chain and the resulting H^+ gradient

formation. Prokaryotes, as already mentioned, generate H^+ gradients across their plasma membranes. They then tap the proton-motive force not only to make ATP inside the cell but also to rotate their flagella and to pump nutrients and waste products across the membrane. Because of its central importance to energy conversions in prokaryotes and eukaryotes, chemiosmosis has helped unify the study of bioenergetics. Peter Mitchell was awarded the Nobel Prize in 1978 for originally proposing the chemiosmotic model.

An Accounting of ATP Production by Cellular Respiration

In the last few sections, we have looked rather closely at the key processes of cellular respiration. Now let's take a step back and remind ourselves of its overall function: harvesting the energy of glucose for ATP synthesis.

During respiration, most energy flows in this sequence: glucose → NADH → electron transport chain → proton-motive force → ATP. We can do some bookkeeping to calculate the ATP profit when cellular respiration oxidizes a molecule of glucose to six molecules of carbon dioxide. The three main departments of this metabolic enterprise are glycolysis, pyruvate oxidation and the citric acid cycle, and the electron transport chain, which drives oxidative phosphorylation. Figure 10.16 gives a detailed accounting of the ATP yield for each glucose molecule that is oxidized. The tally adds the

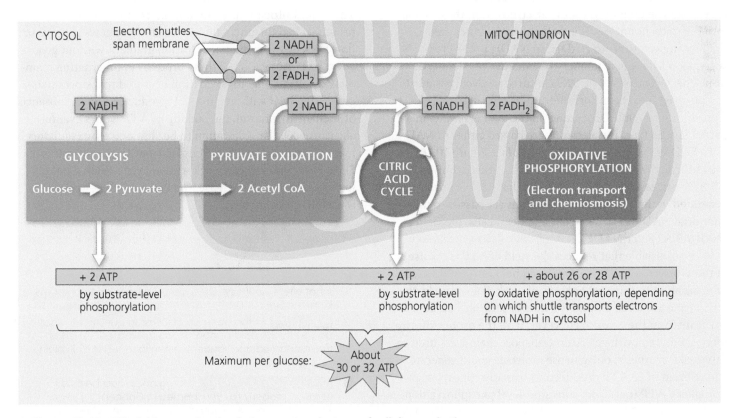

▲ Figure 10.16 **ATP yield per molecule of glucose at each stage of cellular respiration.**

? *Explain exactly how the total of 26 or 28 ATP (see the yellow bar in the figure) was calculated.*

4 ATP produced directly by substrate-level phosphorylation during glycolysis and the citric acid cycle to the many more molecules of ATP generated by oxidative phosphorylation. Each NADH that transfers a pair of electrons from glucose to the electron transport chain contributes enough to the proton-motive force to generate a maximum of about 3 ATP.

Why are the numbers in Figure 10.16 inexact? There are three reasons we cannot state an exact number of ATP molecules generated by the breakdown of one molecule of glucose. First, phosphorylation and the redox reactions are not directly coupled to each other, so the ratio of the number of NADH molecules to the number of ATP molecules is not a whole number. We know that 1 NADH results in 10 H^+ being transported out across the inner mitochondrial membrane, but the exact number of H^+ that must reenter the mitochondrial matrix via ATP synthase to generate 1 ATP has long been debated. Based on experimental data, however, most biochemists now agree that the most accurate number is 4 H^+. Therefore, a single molecule of NADH generates enough proton-motive force for the synthesis of 2.5 ATP. The citric acid cycle also supplies electrons to the electron transport chain via $FADH_2$, but since its electrons enter later in the chain, each molecule of this electron carrier is responsible for transport of only enough H^+ for the synthesis of 1.5 ATP. These numbers also take into account the slight energetic cost of moving the ATP formed in the mitochondrion out into the cytosol, where it will be used.

Second, the ATP yield varies slightly depending on the type of shuttle used to transport electrons from the cytosol into the mitochondrion. The mitochondrial inner membrane is impermeable to NADH, so NADH in the cytosol is segregated from the machinery of oxidative phosphorylation. The 2 electrons of NADH captured in glycolysis must be conveyed into the mitochondrion by one of several electron shuttle systems. Depending on the kind of shuttle in a particular cell type, the electrons are passed either to NAD^+ or to FAD in the mitochondrial matrix (see Figure 10.16). If the electrons are passed to FAD, as in brain cells, only about 1.5 ATP can result from each NADH that was originally generated in the cytosol. If the electrons are passed to mitochondrial NAD^+, as in liver cells and heart cells, the yield is about 2.5 ATP per NADH.

A third variable that reduces the yield of ATP is the use of the proton-motive force generated by the redox reactions of respiration to drive other kinds of work. For example, the proton-motive force powers the mitochondrion's uptake of pyruvate from the cytosol. However, if *all* the proton-motive force generated by the electron transport chain were used to drive ATP synthesis, one glucose molecule could generate a maximum of 28 ATP produced by oxidative phosphorylation plus 4 ATP (net) from substrate-level phosphorylation to give a total yield of about 32 ATP (or only about 30 ATP if the less efficient shuttle were functioning).

We can now roughly estimate the efficiency of respiration—that is, the percentage of chemical energy in glucose that has been transferred to ATP. Recall that the complete oxidation of a mole of glucose releases 686 kcal of energy under standard conditions ($\Delta G = -686$ kcal/mol). Phosphorylation of ADP to form ATP stores at least 7.3 kcal per mole of ATP. Therefore, the efficiency of respiration is 7.3 kcal per mole of ATP times 32 moles of ATP per mole of glucose divided by 686 kcal per mole of glucose, which equals 0.34. Thus, about 34% of the potential chemical energy in glucose has been transferred to ATP; the actual percentage is bound to vary as ΔG varies under different cellular conditions. Cellular respiration is remarkably efficient in its energy conversion. By comparison, even the most efficient automobile converts only about 25% of the energy stored in gasoline to energy that moves the car.

The rest of the energy stored in glucose is lost as heat. We humans use some of this heat to maintain our relatively high body temperature (37°C), and we dissipate the rest through sweating and other cooling mechanisms.

Surprisingly, perhaps, it may be beneficial under certain conditions to reduce the efficiency of cellular respiration. A remarkable adaptation is shown by hibernating mammals, which overwinter in a state of inactivity and lowered metabolism. Although their internal body temperature is lower than normal, it still must be kept significantly higher than the external air temperature. One type of tissue, called brown fat, is made up of cells packed full of mitochondria. The inner mitochondrial membrane contains a channel protein called the uncoupling protein that allows protons to flow back down their concentration gradient without generating ATP. Activation of these proteins in hibernating mammals results in ongoing oxidation of stored fuel stores (fats), generating heat without any ATP production. In the absence of such an adaptation, the buildup of ATP would eventually cause cellular respiration to be shut down by regulatory mechanisms that will be discussed later. In the Scientific Skills Exercise, you can work with data in a related but different case where a decrease in metabolic efficiency in cells is used to generate heat.

CONCEPT CHECK 10.4

1. What effect would an absence of O_2 have on the process shown in Figure 10.15?

2. **WHAT IF?** In the absence of O_2, as in question 1, what do you think would happen if you decreased the pH of the intermembrane space of the mitochondrion? Explain your answer.

3. **MAKE CONNECTIONS** Membranes must be fluid to function properly (as you learned in Concept 7.1). How does the operation of the electron transport chain support that assertion?

Making a Bar Graph and Evaluating a Hypothesis

Does Thyroid Hormone Level Affect Oxygen Consumption in Cells? Some animals, such as mammals and birds, maintain a relatively constant body temperature, above that of their environment, by using heat produced as a by-product of metabolism. When the core temperature of these animals drops below an internal set point, their cells are triggered to reduce the efficiency of ATP production by the electron transport chains in mitochondria. At lower efficiency, extra fuel must be consumed to produce the same number of ATPs, generating additional heat. Because this response is moderated by the endocrine system, researchers hypothesized that thyroid hormone might trigger this cellular response. In this exercise, you will use a bar graph to visualize data from an experiment that compared the metabolic rate (by measuring oxygen consumption) in mitochondria of cells from animals with different levels of thyroid hormone.

How the Experiment Was Done Liver cells were isolated from sibling rats that had low, normal, or elevated thyroid hormone levels. The oxygen consumption rate due to activity of the mitochondrial electron transport chains of each type of cell was measured under controlled conditions.

Data from the Experiment

Thyroid Hormone Level	Oxygen Consumption Rate (nmol O_2/min · mg cells)
Low	4.3
Normal	4.8
Elevated	8.7

Interpret the Data

1. To visualize any differences in oxygen consumption between cell types, it will be useful to graph the data in a bar graph. First, set up the axes. (a) What is the independent variable (intentionally varied by the researchers), which goes on the x-axis? List the categories along the x-axis; because they are discrete rather than continuous, you can list them in any order. (b) What is the dependent variable (measured by the researchers), which goes on the y-axis? (c) What units (abbreviated) should go on the y-axis? Label the y-axis, including the units specified in the data table. Determine the range of values of the data that will need to go on the y-axis. What is the largest value? Draw evenly spaced tick marks and label them, starting with 0 at the bottom.

2. Graph the data for each sample. Match each x-value with its y-value and place a mark on the graph at that coordinate, then draw a bar from the x-axis up to the correct height for each sample. Why is a bar graph more appropriate than a scatter plot or line graph?

3. Examine your graph and look for a pattern in the data. (a) Which cell type had the highest rate of oxygen consumption, and which had the lowest? (b) Does this support the researchers' hypothesis? Explain. (c) Based on what you know about mitochondrial electron transport and heat production, predict which rats had the highest, and which had the lowest, body temperature.

(MB) A version of this Scientific Skills Exercise can be assigned in MasteringBiology.

Data from M. E. Harper and M. D. Brand, The quantitative contributions of mitochondrial proton leak and ATP turnover reactions to the changed respiration rates of hepatocytes from rats of different thyroid status, *Journal of Biological Chemistry* 268:14850–14860 (1993).

CONCEPT 10.5

Fermentation and anaerobic respiration enable cells to produce ATP without the use of oxygen

Because most of the ATP generated by cellular respiration is due to the work of oxidative phosphorylation, our estimate of ATP yield from aerobic respiration is contingent on an adequate supply of oxygen to the cell. Without the electronegative oxygen to pull electrons down the transport chain, oxidative phosphorylation eventually ceases. However, there are two general mechanisms by which certain cells can oxidize organic fuel and generate ATP *without* the use of oxygen: anaerobic respiration and fermentation. The distinction between these two is that an electron transport chain is used in anaerobic respiration but not in fermentation. (The electron transport chain is also called the respiratory chain because of its role in both types of cellular respiration.)

We have already mentioned anaerobic respiration, which takes place in certain prokaryotic organisms that live in environments without oxygen. These organisms have an electron transport chain but do not use oxygen as a final electron acceptor at the end of the chain. Oxygen performs this function very well because it is extremely electronegative, but other, less electronegative substances can also serve as final electron acceptors. Some "sulfate-reducing" marine bacteria, for instance, use the sulfate ion (SO_4^{2-}) at the end of their respiratory chain. Operation of the chain builds up a proton-motive force used to produce ATP, but H_2S (hydrogen sulfide) is made as a by-product rather than water. The rotten-egg odor you may have smelled while walking through a salt marsh or a mudflat signals the presence of sulfate-reducing bacteria.

Fermentation is a way of harvesting chemical energy without using either oxygen or any electron transport chain—in other words, without cellular respiration. How can food be oxidized without cellular respiration? Remember, oxidation simply refers to the loss of electrons to an electron acceptor, so it does not need to involve oxygen. Glycolysis oxidizes glucose to two molecules of pyruvate. The oxidizing agent of glycolysis is NAD^+, and neither oxygen nor any electron transfer chain is involved. Overall, glycolysis is exergonic, and some of the energy made available is used to produce 2 ATP (net) by substrate-level phosphorylation. If oxygen *is* present, then additional ATP is made by oxidative phosphorylation when NADH passes electrons removed from glucose to the electron transport chain. But glycolysis generates 2 ATP whether oxygen is present or not—that is, whether conditions are aerobic or anaerobic.

As an alternative to respiratory oxidation of organic nutrients, fermentation is an extension of glycolysis that allows continuous generation of ATP by the substrate-level phosphorylation of glycolysis. For this to occur, there must be a sufficient supply of NAD^+ to accept electrons during the oxidation step of glycolysis. Without some mechanism to recycle NAD^+ from NADH, glycolysis would soon deplete the cell's pool of NAD^+ by reducing it all to NADH and would shut itself down for lack of an oxidizing agent. Under aerobic conditions, NAD^+ is recycled from NADH by the transfer of electrons to the electron transport chain. An anaerobic alternative is to transfer electrons from NADH to pyruvate, the end product of glycolysis.

Types of Fermentation

Fermentation consists of glycolysis plus reactions that regenerate NAD^+ by transferring electrons from NADH to pyruvate or derivatives of pyruvate. The NAD^+ can then be reused to oxidize sugar by glycolysis, which nets two molecules of ATP by substrate-level phosphorylation. There are many types of fermentation, differing in the end products formed from pyruvate. Two types commonly harnessed by humans for food and industrial production are alcohol fermentation and lactic acid fermentation.

In **alcohol fermentation (Figure 10.17a)**, pyruvate is converted to ethanol (ethyl alcohol) in two steps. The first step releases carbon dioxide from the pyruvate, which is

(a) Alcohol fermentation

(b) Lactic acid fermentation

▲ **Figure 10.17 Fermentation.** In the absence of oxygen, many cells use fermentation to produce ATP by substrate-level phosphorylation. Pyruvate, the end product of glycolysis, serves as an electron acceptor for oxidizing NADH back to NAD^+, which can then be reused in glycolysis. Two of the common end products formed from fermentation are **(a)** ethanol and **(b)** lactate, the ionized form of lactic acid.

converted to the two-carbon compound acetaldehyde. In the second step, acetaldehyde is reduced by NADH to ethanol. This regenerates the supply of NAD^+ needed for the continuation of glycolysis. Many bacteria carry out alcohol fermentation under anaerobic conditions. Yeast (a fungus) also carries out alcohol fermentation. For thousands of years, humans have used yeast in brewing, winemaking, and baking. The CO_2 bubbles generated by baker's yeast during alcohol fermentation allow bread to rise.

During **lactic acid fermentation (Figure 10.17b)**, pyruvate is reduced directly by NADH to form lactate as an end product, with no release of CO_2. (Lactate is the ionized form of lactic acid.) Lactic acid fermentation by certain fungi and bacteria is used in the dairy industry to make cheese and yogurt.

Human muscle cells make ATP by lactic acid fermentation when oxygen is scarce. This occurs during strenuous exercise, when sugar catabolism for ATP production outpaces the muscle's supply of oxygen from the blood. Under these conditions, the cells switch from aerobic respiration to fermentation. The lactate that accumulates was previously thought to cause muscle fatigue and pain, but recent research suggests instead that increased levels of potassium ions (K^+) may be to blame, while lactate appears to enhance muscle performance. In any case, the excess lactate is gradually carried away by the blood to the liver, where it is converted back to pyruvate by liver cells. Because oxygen is available, this pyruvate can then enter the mitochondria in liver cells and complete cellular respiration.

Comparing Fermentation with Anaerobic and Aerobic Respiration

Fermentation, anaerobic respiration, and aerobic respiration are three alternative cellular pathways for producing ATP by harvesting the chemical energy of food. All three use glycolysis to oxidize glucose and other organic fuels to pyruvate, with a net production of 2 ATP by substrate-level phosphorylation. And in all three pathways, NAD^+ is the oxidizing agent that accepts electrons from food during glycolysis.

A key difference is the contrasting mechanisms for oxidizing NADH back to NAD^+, which is required to sustain glycolysis. In fermentation, the final electron acceptor is an organic molecule such as pyruvate (lactic acid fermentation) or acetaldehyde (alcohol fermentation). In cellular respiration, by contrast, electrons carried by NADH are transferred to an electron transport chain, which regenerates the NAD^+ required for glycolysis.

Another major difference is the amount of ATP produced. Fermentation yields 2 molecules of ATP, produced by substrate-level phosphorylation. In the absence of an electron transport chain, the energy stored in pyruvate is unavailable. In cellular respiration, however, pyruvate is completely oxidized in the mitochondrion. Most of the chemical energy from this process is shuttled by NADH and $FADH_2$ in the form of electrons to the electron transport chain. There, the electrons move stepwise down a series of redox reactions to a final electron acceptor. (In aerobic respiration, the final electron acceptor is oxygen; in anaerobic respiration, the final acceptor is another molecule that is electronegative, although less so than oxygen.) Stepwise electron transport drives oxidative phosphorylation, yielding ATPs. Thus, cellular respiration harvests much more energy from each sugar molecule than fermentation can. In fact, aerobic respiration yields up to 32 molecules of ATP per glucose molecule—up to 16 times as much as does fermentation.

Some organisms, called **obligate anaerobes**, carry out only fermentation or anaerobic respiration. In fact, these

▲ **Figure 10.18 Pyruvate as a key juncture in catabolism.** Glycolysis is common to fermentation and cellular respiration. The end product of glycolysis, pyruvate, represents a fork in the catabolic pathways of glucose oxidation. In a facultative anaerobe or a muscle cell, which are capable of both aerobic cellular respiration and fermentation, pyruvate is committed to one of those two pathways, usually depending on whether or not oxygen is present.

organisms cannot survive in the presence of oxygen, some forms of which can actually be toxic if protective systems are not present in the cell. A few cell types, such as cells of the vertebrate brain, can carry out only aerobic oxidation of pyruvate, not fermentation. Other organisms, including yeasts and many bacteria, can make enough ATP to survive using either fermentation or respiration. Such species are called **facultative anaerobes**. On the cellular level, our muscle cells behave as facultative anaerobes. In such cells, pyruvate is a fork in the metabolic road that leads to two alternative catabolic routes **(Figure 10.18)**. Under aerobic conditions, pyruvate can be converted to acetyl CoA, and oxidation continues in the citric acid cycle via aerobic respiration. Under anaerobic conditions, lactic acid fermentation occurs: Pyruvate is diverted from the citric acid cycle, serving instead as an electron acceptor to recycle NAD^+. To make the same amount of ATP, a facultative anaerobe has to consume sugar at a much faster rate when fermenting than when respiring.

The Evolutionary Significance of Glycolysis

EVOLUTION The role of glycolysis in both fermentation and respiration has an evolutionary basis. Ancient prokaryotes are thought to have used glycolysis to make ATP long before oxygen was present in Earth's atmosphere. The oldest known fossils of bacteria date back 3.5 billion years, but appreciable quantities of oxygen probably did not begin to accumulate in the atmosphere until about 2.7 billion years ago. Cyanobacteria produced this O_2 as a by-product of photosynthesis. Therefore, early prokaryotes may have generated ATP exclusively from glycolysis. The fact that glycolysis is today the most widespread metabolic pathway among Earth's organisms suggests that it evolved very early in the history of life. The cytosolic location of glycolysis also implies great antiquity; the pathway does not require any of the membrane-enclosed organelles of the eukaryotic cell, which evolved approximately 1 billion years after the first prokaryotic cell. Glycolysis is a metabolic heirloom from early cells that continues to function in fermentation and as the first stage in the breakdown of organic molecules by respiration.

CONCEPT CHECK 10.5

1. Consider the NADH formed during glycolysis. What is the final acceptor for its electrons during fermentation? What is the final acceptor for its electrons during aerobic respiration?
2. **WHAT IF?** A glucose-fed yeast cell is moved from an aerobic environment to an anaerobic one. How would its rate of glucose consumption change if ATP were to be generated at the same rate?

CONCEPT 10.6

Glycolysis and the citric acid cycle connect to many other metabolic pathways

So far, we have treated the oxidative breakdown of glucose in isolation from the cell's overall metabolic economy. In this section, you will learn that glycolysis and the citric acid cycle are major intersections of the cell's catabolic (breakdown) and anabolic (biosynthetic) pathways.

The Versatility of Catabolism

Throughout this chapter, we have used glucose as an example of a fuel for cellular respiration. But free glucose molecules are not common in the diets of humans and other animals. We obtain most of our calories in the form of fats, proteins, sucrose and other disaccharides, and starch, a polysaccharide. All these organic molecules in food can be used by cellular respiration to make ATP (**Figure 10.19**).

Glycolysis can accept a wide range of carbohydrates for catabolism. In the digestive tract, starch is hydrolyzed to glucose, which can then be broken down in the cells by glycolysis and the citric acid cycle. Similarly, glycogen, the polysaccharide that humans and many other animals store

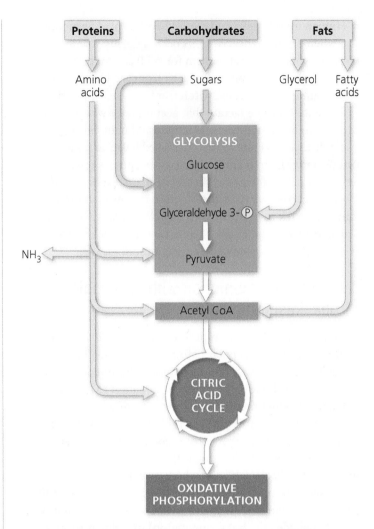

▲ **Figure 10.19 The catabolism of various molecules from food.** Carbohydrates, fats, and proteins can all be used as fuel for cellular respiration. Monomers of these molecules enter glycolysis or the citric acid cycle at various points. Glycolysis and the citric acid cycle are catabolic funnels through which electrons from all kinds of organic molecules flow on their exergonic fall to oxygen.

in their liver and muscle cells, can be hydrolyzed to glucose between meals as fuel for respiration. The digestion of disaccharides, including sucrose, provides glucose and other monosaccharides as fuel for respiration.

Proteins can also be used for fuel, but first they must be digested to their constituent amino acids. Many of the amino acids are used by the organism to build new proteins. Amino acids present in excess are converted by enzymes to intermediates of glycolysis and the citric acid cycle. Before amino acids can feed into glycolysis or the citric acid cycle, their amino groups must be removed, a process called *deamination*. The nitrogenous refuse is excreted from the animal in the form of ammonia (NH_3), urea, or other waste products.

Catabolism can also harvest energy stored in fats obtained either from food or from storage cells in the body. After fats are digested to glycerol and fatty acids, the glycerol is converted to glyceraldehyde 3-phosphate, an intermediate of glycolysis. Most of the energy of a fat is stored in the fatty acids. A metabolic sequence called **beta oxidation** breaks the fatty acids down to two-carbon fragments, which enter the citric acid cycle as acetyl CoA. NADH and FADH$_2$ are also generated during beta oxidation; they can enter the electron transport chain, leading to further ATP production. Fats make excellent fuels, in large part due to their chemical structure and the high energy level of their electrons (equally shared between carbon and hydrogen) compared to those of carbohydrates. A gram of fat oxidized by respiration produces more than twice as much ATP as a gram of carbohydrate. Unfortunately, this also means that a person trying to lose weight must work hard to use up fat stored in the body because so many calories are stockpiled in each gram of fat.

Biosynthesis (Anabolic Pathways)

Cells need substance as well as energy. Not all the organic molecules of food are destined to be oxidized as fuel to make ATP. In addition to calories, food must also provide the carbon skeletons that cells require to make their own molecules. Some organic monomers obtained from digestion can be used directly. For example, as previously mentioned, amino acids from the hydrolysis of proteins in food can be incorporated into the organism's own proteins. Often, however, the body needs specific molecules that are not present as such in food. Compounds formed as intermediates of glycolysis and the citric acid cycle can be diverted into anabolic pathways as precursors from which the cell can synthesize the molecules it requires. For example, humans can make about half of the 20 amino acids in proteins by modifying compounds siphoned away from the citric acid cycle; the rest are "essential amino acids" that must be obtained in the diet. Also, glucose can be made from pyruvate, and fatty acids can be synthesized from acetyl CoA. Of course, these anabolic, or biosynthetic, pathways do not generate ATP, but instead consume it.

In addition, glycolysis and the citric acid cycle function as metabolic interchanges that enable our cells to convert some kinds of molecules to others as we need them. For example, an intermediate compound generated during glycolysis, dihydroxyacetone phosphate (see Figure 10.9, step 5), can be converted to one of the major precursors of fats. If we eat more food than we need, we store fat even if our diet is fat-free. Metabolism is remarkably versatile and adaptable.

Regulation of Cellular Respiration via Feedback Mechanisms

Basic principles of supply and demand regulate the metabolic economy. The cell does not waste energy making more of a particular substance than it needs. If there is a glut of a certain amino acid, for example, the anabolic pathway that synthesizes that amino acid from an intermediate of the citric acid cycle is switched off. The most common mechanism for this control is feedback inhibition: The end product of the anabolic pathway inhibits the enzyme that catalyzes an early step of the pathway (see Figure 9.21). This prevents the needless diversion of key metabolic intermediates from uses that are more urgent.

The cell also controls its catabolism. If the cell is working hard and its ATP concentration begins to drop, respiration speeds up. When there is plenty of ATP to meet demand, respiration slows down, sparing valuable organic molecules for other functions. Again, control is based mainly on regulating the activity of enzymes at strategic points in the catabolic pathway. As shown in **Figure 10.20**, one important

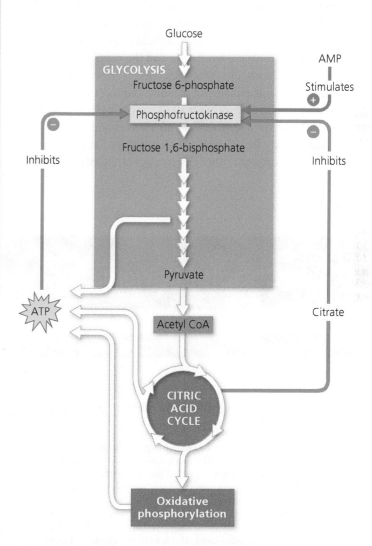

▲ **Figure 10.20 The control of cellular respiration.** Allosteric enzymes at certain points in the respiratory pathway respond to inhibitors and activators that help set the pace of glycolysis and the citric acid cycle. Phosphofructokinase, which catalyzes an early step in glycolysis (see Figure 10.9, step 3), is one such enzyme. It is stimulated by AMP (derived from ADP) but is inhibited by ATP and by citrate. This feedback regulation adjusts the rate of respiration as the cell's catabolic and anabolic demands change.

switch is phosphofructokinase, the enzyme that catalyzes step 3 of glycolysis (see Figure 10.9). That is the first step that commits the substrate irreversibly to the glycolytic pathway. By controlling the rate of this step, the cell can speed up or slow down the entire catabolic process. Phosphofructokinase can thus be considered the pacemaker of respiration.

Phosphofructokinase is an allosteric enzyme with receptor sites for specific inhibitors and activators. It is inhibited by ATP and stimulated by AMP (adenosine monophosphate), which the cell derives from ADP. As ATP accumulates, inhibition of the enzyme slows down glycolysis. The enzyme becomes active again as cellular work converts ATP to ADP (and AMP) faster than ATP is being regenerated. Phosphofructokinase is also sensitive to citrate, the first product of the citric acid cycle. If citrate accumulates in mitochondria, some of it passes into the cytosol and inhibits phosphofructokinase. This mechanism helps synchronize the rates of glycolysis and the citric acid cycle. As citrate accumulates, glycolysis slows down, and the supply of acetyl groups to the citric acid cycle decreases. If citrate consumption increases, either because of a demand for more ATP or because anabolic pathways are draining off intermediates of the citric acid cycle, glycolysis accelerates and meets the demand. Metabolic balance is augmented by the control of enzymes that catalyze other key steps of glycolysis and the citric acid cycle. Cells are thrifty, expedient, and responsive in their metabolism.

Cellular respiration and metabolic pathways play a role of central importance in organisms. Examine Figure 10.2 again to put cellular respiration into the broader context of energy flow and chemical cycling in ecosystems. The energy that keeps us alive is *released*, not *produced*, by cellular respiration. We are tapping energy that was stored in food by photosynthesis. In the next chapter, you will learn how photosynthesis captures light and converts it to chemical energy.

CONCEPT CHECK 10.6

1. **MAKE CONNECTIONS** Compare the structure of a fat (see Figure 5.9) with that of a carbohydrate (see Figure 5.3). What features of their structures make fat a much better fuel?

2. Under what circumstances might your body synthesize fat molecules?

3. **WHAT IF?** What will happen in a muscle cell that has used up its supply of oxygen and ATP? (Review Figures 10.18 and 10.20.)

4. **WHAT IF?** During intense exercise, can a muscle cell use fat as a concentrated source of chemical energy? Explain. (Review Figures 10.18 and 10.19.)

---

10 Chapter Review

SUMMARY OF KEY CONCEPTS

CONCEPT 10.1

Catabolic pathways yield energy by oxidizing organic fuels (pp. 187–191)

- Cells break down glucose and other organic fuels to yield chemical energy in the form of ATP. **Fermentation** is a process that results in the partial degradation of glucose without the use of oxygen. **Cellular respiration** is a more complete breakdown of glucose; in **aerobic respiration**, oxygen is used as a reactant. The cell taps the energy stored in food molecules through **redox reactions**, in which one substance partially or totally shifts electrons to another. **Oxidation** is the loss of electrons from one substance, while **reduction** is the addition of electrons to the other.

- During aerobic respiration, glucose ($C_6H_{12}O_6$) is oxidized to CO_2, and O_2 is reduced to H_2O. Electrons lose potential energy during their transfer from glucose or other organic compounds to oxygen. Electrons are usually passed first to NAD^+, reducing it to NADH, and then from NADH to an **electron transport chain**, which conducts them to O_2 in energy-releasing steps. The energy is used to make ATP.

- Aerobic respiration occurs in three stages: (1) **glycolysis**, (2) pyruvate oxidation and the **citric acid cycle**, and (3) **oxidative phosphorylation** (electron transport and chemiosmosis).

  ? *Describe the difference between the two processes in cellular respiration that produce ATP: oxidative phosphorylation and substrate-level phosphorylation.*

CONCEPT 10.2

Glycolysis harvests chemical energy by oxidizing glucose to pyruvate (pp. 192–193)

- Glycolysis ("splitting of sugar") is a series of reactions that break down glucose into two pyruvate molecules, which may go on to enter the citric acid cycle, and nets 2 ATP and 2 NADH per glucose molecule.

Inputs		Outputs
Glucose	GLYCOLYSIS →	2 Pyruvate + 2 ATP + 2 NADH

  ? *Which reactions in glycolysis are the source of energy for the formation of ATP and NADH?*

CONCEPT 10.3

After pyruvate is oxidized, the citric acid cycle completes the energy-yielding oxidation of organic molecules (pp. 193–196)

- In eukaryotic cells, pyruvate enters the mitochondrion and is oxidized to **acetyl CoA**, which is further oxidized in the citric acid cycle.

Inputs		Outputs

? *What molecular products indicate the complete oxidation of glucose during cellular respiration?*

CONCEPT 10.4

During oxidative phosphorylation, chemiosmosis couples electron transport to ATP synthesis (pp. 196–201)

- NADH and FADH$_2$ transfer electrons to the electron transport chain. Electrons move down the chain, losing energy in several energy-releasing steps. Finally, electrons are passed to O$_2$, reducing it to H$_2$O.

- At certain steps along the electron transport chain, electron transfer causes protein complexes to move H$^+$ from the mitochondrial matrix (in eukaryotes) to the intermembrane space, storing energy as a **proton-motive force** (H$^+$ gradient). As H$^+$ diffuses back into the matrix through **ATP synthase**, its passage drives the phosphorylation of ADP to form ATP, a process called **chemiosmosis**.

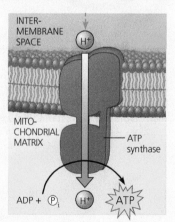

- About 34% of the energy stored in a glucose molecule is transferred to ATP during cellular respiration, producing a maximum of about 32 ATP.

? *Briefly explain the mechanism by which ATP synthase produces ATP. List three locations in which ATP synthases are found.*

CONCEPT 10.5

Fermentation and anaerobic respiration enable cells to produce ATP without the use of oxygen (pp. 201–204)

- Glycolysis nets 2 ATP by substrate-level phosphorylation, whether oxygen is present or not. Under anaerobic conditions, either anaerobic respiration or fermentation can take place. In anaerobic respiration, an electron transport chain is present with a final electron acceptor other than oxygen. In fermentation, the electrons from NADH are passed to pyruvate or a derivative of pyruvate, regenerating the NAD$^+$ required to oxidize more glucose. Two common types of fermentation are **alcohol fermentation** and **lactic acid fermentation**.
- Fermentation and anaerobic or aerobic respiration all use glycolysis to oxidize glucose, but they differ in their final electron acceptor and whether an electron transport chain is used (respiration) or not (fermentation). Respiration yields more ATP; aerobic respiration, with O$_2$ as the final electron acceptor, yields about 16 times as much ATP as does fermentation.
- Glycolysis occurs in nearly all organisms and is thought to have evolved in ancient prokaryotes before there was O$_2$ in the atmosphere.

? *Which process yields more ATP, fermentation or anaerobic respiration? Explain.*

CONCEPT 10.6

Glycolysis and the citric acid cycle connect to many other metabolic pathways (pp. 204–206)

- Catabolic pathways funnel electrons from many kinds of organic molecules into cellular respiration. Many carbohydrates can enter glycolysis, most often after conversion to glucose. Amino acids of proteins must be deaminated before being oxidized. The fatty acids of fats undergo **beta oxidation** to two-carbon fragments and then enter the citric acid cycle as acetyl CoA. Anabolic pathways can use small molecules from food directly or build other substances using intermediates of glycolysis or the citric acid cycle.
- Cellular respiration is controlled by allosteric enzymes at key points in glycolysis and the citric acid cycle.

? *Describe how the catabolic pathways of glycolysis and the citric acid cycle intersect with anabolic pathways in the metabolism of a cell.*

TEST YOUR UNDERSTANDING

LEVEL 1: KNOWLEDGE/COMPREHENSION

1. The *immediate* energy source that drives ATP synthesis by ATP synthase during oxidative phosphorylation is the
   a. oxidation of glucose and other organic compounds.
   b. flow of electrons down the electron transport chain.
   c. H$^+$ concentration gradient across the membrane holding ATP synthase.
   d. transfer of phosphate to ADP.

2. Which metabolic pathway is common to both fermentation and cellular respiration of a glucose molecule?
   a. the citric acid cycle
   b. the electron transport chain
   c. glycolysis
   d. reduction of pyruvate to lactate

3. The final electron acceptor of the electron transport chain that functions in aerobic oxidative phosphorylation is
   a. oxygen.   b. water.   c. NAD$^+$.   d. pyruvate.

4. In mitochondria, exergonic redox reactions
   a. are the source of energy driving prokaryotic ATP synthesis.
   b. provide the energy that establishes the proton gradient.
   c. reduce carbon atoms to carbon dioxide.
   d. are coupled via phosphorylated intermediates to endergonic processes.

LEVEL 2: APPLICATION/ANALYSIS

5. What is the oxidizing agent in the following reaction?

   $$\text{Pyruvate} + \text{NADH} + \text{H}^+ \rightarrow \text{Lactate} + \text{NAD}^+$$

   a. oxygen
   b. NADH
   c. lactate
   d. pyruvate

6. When electrons flow along the electron transport chains of mitochondria, which of the following changes occurs?
   a. The pH of the matrix increases.
   b. ATP synthase pumps protons by active transport.
   c. The electrons gain free energy.
   d. NAD^+ is oxidized.

7. Most CO_2 from catabolism is released during
   a. glycolysis.
   b. the citric acid cycle.
   c. lactate fermentation.
   d. electron transport.

8. **MAKE CONNECTIONS** Step 3 in Figure 10.9 is a major point of regulation of glycolysis. The enzyme phosphofructokinase is allosterically regulated by ATP and related molecules (see Concept 11.5). Considering the overall result of glycolysis, would you expect ATP to inhibit or stimulate activity of this enzyme? Explain. (*Hint:* Make sure you consider the role of ATP as an allosteric regulator, not as a substrate of the enzyme.)

9. **MAKE CONNECTIONS** The proton pump shown in Figure 7.17 is depicted as a simplified oval purple shape, but it is, in fact, an ATP synthase (see Figure 10.14). Compare the processes shown in the two figures, and say whether they are involved in active or passive transport (see Concepts 7.3 and 7.4).

LEVEL 3: SYNTHESIS/EVALUATION

10. **INTERPRET THE DATA**

    Phosphofructokinase is an enzyme that acts on fructose 6-phosphate at an early step in glucose breakdown. Regulation of this enzyme controls whether the sugar will continue on in the glycolytic pathway. Considering this graph, under which condition is phosphofructokinase more active? Given what you know about glycolysis and regulation of metabolism by this enzyme, explain the mechanism by which phosphofructokinase activity differs depending on ATP concentration.

11. **DRAW IT** The graph here shows the pH difference across the inner mitochondrial membrane over time in an actively respiring cell. At the time indicated by the vertical arrow, a metabolic poison is added that specifically and completely inhibits all function of mitochondrial ATP synthase. Draw what you would expect to see for the rest of the graphed line, and explain your reasoning for drawing the line as you did.

12. **EVOLUTION CONNECTION**
    ATP synthases are found in the prokaryotic plasma membrane and in mitochondria and chloroplasts. What does this suggest about the evolutionary relationship of these eukaryotic organelles to prokaryotes? How might the amino acid sequences of the ATP synthases from the different sources support or refute your hypothesis?

13. **SCIENTIFIC INQUIRY**
    In the 1930s, some physicians prescribed low doses of a compound called dinitrophenol (DNP) to help patients lose weight. This unsafe method was abandoned after some patients died. DNP uncouples the chemiosmotic machinery by making the lipid bilayer of the inner mitochondrial membrane leaky to H^+. Explain how this could cause weight loss and death.

14. **WRITE ABOUT A THEME: ORGANIZATION**
    In a short essay (100–150 words), explain how oxidative phosphorylation—production of ATP using energy from the redox reactions of a spatially organized electron transport chain followed by chemiosmosis—is an example of how new properties emerge at each level of the biological hierarchy.

15. **SYNTHESIZE YOUR KNOWLEDGE**

    Coenzyme Q (CoQ) is sold as a nutritional supplement. One company uses this marketing slogan for CoQ: "Give your heart the fuel it craves most." Considering the role of coenzyme Q, how do you think this product might function as a nutritional supplement to benefit the heart? Is CoQ used as a "fuel" during cellular respiration?

MasteringBiology®

Students Go to **MasteringBiology** for assignments, the eText, and the Study Area with practice tests, animations, and activities.

Instructors Go to **MasteringBiology** for automatically graded tutorials and questions that you can assign to your students, plus Instructor Resources.

11 Photosynthesis

▲ Other organisms also benefit from photosynthesis.

▲ Figure 11.1 How does sunlight help build the trunk, branches, and leaves of this broadleaf tree?

The Process That Feeds the Biosphere

Life on Earth is solar powered. The chloroplasts in plants and other photosynthetic organisms capture light energy that has traveled 150 million kilometers from the sun and convert it to chemical energy that is stored in sugar and other organic molecules. This conversion process is called **photosynthesis**. Let's begin by placing photosynthesis in its ecological context.

Photosynthesis nourishes almost the entire living world directly or indirectly. An organism acquires the organic compounds it uses for energy and carbon skeletons by one of two major modes: autotrophic nutrition or heterotrophic nutrition. **Autotrophs** are "self-feeders" (*auto-* means "self," and *trophos* means "feeder"); they sustain themselves without eating anything derived from other living beings. Autotrophs produce their organic molecules from CO_2 and other inorganic raw materials obtained from the environment. They are the ultimate sources of organic compounds for all nonautotrophic organisms, and for this reason, biologists refer to autotrophs as the *producers* of the biosphere.

Almost all plants are autotrophs; the only nutrients they require are water and minerals from the soil and carbon dioxide from the air. Specifically, plants are *photo*autotrophs, organisms that use light as a source of energy to synthesize organic substances (Figure 11.1). Photosynthesis also occurs in algae, certain other unicellular eukaryotes, and some prokaryotes (**Figure 11.2**). In this chapter, we will touch on these other groups in passing, but our emphasis will be on plants.

(a) Plants

(b) Multicellular alga

10 μm

(c) Unicellular eukaryotes

(d) Cyanobacteria   40 μm

1 μm

(e) Purple sulfur bacteria

▲ **Figure 11.2 Photoautotrophs.** These organisms use light energy to drive the synthesis of organic molecules from carbon dioxide and (in most cases) water. They feed themselves and the entire living world. **(a)** On land, plants are the predominant producers of food. In aquatic environments, photoautotrophs include unicellular and **(b)** multicellular algae, such as this kelp; **(c)** some non-algal unicellular eukaryotes, such as *Euglena*; **(d)** the prokaryotes called cyanobacteria; and **(e)** other photosynthetic prokaryotes, such as these purple sulfur bacteria, which produce sulfur (the yellow globules within the cells) (c–e, LMs).

Heterotrophs obtain organic material by the second major mode of nutrition. Unable to make their own food, they live on compounds produced by other organisms (*hetero-* means "other"). Heterotrophs are the biosphere's *consumers*. The most obvious "other-feeding" occurs when an animal eats plants or other animals. But heterotrophic nutrition may be more subtle. Some heterotrophs consume the remains of dead organisms by decomposing and feeding on organic litter such as carcasses, feces, and fallen leaves; these types of organisms are known as decomposers. Most fungi and many types of prokaryotes get their nourishment this way. Almost all heterotrophs, including humans, are completely dependent, either directly or indirectly, on photoautotrophs for food—and also for oxygen, a by-product of photosynthesis.

The Earth's supply of fossil fuels was formed from remains of organisms that died hundreds of millions of years ago. In a sense, then, fossil fuels represent stores of the sun's energy from the distant past. Because these resources are being used at a much higher rate than they are replenished, researchers are exploring methods of capitalizing on the photosynthetic process to provide alternative fuels (**Figure 11.3**).

In this chapter, you'll learn how photosynthesis works. After discussing general principles of photosynthesis, we'll consider the two stages of photosynthesis: the light reactions, which capture solar energy and transform it into chemical energy; and the Calvin cycle, which uses that chemical energy to make the organic molecules of food. Finally, we will consider some aspects of photosynthesis from an evolutionary perspective.

▲ **Figure 11.3 Alternative fuels from algae.** The power of sunlight can be tapped to generate a sustainable alternative to fossil fuels. Species of unicellular algae that are prolific producers of plant oils can be cultured in long, transparent tanks called photobioreactors, such as the one shown here at Arizona State University. A simple chemical process can yield "biodiesel," which can be mixed with gasoline or used alone to power vehicles.

WHAT IF? *The main product of fossil fuel combustion is CO_2, and this is the source of the increase in atmospheric CO_2 concentration. Scientists have proposed strategically situating containers of these algae near industrial plants or near highly congested city streets. Considering the process of photosynthesis, how does this arrangement make sense?*

Photosynthesis converts light energy to the chemical energy of food

The remarkable ability of an organism to harness light energy and use it to drive the synthesis of organic compounds emerges from structural organization in the cell: Photosynthetic enzymes and other molecules are grouped together in a biological membrane, enabling the necessary series of chemical reactions to be carried out efficiently. The process of photosynthesis most likely originated in a group of bacteria that had infolded regions of the plasma membrane containing clusters of such molecules. In existing photosynthetic bacteria, infolded photosynthetic membranes function similarly to the internal membranes of the chloroplast, a eukaryotic organelle. According to what has come to be known as the endosymbiont theory, the original chloroplast was a photosynthetic prokaryote that lived inside an ancestor of eukaryotic cells. (You learned about this theory in Chapter 6.) Chloroplasts are present in a variety of photosynthesizing organisms (see some examples in Figure 11.2), but here we focus on chloroplasts in plants.

Chloroplasts: The Sites of Photosynthesis in Plants

All green parts of a plant, including green stems and unripened fruit, have chloroplasts, but the leaves are the major sites of photosynthesis in most plants **(Figure 11.4)**. There are about half a million chloroplasts in a chunk of leaf with a top surface area of 1 mm^2. Chloroplasts are found mainly in the cells of the **mesophyll**, the tissue in the interior of the leaf. Carbon dioxide enters the leaf, and oxygen exits, by way of microscopic pores called **stomata** (singular, *stoma*; from the Greek, meaning "mouth"). Water absorbed by the roots is delivered to the leaves in veins. Leaves also use veins to export sugar to roots and other nonphotosynthetic parts of the plant.

A typical mesophyll cell has about 30–40 chloroplasts, each measuring about 2–4 μm by 4–7 μm. A chloroplast has an envelope of two membranes surrounding a dense fluid called the **stroma**. Suspended within the stroma is a third membrane system, made up of sacs called **thylakoids**, which segregates the stroma from the *thylakoid space* inside these sacs. In some places, thylakoid sacs are stacked in columns called *grana* (singular, *granum*). **Chlorophyll**, the green pigment that gives leaves their color, resides in the thylakoid membranes of the chloroplast. (The internal photosynthetic membranes of some prokaryotes are also called thylakoid

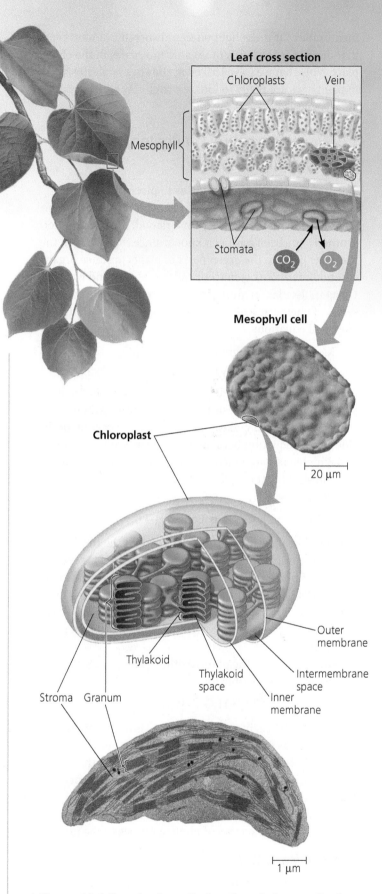

Leaf cross section

Chloroplasts Vein

Mesophyll

Stomata CO_2 O_2

Mesophyll cell

Chloroplast

20 μm

Thylakoid

Thylakoid space

Outer membrane

Intermembrane space

Inner membrane

Stroma Granum

1 μm

▲ **Figure 11.4 Zooming in on the location of photosynthesis in a plant.** Leaves are the major organs of photosynthesis in plants. These pictures take you into a leaf, then into a cell, and finally into a chloroplast, the organelle where photosynthesis occurs (middle, LM; bottom, TEM).

membranes.) It is the light energy absorbed by chlorophyll that drives the synthesis of organic molecules in the chloroplast. Now that we have looked at the sites of photosynthesis in plants, we are ready to look more closely at the process of photosynthesis.

Tracking Atoms Through Photosynthesis: *Scientific Inquiry*

Scientists have tried for centuries to piece together the process by which plants make food. Although some of the steps are still not completely understood, the overall photosynthetic equation has been known since the 1800s: In the presence of light, the green parts of plants produce organic compounds and oxygen from carbon dioxide and water. Using molecular formulas, we can summarize the complex series of chemical reactions in photosynthesis with this chemical equation:

$$6\ CO_2 + 12\ H_2O + \text{Light energy} \rightarrow C_6H_{12}O_6 + 6\ O_2 + 6\ H_2O$$

We use glucose ($C_6H_{12}O_6$) here to simplify the relationship between photosynthesis and respiration, but the direct product of photosynthesis is actually a three-carbon sugar that can be used to make glucose. Water appears on both sides of the equation because 12 molecules are consumed and 6 molecules are newly formed during photosynthesis. We can simplify the equation by indicating only the net consumption of water:

$$6\ CO_2 + 6\ H_2O + \text{Light energy} \rightarrow C_6H_{12}O_6 + 6\ O_2$$

Writing the equation in this form, we can see that the overall chemical change during photosynthesis is the reverse of the one that occurs during cellular respiration (see Concept 9.1). Both of these metabolic processes occur in plant cells. However, as you will soon learn, chloroplasts do not synthesize sugars by simply reversing the steps of respiration.

Now let's divide the photosynthetic equation by 6 to put it in its simplest possible form:

$$CO_2 + H_2O \rightarrow [CH_2O] + O_2$$

Here, the brackets indicate that CH_2O is not an actual sugar but represents the general formula for a carbohydrate (see Concept 5.2). In other words, we are imagining the synthesis of a sugar molecule one carbon at a time. Six repetitions would theoretically produce a glucose molecule ($C_6H_{12}O_6$). Let's now see how researchers tracked the elements C, H, and O from the reactants of photosynthesis to the products.

The Splitting of Water

One of the first clues to the mechanism of photosynthesis came from the discovery that the O_2 given off by plants is derived from H_2O and not from CO_2. The chloroplast splits water into hydrogen and oxygen. Before this discovery, the prevailing hypothesis was that photosynthesis split carbon dioxide ($CO_2 \rightarrow C + O_2$) and then added water to the carbon ($C + H_2O \rightarrow [CH_2O]$). This hypothesis predicted that the O_2 released during photosynthesis came from CO_2. This idea was challenged in the 1930s by C. B. van Niel, of Stanford University. Van Niel was investigating photosynthesis in bacteria that make their carbohydrate from CO_2 but do not release O_2. He concluded that, at least in these bacteria, CO_2 is not split into carbon and oxygen. One group of bacteria used hydrogen sulfide (H_2S) rather than water for photosynthesis, forming yellow globules of sulfur as a waste product (these globules are visible in Figure 11.2e). Here is the chemical equation for photosynthesis in these sulfur bacteria:

$$CO_2 + 2\ H_2S \rightarrow [CH_2O] + H_2O + 2\ S$$

Van Niel reasoned that the bacteria split H_2S and used the hydrogen atoms to make sugar. He then generalized that idea, proposing that all photosynthetic organisms require a hydrogen source but that the source varies:

$$\text{Sulfur bacteria: } CO_2 + 2\ H_2S \rightarrow [CH_2O] + H_2O + 2\ S$$
$$\text{Plants: } CO_2 + 2\ H_2O \rightarrow [CH_2O] + H_2O + O_2$$
$$\text{General: } CO_2 + 2\ H_2X \rightarrow [CH_2O] + H_2O + 2\ X$$

Thus, van Niel hypothesized that plants split H_2O as a source of electrons from hydrogen atoms, releasing O_2 as a by-product.

Nearly 20 years later, scientists confirmed van Niel's hypothesis by using oxygen-18 (^{18}O), a heavy isotope, as a tracer to follow the fate of oxygen atoms during photosynthesis. The experiments showed that the O_2 from plants was labeled with ^{18}O *only* if water was the source of the tracer (experiment 1). If the ^{18}O was introduced to the plant in the form of CO_2, the label did not turn up in the released O_2 (experiment 2). In the following summary, red denotes labeled atoms of oxygen (^{18}O):

$$\text{Experiment 1: } CO_2 + 2\ H_2O \rightarrow [CH_2O] + H_2O + O_2$$
$$\text{Experiment 2: } CO_2 + 2\ H_2O \rightarrow [CH_2O] + H_2O + O_2$$

A significant result of the shuffling of atoms during photosynthesis is the extraction of hydrogen from water and its incorporation into sugar. The waste product of photosynthesis, O_2, is released to the atmosphere. **Figure 11.5** shows the fates of all atoms in photosynthesis.

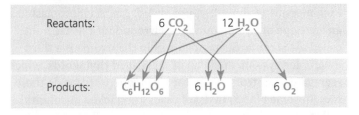

▲ **Figure 11.5 Tracking atoms through photosynthesis.** The atoms from CO_2 are shown in magenta, and the atoms from H_2O are shown in blue.

Photosynthesis as a Redox Process

Let's briefly compare photosynthesis with cellular respiration. Both processes involve redox reactions. During cellular respiration, energy is released from sugar when electrons associated with hydrogen are transported by carriers to oxygen, forming water as a by-product. The electrons lose potential energy as they "fall" down the electron transport chain toward electronegative oxygen, and the mitochondrion harnesses that energy to synthesize ATP (see Figure 8.15). Photosynthesis reverses the direction of electron flow. Water is split, and electrons are transferred along with hydrogen ions from the water to carbon dioxide, reducing it to sugar.

$$\text{Energy} \ + \ 6\,CO_2 \ + \ 6\,H_2O \ \longrightarrow \ C_6H_{12}O_6 \ + \ 6\,O_2$$

becomes reduced ⟶ (over the left side)
becomes oxidized ⟶ (under to O_2)

Because the electrons increase in potential energy as they move from water to sugar, this process requires energy—in other words is endergonic. This energy boost that occurs during photosynthesis is provided by light.

The Two Stages of Photosynthesis: *A Preview*

The equation for photosynthesis is a deceptively simple summary of a very complex process. Actually, photosynthesis is not a single process, but two processes, each with multiple steps. These two stages of photosynthesis are known as the **light reactions** (the *photo* part of photosynthesis) and the **Calvin cycle** (the *synthesis* part) **(Figure 11.6)**.

The light reactions are the steps of photosynthesis that convert solar energy to chemical energy. Water is split, providing a source of electrons and protons (hydrogen ions, H^+) and giving off O_2 as a by-product. Light absorbed by chlorophyll drives a transfer of the electrons and hydrogen ions from water to an acceptor called **NADP$^+$** (nicotinamide adenine dinucleotide phosphate), where they are temporarily stored. The electron acceptor NADP$^+$ is first cousin to NAD$^+$, which functions as an electron carrier in cellular respiration; the two molecules differ only by the presence of an extra phosphate group in the NADP$^+$ molecule. The light reactions use solar energy to reduce NADP$^+$ to NADPH by adding a pair of electrons along with an H^+. The light reactions also generate ATP, using chemiosmosis to power the addition of a phosphate group to ADP, a process called **photophosphorylation**. Thus, light energy is initially converted to chemical energy in the form of two compounds: NADPH and ATP. NADPH, a source of electrons, acts as "reducing power" that can be passed along to an electron acceptor, reducing it, while ATP is the versatile energy currency of cells. Notice that the light reactions produce no sugar; that happens in the second stage of photosynthesis, the Calvin cycle.

The Calvin cycle is named for Melvin Calvin, who, along with his colleagues James Bassham and Andrew Benson, began to elucidate its steps in the late 1940s. The cycle begins by incorporating CO$_2$ from the air into organic molecules already present in the chloroplast. This initial incorporation of carbon into organic compounds is known as **carbon fixation**. The Calvin cycle then reduces the fixed carbon

▶ **Figure 11.6 An overview of photosynthesis: cooperation of the light reactions and the Calvin cycle.** In the chloroplast, the thylakoid membranes (green) are the sites of the light reactions, whereas the Calvin cycle occurs in the stroma (gray). The light reactions use solar energy to make ATP and NADPH, which supply chemical energy and reducing power, respectively, to the Calvin cycle. The Calvin cycle incorporates CO$_2$ into organic molecules, which are converted to sugar. (Recall that most simple sugars have formulas that are some multiple of CH$_2$O.)

to carbohydrate by the addition of electrons. The reducing power is provided by NADPH, which acquired its cargo of electrons in the light reactions. To convert CO_2 to carbohydrate, the Calvin cycle also requires chemical energy in the form of ATP, which is also generated by the light reactions. Thus, it is the Calvin cycle that makes sugar, but it can do so only with the help of the NADPH and ATP produced by the light reactions. The metabolic steps of the Calvin cycle are sometimes referred to as the dark reactions, or light-independent reactions, because none of the steps requires light *directly*. Nevertheless, the Calvin cycle in most plants occurs during daylight, for only then can the light reactions provide the NADPH and ATP that the Calvin cycle requires. In essence, the chloroplast uses light energy to make sugar by coordinating the two stages of photosynthesis.

As Figure 11.6 indicates, the thylakoids of the chloroplast are the sites of the light reactions, while the Calvin cycle occurs in the stroma. On the outside of the thylakoids, molecules of $NADP^+$ and ADP pick up electrons and phosphate, respectively, and NADPH and ATP are then released to the stroma, where they play crucial roles in the Calvin cycle. The two stages of photosynthesis are treated in this figure as metabolic modules that take in ingredients and crank out products. In the next two sections, we'll look more closely at how the two stages work, beginning with the light reactions.

CONCEPT CHECK 11.1

1. How do the reactant molecules of photosynthesis reach the chloroplasts in leaves?
2. How did the use of an oxygen isotope help elucidate the chemistry of photosynthesis?
3. **WHAT IF?** The Calvin cycle requires ATP and NADPH, products of the light reactions. If a classmate asserted that the light reactions don't depend on the Calvin cycle and, with continual light, could just keep on producing ATP and NADPH, how would you respond?

CONCEPT 11.2

The light reactions convert solar energy to the chemical energy of ATP and NADPH

Chloroplasts are chemical factories powered by the sun. Their thylakoids transform light energy into the chemical energy of ATP and NADPH, which will be used to synthesize glucose and other molecules that can be used as energy sources. To better understand the conversion of light to chemical energy, we need to know about some important properties of light.

The Nature of Sunlight

Light is a form of energy known as electromagnetic energy, also called electromagnetic radiation. Electromagnetic energy travels in rhythmic waves analogous to those created by dropping a pebble into a pond. Electromagnetic waves, however, are disturbances of electric and magnetic fields rather than disturbances of a material medium such as water.

The distance between the crests of electromagnetic waves is called the **wavelength**. Wavelengths range from less than a nanometer (for gamma rays) to more than a kilometer (for radio waves). This entire range of radiation is known as the **electromagnetic spectrum** (Figure 11.7). The segment most important to life is the narrow band from about 380 nm to 750 nm in wavelength. This radiation is known as **visible light** because it can be detected as various colors by the human eye.

The model of light as waves explains many of light's properties, but in certain respects light behaves as though it consists of discrete particles, called **photons**. Photons are not tangible objects, but they act like objects in that each of them has a fixed quantity of energy. The amount of energy is inversely related to the wavelength of the light: the shorter the wavelength, the greater the energy of each photon of that light. Thus, a photon of violet light packs nearly twice as much energy as a photon of red light (see Figure 11.7).

Although the sun radiates the full spectrum of electromagnetic energy, the atmosphere acts like a selective window, allowing visible light to pass through while screening out a substantial fraction of other radiation. The part of the spectrum we can see—visible light—is also the radiation that drives photosynthesis.

▲ **Figure 11.7 The electromagnetic spectrum.** White light is a mixture of all wavelengths of visible light. A prism can sort white light into its component colors by bending light of different wavelengths at different angles. (Droplets of water in the atmosphere can act as prisms, causing a rainbow to form.) Visible light drives photosynthesis.

Photosynthetic Pigments: The Light Receptors

When light meets matter, it may be reflected, transmitted, or absorbed. Substances that absorb visible light are known as *pigments*. Different pigments absorb light of different wavelengths, and the wavelengths that are absorbed disappear. If a pigment is illuminated with white light, the color we see is the color most reflected or transmitted by the pigment. (If a pigment absorbs all wavelengths, it appears black.) We see green when we look at a leaf because chlorophyll absorbs violet-blue and red light while transmitting and reflecting green light (**Figure 11.8**). The ability of a pigment to absorb various wavelengths of light can be measured with an instrument called a **spectrophotometer**. This machine directs beams of light of different wavelengths through a solution of the pigment and measures the fraction of the light transmitted at each wavelength. A graph plotting a pigment's light absorption versus wavelength is called an **absorption spectrum** (**Figure 11.9**).

The absorption spectra of chloroplast pigments provide clues to the relative effectiveness of different wavelengths for driving photosynthesis, since light can perform work in chloroplasts only if it is absorbed. **Figure 11.10a** shows the absorption spectra of three types of pigments in chloroplasts: **chlorophyll *a***, the key light-capturing pigment that participates directly in the light reactions; the accessory pigment **chlorophyll *b***; and a separate group of accessory pigments called carotenoids. The spectrum of chlorophyll

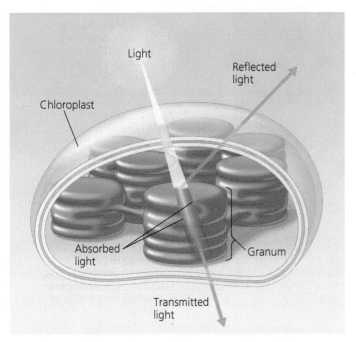

▲ **Figure 11.8 Why leaves are green: interaction of light with chloroplasts.** The chlorophyll molecules of chloroplasts absorb violet-blue and red light (the colors most effective in driving photosynthesis) and reflect or transmit green light. This is why leaves appear green.

▼ Figure 11.9 **Research Method**

Determining an Absorption Spectrum

Application An absorption spectrum is a visual representation of how well a particular pigment absorbs different wavelengths of visible light. Absorption spectra of various chloroplast pigments help scientists decipher the role of each pigment in a plant.

Technique A spectrophotometer measures the relative amounts of light of different wavelengths absorbed and transmitted by a pigment solution.

1. White light is separated into colors (wavelengths) by a prism.

2. One by one, the different colors of light are passed through the sample (chlorophyll in this example). Green light and blue light are shown here.

3. The transmitted light strikes a photoelectric tube, which converts the light energy to electricity.

4. The electric current is measured by a galvanometer. The meter indicates the fraction of light transmitted through the sample, from which we can determine the amount of light absorbed.

Results See Figure 11.10a for absorption spectra of three types of chloroplast pigments.

a suggests that violet-blue and red light work best for photosynthesis, since they are absorbed, while green is the least effective color. This is confirmed by an **action spectrum** for photosynthesis (**Figure 11.10b**), which profiles the relative effectiveness of different wavelengths of radiation in driving the process. An action spectrum is prepared by illuminating chloroplasts with light of different colors and then plotting wavelength against some measure of photosynthetic rate,

▼ Figure 11.10 | Inquiry

Which wavelengths of light are most effective in driving photosynthesis?

Experiment Absorption and action spectra, along with a classic experiment by Theodor W. Engelmann, reveal which wavelengths of light are photosynthetically important.

Results

(a) Absorption spectra. The three curves show the wavelengths of light best absorbed by three types of chloroplast pigments.

(b) Action spectrum. This graph plots the rate of photosynthesis versus wavelength. The resulting action spectrum resembles the absorption spectrum for chlorophyll *a* but does not match exactly (see part a). This is partly due to the absorption of light by accessory pigments such as chlorophyll *b* and carotenoids.

(c) Engelmann's experiment. In 1883, Theodor W. Engelmann illuminated a filamentous alga with light that had been passed through a prism, exposing different segments of the alga to different wavelengths. He used aerobic bacteria, which concentrate near an oxygen source, to determine which segments of the alga were releasing the most O₂ and thus photosynthesizing most. Bacteria congregated in greatest numbers around the parts of the alga illuminated with violet-blue or red light.

Conclusion Light in the violet-blue and red portions of the spectrum is most effective in driving photosynthesis.

Source: T. W. Engelmann, *Bacterium photometricum. Ein Beitrag zur vergleichenden Physiologie des Licht-und Farbensinnes, Archiv. für Physiologie* 30:95–124 (1883).

(MB) An Experimental Inquiry Tutorial can be assigned in MasteringBiology.

INTERPRET THE DATA *What wavelengths of light drive the highest rates of photosynthesis?*

such as CO₂ consumption or O₂ release. The action spectrum for photosynthesis was first demonstrated by Theodor W. Engelmann, a German botanist, in 1883. Before equipment for measuring O₂ levels had even been invented, Engelmann performed a clever experiment in which he used bacteria to measure rates of photosynthesis in filamentous algae (**Figure 11.10c**). His results are a striking match to the modern action spectrum shown in Figure 11.10b.

Notice by comparing Figures 11.10a and 11.10b that the action spectrum for photosynthesis is much broader than the absorption spectrum of chlorophyll *a*. The absorption spectrum of chlorophyll *a* alone underestimates the effectiveness of certain wavelengths in driving photosynthesis. This is partly because accessory pigments with different absorption spectra also present in chloroplasts—including chlorophyll *b* and carotenoids—broaden the spectrum of colors that can be used for photosynthesis. **Figure 11.11** shows the structure of chlorophyll *a* compared with that of chlorophyll *b*. A slight structural difference between them is enough to cause the two pigments to absorb at slightly different wavelengths in the red and blue parts of the spectrum (see Figure 11.10a). As a result, chlorophyll *a* appears blue green and chlorophyll *b* olive green under visible light.

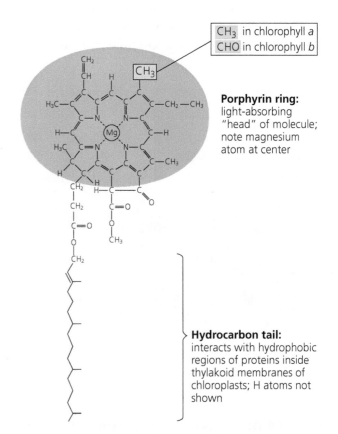

▲ **Figure 11.11 Structure of chlorophyll molecules in chloroplasts of plants.** Chlorophyll *a* and chlorophyll *b* differ only in one of the functional groups bonded to the porphyrin ring. (Also see the space-filling model of chlorophyll in Figure 1.3.)

Other accessory pigments include **carotenoids**, hydrocarbons that are various shades of yellow and orange because they absorb violet and blue-green light (see Figure 11.10a). Carotenoids may broaden the spectrum of colors that can drive photosynthesis. However, a more important function of at least some carotenoids seems to be *photoprotection*: These compounds absorb and dissipate excessive light energy that would otherwise damage chlorophyll or interact with oxygen, forming reactive oxidative molecules that are dangerous to the cell. Interestingly, carotenoids similar to the photoprotective ones in chloroplasts have a photoprotective role in the human eye. (Remember being told to eat your carrots for improved night vision?) These and related molecules are, of course, found naturally in many vegetables and fruits. They are also often advertised in health food products as "phytochemicals" (from the Greek *phyton*, plant), some of which have antioxidant properties. Plants can synthesize all the antioxidants they require, but humans and other animals must obtain some of them from their diets.

Excitation of Chlorophyll by Light

What exactly happens when chlorophyll and other pigments absorb light? The colors corresponding to the absorbed wavelengths disappear from the spectrum of the transmitted and reflected light, but energy cannot disappear. When a molecule absorbs a photon of light, one of the molecule's electrons is elevated to an orbital where it has more potential energy (see Figure 2.6b). When the electron is in its normal orbital, the pigment molecule is said to be in its ground state. Absorption of a photon boosts an electron to an orbital of higher energy, and the pigment molecule is then said to be in an excited state. The only photons absorbed are those whose energy is exactly equal to the energy difference between the ground state and an excited state, and this energy difference varies from one kind of molecule to another. Thus, a particular compound absorbs only photons corresponding to specific wavelengths, which is why each pigment has a unique absorption spectrum.

Once absorption of a photon raises an electron to an excited state, the electron cannot stay there long. The excited state, like all high-energy states, is unstable. Generally, when isolated pigment molecules absorb light, their excited electrons drop back down to the ground-state orbital in a billionth of a second, releasing their excess energy as heat. This conversion of light energy to heat is what makes the top of an automobile so hot on a sunny day. (White cars are coolest because their paint reflects all wavelengths of visible light.) In isolation, some pigments, including chlorophyll, emit light as well as heat after absorbing photons. As excited electrons fall back to the ground state, photons are given off, an afterglow called fluorescence. An illuminated solution of chlorophyll isolated from chloroplasts will fluoresce in the red part of the spectrum and also give off heat (Figure 11.12). This is best seen by illuminating with ultraviolet light, which chlorophyll can also absorb (see Figures 11.7 and 11.10a). Viewed under visible light, the fluorescence would be harder to see against the green of the solution.

A Photosystem: A Reaction-Center Complex Associated with Light-Harvesting Complexes

Chlorophyll molecules excited by the absorption of light energy produce very different results in an intact chloroplast than they do in isolation (see Figure 11.12). In their native environment of the thylakoid membrane, chlorophyll molecules are organized along with other small organic molecules and proteins into complexes called photosystems.

▶ **Figure 11.12 Excitation of isolated chlorophyll by light. (a)** Absorption of a photon causes a transition of the chlorophyll molecule from its ground state to its excited state. The photon boosts an electron to an orbital where it has more potential energy. If the illuminated molecule exists in isolation, its excited electron immediately drops back down to the ground-state orbital, and its excess energy is given off as heat and fluorescence (light). **(b)** A chlorophyll solution excited with ultraviolet light fluoresces with a red-orange glow.

WHAT IF? *If a leaf containing a similar concentration of chlorophyll as the solution was exposed to the same ultraviolet light, no fluorescence would be seen. Propose an explanation for the difference in fluorescence emission between the solution and the leaf.*

(a) Excitation of isolated chlorophyll molecule

(b) Fluorescence

A **photosystem** is composed of a **reaction-center complex** surrounded by several light-harvesting complexes (**Figure 11.13**). The reaction-center complex is an organized association of proteins holding a special pair of chlorophyll *a* molecules. Each **light-harvesting complex** consists of various pigment molecules (which may include chlorophyll *a*, chlorophyll *b*, and multiple carotenoids) bound to proteins. The number and variety of pigment molecules enable a photosystem to harvest light over a larger surface area and a larger portion of the spectrum than could any single pigment molecule alone. Together, these light-harvesting complexes act as an antenna for the reaction-center complex. When a pigment molecule absorbs a photon, the energy is transferred from pigment molecule to pigment molecule within a light-harvesting complex, somewhat like a human "wave" at a sports arena, until it is passed into the reaction-center complex. The reaction-center complex also contains a molecule capable of accepting electrons and becoming reduced; this is called the **primary electron acceptor**. The pair of chlorophyll *a* molecules in the reaction-center complex are special because their molecular environment—their location and the other molecules with which they are associated—enables them to use the energy from light not only to boost one of their electrons to a higher energy level, but also to transfer it to a different molecule—the primary electron acceptor.

The solar-powered transfer of an electron from the reaction-center chlorophyll *a* pair to the primary electron acceptor is the first step of the light reactions. As soon as the chlorophyll electron is excited to a higher energy level, the primary electron acceptor captures it; this is a redox reaction. In the flask shown in Figure 11.12b, isolated chlorophyll fluoresces because there is no electron acceptor, so electrons of photoexcited chlorophyll drop right back to the ground state. In the structured environment of a chloroplast, however, an electron acceptor is readily available, and the potential energy represented by the excited electron is not dissipated as light and heat. Thus, each photosystem—a reaction-center complex surrounded by light-harvesting complexes—functions in the chloroplast as a unit. It converts light energy to chemical energy, which will ultimately be used for the synthesis of sugar.

The thylakoid membrane is populated by two types of photosystems that cooperate in the light reactions of photosynthesis. They are called **photosystem II (PS II)** and **photosystem I (PS I)**. (They were named in order of their discovery, but photosystem II functions first in the light reactions.) Each has a characteristic reaction-center complex—a particular kind of primary electron acceptor next to a special pair of chlorophyll *a* molecules associated with specific proteins. The reaction-center chlorophyll *a* of photosystem II is known as P680 because this pigment is best at absorbing

(a) **How a photosystem harvests light.** When a photon strikes a pigment molecule in a light-harvesting complex, the energy is passed from molecule to molecule until it reaches the reaction-center complex. Here, an excited electron from the special pair of chlorophyll *a* molecules is transferred to the primary electron acceptor.

(b) **Structure of a photosystem.** This computer model, based on X-ray crystallography, shows two photosystem complexes side by side, oriented opposite to each other. Chlorophyll molecules (small green ball-and-stick models) are interspersed with protein subunits (cylinders and ribbons). For simplicity, this photosystem will be shown as a single complex in the rest of the chapter.

▲ **Figure 11.13 The structure and function of a photosystem.**

light having a wavelength of 680 nm (in the red part of the spectrum). The chlorophyll *a* at the reaction-center complex of photosystem I is called P700 because it most effectively absorbs light of wavelength 700 nm (in the far-red part of the spectrum). These two pigments, P680 and P700, are nearly identical chlorophyll *a* molecules. However, their association with different proteins in the thylakoid membrane affects the electron distribution in the two pigments and accounts for the slight differences in their light-absorbing properties. Now let's see how the two photosystems work together in using light energy to generate ATP and NADPH, the two main products of the light reactions.

Linear Electron Flow

Light drives the synthesis of ATP and NADPH by energizing the two photosystems embedded in the thylakoid membranes of chloroplasts. The key to this energy transformation is a flow of electrons through the photosystems and other molecular components built into the thylakoid membrane. This is called **linear electron flow**, and it occurs during the light reactions of photosynthesis, as shown in **Figure 11.14**. The numbered steps in the text correspond to the numbered steps in the figure.

① A photon of light strikes one of the pigment molecules in a light-harvesting complex of PS II, boosting one of its electrons to a higher energy level. As this electron falls back to its ground state, an electron in a nearby pigment molecule is simultaneously raised to an excited state. The process continues, with the energy being relayed to other pigment molecules until it reaches the P680 pair of chlorophyll *a* molecules in the PS II reaction-center complex. It excites an electron in this pair of chlorophylls to a higher energy state.

② This electron is transferred from the excited P680 to the primary electron acceptor. We can refer to the resulting form of P680, missing an electron, as P680$^+$.

③ An enzyme catalyzes the splitting of a water molecule into two electrons, two hydrogen ions (H$^+$), and an oxygen atom. The electrons are supplied one by one to the P680$^+$ pair, each electron replacing one transferred to the primary electron acceptor. (P680$^+$ is the strongest biological oxidizing agent known; its electron "hole" must be filled. This greatly facilitates the transfer of electrons from the split water molecule.) The H$^+$ are released into

▼ Figure 11.14 **How linear electron flow during the light reactions generates ATP and NADPH.** The gold arrows trace the flow of light-driven electrons from water to NADPH. The black arrows trace the transfer of energy from pigment molecule to pigment molecule.

the thylakoid space. The oxygen atom immediately combines with an oxygen atom generated by the splitting of another water molecule, forming O_2.

4 Each photoexcited electron passes from the primary electron acceptor of PS II to PS I via an electron transport chain, the components of which are similar to those of the electron transport chain that functions in cellular respiration. The electron transport chain between PS II and PS I is made up of the electron carrier plastoquinone (Pq), a cytochrome complex, and a protein called plastocyanin (Pc).

5 The exergonic "fall" of electrons to a lower energy level provides energy for the synthesis of ATP. As electrons pass through the cytochrome complex, H^+ are pumped into the thylakoid space, contributing to the proton gradient that is subsequently used in chemiosmosis.

6 Meanwhile, light energy has been transferred via light-harvesting complex pigments to the PS I reaction-center complex, exciting an electron of the P700 pair of chlorophyll *a* molecules located there. The photoexcited electron is then transferred to PS I's primary electron acceptor, creating an electron "hole" in the P700—which we now can call $P700^+$. In other words, $P700^+$ can now act as an electron acceptor, accepting an electron that reaches the bottom of the electron transport chain from PS II.

7 Photoexcited electrons are passed in a series of redox reactions from the primary electron acceptor of PS I down a second electron transport chain through the protein ferredoxin (Fd). (This chain does not create a proton gradient and thus does not produce ATP.)

8 The enzyme $NADP^+$ reductase catalyzes the transfer of electrons from Fd to $NADP^+$. Two electrons are required for its reduction to NADPH. This molecule is at a higher energy level than water, so its electrons are more readily available for the reactions of the Calvin cycle. This process also removes an H^+ from the stroma.

▲ **Figure 11.15 A mechanical analogy for linear electron flow during the light reactions.**

The energy changes of electrons during their linear flow through the light reactions are shown in a mechanical analogy in **Figure 11.15**. Although the scheme shown in Figures 11.14 and 11.15 may seem complicated, do not lose track of the big picture: The light reactions use solar power to generate ATP and NADPH, which provide chemical energy and reducing power, respectively, to the carbohydrate-synthesizing reactions of the Calvin cycle.

Cyclic Electron Flow

In certain cases, photoexcited electrons can take an alternative path called **cyclic electron flow**, which uses photosystem I but not photosystem II. You can see in **Figure 11.16** that cyclic flow is a short circuit: The electrons cycle back from ferredoxin (Fd) to the cytochrome complex and from there continue on to a P700 chlorophyll in the PS I reaction-center

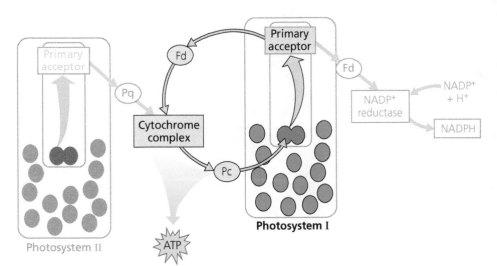

◀ **Figure 11.16 Cyclic electron flow.** Photoexcited electrons from PS I are occasionally shunted back from ferredoxin (Fd) to chlorophyll via the cytochrome complex and plastocyanin (Pc). This electron shunt supplements the supply of ATP (via chemiosmosis) but produces no NADPH. The "shadow" of linear electron flow is included in the diagram for comparison with the cyclic route. The two Fd molecules in this diagram are actually one and the same—the final electron carrier in the electron transport chain of PS I—although it is depicted twice to clearly show its role in two parts of the process.

? *Look at Figure 11.15, and explain how you would alter it to show a mechanical analogy for cyclic electron flow.*

complex. There is no production of NADPH and no release of oxygen that results from this process. On the other hand, cyclic flow does generate ATP.

Rather than having both PSII and PSI, several of the currently existing groups of photosynthetic bacteria are known to have a single photosystem related to either PSII or PSI. For these species, which include the purple sulfur bacteria (see Figure 11.2e) and the green sulfur bacteria, cyclic electron flow is the one and only means of generating ATP during the process of photosynthesis. Evolutionary biologists hypothesize that these bacterial groups are descendants of ancestral bacteria in which photosynthesis first evolved, in a form similar to cyclic electron flow.

Cyclic electron flow can also occur in photosynthetic species that possess both photosystems; this includes some prokaryotes, such as the cyanobacteria shown in Figure 11.2d, as well as the eukaryotic photosynthetic species that have been tested thus far. Although the process is probably in part an "evolutionary leftover," research suggests it plays at least one beneficial role for these organisms. Mutant plants that are not able to carry out cyclic electron flow are capable of growing well in low light, but do not grow well where light is intense. This is evidence for the idea that cyclic electron flow may be photoprotective. Later you'll learn more about cyclic electron flow as it relates to a particular adaptation of photosynthesis (C_4 plants; see Concept 11.4).

Whether ATP synthesis is driven by linear or cyclic electron flow, the actual mechanism is the same. Before we move on to consider the Calvin cycle, let's review chemiosmosis, the process that uses membranes to couple redox reactions to ATP production.

A Comparison of Chemiosmosis in Chloroplasts and Mitochondria

Chloroplasts and mitochondria generate ATP by the same basic mechanism: chemiosmosis. An electron transport chain pumps protons (H^+) across a membrane as electrons are passed through a series of carriers that are progressively more electronegative. Thus, electron transport chains transform redox energy to a proton-motive force, potential energy stored in the form of an H^+ gradient across a membrane. An ATP synthase complex in the same membrane couples the diffusion of hydrogen ions down their gradient to the phosphorylation of ADP, forming ATP.

Some of the electron carriers, including the iron-containing proteins called cytochromes, are very similar in chloroplasts and mitochondria. The ATP synthase complexes of the two organelles are also quite similar. But there are noteworthy differences between photophosphorylation in chloroplasts and oxidative phosphorylation in mitochondria. In chloroplasts, the high-energy electrons dropped down the transport chain come from water, while in mitochondria, they are extracted from organic molecules (which are thus oxidized). Chloroplasts do not need molecules from food to make ATP; their photosystems capture light energy and use it to drive the electrons from water to the top of the transport chain. In other words, mitochondria use chemiosmosis to transfer chemical energy from food molecules to ATP, whereas chloroplasts transform light energy into chemical energy in ATP.

Although the spatial organization of chemiosmosis differs slightly between chloroplasts and mitochondria, it is easy to see similarities in the two (**Figure 11.17**). The inner

▶ **Figure 11.17 Comparison of chemiosmosis in mitochondria and chloroplasts.** In both kinds of organelles, electron transport chains pump protons (H^+) across a membrane from a region of low H^+ concentration (light gray in this diagram) to one of high H^+ concentration (dark gray). The protons then diffuse back across the membrane through ATP synthase, driving the synthesis of ATP.

membrane of the mitochondrion pumps protons from the mitochondrial matrix out to the intermembrane space, which then serves as a reservoir of hydrogen ions. The thylakoid membrane of the chloroplast pumps protons from the stroma into the thylakoid space (interior of the thylakoid), which functions as the H^+ reservoir. If you imagine the cristae of mitochondria pinching off from the inner membrane, this may help you see how the thylakoid space and the intermembrane space are comparable spaces in the two organelles, while the mitochondrial matrix is analogous to the stroma of the chloroplast.

In the mitochondrion, protons diffuse down their concentration gradient from the intermembrane space through ATP synthase to the matrix, driving ATP synthesis. In the chloroplast, ATP is synthesized as the hydrogen ions diffuse from the thylakoid space back to the stroma through ATP synthase complexes, whose catalytic knobs are on the stroma side of the membrane (Figure 11.18). Thus, ATP forms in the stroma, where it is used to help drive sugar synthesis during the Calvin cycle.

The proton (H^+) gradient, or pH gradient, across the thylakoid membrane is substantial. When chloroplasts in an

▲ Figure 11.18 The light reactions and chemiosmosis: Current model of the organization of the thylakoid membrane. The gold arrows track the linear electron flow outlined in Figure 11.14. At least three steps in the light reactions contribute to the H^+ gradient by increasing H^+ concentration in the thylakoid space: ❶ Water is split by photosystem II on the side of the membrane facing the thylakoid space; ❷ as plastoquinone (Pq) transfers electrons to the cytochrome complex, four protons are translocated across the membrane into the thylakoid space; and ❸ a hydrogen ion is removed from the stroma when it is taken up by $NADP^+$. Notice that in step 2, hydrogen ions are being pumped from the stroma into the thylakoid space, as in Figure 11.17. The diffusion of H^+ from the thylakoid space back to the stroma (along the H^+ concentration gradient) powers the ATP synthase. These light-driven reactions store chemical energy in NADPH and ATP, which shuttle the energy to the carbohydrate-producing Calvin cycle.

experimental setting are illuminated, the pH in the thylakoid space drops to about 5 (the H^+ concentration increases), and the pH in the stroma increases to about 8 (the H^+ concentration decreases). This gradient of three pH units corresponds to a thousandfold difference in H^+ concentration. If the lights are then turned off, the pH gradient is abolished, but it can quickly be restored by turning the lights back on. Experiments such as this provided strong evidence in support of the chemiosmotic model.

The currently-accepted model for the organization of the light-reaction "machinery" within the thylakoid membrane is based on several research studies. Each of the molecules and molecular complexes in the figure is present in numerous copies in each thylakoid. Notice that NADPH, like ATP, is produced on the side of the membrane facing the stroma, where the Calvin cycle reactions take place.

Let's summarize the light reactions. Electron flow pushes electrons from water, where they are at a low state of potential energy, ultimately to NADPH, where they are stored at a high state of potential energy. The light-driven electron flow also generates ATP. Thus, the equipment of the thylakoid membrane converts light energy to chemical energy stored in ATP and NADPH. (Oxygen is a by-product.) Let's now see how the Calvin cycle uses the products of the light reactions to synthesize sugar from CO_2.

CONCEPT CHECK 11.2

1. What color of light is *least* effective in driving photosynthesis? Explain.

2. In the light reactions, what is the initial electron donor? Where do the electrons finally end up?

3. **WHAT IF?** In an experiment, isolated chloroplasts placed in an illuminated solution with the appropriate chemicals can carry out ATP synthesis. Predict what would happen to the rate of synthesis if a compound is added to the solution that makes membranes freely permeable to hydrogen ions.

CONCEPT 11.3

The Calvin cycle uses the chemical energy of ATP and NADPH to reduce CO_2 to sugar

The Calvin cycle is similar to the citric acid cycle in that a starting material is regenerated after some molecules enter the cycle and others exit the cycle. However, the citric acid cycle is catabolic, oxidizing acetyl CoA and using the energy to synthesize ATP. In contrast, the Calvin cycle is anabolic, building carbohydrates from smaller molecules and consuming energy. Carbon enters the Calvin cycle in the form of CO_2 and leaves in the form of sugar. The cycle spends ATP as an energy source and consumes NADPH as reducing power for adding high-energy electrons to make the sugar.

As we mentioned previously (in Concept 11.1), the carbohydrate produced directly from the Calvin cycle is actually not glucose, but a three-carbon sugar; the name of this sugar is **glyceraldehyde 3-phosphate (G3P)**. For the net synthesis of *one* molecule of G3P, the cycle must take place three times, fixing *three* molecules of CO_2—one per turn of the cycle. (Recall that the term carbon fixation refers to the initial incorporation of CO_2 into organic material.) As we trace the steps of the cycle, it's important to keep in mind that we are following three molecules of CO_2 through the reactions. **Figure 11.19** divides the Calvin cycle into three phases: carbon fixation, reduction, and regeneration of the CO_2 acceptor.

Phase 1: Carbon fixation. The Calvin cycle incorporates each CO_2 molecule, one at a time, by attaching it to a five-carbon sugar named ribulose bisphosphate (abbreviated RuBP). The enzyme that catalyzes this first step is RuBP carboxylase-oxygenase, or **rubisco**. (This is the most abundant protein in chloroplasts and is also thought to be the most abundant protein on Earth.) The product of the reaction is a six-carbon intermediate that is short-lived because it is so energetically unstable that it immediately splits in half, forming two molecules of 3-phosphoglycerate (for each CO_2 fixed).

Phase 2: Reduction. Each molecule of 3-phosphoglycerate receives an additional phosphate group from ATP, becoming 1,3-bisphosphoglycerate. Next, a pair of electrons donated from NADPH reduces 1,3-bisphosphoglycerate, which also loses a phosphate group in the process, becoming glyceraldehyde 3-phosphate (G3P). Specifically, the electrons from NADPH reduce a carboxyl group on 1,3-bisphosphoglycerate to the aldehyde group of G3P, which stores more potential energy. G3P is a sugar—the same three-carbon sugar formed in glycolysis by the splitting of glucose (see Figure 8.9). Notice in Figure 11.19 that for every *three* molecules of CO_2 that enter the cycle, there are *six* molecules of G3P formed. But only one molecule of this three-carbon sugar can be counted as a net gain of carbohydrate because the rest are required to complete the cycle. The cycle began with 15 carbons' worth of carbohydrate in the form of three molecules of the five-carbon sugar RuBP. Now there are 18 carbons' worth of carbohydrate in the form of six molecules of G3P. One molecule exits the cycle to be used by the plant cell, but the other five molecules must be recycled to regenerate the three molecules of RuBP.

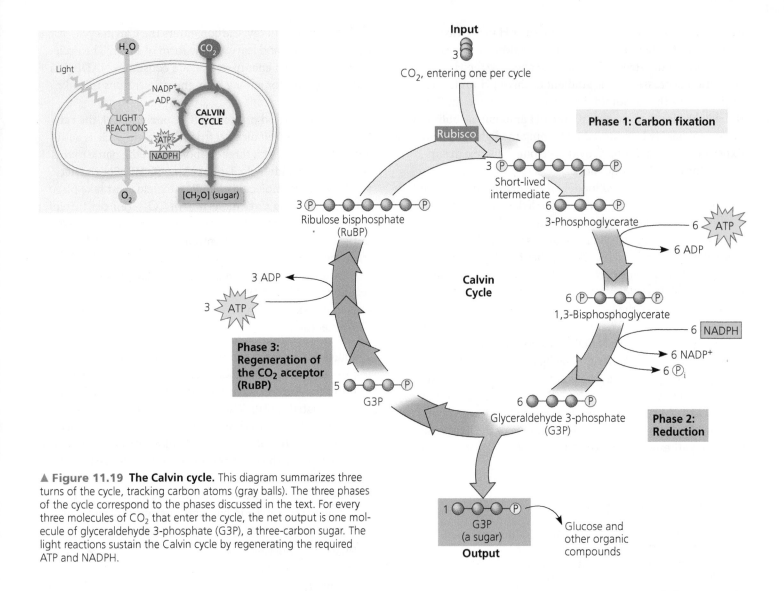

Input

3 ⬤⬤⬤

CO_2, entering one per cycle

Rubisco

Phase 1: Carbon fixation

3 Ⓟ⬤⬤⬤⬤⬤Ⓟ

Short-lived intermediate

6 ⬤⬤⬤Ⓟ

3-Phosphoglycerate

6 ATP

6 ADP

3 Ⓟ⬤⬤⬤⬤⬤Ⓟ

Ribulose bisphosphate (RuBP)

Calvin Cycle

6 Ⓟ⬤⬤⬤Ⓟ

1,3-Bisphosphoglycerate

6 NADPH

6 NADP⁺

6 Ⓟᵢ

3 ADP

3 ATP

Phase 3: Regeneration of the CO_2 acceptor (RuBP)

5 ⬤⬤⬤Ⓟ

G3P

6 ⬤⬤⬤Ⓟ

Glyceraldehyde 3-phosphate (G3P)

Phase 2: Reduction

1 ⬤⬤⬤Ⓟ

G3P (a sugar)

Output

Glucose and other organic compounds

▲ Figure 11.19 The Calvin cycle. This diagram summarizes three turns of the cycle, tracking carbon atoms (gray balls). The three phases of the cycle correspond to the phases discussed in the text. For every three molecules of CO_2 that enter the cycle, the net output is one molecule of glyceraldehyde 3-phosphate (G3P), a three-carbon sugar. The light reactions sustain the Calvin cycle by regenerating the required ATP and NADPH.

Phase 3: Regeneration of the CO_2 acceptor (RuBP). In a complex series of reactions, the carbon skeletons of five molecules of G3P are rearranged by the last steps of the Calvin cycle into three molecules of RuBP. To accomplish this, the cycle spends three more molecules of ATP. The RuBP is now prepared to receive CO_2 again, and the cycle continues.

For the net synthesis of one G3P molecule, the Calvin cycle consumes a total of nine molecules of ATP and six molecules of NADPH. The light reactions regenerate the ATP and NADPH. The G3P spun off from the Calvin cycle becomes the starting material for metabolic pathways that synthesize other organic compounds, including glucose (formed by combining two molecules of G3P), the disaccharide sucrose, and other carbohydrates. Neither the light reactions nor the Calvin cycle alone can make sugar from CO_2. Photosynthesis is an emergent property of the intact chloroplast, which integrates the two stages of photosynthesis.

CONCEPT CHECK 11.3

1. To synthesize one glucose molecule, the Calvin cycle uses _____ molecules of CO_2, _____ molecules of ATP, and _____ molecules of NADPH.

2. How are the large numbers of ATP and NADPH molecules used during the Calvin cycle consistent with the high value of glucose as an energy source?

3. **WHAT IF?** Explain why a poison that inhibits an enzyme of the Calvin cycle will also inhibit the light reactions.

4. **DRAW IT** Redraw the cycle in Figure 11.19 using numerals to indicate the numbers of carbons instead of gray balls, multiplying at each step to ensure that you have accounted for all carbons. In what forms do the carbon atoms enter and leave the cycle?

5. **MAKE CONNECTIONS** Review Figures 8.9 and 11.19. Discuss the roles of intermediate and product played by glyceraldehyde 3-phosphate (G3P) in the two processes shown in these figures.

CONCEPT 11.4

Alternative mechanisms of carbon fixation have evolved in hot, arid climates

EVOLUTION Ever since plants first moved onto land about 475 million years ago, they have been adapting to the problems of terrestrial life, particularly the problem of dehydration. We will consider anatomical adaptations that help plants conserve water, while in this chapter we are concerned with metabolic adaptations. The solutions often involve trade-offs. An important example is the compromise between photosynthesis and the prevention of excessive water loss from the plant. The CO_2 required for photosynthesis enters a leaf (and the resulting O_2 exits) via stomata, the pores on the leaf surface (see Figure 11.4). However, stomata are also the main avenues of transpiration, the evaporative loss of water from leaves. On a hot, dry day, most plants close their stomata, a response that conserves water. This response also reduces photosynthetic yield by limiting access to CO_2. With stomata even partially closed, CO_2 concentrations begin to decrease in the air spaces within the leaf, and the concentration of O_2 released from the light reactions begins to increase. These conditions within the leaf favor an apparently wasteful process called photorespiration.

Photorespiration: An Evolutionary Relic?

In most plants, initial fixation of carbon occurs via rubisco, the Calvin cycle enzyme that adds CO_2 to ribulose bisphosphate. Such plants are called **C_3 plants** because the first organic product of carbon fixation is a three-carbon compound, 3-phosphoglycerate (see Figure 11.19). Rice, wheat, and soybeans are C_3 plants that are important in agriculture. When their stomata partially close on hot, dry days, C_3 plants produce less sugar because the declining level of CO_2 in the leaf starves the Calvin cycle. In addition, rubisco is capable of binding O_2 in place of CO_2. As CO_2 becomes scarce within the air spaces of the leaf and O_2 builds up, rubisco adds O_2 to the Calvin cycle instead of CO_2. The product splits, and a two-carbon compound leaves the chloroplast. Peroxisomes and mitochondria within the plant cell rearrange and split this compound, releasing CO_2. The process is called **photorespiration** because it occurs in the light (*photo*) and consumes O_2 while producing CO_2 (*respiration*). However, unlike normal cellular respiration, photorespiration uses ATP rather than generating it. And unlike photosynthesis, photorespiration produces no sugar. In fact, photorespiration *decreases* photosynthetic output by siphoning organic material from the Calvin cycle and

releasing CO_2 that would otherwise be fixed. This CO_2 can eventually be fixed if it is still in the leaf once the CO_2 concentration is high enough. In the meantime, though, the process is energetically costly, much like a hamster running on its wheel.

How can we explain the existence of a metabolic process that seems to be counterproductive for the plant? According to one hypothesis, photorespiration is evolutionary baggage—a metabolic relic from a much earlier time when the atmosphere had less O_2 and more CO_2 than it does today. In the ancient atmosphere that prevailed when rubisco first evolved, the inability of the enzyme's active site to exclude O_2 would have made little difference. The hypothesis suggests that modern rubisco retains some of its chance affinity for O_2, which is now so concentrated in the atmosphere that a certain amount of photorespiration is inevitable.

We now know that, at least in some cases, photorespiration plays a protective role in plants. Plants that are impaired in their ability to carry out photorespiration (due to defective genes) are more susceptible to damage induced by excess light. Researchers consider this clear evidence that photorespiration acts to neutralize the otherwise damaging products of the light reactions, which build up when a low CO_2 concentration limits the progress of the Calvin cycle. Whether there are other benefits of photorespiration is still unknown. In many types of plants—including a significant number of crop plants—photorespiration drains away as much as 50% of the carbon fixed by the Calvin cycle. As heterotrophs that depend on carbon fixation in chloroplasts for our food, we naturally view photorespiration as wasteful. Indeed, if photorespiration could be reduced in certain plant species without otherwise affecting photosynthetic productivity, crop yields and food supplies might increase.

In some plant species, alternate modes of carbon fixation have evolved that minimize photorespiration and optimize the Calvin cycle—even in hot, arid climates. The two most important of these photosynthetic adaptations are C_4 photosynthesis and crassulacean acid metabolism (CAM).

C_4 Plants

The **C_4 plants** are so named because they preface the Calvin cycle with an alternate mode of carbon fixation that forms a four-carbon compound as its first product. The C_4 pathway is believed to have evolved independently at least 45 separate times and is used by several thousand species in at least 19 plant families. Among the C_4 plants important to agriculture are sugarcane and corn, members of the grass family.

The anatomy of a C_4 leaf is correlated with the mechanism of C_4 photosynthesis. In C_4 plants, there are two distinct types of photosynthetic cells: bundle-sheath cells and mesophyll cells. **Bundle-sheath cells** are arranged into tightly

Photosynthetic cells of C₄ plant leaf { Mesophyll cell, Bundle-sheath cell

Vein (vascular tissue)

C₄ leaf anatomy

Stoma

Mesophyll cell

PEP carboxylase

CO_2

The C₄ pathway

Oxaloacetate (4C) PEP (3C)

ADP

Malate (4C) ATP

Pyruvate (3C)

CO_2

Bundle-sheath cell

Calvin Cycle

Sugar

Vascular tissue

❶ In mesophyll cells, the enzyme PEP carboxylase adds carbon dioxide to PEP.

❷ A four-carbon compound (such as malate) conveys the atoms of the CO_2 into a bundle-sheath cell via plasmodesmata.

❸ In bundle-sheath cells, CO_2 is released and enters the Calvin cycle.

▲ **Figure 11.20 C₄ leaf anatomy and the C₄ pathway.** The structure and biochemical functions of the leaves of C₄ plants are an evolutionary adaptation to hot, dry climates. This adaptation maintains a CO_2 concentration in the bundle sheath that favors photosynthesis over photorespiration.

packed sheaths around the veins of the leaf (**Figure 11.20**). Between the bundle sheath and the leaf surface are the more loosely arranged mesophyll cells, which, in C₄ leaves, are closely associated and never more than two to three cells away from the bundle-sheath cells. The Calvin cycle is confined to the chloroplasts of the bundle-sheath cells. However, the Calvin cycle is preceded by incorporation of CO_2 into organic compounds in the mesophyll cells. See the numbered steps in Figure 11.20, which are also described here:

❶ The first step is carried out by an enzyme present only in mesophyll cells called **PEP carboxylase**. This enzyme adds CO_2 to phosphoenolpyruvate (PEP), forming the four-carbon product oxaloacetate. PEP carboxylase has a much higher affinity for CO_2 than does rubisco and no affinity for O_2. Therefore, PEP carboxylase can fix carbon efficiently when rubisco cannot—that is, when it is hot and dry and stomata are partially closed, causing CO_2 concentration in the leaf to be lower and O_2 concentration to be relatively higher.

❷ After the C₄ plant fixes carbon from CO_2, the mesophyll cells export their four-carbon products (malate in the example shown in Figure 11.20) to bundle-sheath cells through plasmodesmata (see Figure 6.29).

❸ Within the bundle-sheath cells, the four-carbon compounds release CO_2, which is reassimilated into organic material by rubisco and the Calvin cycle. The same reaction regenerates pyruvate, which is transported to mesophyll cells. There, ATP is used to convert pyruvate to PEP, allowing the reaction cycle to continue.

This ATP can be thought of, in a sense, as the "price" of concentrating CO_2 in the bundle-sheath cells. To generate this extra ATP, bundle-sheath cells carry out cyclic electron flow, the process described earlier in this chapter (see Figure 11.16). In fact, these cells contain PS I but no PS II, so cyclic electron flow is their only photosynthetic mode of generating ATP.

In effect, the mesophyll cells of a C₄ plant pump CO_2 into the bundle sheath, keeping the CO_2 concentration in the bundle-sheath cells high enough for rubisco to bind CO_2 rather than O_2. The cyclic series of reactions involving PEP carboxylase and the regeneration of PEP can be thought of as a CO_2-concentrating pump that is powered by ATP. In this way, C₄ photosynthesis spends ATP energy to minimize photorespiration and enhance sugar production. This adaptation is especially advantageous in hot regions with intense sunlight, where stomata partially close during the day, and it is in such environments that C₄ plants evolved and thrive today.

The concentration of CO_2 in the atmosphere has drastically increased since the Industrial Revolution began in the 1800s, and it continues to rise today due to human activities such as the burning of fossil fuels. The resulting global climate change, including an increase in average temperatures around the planet, may have far-reaching effects on plant species. Scientists are concerned that increasing CO_2 concentration and temperature may affect C₃ and C₄ plants differently, thus changing the relative abundance of these species in a given plant community.

Which type of plant would stand to gain more from increasing CO_2 levels? Recall that in C_3 plants, the binding of O_2 rather than CO_2 by rubisco leads to photorespiration, lowering the efficiency of photosynthesis. C_4 plants overcome this problem by concentrating CO_2 in the bundle-sheath cells at the cost of ATP. Rising CO_2 levels should benefit C_3 plants by lowering the amount of photorespiration that occurs. At the same time, rising temperatures have the opposite effect, increasing photorespiration. (Other factors such as water availability may also come into play.) In contrast, many C_4 plants could be largely unaffected by increasing CO_2 levels or temperature. Researchers have investigated aspects of this question in several studies; you can work with data from one such experiment in the Scientific Skills Exercise. In different regions, the particular combination of CO_2 concentration and temperature is likely to alter the balance of C_3 and C_4 plants in varying ways. The effects of such a widespread and variable change in community structure are unpredictable and thus a cause of legitimate concern.

CAM Plants

A second photosynthetic adaptation to arid conditions has evolved in many succulent (water-storing) plants, numerous cacti, pineapples, and representatives of several other plant families. These plants open their stomata during the night

---

SCIENTIFIC SKILLS EXERCISE

Making Scatter Plots with Regression Lines

Does Atmospheric CO₂ Concentration Affect the Productivity of Agricultural Crops? Atmospheric concentration of CO_2 has been rising globally, and scientists wondered whether this would affect C_3 and C_4 plants differently. In this exercise, you will make a scatter plot to examine the relationship between CO_2 concentration and growth of corn (maize), a C_4 crop plant, and velvetleaf, a C_3 weed found in cornfields.

How the Experiment Was Done Researchers grew corn and velvetleaf plants under controlled conditions for 45 days, where all plants received the same amounts of water and light. The plants were divided into three groups, and each was exposed to a different concentration of CO_2 in the air: 350, 600, or 1,000 ppm (parts per million).

Data from the Experiment The table shows the dry mass (in grams) of corn and velvetleaf plants grown at the three concentrations of CO_2. The dry mass values are averages of the leaves, stems, and roots of eight plants.

▶ Corn plant surrounded by invasive velvetleaf plants

	350 ppm CO₂	600 ppm CO₂	1,000 ppm CO₂
Average dry mass of one corn plant (g)	91	89	80
Average dry mass of one velvetleaf plant (g)	35	48	54

Interpret the Data

1. To explore the relationship between the two variables, it is useful to graph the data in a scatter plot, and then draw a regression line. (a) First, place labels for the dependent and independent variables on the appropriate axes. Explain your choices. (b) Now plot the data points for corn and velvetleaf using different symbols for each set of data, and add a key for the two symbols.

2. Draw a "best-fit" line for each set of points. A best-fit line does not necessarily pass through all or even most points. Instead, it is a straight line that passes as close as possible to all data points from that set. Draw a best-fit line for each set of data. Because placement of the line is a matter of judgment, two individuals may draw two slightly different lines for a given set of points. The line that actually fits best, a regression line, can be identified by squaring the distances of all points to any candidate line, then selecting the line that minimizes the sum of the squares. (See the graph in the Scientific Skills Exercise in Chapter 3 for an example of a linear regression line.) Excel or other software programs, including those on a graphing calculator, can plot a regression line once data points are entered. Using either Excel or a graphing calculator, enter the data points for each data set and have the program draw the two regression lines. Compare them to the lines you drew.

3. Describe the trends shown by the regression lines in your scatter plot. (a) Compare the relationship between increasing concentration of CO_2 and the dry mass of corn to that of velvetleaf. (b) Considering that velvetleaf is a weed invasive to cornfields, predict how increased CO_2 concentration may affect interactions between the two species.

4. Based on the data in the scatter plot, estimate the percentage change in dry mass of corn and velvetleaf plants if atmospheric CO_2 concentration increased from 390 ppm (current levels) to 800 ppm. (a) What is the estimated dry mass of corn and velvetleaf plants at 390 ppm? 800 ppm? (b) To calculate the percentage change in mass for each plant, subtract the mass at 390 ppm from the mass at 800 ppm (change in mass), divide by the mass at 390 ppm (initial mass), and multiply by 100. What is the estimated percentage change in dry mass for corn? For velvetleaf? (c) Do these results support the conclusion from other experiments that C_3 plants grow better than C_4 plants under increased CO_2 concentration? Why or why not?

(MB) A version of this Scientific Skills Exercise can be assigned in MasteringBiology.

Data from D. T. Patterson and E. P. Flint, Potential effects of global atmospheric CO_2 enrichment on the growth and competitiveness of C_3 and C_4 weed and crop plants, *Weed Science* 28(1):71–75 (1980).

and close them during the day, just the reverse of how other plants behave. Closing stomata during the day helps desert plants conserve water, but it also prevents CO_2 from entering the leaves. During the night, when their stomata are open, these plants take up CO_2 and incorporate it into a variety of organic acids. This mode of carbon fixation is called **crassulacean acid metabolism**, or **CAM**, after the plant family Crassulaceae, the succulents in which the process was first discovered. The mesophyll cells of **CAM plants** store the organic acids they make during the night in their vacuoles until morning, when the stomata close. During the day, when the light reactions can supply ATP and NADPH for the Calvin cycle, CO_2 is released from the organic acids made the night before to become incorporated into sugar in the chloroplasts.

Notice in **Figure 11.21** that the CAM pathway is similar to the C_4 pathway in that carbon dioxide is first incorporated into organic intermediates before it enters the Calvin cycle. The difference is that in C_4 plants, the initial steps of carbon fixation are separated structurally from the Calvin cycle, whereas in CAM plants, the two steps occur at separate times but within the same cell. (Keep in mind that CAM, C_4, and C_3 plants all eventually use the Calvin cycle to make sugar from carbon dioxide.)

Sugarcane

Pineapple

C_4

CAM

(a) **Spatial separation of steps.** In C_4 plants, carbon fixation and the Calvin cycle occur in different types of cells.

(b) **Temporal separation of steps.** In CAM plants, carbon fixation and the Calvin cycle occur in the same cell at different times.

▲ **Figure 11.21 C_4 and CAM photosynthesis compared.** Both adaptations are characterized by ❶ preliminary incorporation of CO_2 into organic acids, followed by ❷ transfer of CO_2 to the Calvin cycle. The C_4 and CAM pathways are two evolutionary solutions to the problem of maintaining photosynthesis with stomata partially or completely closed on hot, dry days.

The Importance of Photosynthesis: *A Review*

In this chapter, we have followed photosynthesis from photons to food. The light reactions capture solar energy and use it to make ATP and transfer electrons from water to $NADP^+$, forming NADPH. The Calvin cycle uses the ATP and NADPH to produce sugar from carbon dioxide. The energy that enters the chloroplasts as sunlight becomes stored as chemical energy in organic compounds. The entire process is reviewed visually in **Figure 11.22**, where photosynthesis is also put in its natural context.

As for the fates of photosynthetic products, enzymes in the chloroplast and cytosol convert the G3P made in the Calvin cycle to many other organic compounds. In fact, the sugar made in the chloroplasts supplies the entire plant with chemical energy and carbon skeletons for the synthesis of all the major organic molecules of plant cells. About 50% of the organic material made by photosynthesis is consumed as fuel for cellular respiration in plant cell mitochondria.

Technically, green cells are the only autotrophic parts of the plant. The rest of the plant depends on organic molecules exported from leaves via veins (see Figure 11.22, top). In most plants, carbohydrate is transported out of the leaves to the rest of the plant in the form of sucrose, a disaccharide. After arriving at nonphotosynthetic cells, the sucrose provides raw material for cellular respiration and a multitude of anabolic pathways that synthesize proteins, lipids, and other products. A considerable amount of sugar in the form of glucose is linked together to make the polysaccharide cellulose (see Figure 5.6c), especially in plant cells that are still growing and maturing. Cellulose, the main ingredient of cell walls, is the most abundant organic molecule in the plant—and probably on the surface of the planet.

Most plants and other photosynthesizers make more organic material each day than they need to use as respiratory fuel and precursors for biosynthesis. They stockpile the extra sugar by synthesizing starch, storing some in the chloroplasts themselves and some in storage cells of roots, tubers, seeds, and fruits. In accounting for the consumption of the food molecules produced by photosynthesis, let's not forget that most plants lose leaves, roots, stems, fruits, and sometimes their entire bodies to heterotrophs, including humans.

On a global scale, photosynthesis is the process responsible for the presence of oxygen in our atmosphere.

Furthermore, while each chloroplast is minuscule, their collective productivity in terms of food production is prodigious: Photosynthesis makes an estimated 150 billion metric tons of carbohydrate per year (a metric ton is 1,000 kg, about 1.1 tons). That's organic matter equivalent in mass to a stack of about 60 trillion biology textbooks—17 stacks of books reaching from Earth to the sun! No chemical process is more important than photosynthesis to the welfare of life on Earth.

In Chapters 5 through 10, you have learned about many activities of cells. **Figure 11.23** integrates these processes in the context of a working plant cell. As you study the figure, reflect on how each process fits into the big picture: As the most basic unit of living organisms, a cell performs all functions characteristic of life.

▼ **Figure 11.22 A review of photosynthesis.** This diagram shows the main reactants and products of photosynthesis as they move through the tissues of a tree (left) and a chloroplast (right).

MAKE CONNECTIONS *Can plants use the sugar they produce during photosynthesis to directly power the work of the cell? Explain. (See Figures 9.10, 9.11, and 10.6.)*

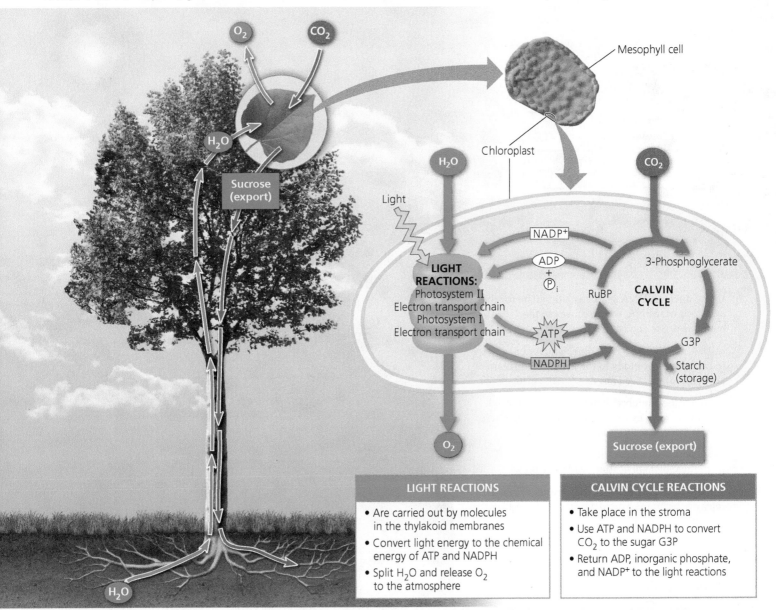

LIGHT REACTIONS	CALVIN CYCLE REACTIONS
• Are carried out by molecules in the thylakoid membranes	• Take place in the stroma
• Convert light energy to the chemical energy of ATP and NADPH	• Use ATP and NADPH to convert CO_2 to the sugar G3P
• Split H_2O and release O_2 to the atmosphere	• Return ADP, inorganic phosphate, and $NADP^+$ to the light reactions

MAKE CONNECTIONS

The Working Cell

This figure illustrates how a generalized plant cell functions, integrating the cellular activities you learned about in Chapters 5–10.

Flow of Genetic Information in the Cell: DNA → RNA → Protein (Chapters 5–7)

1 In the nucleus, DNA serves as a template for the synthesis of mRNA, which moves to the cytoplasm. *See Figures 5.23 and 6.9.*

2 mRNA attaches to a ribosome, which remains free in the cytosol or binds to the rough ER. Proteins are synthesized. *See Figures 5.23 and 6.10.*

3 Proteins and membrane produced by the rough ER flow in vesicles to the Golgi apparatus, where they are processed. *See Figures 6.15 and 7.9.*

4 Transport vesicles carrying proteins pinch off from the Golgi apparatus. *See Figure 6.15.*

5 Some vesicles merge with the plasma membrane, releasing proteins by exocytosis. *See Figure 7.9.*

6 Proteins synthesized on free ribosomes stay in the cell and perform specific functions; examples include the enzymes that catalyze the reactions of cellular respiration and photosynthesis. *See Figures 10.7, 10.9, and 11.19.*

Labels in figure: Nucleus, DNA, mRNA, Nuclear pore, Protein, Protein in vesicle, Rough endoplasmic reticulum (ER), Ribosome, mRNA, Golgi apparatus, Vesicle forming, Protein, Plasma membrane, Cell wall

Energy Transformations in the Cell: Photosynthesis and Cellular Respiration (Chapters 9–11)

7 In chloroplasts, the process of photosynthesis uses the energy of light to convert CO_2 and H_2O to organic molecules, with O_2 as a by-product. *See Figure 11.22.*

8 In mitochondria, organic molecules are broken down by cellular respiration, capturing energy in molecules of ATP, which are used to power the work of the cell, such as protein synthesis and active transport. CO_2 and H_2O are by-products. *See Figures 9.9–9.11, 10.2, and 10.16.*

Vacuole

Movement Across Cell Membranes (Chapter 7)

9 Water diffuses into and out of the cell directly through the plasma membrane and by facilitated diffusion through aquaporins. *See Figure 7.1.*

10 By passive transport, the CO_2 used in photosynthesis diffuses into the cell and the O_2 formed as a by-product of photosynthesis diffuses out of the cell. Both solutes move down their concentration gradients. *See Figures 7.10 and 11.22.*

11 In active transport, energy (usually supplied by ATP) is used to transport a solute against its concentration gradient. *See Figure 7.16.*

Exocytosis (shown in step 5) and endocytosis move larger materials out of and into the cell. *See Figures 7.9 and 7.19.*

7 Photosynthesis in chloroplast

CO_2

H_2O

Organic molecules

O_2

8 Cellular respiration in mitochondrion

ATP

ATP

ATP

ATP

Transport pump

11

9

10

O_2

CO_2

H_2O

MAKE CONNECTIONS *The first enzyme that functions in glycolysis is hexokinase. In this plant cell, describe the entire process by which this enzyme is produced and where it functions, specifying the locations for each step. (See Figures 5.18, 5.23, and 10.9.)*

ANIMATION *BioFlix* Visit the Study Area in **MasteringBiology** for BioFlix® 3-D Animations in Chapters 6, 7, 10, and 11. BioFlix Tutorials can also be assigned in MasteringBiology.

CONCEPT 11.1

Photosynthesis converts light energy to the chemical energy of food (pp. 211–214)

- In **autotrophic** eukaryotes, photosynthesis occurs in chloroplasts, organelles containing **thylakoids**. Stacks of thylakoids form grana. **Photosynthesis** is summarized as

$$6\,CO_2 + 12\,H_2O + \text{Light energy} \rightarrow C_6H_{12}O_6 + 6\,O_2 + 6\,H_2O.$$

Chloroplasts split water into hydrogen and oxygen, incorporating the electrons of hydrogen into sugar molecules. Photosynthesis is a redox process: H_2O is oxidized, and CO_2 is reduced. The **light reactions** in the thylakoid membranes split water, releasing O_2, producing ATP, and forming **NADPH**. The **Calvin cycle** in the **stroma** forms sugar from CO_2, using ATP for energy and NADPH for reducing power.

? *Compare the roles of CO_2 and H_2O in respiration and photosynthesis.*

CONCEPT 11.2

The light reactions convert solar energy to the chemical energy of ATP and NADPH (pp. 214–223)

- Light is a form of electromagnetic energy. The colors we see as **visible light** include those **wavelengths** that drive photosynthesis. A pigment absorbs light of specific wavelengths; **chlorophyll *a*** is the main photosynthetic pigment in plants. Other accessory pigments absorb different wavelengths of light and pass the energy on to chlorophyll *a*.
- A pigment goes from a ground state to an excited state when a **photon** of light boosts one of the pigment's electrons to a higher-energy orbital. This excited state is unstable. Electrons from isolated pigments tend to fall back to the ground state, giving off heat and/or light.
- A **photosystem** is composed of a **reaction-center complex** surrounded by **light-harvesting complexes** that funnel the energy of photons to the reaction-center complex. When a special pair of reaction-center chlorophyll *a* molecules absorbs energy, one of its electrons is boosted to a higher energy level and transferred to the **primary electron acceptor**. Photosystem II contains P680 chlorophyll *a* molecules in the reaction-center complex; **photosystem I** contains P700 molecules.
- **Linear electron flow** during the light reactions uses both photosystems and produces NADPH, ATP, and oxygen:

- **Cyclic electron flow** employs only one photosystem, producing ATP but no NADPH or O_2.
- During chemiosmosis in both mitochondria and chloroplasts, electron transport chains generate an H^+ gradient across a membrane. ATP synthase uses this proton-motive force to make ATP.

? *The absorption spectrum of chlorophyll a differs from the action spectrum of photosynthesis. Explain this observation.*

CONCEPT 11.3

The Calvin cycle uses the chemical energy of ATP and NADPH to reduce CO_2 to sugar (pp. 223–224)

- The Calvin cycle occurs in the stroma, using electrons from NADPH and energy from ATP. One molecule of **G3P** exits the cycle per three CO_2 molecules fixed and is converted to glucose and other organic molecules.

DRAW IT *On the diagram above, draw where ATP and NADPH are used and where rubisco functions. Describe these steps.*

CONCEPT 11.4

Alternative mechanisms of carbon fixation have evolved in hot, arid climates (pp. 225–231)

- On dry, hot days, **C₃ plants** close their stomata, conserving water. Oxygen from the light reactions builds up. In **photorespiration**, O_2 substitutes for CO_2 in the active site of rubisco. This process consumes organic fuel and releases CO_2 without producing ATP or carbohydrate. Photorespiration may be an evolutionary relic, and it may play a photoprotective role.
- **C₄ plants** minimize the cost of photorespiration by incorporating CO_2 into four-carbon compounds in mesophyll cells. These compounds are exported to **bundle-sheath cells**, where they release carbon dioxide for use in the Calvin cycle.
- **CAM plants** open their stomata at night, incorporating CO_2 into organic acids, which are stored in mesophyll cells. During the day, the stomata close, and the CO_2 is released from the organic acids for use in the Calvin cycle.
- Organic compounds produced by photosynthesis provide the energy and building material for Earth's ecosystems.

? *Why are C₄ and CAM photosynthesis more energetically expensive than C₃ photosynthesis? What climate conditions would favor C₄ and CAM plants?*

LEVEL 1: KNOWLEDGE/COMPREHENSION

1. The light reactions of photosynthesis supply the Calvin cycle with
   a. light energy.
   b. CO_2 and ATP.
   c. H_2O and NADPH.
   d. ATP and NADPH.

2. Which of the following sequences correctly represents the flow of electrons during photosynthesis?
   a. NADPH $\rightarrow O_2 \rightarrow CO_2$
   b. $H_2O \rightarrow$ NADPH $\rightarrow$ Calvin cycle
   c. $H_2O \rightarrow$ photosystem I $\rightarrow$ photosystem II
   d. NADPH $\rightarrow$ electron transport chain $\rightarrow O_2$

3. How is photosynthesis similar in C_4 plants and CAM plants?
   a. In both cases, only photosystem I is used.
   b. Both types of plants make sugar without the Calvin cycle.
   c. In both cases, rubisco is not used to fix carbon initially.
   d. Both types of plants make most of their sugar in the dark.

4. Which of the following statements is a correct distinction between autotrophs and heterotrophs?
   a. Autotrophs, but not heterotrophs, can nourish themselves beginning with CO_2 and other nutrients that are inorganic.
   b. Only heterotrophs require chemical compounds from the environment.
   c. Cellular respiration is unique to heterotrophs.
   d. Only heterotrophs have mitochondria.

5. Which of the following does *not* occur during the Calvin cycle?
   a. carbon fixation
   b. oxidation of NADPH
   c. release of oxygen
   d. regeneration of the CO_2 acceptor

LEVEL 2: APPLICATION/ANALYSIS

6. In mechanism, photophosphorylation is most similar to
   a. substrate-level phosphorylation in glycolysis.
   b. oxidative phosphorylation in cellular respiration.
   c. carbon fixation.
   d. reduction of $NADP^+$.

7. Which process is most directly driven by light energy?
   a. creation of a pH gradient by pumping protons across the thylakoid membrane
   b. reduction of $NADP^+$ molecules
   c. removal of electrons from chlorophyll molecules
   d. ATP synthesis

LEVEL 3: SYNTHESIS/EVALUATION

8. SCIENCE, TECHNOLOGY, AND SOCIETY
   Scientific evidence indicates that the CO_2 added to the air by the burning of wood and fossil fuels is contributing to global warming, a rise in global temperature. Tropical rain forests are estimated to be responsible for approximately 20% of global photosynthesis, yet the consumption of large amounts of CO_2 by living trees is thought to make little or no *net* contribution to reduction of global warming. Why might this be? (*Hint*: What processes in both living and dead trees produce CO_2?)

9. EVOLUTION CONNECTION
   Photorespiration can decrease soybeans' photosynthetic output by about 50%. Would you expect this figure to be higher or lower in wild relatives of soybeans? Why?

10. SCIENTIFIC INQUIRY
    MAKE CONNECTIONS The following diagram represents an experiment with isolated thylakoids. The thylakoids were first made acidic by soaking them in a solution at pH 4. After the thylakoid space reached pH 4, the thylakoids were transferred to a basic solution at pH 8. The thylakoids then made ATP in the dark. (See Concept 3.3 to review pH.)

Draw an enlargement of part of the thylakoid membrane in the beaker with the solution at pH 8. Draw ATP synthase. Label the areas of high H^+ concentration and low H^+ concentration. Show the direction protons flow through the enzyme, and show the reaction where ATP is synthesized. Would ATP end up in the thylakoid or outside of it? Explain why the thylakoids in the experiment were able to make ATP in the dark.

11. WRITE ABOUT A THEME: ENERGY AND MATTER
    Life is solar powered. Almost all the producers of the biosphere depend on energy from the sun to produce the organic molecules that supply the energy and carbon skeletons needed for life. In a short essay (100–150 words), describe how the process of photosynthesis in the chloroplasts of plants transforms the energy of sunlight into the chemical energy of sugar molecules.

12. SYNTHESIZE YOUR KNOWLEDGE

The photo shows "watermelon snow" in Antarctica, caused by a species of photosynthetic green algae that thrives in subzero temperatures (*Chlamydomonas nivalis*). These algae are also found in high altitude year-round snowfields. In both locations, UV light levels tend to be high. Based on what you learned in this chapter, propose an explanation for why this photosynthetic alga appears reddish-pink.

MasteringBiology®

12

The Cell Cycle

▲ Chromosomes (blue) are moved by cell machinery (red) during division of a rat kangaroo cell.

▲ **Figure 12.1 How do dividing cells distribute chromosomes to daughter cells?**

The Key Roles of Cell Division

The ability of organisms to produce more of their own kind is the one characteristic that best distinguishes living things from nonliving matter. This unique capacity to procreate, like all biological functions, has a cellular basis. Rudolf Virchow, a German physician, put it this way in 1855: "Where a cell exists, there must have been a preexisting cell, just as the animal arises only from an animal and the plant only from a plant." He summarized this concept with the Latin axiom "*Omnis cellula e cellula*," meaning "Every cell from a cell." The continuity of life is based on the reproduction of cells, or **cell division**. The series of confocal fluorescence micrographs in **Figure 12.1**, starting at the upper left, follows the events of cell division as the cells of a two-celled embryo become four.

Cell division plays several important roles in life. When a prokaryotic cell divides, it is actually reproducing, since the process gives rise to a new organism (another cell). The same is true of any unicellular eukaryote, such as the amoeba shown in **Figure 12.2a**. As for multicellular eukaryotes, cell division enables each of these organisms to develop from a single cell—the fertilized egg. A two-celled embryo, the first stage in this process, is shown in **Figure 12.2b**. And cell division continues to function in renewal and repair in fully grown multicellular eukaryotes, replacing cells that die from normal wear and tear or accidents. For example, dividing cells in your bone marrow continuously make new blood cells (**Figure 12.2c**).

◀ **(a) Reproduction.** An amoeba, a single-celled eukaryote, is dividing into two cells. Each new cell will be an individual organism (LM).

▶ **(b) Growth and development.** This micrograph shows a sand dollar embryo shortly after the fertilized egg divided, forming two cells (LM).

◀ **(c) Tissue renewal.** These dividing bone marrow cells will give rise to new blood cells (LM).

▲ **Figure 12.2 The functions of cell division.**

The cell division process is an integral part of the **cell cycle**, the life of a cell from the time it is first formed during division of a parent cell until its own division into two daughter cells. (Our use of the words *daughter* or *sister* in relation to cells is not meant to imply gender.) Passing identical genetic material to cellular offspring is a crucial function of cell division. In this chapter, you will learn how this process occurs. After studying the cellular mechanics of cell division in eukaryotes and bacteria, you will learn about the molecular control system that regulates progress through the eukaryotic cell cycle and what happens when the control system malfunctions. Because a breakdown in cell cycle control plays a major role in cancer development, this aspect of cell biology is an active area of research.

CONCEPT 12.1

Most cell division results in genetically identical daughter cells

The reproduction of a cell, with all of its complexity, cannot occur by a mere pinching in half; a cell is not like a soap bubble that simply enlarges and splits in two. In both prokaryotes and eukaryotes, most cell division involves the distribution of identical genetic material—DNA—to two daughter cells. (The exception is meiosis, the special type of eukaryotic cell division that can produce sperm and eggs.) What is most remarkable about cell division is the fidelity with which the DNA is passed from one generation of cells to the next. A dividing cell replicates its DNA, allocates the two copies to opposite ends of the cell, and only then splits into daughter cells.

Cellular Organization of the Genetic Material

A cell's endowment of DNA, its genetic information, is called its **genome**. Although a prokaryotic genome is often a single DNA molecule, eukaryotic genomes usually consist of a number of DNA molecules. The overall length of DNA in a eukaryotic cell is enormous. A typical human cell, for example, has about 2 m of DNA—a length about 250,000 times greater than the cell's diameter. Before the cell can divide to form genetically identical daughter cells, all of this DNA must be copied, or replicated, and then the two copies must be separated so that each daughter cell ends up with a complete genome.

The replication and distribution of so much DNA is manageable because the DNA molecules are packaged into structures called **chromosomes**, so named because they take up certain dyes used in microscopy (from the Greek *chroma*, color, and *soma*, body; **Figure 12.3**). Each eukaryotic chromosome consists of one very long, linear DNA molecule associated with many proteins (see Figure 6.9). The DNA molecule carries several hundred to a few thousand genes, the units of information that specify an organism's inherited traits. The associated proteins maintain the structure of the chromosome and help control the activity of the genes. Together, the entire complex of DNA and proteins that is the building material of chromosomes is referred to as **chromatin**. As you will soon see, the chromatin of a chromosome varies in its degree of condensation during the process of cell division.

Every eukaryotic species has a characteristic number of chromosomes in each cell's nucleus. For example, the nuclei of human **somatic cells** (all body cells except the reproductive cells) each contain 46 chromosomes, made up of two sets of 23, one set inherited from each parent. Reproductive

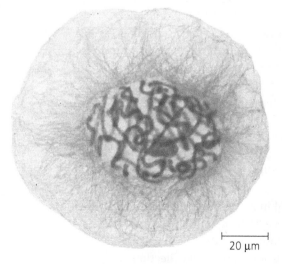

▲ **Figure 12.3 Eukaryotic chromosomes.** Chromosomes (stained purple) are visible within the nucleus of this cell from an African blood lily. The thinner red threads in the surrounding cytoplasm are the cytoskeleton. The cell is preparing to divide (LM).

cells, or **gametes**—sperm and eggs—have one set, or half as many chromosomes as somatic cells; in our example, human gametes have one set of 23 chromosomes. The number of chromosomes in somatic cells varies widely among species: 18 in cabbage plants, 48 in chimpanzees, 56 in elephants, 90 in hedgehogs, and 148 in one species of alga. We'll now consider how these chromosomes behave during cell division.

Distribution of Chromosomes During Eukaryotic Cell Division

When a cell is not dividing, and even as it replicates its DNA in preparation for cell division, each chromosome is in the form of a long, thin chromatin fiber. After DNA replication, however, the chromosomes condense as a part of cell division: Each chromatin fiber becomes densely coiled and folded, making the chromosomes much shorter and so thick that we can see them with a light microscope.

Each duplicated chromosome has two **sister chromatids**, which are joined copies of the original chromosome **(Figure 12.4)**. The two chromatids, each containing an identical DNA molecule, are initially attached all along their lengths by protein complexes called *cohesins*; this attachment is known as *sister chromatid cohesion*. Each sister chromatid has a **centromere**, a region of the chromosomal DNA where the chromatid is attached most closely to its sister chromatid. This attachment is mediated by proteins bound to the centromeric DNA; other bound proteins condense the DNA, giving the duplicated chromosome a narrow "waist." The portion of a chromatid to either side of the centromere is referred to as an *arm* of the chromatid. (An unduplicated chromosome has a single centromere, distinguished by the proteins that bind there, and two arms.)

Later in the cell division process, the two sister chromatids of each duplicated chromosome separate and move into two new nuclei, one forming at each end of the cell. Once the sister chromatids separate, they are no longer called sister chromatids but are considered individual chromosomes; this step essentially doubles the number of chromosomes in the cell. Thus, each new nucleus receives a collection of chromosomes identical to that of the parent cell **(Figure 12.5)**. **Mitosis**, the

▲ **Figure 12.4 A highly condensed, duplicated human chromosome (SEM).**

DRAW IT *Circle one sister chromatid of the chromosome in this micrograph.*

division of the genetic material in the nucleus, is usually followed immediately by **cytokinesis**, the division of the cytoplasm. One cell has become two, each the genetic equivalent of the parent cell.

From a fertilized egg, mitosis and cytokinesis produced the 200 trillion somatic cells that now make up your body, and the same processes continue to generate new cells to

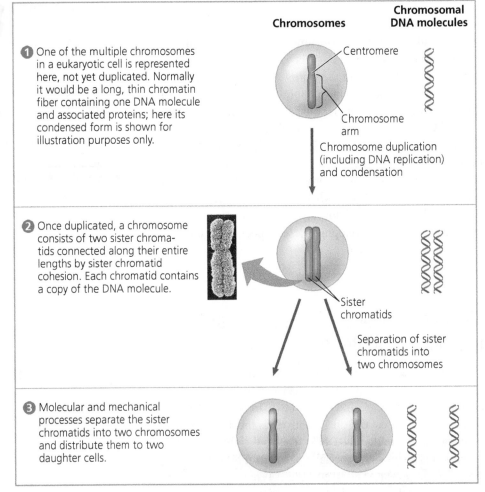

Chromosomes   **Chromosomal DNA molecules**

1 One of the multiple chromosomes in a eukaryotic cell is represented here, not yet duplicated. Normally it would be a long, thin chromatin fiber containing one DNA molecule and associated proteins; here its condensed form is shown for illustration purposes only.

Centromere

Chromosome arm

Chromosome duplication (including DNA replication) and condensation

2 Once duplicated, a chromosome consists of two sister chromatids connected along their entire lengths by sister chromatid cohesion. Each chromatid contains a copy of the DNA molecule.

Sister chromatids

Separation of sister chromatids into two chromosomes

3 Molecular and mechanical processes separate the sister chromatids into two chromosomes and distribute them to two daughter cells.

▲ **Figure 12.5 Chromosome duplication and distribution during cell division.**

? *How many chromatid arms does the chromosome in* **2** *have?*

replace dead and damaged ones. In contrast, you produce gametes—eggs or sperm—by a variation of cell division called *meiosis*, which yields daughter cells with only one set of chromosomes, half as many chromosomes as the parent cell. Meiosis in humans occurs only in special cells in the ovaries or testes (the gonads). Generating gametes, meiosis reduces the chromosome number from 46 (two sets) to 23 (one set). Fertilization fuses two gametes together and returns the chromosome number to 46 (two sets). Mitosis then conserves that number in every somatic cell nucleus of the new human individual. In Chapter 13, we will examine the role of meiosis in reproduction and inheritance in more detail. In the remainder of this chapter, we focus on mitosis and the rest of the cell cycle in eukaryotes.

CONCEPT CHECK 12.1

1. How many chromosomes are drawn in each part of Figure 12.5? (Ignore the micrograph in part 2.)
2. **WHAT IF?** A chicken has 78 chromosomes in its somatic cells. How many chromosomes did the chicken inherit from each parent? How many chromosomes are in each of the chicken's gametes? How many chromosomes will be in each somatic cell of the chicken's offspring?

CONCEPT 12.2

The mitotic phase alternates with interphase in the cell cycle

In 1882, a German anatomist named Walther Flemming developed dyes that allowed him to observe, for the first time, the behavior of chromosomes during mitosis and cytokinesis. (In fact, Flemming coined the terms *mitosis* and *chromatin*.) During the period between one cell division and the next, it appeared to Flemming that the cell was simply growing larger. But we now know that many critical events occur during this stage in the life of a cell.

Phases of the Cell Cycle

Mitosis is just one part of the cell cycle **(Figure 12.6)**. In fact, the **mitotic (M) phase**, which includes both mitosis and cytokinesis, is usually the shortest part of the cell cycle. The mitotic phase alternates with a much longer stage called **interphase**, which often accounts for about 90% of the cycle. Interphase can be divided into subphases: the **G₁ phase** ("first gap"), the **S phase** ("synthesis"), and the **G₂ phase** ("second gap"). The G phases were misnamed as "gaps" when they were first observed because the cells appeared inactive, but we now know that intense metabolic activity and growth occur throughout interphase. During all three

▲ **Figure 12.6 The cell cycle.** In a dividing cell, the mitotic (M) phase alternates with interphase, a growth period. The first part of interphase (G_1) is followed by the S phase, when the chromosomes duplicate; G_2 is the last part of interphase. In the M phase, mitosis distributes the daughter chromosomes to daughter nuclei, and cytokinesis divides the cytoplasm, producing two daughter cells.

subphases of interphase, in fact, a cell grows by producing proteins and cytoplasmic organelles such as mitochondria and endoplasmic reticulum. Duplication of the chromosomes, crucial for eventual division of the cell, occurs entirely during the S phase. (We will discuss synthesis of DNA in Chapter 16.) Thus, a cell grows (G_1), continues to grow as it copies its chromosomes (S), grows more as it completes preparations for cell division (G_2), and divides (M). The daughter cells may then repeat the cycle.

A particular human cell might undergo one division in 24 hours. Of this time, the M phase would occupy less than 1 hour, while the S phase might occupy about 10–12 hours, or about half the cycle. The rest of the time would be apportioned between the G_1 and G_2 phases. The G_2 phase usually takes 4–6 hours; in our example, G_1 would occupy about 5–6 hours. G_1 is the most variable in length in different types of cells. Some cells in a multicellular organism divide very infrequently or not at all. These cells spend their time in G_1 (or a related phase called G_0) doing their job in the organism—a nerve cell carries impulses, for example.

Mitosis is conventionally broken down into five stages: **prophase**, **prometaphase**, **metaphase**, **anaphase**, and **telophase**. Overlapping with the latter stages of mitosis, cytokinesis completes the mitotic phase. **Figure 12.7** describes these stages in an animal cell. Study this figure thoroughly before progressing to the next two sections, which examine mitosis and cytokinesis more closely.

The Mitotic Spindle: *A Closer Look*

Many of the events of mitosis depend on the **mitotic spindle**, which begins to form in the cytoplasm during prophase. This structure consists of fibers made of microtubules and

Exploring Mitosis in an Animal Cell

| G₂ of Interphase | Prophase | Prometaphase |

  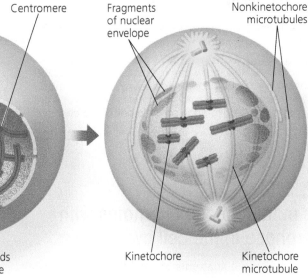

G₂ of Interphase labels: Centrosomes (with centriole pairs); Chromosomes (duplicated, uncondensed); Nucleolus; Nuclear envelope; Plasma membrane

Prophase labels: Early mitotic spindle; Aster; Centromere; Two sister chromatids of one chromosome

Prometaphase labels: Fragments of nuclear envelope; Nonkinetochore microtubules; Kinetochore; Kinetochore microtubule

G₂ of Interphase

- A nuclear envelope encloses the nucleus.
- The nucleus contains one or more nucleoli (singular, *nucleolus*).
- Two centrosomes have formed by duplication of a single centrosome. Centrosomes are regions in animal cells that organize the microtubules of the spindle. Each centrosome contains two centrioles.
- Chromosomes, duplicated during S phase, cannot be seen individually because they have not yet condensed.

The fluorescence micrographs show dividing lung cells from a newt; this species has 22 chromosomes. Chromosomes appear blue, microtubules green, and intermediate filaments red. For simplicity, the drawings show only 6 chromosomes.

Prophase

- The chromatin fibers become more tightly coiled, condensing into discrete chromosomes observable with a light microscope.
- The nucleoli disappear.
- Each duplicated chromosome appears as two identical sister chromatids joined at their centromeres and, in some species, all along their arms by cohesins (sister chromatid cohesion).
- The mitotic spindle (named for its shape) begins to form. It is composed of the centrosomes and the microtubules that extend from them. The radial arrays of shorter microtubules that extend from the centrosomes are called asters ("stars").
- The centrosomes move away from each other, propelled partly by the lengthening microtubules between them.

Prometaphase

- The nuclear envelope fragments.
- The microtubules extending from each centrosome can now invade the nuclear area.
- The chromosomes have become even more condensed.
- Each of the two chromatids of each chromosome now has a kinetochore, a specialized protein structure at the centromere.
- Some of the microtubules attach to the kinetochores, becoming "kinetochore microtubules," which jerk the chromosomes back and forth.
- Nonkinetochore microtubules interact with those from the opposite pole of the spindle.

? *How many molecules of DNA are in the prometaphase drawing? How many molecules per chromosome? How many double helices are there per chromosome? Per chromatid?*

10 μm

| **Metaphase** | **Anaphase** | **Telophase and Cytokinesis** |

 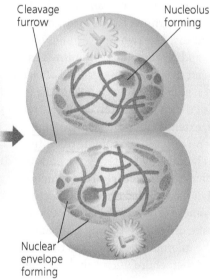

Metaphase plate

Spindle

Centrosome at one spindle pole

Daughter chromosomes

Cleavage furrow

Nucleolus forming

Nuclear envelope forming

Metaphase

- The centrosomes are now at opposite poles of the cell.
- The chromosomes have all arrived at the *metaphase plate*, a plane that is equidistant between the spindle's two poles. The chromosomes' centromeres lie at the metaphase plate.
- For each chromosome, the kinetochores of the sister chromatids are attached to kinetochore microtubules coming from opposite poles.

Anaphase

- Anaphase is the shortest stage of mitosis, often lasting only a few minutes.
- Anaphase begins when the cohesin proteins are cleaved. This allows the two sister chromatids of each pair to part suddenly. Each chromatid thus becomes a full-fledged chromosome.
- The two liberated daughter chromosomes begin moving toward opposite ends of the cell as their kinetochore microtubules shorten. Because these microtubules are attached at the centromere region, the chromosomes move centromere first (at about 1 μm/min).
- The cell elongates as the nonkinetochore microtubules lengthen.
- By the end of anaphase, the two ends of the cell have equivalent—and complete—collections of chromosomes.

Telophase

- Two daughter nuclei form in the cell. Nuclear envelopes arise from the fragments of the parent cell's nuclear envelope and other portions of the endomembrane system.
- Nucleoli reappear.
- The chromosomes become less condensed.
- Any remaining spindle microtubules are depolymerized.
- Mitosis, the division of one nucleus into two genetically identical nuclei, is now complete.

Cytokinesis

- The division of the cytoplasm is usually well under way by late telophase, so the two daughter cells appear shortly after the end of mitosis.
- In animal cells, cytokinesis involves the formation of a cleavage furrow, which pinches the cell in two.

ANIMATION

BioFlix Visit the Study Area in **MasteringBiology** for the BioFlix® 3-D Animation on Mitosis. BioFlix Tutorials can also be assigned in MasteringBiology.

associated proteins. While the mitotic spindle assembles, the other microtubules of the cytoskeleton partially disassemble, providing the material used to construct the spindle. The spindle microtubules elongate (polymerize) by incorporating more subunits of the protein tubulin (see Table 6.1) and shorten (depolymerize) by losing subunits.

In animal cells, the assembly of spindle microtubules starts at the **centrosome**, a subcellular region containing material that functions throughout the cell cycle to organize the cell's microtubules. (It is also a type of *microtubule-organizing center*.) A pair of centrioles is located at the center of the centrosome, but they are not essential for cell division: If the centrioles are destroyed with a laser microbeam, a spindle nevertheless forms during mitosis. In fact, centrioles are not even present in plant cells, which do form mitotic spindles.

During interphase in animal cells, the single centrosome duplicates, forming two centrosomes, which remain near the nucleus. The two centrosomes move apart during prophase and prometaphase of mitosis as spindle microtubules grow out from them. By the end of prometaphase, the two centrosomes, one at each pole of the spindle, are at opposite ends of the cell. An **aster**, a radial array of short microtubules, extends from each centrosome. The spindle includes the centrosomes, the spindle microtubules, and the asters.

Each of the two sister chromatids of a duplicated chromosome has a **kinetochore**, a structure made up of proteins that have assembled on specific sections of DNA at each centromere. The chromosome's two kinetochores face in opposite directions. During prometaphase, some of the spindle microtubules attach to the kinetochores; these are called kinetochore microtubules. (The number of microtubules attached to a kinetochore varies among species, from one microtubule in yeast cells to 40 or so in some mammalian cells.) When one of a chromosome's kinetochores is "captured" by microtubules, the chromosome begins to move toward the pole from which those microtubules extend. However, this movement is checked as soon as microtubules from the opposite pole attach to the kinetochore on the other chromatid. What happens next is like a tug-of-war that ends in a draw. The chromosome moves first in one direction, then in the other, back and forth, finally settling midway between the two ends of the cell. At metaphase, the centromeres of all the duplicated chromosomes are on a plane midway between the spindle's two poles. This plane is called the **metaphase plate**, which is an imaginary plate rather than an actual cellular structure (**Figure 12.8**). Meanwhile, microtubules that do not attach to kinetochores have been elongating, and by metaphase they overlap and interact with other nonkinetochore microtubules from the opposite pole of the spindle. By metaphase, the microtubules of the asters have also grown and are in contact with the plasma membrane. The spindle is now complete.

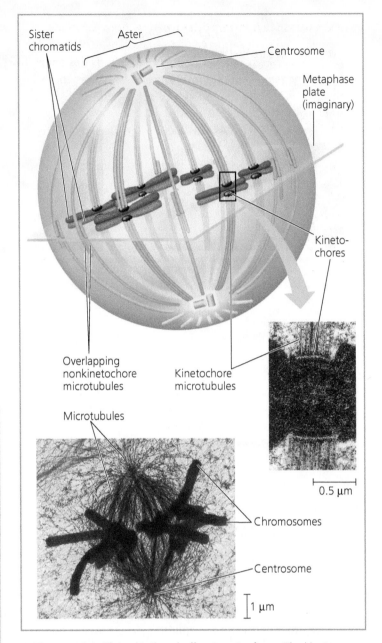

▲ **Figure 12.8 The mitotic spindle at metaphase.** The kinetochores of each chromosome's two sister chromatids face in opposite directions. Here, each kinetochore is attached to a cluster of kinetochore microtubules extending from the nearest centrosome. Nonkinetochore microtubules overlap at the metaphase plate (TEMs).

DRAW IT *On the lower micrograph, draw a line indicating the position of the metaphase plate. Circle an aster. Draw arrows indicating the directions of chromosome movement once anaphase begins.*

The structure of the spindle correlates well with its function during anaphase. Anaphase begins suddenly when the cohesins holding together the sister chromatids of each chromosome are cleaved by an enzyme called *separase*. Once separated, the chromatids become full-fledged chromosomes that move toward opposite ends of the cell.

How do the kinetochore microtubules function in this poleward movement of chromosomes? Apparently, two mechanisms are in play, both involving motor proteins. (To review how motor proteins move an object along a microtubule, see Figure 6.21.) Results of a cleverly designed experiment suggested that motor proteins on the kinetochores "walk" the chromosomes along the microtubules, which depolymerize at their kinetochore ends after the motor proteins have passed (Figure 12.9). (This is referred to as the "Pac-man" mechanism because of its resemblance to the arcade game character that moves by eating all the dots in its path.) However, other researchers, working with different cell types or cells from other species, have shown that chromosomes are "reeled in" by motor proteins at the spindle poles and that the microtubules depolymerize after they pass by these motor proteins. The general consensus now is that both mechanisms are used and that their relative contributions vary among cell types.

In a dividing animal cell, the nonkinetochore microtubules are responsible for elongating the whole cell during anaphase. Nonkinetochore microtubules from opposite poles overlap each other extensively during metaphase (see Figure 12.8). During anaphase, the region of overlap is reduced as motor proteins attached to the microtubules walk them away from one another, using energy from ATP. As the microtubules push apart from each other, their spindle poles are pushed apart, elongating the cell. At the same time, the microtubules lengthen somewhat by the addition of tubulin subunits to their overlapping ends. As a result, the microtubules continue to overlap.

At the end of anaphase, duplicate groups of chromosomes have arrived at opposite ends of the elongated parent cell. Nuclei re-form during telophase. Cytokinesis generally begins during anaphase or telophase, and the spindle eventually disassembles by depolymerization of microtubules.

Cytokinesis: *A Closer Look*

In animal cells, cytokinesis occurs by a process known as **cleavage**. The first sign of cleavage is the appearance of a **cleavage furrow**, a shallow groove in the cell surface near the old metaphase plate (Figure 12.10a). On the cytoplasmic side of the furrow is a contractile ring of actin microfilaments associated with molecules of the protein myosin. The actin microfilaments interact with the myosin molecules, causing the ring to contract. The contraction of the dividing cell's ring of microfilaments is like the pulling of a drawstring. The cleavage furrow deepens until the parent cell is pinched in two, producing two completely separated cells, each with its own nucleus and its own share of cytosol, organelles, and other subcellular structures.

Cytokinesis in plant cells, which have cell walls, is markedly different. There is no cleavage furrow. Instead, during telophase, vesicles derived from the Golgi apparatus move along microtubules to the middle of the cell, where they

▼ **Figure 12.9**   Inquiry

At which end do kinetochore microtubules shorten during anaphase?

Experiment Gary Borisy and colleagues at the University of Wisconsin wanted to determine whether kinetochore microtubules depolymerize at the kinetochore end or the pole end as chromosomes move toward the poles during mitosis. First they labeled the microtubules of a pig kidney cell in early anaphase with a yellow fluorescent dye.

Then they marked a region of the kinetochore microtubules between one spindle pole and the chromosomes by using a laser to eliminate the fluorescence from that region, while leaving the microtubules intact (see below). As anaphase proceeded, they monitored the changes in microtubule length on either side of the mark.

Results As the chromosomes moved poleward, the microtubule segments on the kinetochore side of the mark shortened, while those on the spindle pole side stayed the same length.

Conclusion During anaphase in this cell type, chromosome movement is correlated with kinetochore microtubules shortening at their kinetochore ends and not at their spindle pole ends. This experiment supports the hypothesis that during anaphase, a chromosome is walked along a microtubule as the microtubule depolymerizes at its kinetochore end, releasing tubulin subunits.

Source: G. J. Gorbsky, P. J. Sammak, and G. G. Borisy, Chromosomes move poleward in anaphase along stationary microtubules that coordinately disassemble from their kinetochore ends, *Journal of Cell Biology* 104:9–18 (1987).

WHAT IF? *If this experiment had been done on a cell type in which "reeling in" at the poles was the main cause of chromosome movement, how would the mark have moved relative to the poles? How would the microtubule lengths have changed?*

(a) Cleavage of an animal cell (SEM)

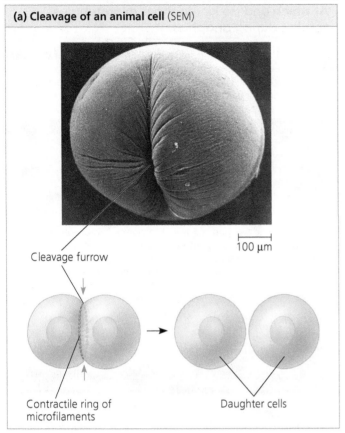

100 μm

Cleavage furrow

Contractile ring of
microfilaments

Daughter cells

(b) Cell plate formation in a plant cell (TEM)

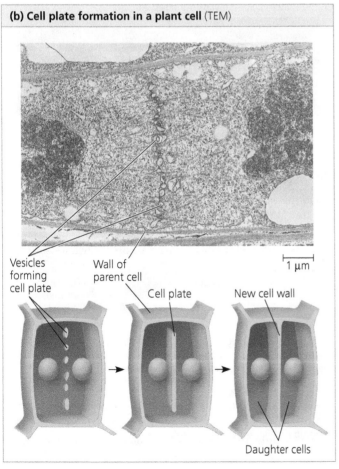

1 μm

Vesicles
forming
cell plate

Wall of
parent cell

Cell plate

New cell wall

Daughter cells

coalesce, producing a **cell plate** (Figure 12.10b). Cell wall materials carried in the vesicles collect inside the cell plate as it grows. The cell plate enlarges until its surrounding membrane fuses with the plasma membrane along the perimeter of the cell. Two daughter cells result, each with its own plasma membrane. Meanwhile, a new cell wall arising from the contents of the cell plate has formed between the daughter cells.

Figure 12.11 is a series of micrographs of a dividing plant cell. Examining this figure will help you review mitosis and cytokinesis.

Binary Fission in Bacteria

Prokaryotes (bacteria and archaea) can undergo a type of reproduction in which the cell grows to roughly double its size and then divides to form two cells. The term **binary fission**, meaning "division in half," refers to this process and to the asexual reproduction of single-celled eukaryotes, such as the amoeba in Figure 12.2a. However, the process in eukaryotes involves mitosis, while that in prokaryotes does not.

In bacteria, most genes are carried on a single bacterial chromosome that consists of a circular DNA molecule and associated proteins. Although bacteria are smaller and simpler than eukaryotic cells, the challenge of replicating their genomes in an orderly fashion and distributing the copies equally to two daughter cells is still formidable. The chromosome of the bacterium *Escherichia coli*, for example, when it is fully stretched out, is about 500 times as long as the cell. For such a long chromosome to fit within the cell requires that it be highly coiled and folded.

In *E. coli*, the process of cell division is initiated when the DNA of the bacterial chromosome begins to replicate at a specific place on the chromosome called the **origin of replication**, producing two origins. As the chromosome continues to replicate, one origin moves rapidly toward the opposite end of the cell (Figure 12.12). While the chromosome is replicating, the cell elongates. When replication is complete and the bacterium has reached about twice its initial size, its plasma membrane pinches inward, dividing the parent *E. coli* cell into two daughter cells. In this way, each cell inherits a complete genome.

Using the techniques of modern DNA technology to tag the origins of replication with molecules that glow green in fluorescence microscopy (see Figure 6.3), researchers have directly observed the movement of bacterial chromosomes. This movement is reminiscent of the poleward movements of the centromere regions of eukaryotic chromosomes during anaphase of mitosis, but bacteria don't have visible mitotic spindles or even microtubules. In most bacterial species studied, the two origins of replication end up at opposite ends of the cell or in some other very specific location, possibly anchored there by one or more proteins. How bacterial chromosomes move and how their specific location is

Nucleus
Nucleolus
Chromosomes condensing
Chromosomes
Cell plate
10 μm

1 Prophase. The chromosomes are condensing and the nucleolus is beginning to disappear. Although not yet visible in the micrograph, the mitotic spindle is starting to form.

2 Prometaphase. Discrete chromosomes are now visible; each consists of two aligned, identical sister chromatids. Later in prometaphase, the nuclear envelope will fragment.

3 Metaphase. The spindle is complete, and the chromosomes, attached to microtubules at their kinetochores, are all at the metaphase plate.

4 Anaphase. The chromatids of each chromosome have separated, and the daughter chromosomes are moving to the ends of the cell as their kinetochore microtubules shorten.

5 Telophase. Daughter nuclei are forming. Meanwhile, cytokinesis has started: The cell plate, which will divide the cytoplasm in two, is growing toward the perimeter of the parent cell.

▲ **Figure 12.11 Mitosis in a plant cell.** These light micrographs show mitosis in cells of an onion root.

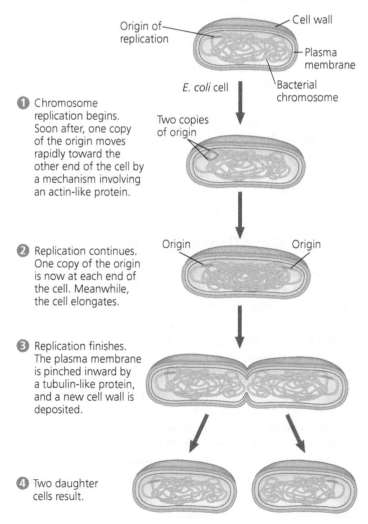

Origin of replication
Cell wall
Plasma membrane
E. coli cell
Bacterial chromosome

1 Chromosome replication begins. Soon after, one copy of the origin moves rapidly toward the other end of the cell by a mechanism involving an actin-like protein.

Two copies of origin

2 Replication continues. One copy of the origin is now at each end of the cell. Meanwhile, the cell elongates.

Origin   Origin

3 Replication finishes. The plasma membrane is pinched inward by a tubulin-like protein, and a new cell wall is deposited.

4 Two daughter cells result.

▲ **Figure 12.12 Bacterial cell division by binary fission.** The bacterium *E. coli*, shown here, has a single, circular chromosome.

established and maintained are active areas of research. Several proteins have been identified that play important roles. Polymerization of one protein resembling eukaryotic actin apparently functions in bacterial chromosome movement during cell division, and another protein that is related to tubulin helps pinch the plasma membrane inward, separating the two bacterial daughter cells.

The Evolution of Mitosis

EVOLUTION Given that prokaryotes preceded eukaryotes on Earth by more than a billion years, we might hypothesize that mitosis evolved from simpler prokaryotic mechanisms of cell reproduction. The fact that some of the proteins involved in bacterial binary fission are related to eukaryotic proteins that function in mitosis supports that hypothesis.

As eukaryotes with nuclear envelopes and larger genomes evolved, the ancestral process of binary fission, seen today in bacteria, somehow gave rise to mitosis. Variations on cell division exist in different groups of organisms. These variant processes may be similar to mechanisms used by ancestral species and thus may resemble steps in the evolution of mitosis from a binary fission-like process presumably carried out by very early bacteria. Possible intermediate stages are suggested by two unusual types of nuclear division found today in certain unicellular eukaryotes—dinoflagellates, diatoms, and some yeasts (**Figure 12.13**). These two modes of nuclear division are thought to be cases where ancestral mechanisms have remained relatively unchanged over evolutionary time. In both types, the nuclear envelope remains intact, in contrast to what happens in most eukaryotic cells.

Bacterial
chromosome

(a) Bacteria. During binary fission in bacteria, the origins of the daughter chromosomes move to opposite ends of the cell. The mechanism involves polymerization of actin-like molecules, and possibly proteins that may anchor the daughter chromosomes to specific sites on the plasma membrane.

Chromosomes

Microtubules

Intact nuclear
envelope

(b) Dinoflagellates. In unicellular protists called dinoflagellates, the chromosomes attach to the nuclear envelope, which remains intact during cell division. Microtubules pass through the nucleus inside cytoplasmic tunnels, reinforcing the spatial orientation of the nucleus, which then divides in a process reminiscent of bacterial binary fission.

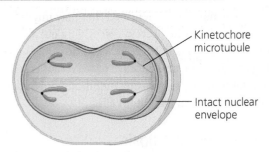

Kinetochore
microtubule

Intact nuclear
envelope

(c) Diatoms and some yeasts. In these two other groups of unicellular eukaryotes, the nuclear envelope also remains intact during cell division. In these organisms, the microtubules form a spindle *within* the nucleus. Microtubules separate the chromosomes, and the nucleus splits into two daughter nuclei.

Kinetochore
microtubule

Fragments of
nuclear envelope

(d) Most eukaryotes. In most other eukaryotes, including plants and animals, the spindle forms outside the nucleus, and the nuclear envelope breaks down during mitosis. Microtubules separate the chromosomes, and two nuclear envelopes then form.

▲ **Figure 12.13 Mechanisms of cell division in several groups of organisms.** Some unicellular eukaryotes existing today have mechanisms of cell division that may resemble intermediate steps in the evolution of mitosis. Except for (a), these schematic diagrams do not show cell walls.

CONCEPT CHECK **12.2**

1. How many chromosomes are drawn in Figure 12.8? Are they duplicated? How many chromatids are shown?
2. Compare cytokinesis in animal cells and plant cells.
3. During which stages of the cell cycle does a chromosome consist of two identical chromatids?
4. Compare the roles of tubulin and actin during eukaryotic cell division with the roles of tubulin-like and actin-like proteins during bacterial binary fission.
5. A kinetochore has been compared to a coupling device that connects a motor to the cargo that it moves. Explain.
6. MAKE CONNECTIONS What other functions do actin and tubulin carry out? Name the proteins they interact with to do so. (Review Figures 6.21a and 6.26a.)

CONCEPT 12.3

The eukaryotic cell cycle is regulated by a molecular control system

The timing and rate of cell division in different parts of a plant or animal are crucial to normal growth, development, and maintenance. The frequency of cell division varies with the type of cell. For example, human skin cells divide frequently throughout life, whereas liver cells maintain the ability to divide but keep it in reserve until an appropriate need arises—say, to repair a wound. Some of the most specialized cells, such as fully formed nerve cells and muscle cells, do not divide at all in a mature human. These cell cycle differences result from regulation at the molecular level. The mechanisms of this regulation are of great interest, not only to understand the life cycles of normal cells but also to learn how cancer cells manage to escape the usual controls.

The Cell Cycle Control System

What controls the cell cycle? In the early 1970s, a variety of experiments led to the hypothesis that the cell cycle is driven by specific signaling molecules present in the cytoplasm. Some of the first strong evidence for this hypothesis came from experiments with mammalian cells grown in culture. In these experiments, two cells in different phases of the cell cycle were fused to form a single cell with two nuclei **(Figure 12.14)**. If one of the original cells was in the S phase and the other was in G_1, the G_1 nucleus immediately entered the S phase, as though stimulated by signaling molecules present in the cytoplasm of the first cell. Similarly, if a cell undergoing mitosis (M phase) was fused with another cell in any stage of its cell cycle, even G_1, the second nucleus immediately entered mitosis, with condensation of the chromatin and formation of a mitotic spindle.

The experiment shown in Figure 12.14 and other experiments on animal cells and yeasts demonstrated that the

Do molecular signals in the cytoplasm regulate the cell cycle?

Experiment Researchers at the University of Colorado wondered whether a cell's progression through the cell cycle is controlled by cytoplasmic molecules. To investigate this, they selected cultured mammalian cells that were at different phases of the cell cycle and induced them to fuse. Two such experiments are shown here.

Experiment 1	Experiment 2

When a cell in the S phase was fused with a cell in G_1, the G_1 nucleus immediately entered the S phase—DNA was synthesized.

When a cell in the M phase was fused with a cell in G_1, the G_1 nucleus immediately began mitosis—a spindle formed and the chromosomes condensed, even though the chromosomes had not been duplicated.

Conclusion The results of fusing a G_1 cell with a cell in the S or M phase of the cell cycle suggest that molecules present in the cytoplasm during the S or M phase control the progression to those phases.

Source: R. T. Johnson and P. N. Rao, Mammalian cell fusion: Induction of premature chromosome condensation in interphase nuclei, *Nature* 226:717–722 (1970).

WHAT IF? *If the progression of phases did not depend on cytoplasmic molecules and, instead, each phase automatically began when the previous one was complete, how would the results have differed?*

sequential events of the cell cycle are directed by a distinct **cell cycle control system**, a cyclically operating set of molecules in the cell that both triggers and coordinates key events in the cell cycle. The cell cycle control system has been compared to the control device of an automatic washing machine **(Figure 12.15)**. Like the washer's timing device, the cell cycle control system proceeds on its own, according to a built-in clock. However, just as a washer's cycle is subject to both internal control (such as the sensor that detects when the tub is filled with water) and external adjustment (such as starting or stopping the machine), the cell cycle is regulated at certain checkpoints by both internal and external signals that stop or restart the machine. A **checkpoint** is a control point in the cell cycle where stop and go-ahead signals can regulate the cycle. Three important checkpoints are found in the G_1, G_2, and M phases (the red gates in Figure 12.15).

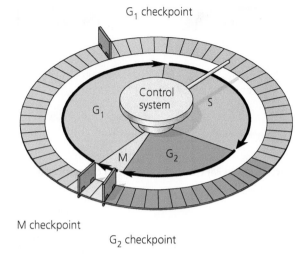

G_1 checkpoint

M checkpoint

G_2 checkpoint

▲ **Figure 12.15 Mechanical analogy for the cell cycle control system.** In this diagram of the cell cycle, the flat "stepping stones" around the perimeter represent sequential events. Like the control device of an automatic washer, the cell cycle control system proceeds on its own, driven by a built-in clock. However, the system is subject to internal and external regulation at various checkpoints; three important checkpoints are shown (red).

To understand how cell cycle checkpoints work, we first need to see what kinds of molecules make up the cell cycle control system (the molecular basis for the cell cycle clock) and how a cell progresses through the cycle. Then we will consider the internal and external checkpoint signals that can make the clock either pause or continue.

The Cell Cycle Clock: Cyclins and Cyclin-Dependent Kinases

Rhythmic fluctuations in the abundance and activity of cell cycle control molecules pace the sequential events of the cell cycle. These regulatory molecules are mainly proteins of two types: protein kinases and cyclins. Protein kinases are enzymes that activate or inactivate other proteins by phosphorylating them (see Chapter 8).

Many of the kinases that drive the cell cycle are actually present at a constant concentration in the growing cell, but much of the time they are in an inactive form. To be active, such a kinase must be attached to a **cyclin**, a protein that gets its name from its cyclically fluctuating concentration in the cell. Because of this requirement, these kinases are called **cyclin-dependent kinases**, or **Cdks**. The activity of a Cdk rises and falls with changes in the concentration of its cyclin partner. **Figure 12.16a** shows the fluctuating activity of **MPF**, the cyclin-Cdk complex that was discovered first (in frog eggs). Note that the peaks of MPF activity correspond to the peaks of cyclin concentration. The cyclin level rises during the S and G_2 phases and then falls abruptly during M phase.

The initials MPF stand for "maturation-promoting factor," but we can think of MPF as "M-phase-promoting factor" because it triggers the cell's passage into the M phase,

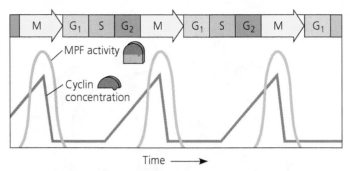

(a) Fluctuation of MPF activity and cyclin concentration during the cell cycle

① Synthesis of cyclin begins in late S phase and continues through G_2. Because cyclin is protected from degradation during this stage, it accumulates.

⑤ During G_1, the degradation of cyclin continues, and the Cdk component of MPF is recycled.

④ During anaphase, the cyclin component of MPF is degraded, terminating the M phase. The cell enters the G_1 phase.

③ MPF promotes mitosis by phosphorylating various proteins. MPF's activity peaks during metaphase.

② Cyclin combines with Cdk, producing MPF. When enough MPF molecules accumulate, the cell passes the G_2 checkpoint and begins mitosis.

(b) Molecular mechanisms that help regulate the cell cycle

▲ **Figure 12.16 Molecular control of the cell cycle at the G_2 checkpoint.** The steps of the cell cycle are timed by rhythmic fluctuations in the activity of cyclin-dependent kinases (Cdks). Here we focus on a cyclin-Cdk complex in animal cells called MPF, which acts at the G_2 checkpoint as a go-ahead signal, triggering the events of mitosis.

[?] *Explain how the events in the diagram in (b) are related to the "Time" axis of the graph in (a), beginning at the left end.*

past the G_2 checkpoint (**Figure 12.16b**). When cyclins that accumulate during G_2 associate with Cdk molecules, the resulting MPF complex phosphorylates a variety of proteins, initiating mitosis. MPF acts both directly as a kinase and indirectly by activating other kinases. For example, MPF causes phosphorylation of various proteins of the nuclear

lamina (see Figure 6.9), which promotes fragmentation of the nuclear envelope during prometaphase of mitosis. There is also evidence that MPF contributes to molecular events required for chromosome condensation and spindle formation during prophase.

During anaphase, MPF helps switch itself off by initiating a process that leads to the destruction of its own cyclin. The noncyclin part of MPF, the Cdk, persists in the cell, inactive until it becomes part of MPF again by associating with new cyclin molecules synthesized during the S and G_2 phases of the next round of the cycle.

The fluctuating activities of different cyclin-Cdk complexes are of major importance in controlling all the stages of the cell cycle and give the go-ahead signals at some checkpoints as well. As mentioned above, MPF controls the cell's passage through the G_2 checkpoint. Cell behavior at the G_1 checkpoint is also regulated by the activity of cyclin-Cdk protein complexes. Animal cells appear to have at least three Cdk proteins and several different cyclins that operate at this checkpoint. Next, let's consider checkpoints in more detail.

Stop and Go Signs: Internal and External Signals at the Checkpoints

Animal cells generally have built-in stop signals that halt the cell cycle at checkpoints until overridden by go-ahead signals. (The signals are transmitted within the cell by the kinds of signal transduction pathways discussed in Chapter 8.) Many signals registered at checkpoints come from cellular surveillance mechanisms inside the cell. These signals report whether crucial cellular processes that should have occurred by that point have in fact been completed correctly and thus whether or not the cell cycle should proceed. Checkpoints also register signals from outside the cell. Three important checkpoints are those in G_1, G_2, and M phases, shown in Figure 12.15.

For many cells, the G_1 checkpoint—dubbed the "restriction point" in mammalian cells—seems to be the most important. If a cell receives a go-ahead signal at the G_1 checkpoint, it will usually complete the G_1, S, G_2, and M phases and divide. If it does not receive a go-ahead signal at that point, it may exit the cycle, switching into a nondividing state called the **G_0 phase** (**Figure 12.17a**). Most cells of the human body are actually in the G_0 phase. As mentioned earlier, mature nerve cells and muscle cells never divide. Other cells, such as liver cells, can be "called back" from the G_0 phase to the cell cycle by external cues, such as growth factors released during injury.

Biologists are currently working out the pathways that link signals originating inside and outside the cell with the responses by cyclin-dependent kinases and other proteins. An example of an internal signal occurs at the third important checkpoint, the M phase checkpoint (**Figure 12.17b**).

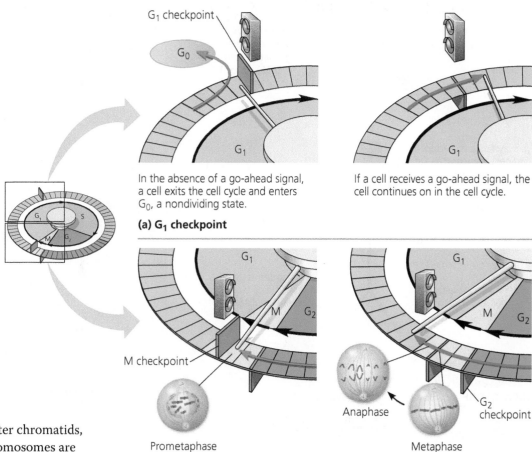

▶ **Figure 12.17 Two important checkpoints.** At certain checkpoints in the cell cycle (red gates), cells do different things depending on the signals they receive. Events of the **(a)** G_1 and **(b)** M checkpoints are shown. In **(b)**, the G_2 checkpoint has already been passed by the cell.

WHAT IF? *What might be the result if the cell ignored either checkpoint and progressed through the cell cycle?*

In the absence of a go-ahead signal, a cell exits the cell cycle and enters G_0, a nondividing state.

(a) G_1 checkpoint

If a cell receives a go-ahead signal, the cell continues on in the cell cycle.

Prometaphase

A cell in mitosis receives a stop signal when any of its chromosomes are not attached to spindle fibers.

(b) M checkpoint

Metaphase

When all chromosomes are attached to spindle fibers from both poles, a go-ahead signal allows the cell to proceed into anaphase.

Anaphase, the separation of sister chromatids, does not begin until all the chromosomes are properly attached to the spindle at the metaphase plate. Researchers have learned that as long as some kinetochores are unattached to spindle microtubules, the sister chromatids remain together, delaying anaphase. Only when the kinetochores of all the chromosomes are properly attached to the spindle does the appropriate regulatory protein complex become activated. (In this case, the regulatory molecule is not a cyclin-Cdk complex but, instead, a different complex made up of several proteins.) Once activated, the complex sets off a chain of molecular events that activates the enzyme separase, which cleaves the cohesins, allowing the sister chromatids to separate. This mechanism ensures that daughter cells do not end up with missing or extra chromosomes.

Studies using animal cells in culture have led to the identification of many external factors, both chemical and physical, that can influence cell division. For example, cells fail to divide if an essential nutrient is lacking in the culture medium. (This is analogous to trying to run a washing machine without the water supply hooked up; an internal sensor won't allow the machine to continue past the point where water is needed.) And even if all other conditions are favorable, most types of mammalian cells divide in culture only if the growth medium includes specific growth factors. As mentioned in Chapter 10, a **growth factor** is a protein released by certain cells that stimulates other cells to divide.

Different cell types respond specifically to different growth factors or combinations of growth factors.

Consider, for example, *platelet-derived growth factor (PDGF)*, which is made by blood cell fragments called platelets. The experiment illustrated in **Figure 12.18** demonstrates that PDGF is required for the division of cultured fibroblasts, a type of connective tissue cell. Fibroblasts have PDGF receptors on their plasma membranes. The binding of PDGF molecules to these receptors (which are receptor tyrosine kinases; see Figure 10.8) triggers a signal transduction pathway that allows the cells to pass the G_1 checkpoint and divide. PDGF stimulates fibroblast division not only in the artificial conditions of cell culture, but also in an animal's body. When an injury occurs, platelets release PDGF in the vicinity. The resulting proliferation of fibroblasts helps heal the wound.

The effect of an external physical factor on cell division is clearly seen in **density-dependent inhibition**, a phenomenon in which crowded cells stop dividing **(Figure 12.19a)**. As first observed many years ago, cultured cells normally divide until they form a single layer of cells on the inner surface of the culture flask, at which point the cells stop dividing. If some cells are removed, those bordering the open

① A sample of human connective tissue is cut up into small pieces.

Scalpels

Petri dish

◀ **Figure 12.18 The effect of platelet-derived growth factor (PDGF) on cell division.**

② Enzymes are used to digest the extracellular matrix in the tissue pieces, resulting in a suspension of free fibroblasts.

③ Cells are transferred to culture vessels containing a basic growth medium consisting of glucose, amino acids, salts, and antibiotics (to prevent bacterial growth).

④ PDGF is added to half the vessels. The culture vessels are incubated at 37°C for 24 hours.

Without PDGF

In the basic growth medium without PDGF (the control), the cells fail to divide.

With PDGF

In the basic growth medium plus PDGF, the cells proliferate. The SEM shows cultured fibroblasts.

MAKE CONNECTIONS
PDGF signals cells by binding to a cell-surface receptor tyrosine kinase. If you added a chemical that blocked phosphorylation, how would the results differ? (See Figure 10.8.)

10 μm

Cells anchor to dish surface and divide (anchorage dependence).

When cells have formed a complete single layer, they stop dividing (density-dependent inhibition).

If some cells are scraped away, the remaining cells divide to fill the gap and then stop once they contact each other (density-dependent inhibition).

20 μm

(a) Normal mammalian cells. Contact with neighboring cells and the availability of nutrients, growth factors, and a substratum for attachment limit cell density to a single layer.

20 μm

(b) Cancer cells. Cancer cells usually continue to divide well beyond a single layer, forming a clump of overlapping cells. They do not exhibit anchorage dependence or density-dependent inhibition.

▲ **Figure 12.19 Density-dependent inhibition and anchorage dependence of cell division.** Individual cells are shown disproportionately large in the drawings.

space begin dividing again and continue until the vacancy is filled. Follow-up studies revealed that the binding of a cell-surface protein to its counterpart on an adjoining cell sends a cell division-inhibiting signal forward in the cell cycle, even in the presence of growth factors.

Most animal cells also exhibit **anchorage dependence** (see Figure 12.19a). To divide, they must be attached to a substratum, such as the inside of a culture flask or the extracellular matrix of a tissue. Experiments suggest that like cell density, anchorage is signaled to the cell cycle control system via pathways involving plasma membrane proteins and elements of the cytoskeleton linked to them.

Density-dependent inhibition and anchorage dependence appear to function not only in cell culture but also in the body's tissues, checking the growth of cells at some optimal density and location during embryonic development and throughout an organism's life. Cancer cells, which we discuss next, exhibit neither density-dependent inhibition nor anchorage dependence **(Figure 12.19b).**

Loss of Cell Cycle Controls in Cancer Cells

Cancer cells do not heed the normal signals that regulate the cell cycle. In culture, they do not stop dividing when growth factors are depleted. A logical hypothesis is that cancer cells do not need growth factors in their culture medium to grow and divide. They may make a required growth factor themselves, or they may have an abnormality in the signaling pathway that conveys the growth factor's signal to the cell cycle control system even in the absence of that factor. Another possibility is an abnormal cell cycle control system. In these scenarios, the underlying basis of the abnormality is almost always a change in one or more genes (for example, a mutation) that alters the function of their protein products, resulting in faulty cell cycle control.

There are other important differences between normal cells and cancer cells that reflect derangements of the cell cycle. If and when they stop dividing, cancer cells do so at random points in the cycle, rather than at the normal checkpoints. Moreover, cancer cells can go on dividing indefinitely in culture if they are given a continual supply of nutrients; in essence, they are "immortal." A striking example is a cell line that has been reproducing in culture since 1951. Cells of this line are called HeLa cells because their original source was a tumor removed from a woman named *Henrietta Lacks*. Cells in culture that acquire the ability to divide indefinitely are said to have undergone **transformation**, the process that causes them to behave like cancer cells. By contrast, nearly all normal, nontransformed mammalian cells growing in culture divide only about 20 to 50 times before they stop dividing, age, and die. Finally, cancer cells evade the normal controls that trigger a cell to undergo apoptosis when something is wrong—for example, when an irreparable mistake has occurred during DNA replication preceding mitosis.

The abnormal behavior of cancer cells can be catastrophic when it occurs in the body. The problem begins when a single cell in a tissue undergoes the first changes of the multistep process that converts a normal cell to a cancer cell. Such a cell often has altered proteins on its surface, and the body's immune system normally recognizes the cell as "nonself"— an insurgent—and destroys it. However, if the cell evades destruction, it may proliferate and form a tumor, a mass of abnormal cells within otherwise normal tissue. The abnormal cells may remain at the original site if they have too few genetic and cellular changes to survive at another site. In that case, the tumor is called a **benign tumor**. Most benign tumors do not cause serious problems and can be removed by surgery. In contrast, a **malignant tumor** includes cells whose genetic and cellular changes enable them to spread to new tissues and impair the functions of one or more organs; these cells are also considered *transformed* cells. An individual with a malignant tumor is said to have cancer; **Figure 12.20** shows the development of breast cancer, as well as a typical breast cancer cell.

The changes that have occurred in cells of malignant tumors show up in many ways besides excessive proliferation. These cells may have unusual numbers of chromosomes, though whether this is a cause or an effect of transformation is a topic of debate. Their metabolism may be altered, and they may cease to function in any constructive way. Abnormal changes on the cell surface cause cancer cells to lose attachments to neighboring cells and the extracellular matrix, allowing them to spread into nearby tissues. Cancer cells may also secrete signaling molecules that cause blood vessels to grow toward the tumor. A few tumor cells may separate from the original tumor, enter blood vessels and lymph vessels, and travel to other parts of the body. There, they may proliferate and form a new tumor. This spread of cancer cells to locations distant from their original site is called **metastasis** (see Figure 12.20).

A tumor that appears to be localized may be treated with high-energy radiation, which damages DNA in cancer cells much more than it does in normal cells, apparently because the majority of cancer cells have lost the ability to repair such damage. To treat known or suspected metastatic tumors, chemotherapy is used, in which drugs that are toxic to actively dividing cells are administered through the circulatory system. As you might expect, chemotherapeutic drugs interfere with specific steps in the cell cycle. For example, the drug Taxol freezes the mitotic spindle by preventing microtubule depolymerization, which stops actively dividing cells from proceeding past metaphase and leads to their destruction. The side effects of chemotherapy are due to the effects of the drugs on normal cells that divide often, due to the function of that cell type in the organism. For example, nausea results from chemotherapy's effects on intestinal cells, hair loss from effects on hair follicle cells, and susceptibility to infection from effects on immune system cells. You'll work

▼ **Figure 12.20 The growth and metastasis of a malignant breast tumor.** A series of genetic and cellular changes contribute to a tumor becoming malignant (cancerous). The cells of malignant tumors grow in an uncontrolled way and can spread to neighboring tissues and, via lymph and blood vessels, to other parts of the body. The spread of cancer cells beyond their original site is called metastasis.

Breast cancer cell (colorized SEM)

❶ A tumor grows from a single cancer cell.

❷ Cancer cells invade neighboring tissue.

❸ Cancer cells spread through lymph and blood vessels to other parts of the body.

❹ A small percentage of cancer cells may metastasize to another part of the body.

with data from an experiment involving a potential chemo-therapeutic agent in the Scientific Skills Exercise.

Over the past several decades, researchers have produced a flood of valuable information about cell-signaling pathways and how their malfunction contributes to the development of cancer through effects on the cell cycle. Coupled with new molecular techniques, such as the ability to rapidly sequence the DNA of cells in a particular tumor, medical treatments for cancer are beginning to become more "personalized" to a particular patient's tumor.

For example, the cells of roughly 20% of breast cancer tumors show abnormally high amounts of a cell-surface receptor tyrosine kinase called HER2, and many show an increase in the number of estrogen receptor (ER) molecules, intracellular receptors that can trigger cell division. Based on lab findings, a physician can prescribe chemotherapy with a molecule that blocks the function of the specific protein (Herceptin for HER2 and tamoxifen for ERs). Treatment using these agents, when appropriate, has led to increased survival rates and fewer cancer recurrences.

CONCEPT CHECK 12.3

1. In Figure 12.14, why do the nuclei resulting from experiment 2 contain different amounts of DNA?
2. How does MPF allow a cell to pass the G_2 phase checkpoint and enter mitosis? (See Figure 12.16.)
3. **MAKE CONNECTIONS** Explain in general how receptor tyrosine kinases and intracellular receptors might function in triggering cell division. (Review Figures 8.8 and 8.9 and Chapter 8.)

SCIENTIFIC SKILLS EXERCISE

Interpreting Histograms

At What Phase Is the Cell Cycle Arrested by an Inhibitor?
Many medical treatments are aimed at stopping cancer cell proliferation by blocking the cell cycle of cancerous tumor cells. One potential treatment is a cell cycle inhibitor derived from human umbilical cord stem cells. In this exercise, you will compare two histograms to determine where in the cell cycle the inhibitor blocks the division of cancer cells.

How the Experiment Was Done In the treated sample, human glioblastoma (brain cancer) cells were grown in tissue culture in the presence of the inhibitor, while control sample cells were grown in its absence. After 72 hours of growth, the two cell samples were harvested. To get a "snapshot" of the phase of the cell cycle each cell was in at that time, the samples were treated with a fluorescent chemical that binds to DNA and then run through a flow cytometer, an instrument that records the fluorescence level of each cell. Computer software then graphed the number of cells in each sample with a particular fluorescence level, as shown below.

Data from the Experiment

The data are plotted in a type of graph called a histogram (above), which groups values for a numeric variable on the x-axis into intervals. A histogram allows you to see how all the experimental subjects (cells, in this case) are distributed along a continuous variable (amount of fluorescence). In these histograms, the bars are so narrow that the data appear to follow a curve for which you can detect peaks and dips. Each narrow bar represents the number of cells observed to have a level of fluorescence in the range of that interval. This in turn indicates the relative amount of DNA in those cells. Overall, comparing the two histograms allows you to see how the DNA content of this cell population is altered by the treatment.

Interpret the Data
1. Familiarize yourself with the data shown in the histograms. (a) Which axis indirectly shows the relative amount of DNA per cell? Explain your answer. (b) In the control sample, compare the first peak in the histogram (in region A) to the second peak (in region C). Which peak shows the population of cells with the higher amount of DNA per cell? Explain.
2. (a) In the control sample histogram, identify the phase of the cell cycle (G_1, S, or G_2) of the population of cells in each region delineated by vertical lines. Label the histogram with these phases and explain your answer. (b) Does the S phase population of cells show a distinct peak in the histogram? Why or why not?
3. The histogram representing the treated sample shows the effect of growing the cancer cells alongside human umbilical cord stem cells that produce the potential inhibitor. (a) Label the histogram with the cell cycle phases. Which phase of the cell cycle has the greatest number of cells in the treated sample? Explain. (b) Compare the distribution of cells among G_1, S, and G_2 phases in the control and treated samples. What does this tell you about the cells in the treated sample? (c) Based on what you learned in Concept 12.3, propose a mechanism by which the stem cell-derived inhibitor might arrest the cancer cell cycle at this stage. (More than one answer is possible.)

(MB) A version of this Scientific Skills Exercise can be assigned in MasteringBiology.

Data from K. K. Velpula et al., Regulation of glioblastoma progression by cord blood stem cells is mediated by downregulation of cyclin D1, *PLoS ONE* 6(3): e18017 (2011).

- Unicellular organisms reproduce by **cell division**; multicellular organisms depend on cell division for their development from a fertilized egg and for growth and repair. Cell division is part of the **cell cycle**, an ordered sequence of events in the life of a cell.

CONCEPT 12.1

Most cell division results in genetically identical daughter cells (pp. 235–237)

- The genetic material (DNA) of a cell—its **genome**—is partitioned among **chromosomes**. Each eukaryotic chromosome consists of one DNA molecule associated with many proteins. Together, the complex of DNA and associated proteins is called **chromatin**. The chromatin of a chromosome exists in different states of condensation at different times. In animals, **gametes** have one set of chromosomes and **somatic cells** have two sets.
- Cells replicate their genetic material before they divide, each daughter cell receiving a copy of the DNA. Prior to cell division, chromosomes are duplicated. Each one then consists of two identical **sister chromatids** joined along their lengths by sister chromatid cohesion and held most tightly together at a constricted region at the **centromeres**. When this cohesion is broken, the chromatids separate during cell division, becoming the chromosomes of the daughter cells. Eukaryotic cell division consists of **mitosis** (division of the nucleus) and **cytokinesis** (division of the cytoplasm).

> **?** *Differentiate between these terms: chromosome, chromatin, and chromatid.*

CONCEPT 12.2

The mitotic phase alternates with interphase in the cell cycle (pp. 237–244)

- Between divisions, a cell is in **interphase**: the G_1, S, and G_2 phases. The cell grows throughout interphase, with DNA being replicated only during the synthesis (S) phase. Mitosis and cytokinesis make up the **mitotic (M) phase** of the cell cycle.

- The **mitotic spindle**, made up of microtubules, controls chromosome movement during mitosis. In animal cells, it arises from the **centrosomes** and includes spindle microtubules and **asters**. Some spindle microtubules attach to the **kinetochores** of chromosomes and move the chromosomes to the **metaphase plate**. After sister chromatids separate, motor proteins move them along kinetochore microtubules toward opposite ends of the cell. The cell elongates when motor proteins push nonkinetochore microtubules from opposite poles away from each other.
- Mitosis is usually followed by cytokinesis. Animal cells carry out cytokinesis by **cleavage**, and plant cells form a **cell plate**.
- During **binary fission** in bacteria, the chromosome replicates and the daughter chromosomes actively move apart. Some of the proteins involved in bacterial binary fission are related to eukaryotic actin and tubulin.
- Since prokaryotes preceded eukaryotes by more than a billion years, it is likely that mitosis evolved from prokaryotic cell division. Certain unicellular eukaryotes exhibit mechanisms of cell division that may be similar to those of ancestors of existing eukaryotes. Such mechanisms might represent intermediate steps in the evolution of mitosis.

> **?** *In which of the three subphases of interphase and the stages of mitosis do chromosomes exist as single DNA molecules?*

CONCEPT 12.3

The eukaryotic cell cycle is regulated by a molecular control system (pp. 244–250)

- Signaling molecules present in the cytoplasm regulate progress through the cell cycle.
- The **cell cycle control system** is molecularly based. Cyclic changes in regulatory proteins work as a cell cycle clock. The key molecules are **cyclins** and **cyclin-dependent kinases (Cdks)**. The clock has specific **checkpoints** where the cell cycle stops until a go-ahead signal is received; important checkpoints occur in G_1, G_2, and M phases. Cell culture has enabled researchers to study the molecular details of cell division. Both internal signals and external signals control the cell cycle checkpoints via signal transduction pathways. Most cells exhibit **density-dependent inhibition** of cell division as well as **anchorage dependence**.
- Cancer cells elude normal cell cycle regulation and divide unchecked, forming tumors. **Malignant tumors** invade nearby tissues and can undergo **metastasis**, exporting cancer cells to other sites, where they may form secondary tumors. Recent cell cycle and cell signaling research, and new techniques for sequencing DNA, have led to improved cancer treatments.

> **?** *Explain the significance of the G_1, G_2, and M checkpoints and the go-ahead signals involved in the cell cycle control system.*

LEVEL 1: KNOWLEDGE/COMPREHENSION

1. Through a microscope, you can see a cell plate beginning to develop across the middle of a cell and nuclei forming on either side of the cell plate. This cell is most likely
   a. an animal cell in the process of cytokinesis.
   b. a plant cell in the process of cytokinesis.
   c. a bacterial cell dividing.
   d. a plant cell in metaphase.

2. Vinblastine is a standard chemotherapeutic drug used to treat cancer. Because it interferes with the assembly of microtubules, its effectiveness must be related to
   a. disruption of mitotic spindle formation.
   b. suppression of cyclin production.
   c. myosin denaturation and inhibition of cleavage furrow formation.
   d. inhibition of DNA synthesis.

3. One difference between cancer cells and normal cells is that cancer cells
   a. are unable to synthesize DNA.
   b. are arrested at the S phase of the cell cycle.
   c. continue to divide even when they are tightly packed together.
   d. cannot function properly because they are affected by density-dependent inhibition.

4. The decline of MPF activity at the end of mitosis is due to
   a. the destruction of the protein kinase Cdk.
   b. decreased synthesis of Cdk.
   c. the degradation of cyclin.
   d. the accumulation of cyclin.

5. In the cells of some organisms, mitosis occurs without cytokinesis. This will result in
   a. cells with more than one nucleus.
   b. cells that are unusually small.
   c. cells lacking nuclei.
   d. cell cycles lacking an S phase.

6. Which of the following does *not* occur during mitosis?
   a. condensation of the chromosomes
   b. replication of the DNA
   c. separation of sister chromatids
   d. spindle formation

LEVEL 2: APPLICATION/ANALYSIS

7. A particular cell has half as much DNA as some other cells in a mitotically active tissue. The cell in question is most likely in
   a. G_1.
   b. G_2.
   c. prophase.
   d. metaphase.

8. The drug cytochalasin B blocks the function of actin. Which of the following aspects of the animal cell cycle would be most disrupted by cytochalasin B?
   a. spindle formation
   b. spindle attachment to kinetochores
   c. cell elongation during anaphase
   d. cleavage furrow formation and cytokinesis

9. In the light micrograph below of dividing cells near the tip of an onion root, identify a cell in each of the following stages: prophase, prometaphase, metaphase, anaphase, and telophase. Describe the major events occurring at each stage.

10. **DRAW IT** Draw one eukaryotic chromosome as it would appear during interphase, during each of the stages of mitosis, and during cytokinesis. Also draw and label the nuclear envelope and any microtubules attached to the chromosome(s).

LEVEL 3: SYNTHESIS/EVALUATION

11. **EVOLUTION CONNECTION**
The result of mitosis is that the daughter cells end up with the same number of chromosomes that the parent cell had. Another way to maintain the number of chromosomes would be to carry out cell division first and then duplicate the chromosomes in each daughter cell. Do you think this would be an equally good way of organizing the cell cycle? Why do you suppose that evolution has not led to this alternative?

12. **SCIENTIFIC INQUIRY**
Although both ends of a microtubule can gain or lose subunits, one end (called the plus end) polymerizes and depolymerizes at a higher rate than the other end (the minus end). For spindle microtubules, the plus ends are in the center of the spindle, and the minus ends are at the poles. Motor proteins that move along microtubules specialize in walking either toward the plus end or toward the minus end; the two types are called plus end–directed and minus end–directed motor proteins, respectively. Given what you know about chromosome movement and spindle changes during anaphase, predict which type of motor proteins would be present on (a) kinetochore microtubules and (b) nonkinetochore microtubules.

13. **WRITE ABOUT A THEME: INFORMATION**
Continuity of life is based on heritable information in the form of DNA. In a short essay (100–150 words), explain how the process of mitosis faithfully parcels out exact copies of this heritable information in the production of genetically identical daughter cells.

14. **SYNTHESIZE YOUR KNOWLEDGE**

Shown here are two HeLa cancer cells that are just completing cytokinesis. Explain how the cell division of cancer cells like these is misregulated. What genetic and other changes might have caused these cells to escape normal cell cycle regulation?

13

Meiosis and Sexual Life Cycles

▲ **Figure 13.1 What accounts for family resemblance?**

Variations on a Theme

We all know that offspring resemble their parents more than they do unrelated individuals. If you examine the family members shown in **Figure 13.1**, you can pick out some similar features among them. The transmission of traits from one generation to the next is called inheritance, or **heredity** (from the Latin *heres*, heir). However, sons and daughters are not identical copies of either parent or of their siblings. Along with inherited similarity, there is also **variation**. What are the biological mechanisms leading to the "family resemblance" evident among the family members in the photo above? The answer to this question eluded biologists until the advance of genetics in the 20th century.

Genetics is the scientific study of heredity and hereditary variation. In this unit, you'll learn about genetics at multiple levels, from organisms to cells to molecules. We begin by examining how chromosomes pass from parents to offspring in sexually reproducing organisms. The processes of meiosis (a special type of cell division) and fertilization (the fusion of sperm and egg, as seen in the photo at the left) maintain a species' chromosome count during the sexual life cycle. We will describe the cellular mechanics of meiosis and explain how this process differs from mitosis. Finally, we will consider how both meiosis and fertilization contribute to genetic variation, such as that seen in Figure 13.1.

CONCEPT 13.1

Offspring acquire genes from parents by inheriting chromosomes

Family friends may tell you that you have your mother's freckles or your father's eyes. Of course, parents do not, in any literal sense, give their children freckles, eyes, hair, or any other traits. What, then, *is* actually inherited?

Inheritance of Genes

Parents endow their offspring with coded information in the form of hereditary units called **genes**. The genes we inherit from our mothers and fathers are our genetic link to our parents, and they account for family resemblances such as shared eye color or freckles. Our genes program the specific traits that emerge as we develop from fertilized eggs into adults.

The genetic program is written in the language of DNA, the polymer of four different nucleotides you learned about in Concepts 1.1 and 5.5. Inherited information is passed on in the form of each gene's specific sequence of DNA nucleotides, much as printed information is communicated in the form of meaningful sequences of letters. In both cases, the language is symbolic. Just as your brain translates the word *apple* into a mental image of the fruit, cells translate genes into freckles and other features. Most genes program cells to synthesize specific enzymes and other proteins, whose cumulative action produces an organism's inherited traits. The programming of these traits in the form of DNA is one of the unifying themes of biology.

The transmission of hereditary traits has its molecular basis in the replication of DNA, which produces copies of genes that can be passed from parents to offspring. In animals and plants, reproductive cells called **gametes** are the vehicles that transmit genes from one generation to the next. During fertilization, male and female gametes (sperm and eggs) unite, passing on genes of both parents to their offspring.

Except for small amounts of DNA in mitochondria and chloroplasts, the DNA of a eukaryotic cell is packaged into chromosomes within the nucleus. Every species has a characteristic number of chromosomes. For example, humans have 46 chromosomes in their **somatic cells**—all cells of the body except the gametes and their precursors. Each chromosome consists of a single long DNA molecule elaborately coiled in association with various proteins. One chromosome includes several hundred to a few thousand genes, each of which is a specific sequence of nucleotides within the DNA molecule. A gene's specific location along the length of a chromosome is called the gene's **locus** (plural, *loci*; from the Latin, meaning "place"). Our genetic endowment (our genome) consists of the genes and other DNA that make up the chromosomes we inherited from our parents.

Comparison of Asexual and Sexual Reproduction

Only organisms that reproduce asexually have offspring that are exact genetic copies of themselves. In **asexual reproduction**, a single individual is the sole parent and passes copies of all its genes to its offspring without the fusion of gametes. For example, single-celled eukaryotic organisms can reproduce asexually by mitotic cell division, in which DNA is copied and allocated equally to two daughter cells. The genomes of the offspring are virtually exact copies of the parent's genome. Some multicellular organisms are also capable of reproducing asexually **(Figure 13.2)**. Because the cells of the offspring are derived by mitosis in the parent, the "chip off the old block" is usually genetically identical to its parent. An individual that reproduces asexually gives rise to a **clone**, a group of genetically identical individuals. Genetic differences occasionally arise in asexually reproducing organisms as a result of changes in the DNA called mutations, which we will discuss in Chapter 17.

In **sexual reproduction**, two parents give rise to offspring that have unique combinations of genes inherited from the two parents. In contrast to a clone, offspring of sexual reproduction vary genetically from their siblings and both parents: They are variations on a common theme of family resemblance, not exact replicas. Genetic variation like that shown in Figure 13.1 is an important consequence of sexual reproduction. What mechanisms generate this genetic variation? The key is the behavior of chromosomes during the sexual life cycle.

(a) Hydra

(b) Redwoods

▲ **Figure 13.2 Asexual reproduction in two multicellular organisms. (a)** This relatively simple animal, a hydra, reproduces by budding. The bud, a localized mass of mitotically dividing cells, develops into a small hydra, which detaches from the parent (LM). **(b)** All the trees in this circle of redwoods arose asexually from a single parent tree, whose stump is in the center of the circle.

1. **MAKE CONNECTIONS** Using what you know of gene expression in a cell, explain what causes the traits of parents (such as hair color) to show up in their offspring. (See Concept 5.5.)

2. How do asexually reproducing eukaryotic organisms produce offspring that are genetically identical to each other and to their parents?

3. **WHAT IF?** A horticulturalist breeds orchids, trying to obtain a plant with a unique combination of desirable traits. After many years, she finally succeeds. To produce more plants like this one, should she cross-breed it with another plant or clone it? Why?

CONCEPT 13.2

Fertilization and meiosis alternate in sexual life cycles

A **life cycle** is the generation-to-generation sequence of stages in the reproductive history of an organism, from conception to production of its own offspring. In this section, we use humans as an example to track the behavior of chromosomes through the sexual life cycle. We begin by considering the chromosome count in human somatic cells and gametes. We will then explore how the behavior of chromosomes relates to the human life cycle and other types of sexual life cycles.

Sets of Chromosomes in Human Cells

In humans, each somatic cell has 46 chromosomes. During mitosis, the chromosomes become condensed enough to be visible under a light microscope. At this point, they can be distinguished from one another by their size, the positions of their centromeres, and the pattern of colored bands produced by certain chromatin-binding stains.

Careful examination of a micrograph of the 46 human chromosomes from a single cell in mitosis reveals that there are two chromosomes of each of 23 types. This becomes clear when images of the chromosomes are arranged in pairs, starting with the longest chromosomes. The resulting ordered display is called a **karyotype (Figure 13.3)**. The two chromosomes of a pair have the same length, centromere position, and staining pattern: These are called **homologous chromosomes**, or **homologs**. Both chromosomes of each pair carry genes controlling the same inherited characters. For example, if a gene for eye color is situated at a particular locus on a certain chromosome, then the homolog of that chromosome will also have a version of the same gene specifying eye color at the equivalent locus.

The two distinct chromosomes referred to as X and Y are an important exception to the general pattern of homologous chromosomes in human somatic cells. Human females

▼ **Figure 13.3** **Research Method**

Preparing a Karyotype

Application A karyotype is a display of condensed chromosomes arranged in pairs. Karyotyping can be used to screen for defective chromosomes or abnormal numbers of chromosomes associated with certain congenital disorders, such as Down syndrome.

Technique Karyotypes are prepared from isolated somatic cells, which are treated with a drug to stimulate mitosis and then grown in culture for several days. Cells arrested in metaphase, when chromosomes are most highly condensed, are stained and then viewed with a microscope equipped with a digital camera. An image of the chromosomes is displayed on a computer monitor, and digital software is used to arrange them in pairs according to their appearance.

Results This karyotype shows the chromosomes from a normal human male, digitally colored to emphasize their banding patterns. The size of the chromosome, position of the centromere, and pattern of stained bands help identify specific chromosomes. Although difficult to discern in the karyotype, each metaphase chromosome consists of two closely attached sister chromatids (see the diagram of a pair of homologous duplicated chromosomes).

have a homologous pair of X chromosomes (XX), but males have one X and one Y chromosome (XY). Only small parts of the X and Y are homologous. Most of the genes carried on the X chromosome do not have counterparts on the tiny Y, and the Y chromosome has genes lacking on the X. Because they determine an individual's sex, the X and Y chromosomes are called **sex chromosomes**. The other chromosomes are called **autosomes**.

The pairs of homologous chromosomes in each human somatic cell is a consequence of our sexual origins. We inherit one chromosome of a pair from each parent. Thus, the 46 chromosomes in our somatic cells are actually two sets of 23 chromosomes—a maternal set (from our mother) and a paternal set (from our father). The number of chromosomes in a single set is represented by n. Any cell with two chromosome sets is called a **diploid cell** and has a diploid number of chromosomes, abbreviated $2n$. For humans, the diploid number is 46 ($2n = 46$), the number of chromosomes in our somatic cells. In a cell in which DNA synthesis has occurred, all the chromosomes are duplicated, and therefore each consists of two identical sister chromatids, associated closely at the centromere and along the arms. (Even though the chromosomes are duplicated, we still say the cell is diploid ($2n$) because it has only two sets of information.) **Figure 13.4** helps clarify the various terms that we use to describe duplicated chromosomes in a diploid cell.

Unlike somatic cells, gametes contain a single set of chromosomes. Such cells are called **haploid cells**, and each has a haploid number of chromosomes (n). For humans, the haploid number is 23 ($n = 23$). The set of 23 consists of the 22 autosomes plus a single sex chromosome. An unfertilized egg contains an X chromosome, but a sperm may contain an X or a Y chromosome.

Each sexually reproducing species has a characteristic diploid and haploid number. For example, the fruit fly *Drosophila melanogaster* has a diploid number ($2n$) of 8 and a haploid number (n) of 4, while for dogs, $2n$ is 78 and n is 39. Now let's consider chromosome behavior during sexual life cycles. We'll use the human life cycle as an example.

Behavior of Chromosome Sets in the Human Life Cycle

The human life cycle begins when a haploid sperm from the father fuses with a haploid egg from the mother **(Figure 13.5)**. This union of gametes, culminating in fusion of their nuclei, is called **fertilization**. The resulting fertilized egg, or **zygote**, is diploid because it contains two haploid sets of chromosomes bearing genes representing the maternal and paternal family

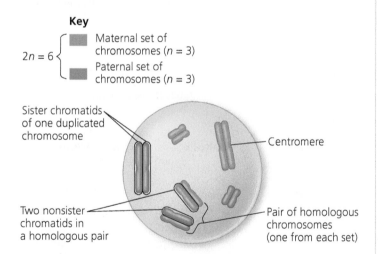

Key

$2n = 6$ {
Maternal set of chromosomes ($n = 3$)
Paternal set of chromosomes ($n = 3$)
}

Sister chromatids of one duplicated chromosome

Centromere

Two nonsister chromatids in a homologous pair

Pair of homologous chromosomes (one from each set)

▲ **Figure 13.4 Describing chromosomes.** A cell from an organism with a diploid number of 6 ($2n = 6$) is depicted here following chromosome duplication and condensation. Each of the six duplicated chromosomes consists of two sister chromatids associated closely along their lengths. Each homologous pair is composed of one chromosome from the maternal set (red) and one from the paternal set (blue). Each set is made up of three chromosomes in this example (long, medium, and short). Together, one maternal and one paternal chromatid in a pair of homologous chromosomes are called nonsister chromatids.

[?] *How many sets of chromosomes are present in this diagram? How many pairs of homologous chromosomes are present?*

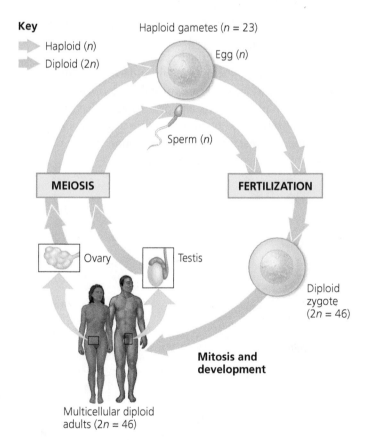

Key

Haploid (n)
Diploid ($2n$)

Haploid gametes ($n = 23$)

Egg (n)

Sperm (n)

MEIOSIS

FERTILIZATION

Ovary

Testis

Diploid zygote ($2n = 46$)

Mitosis and development

Multicellular diploid adults ($2n = 46$)

▲ **Figure 13.5 The human life cycle.** In each generation, the number of chromosome sets doubles at fertilization but is halved during meiosis. For humans, the number of chromosomes in a haploid cell is 23, consisting of one set ($n = 23$); the number of chromosomes in the diploid zygote and all somatic cells arising from it is 46, consisting of two sets ($2n = 46$).

This figure introduces a color code that will be used for other life cycles later in this book. The aqua arrows identify haploid stages of a life cycle, and the tan arrows identify diploid stages.

lines. As a human develops into a sexually mature adult, mitosis of the zygote and its descendant cells generates all the somatic cells of the body. Both chromosome sets in the zygote and all the genes they carry are passed with precision to the somatic cells.

The only cells of the human body not produced by mitosis are the gametes, which develop from specialized cells called *germ cells* in the gonads—ovaries in females and testes in males. Imagine what would happen if human gametes were made by mitosis: They would be diploid like the somatic cells. At the next round of fertilization, when two gametes fused, the normal chromosome number of 46 would double to 92, and each subsequent generation would double the number of chromosomes yet again. This does not happen, however, because in sexually reproducing organisms, gamete formation involves a type of cell division called **meiosis**. This type of cell division reduces the number of sets of chromosomes from two to one in the gametes, counterbalancing the doubling that occurs at fertilization. As a result of meiosis, each human sperm and egg is haploid ($n = 23$). Fertilization restores the diploid condition by combining two haploid sets of chromosomes, and the human life cycle is repeated, generation after generation (see Figure 13.5).

In general, the steps of the human life cycle are typical of many sexually reproducing animals. Indeed, the processes of fertilization and meiosis are the hallmarks of sexual reproduction in plants, fungi, and protists as well as in animals. Fertilization and meiosis alternate in sexual life cycles, maintaining a constant number of chromosomes in each species from one generation to the next.

The Variety of Sexual Life Cycles

Although the alternation of meiosis and fertilization is common to all organisms that reproduce sexually, the timing of these two events in the life cycle varies, depending on the species. These variations can be grouped into three main types of life cycles. In the type that occurs in humans and most other animals, gametes are the only haploid cells **(Figure 13.6a)**. Meiosis occurs in germ cells during the production of gametes, which undergo no further cell division prior to fertilization. After fertilization, the diploid zygote divides by mitosis, producing a multicellular organism that is diploid.

Plants and some species of algae exhibit a second type of life cycle called **alternation of generations (Figure 13.6b)**. This type includes both diploid and haploid stages that are multicellular. The multicellular diploid stage is called the *sporophyte*. Meiosis in the sporophyte produces haploid cells called *spores*. Unlike a gamete, a haploid spore doesn't fuse with another cell but divides mitotically, generating a multicellular haploid stage called the *gametophyte*. Cells of the gametophyte give rise to gametes by mitosis. Fusion of two haploid gametes at fertilization results in a diploid zygote, which develops into the next sporophyte generation. Therefore, in this type of life cycle, the sporophyte generation produces a gametophyte as its offspring, and the gametophyte generation produces the next sporophyte generation (see Figure 13.6b). The term *alternation of generations* fits well as a name for this type of life cycle.

A third type of life cycle occurs in most fungi and some protists, including some algae **(Figure 13.6c)**. After gametes

(a) Animals **(b) Plants and some algae** **(c) Most fungi and some protists**

▲ Figure 13.6 **Three types of sexual life cycles.** The common feature of all three cycles is the alternation of meiosis and fertilization, key events that contribute to genetic variation among offspring. The cycles differ in the timing of these two key events.

fuse and form a diploid zygote, meiosis occurs without a multicellular diploid offspring developing. Meiosis produces not gametes but haploid cells that then divide by mitosis and give rise to either unicellular descendants or a haploid multicellular adult organism. Subsequently, the haploid organism carries out further mitoses, producing the cells that develop into gametes. The only diploid stage found in these species is the single-celled zygote.

Note that *either* haploid or diploid cells can divide by mitosis, depending on the type of life cycle. Only diploid cells, however, can undergo meiosis because haploid cells have only a single set of chromosomes that cannot be further reduced. Though the three types of sexual life cycles differ in the timing of meiosis and fertilization, they share a fundamental result: genetic variation among offspring.

CONCEPT CHECK 13.2

1. **MAKE CONNECTIONS** In Figure 13.4, how many DNA molecules (double helices) are present (see Figure 12.5)? What is the haploid number of this cell? Is a set of chromosomes haploid or diploid?

2. In the karyotype shown in Figure 13.3, how many pairs of chromosomes are present? How many sets?

3. **WHAT IF?** A certain eukaryote lives as a unicellular organism, but during environmental stress, it produces gametes. The gametes fuse, and the resulting zygote undergoes meiosis, generating new single cells. What type of organism could this be?

CONCEPT 13.3

Meiosis reduces the number of chromosome sets from diploid to haploid

Many of the steps of meiosis closely resemble corresponding steps in mitosis. Meiosis, like mitosis, is preceded by the duplication of chromosomes. However, this single duplication is followed by not one but two consecutive cell divisions, called **meiosis I** and **meiosis II**. These two divisions result in four daughter cells (rather than the two daughter cells of mitosis), each with only half as many chromosomes as the parent cell—one set, rather than two.

The Stages of Meiosis

The overview of meiosis in **Figure 13.7** shows, for a single pair of homologous chromosomes in a diploid cell, that both members of the pair are duplicated and the copies sorted into four haploid daughter cells. Recall that sister chromatids are two copies of *one* chromosome, closely associated all

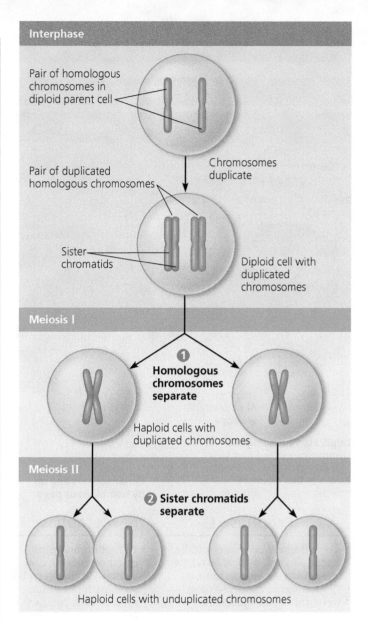

▲ Figure 13.7 **Overview of meiosis: how meiosis reduces chromosome number.** After the chromosomes duplicate in interphase, the diploid cell divides *twice*, yielding four haploid daughter cells. This overview tracks just one pair of homologous chromosomes, which for the sake of simplicity are drawn in the condensed state throughout.

DRAW IT *Redraw the cells in this figure using a simple double helix to represent each DNA molecule.*

along their lengths; this association is called *sister chromatid cohesion*. Together, the sister chromatids make up one duplicated chromosome (see Figure 13.4). In contrast, the two chromosomes of a homologous pair are individual chromosomes that were inherited from different parents. Homologs appear alike in the microscope, but they may have different versions of genes, each called an *allele*, at corresponding loci. Homologs are not associated with each other in any obvious way except during meiosis.

Figure 13.8 describes in detail the stages of the two divisions of meiosis for an animal cell whose diploid number is 6. Study this figure thoroughly before going on.

Exploring Meiosis in an Animal Cell

MEIOSIS I: Separates homologous chromosomes

Prophase I	Metaphase I	Anaphase I	Telophase I and Cytokinesis

Centrosome (with centriole pair)

Sister chromatids

Chiasmata

Spindle

Homologous chromosomes

Fragments of nuclear envelope

Duplicated homologous chromosomes (red and blue) pair and exchange segments; 2n = 6 in this example.

Centromere (with kinetochore)

Metaphase plate

Microtubules attached to kinetochore

Chromosomes line up by homologous pairs.

Sister chromatids remain attached

Homologous chromosomes separate

Each pair of homologous chromosomes separates.

Cleavage furrow

Two haploid cells form; each chromosome still consists of two sister chromatids.

Prophase I

- Centrosome movement, spindle formation, and nuclear envelope breakdown occur as in mitosis. Chromosomes condense progressively throughout prophase I.

- During early prophase I, before the stage shown above, each chromosome pairs with its homolog, aligned gene by gene, and **crossing over** occurs: The DNA molecules of non-sister chromatids are broken (by proteins) and are rejoined to each other.

- At the stage shown above, each homologous pair has one or more X-shaped regions called **chiasmata** (singular, *chiasma*), where crossovers have occurred.

- Later in prophase I, after the stage shown above, microtubules from one pole or the other will attach to the two kinetochores, one at the centromere of each homolog. (The two kinetochores of a homolog, not yet visible above, act as a single kinetochore.) The homologous pairs will then move toward the metaphase plate.

Metaphase I

- Pairs of homologous chromosomes are now arranged at the metaphase plate, with one chromosome in each pair facing each pole.

- Both chromatids of one homolog are attached to kinetochore microtubules from one pole; those of the other homolog are attached to microtubules from the opposite pole.

Anaphase I

- Breakdown of proteins that are responsible for sister chromatid cohesion along chromatid arms allows homologs to separate.

- The homologs move toward opposite poles, guided by the spindle apparatus.

- Sister chromatid cohesion persists at the centromere, causing chromatids to move as a unit toward the same pole.

Telophase I and Cytokinesis

- When telophase I begins, each half of the cell has a complete haploid set of duplicated chromosomes. Each chromosome is composed of two sister chromatids; one or both chromatids include regions of nonsister chromatid DNA.

- Cytokinesis (division of the cytoplasm) usually occurs simultaneously with telophase I, forming two haploid daughter cells.

- In animal cells like these, a cleavage furrow forms. (In plant cells, a cell plate forms.)

- In some species, chromosomes decondense and nuclear envelopes form.

- No chromosome duplication occurs between meiosis I and meiosis II.

MEIOSIS II: Separates sister chromatids

Prophase II	Metaphase II	Anaphase II	Telophase II and Cytokinesis

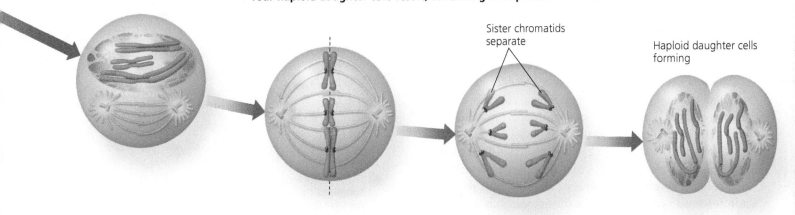

During another round of cell division, the sister chromatids finally separate; four haploid daughter cells result, containing unduplicated chromosomes.

Sister chromatids separate

Haploid daughter cells forming

Prophase II

- A spindle apparatus forms.

- In late prophase II (not shown here), chromosomes, each still composed of two chromatids associated at the centromere, move toward the metaphase II plate.

Metaphase II

- The chromosomes are positioned at the metaphase plate as in mitosis.

- Because of crossing over in meiosis I, the two sister chromatids of each chromosome are *not* genetically identical.

- The kinetochores of sister chromatids are attached to microtubules extending from opposite poles.

Anaphase II

- Breakdown of proteins holding the sister chromatids together at the centromere allows the chromatids to separate. The chromatids move toward opposite poles as individual chromosomes.

Telophase II and Cytokinesis

- Nuclei form, the chromosomes begin decondensing, and cytokinesis occurs.

- The meiotic division of one parent cell produces four daughter cells, each with a haploid set of (unduplicated) chromosomes.

- The four daughter cells are genetically distinct from one another and from the parent cell.

MAKE CONNECTIONS *Look at Figure 12.7 and imagine the two daughter cells undergoing another round of mitosis, yielding four cells. Compare the number of chromosomes in each of those four cells, after mitosis, with the number in each cell in Figure 13.8, after meiosis. What is it about the process of meiosis that accounts for this difference, even though meiosis also includes two cell divisions?*

ANIMATION **BioFlix** Visit the Study Area in **MasteringBiology** for the BioFlix® 3-D Animation on Meiosis. BioFlix Tutorials can also be assigned in MasteringBiology.

Crossing Over and Synapsis During Prophase I

Prophase I of meiosis is a very busy time. The prophase I cell shown in Figure 13.8 is at a point fairly late in prophase I, when homologous pairing, crossing over, and chromosome condensation have already taken place. The sequence of events leading up to that point is shown in more detail in **Figure 13.9**.

After interphase, the chromosomes have been duplicated and the sister chromatids are held together by proteins called *cohesins*. Early in prophase I, the two members of a homologous pair associate loosely along their length. Each gene on one homolog is aligned precisely with the corresponding gene on the other homolog. The DNA of two nonsister chromatids—one maternal and one paternal—is broken by specific proteins at precisely corresponding points. Next, the formation of a zipper-like structure called the **synaptonemal complex** holds one homolog tightly to the other. During this association, called **synapsis**, the DNA breaks are closed up so that each broken end is joined to the corresponding segment of the *nonsister* chromatid. Thus, a paternal chromatid is joined to a piece of maternal chromatid beyond the crossover point, and vice versa.

These points of crossing over become visible as chiasmata (singular, *chiasma*) after the synaptonemal complex disassembles and the homologs move slightly apart from each other. The homologs remain attached because sister chromatids are still held together by sister chromatid cohesion, even though some of the DNA may no longer be attached to its original chromosome. At least one crossover per chromosome must occur in order for the homologous pair to stay together as it moves to the metaphase I plate.

A Comparison of Mitosis and Meiosis

Figure 13.10 summarizes the key differences between meiosis and mitosis in diploid cells. Basically, meiosis reduces the number of chromosome sets from two (diploid) to one (haploid), whereas mitosis conserves the number of chromosome sets. Therefore, meiosis produces cells that differ genetically from their parent cell and from each other, whereas mitosis produces daughter cells that are genetically identical to their parent cell and to each other.

Three events unique to meiosis occur during meiosis I:

1. **Synapsis and crossing over.** During prophase I, duplicated homologs pair up and crossing over occurs, as described above. Synapsis and crossing over normally do not occur during prophase of mitosis.
2. **Homologous pairs at the metaphase plate.** At metaphase I of meiosis, chromosomes are positioned at the metaphase plate as pairs of homologs, rather than individual chromosomes, as in metaphase of mitosis.

① After interphase, the chromosomes have been duplicated and sister chromatids are held together by proteins called cohesins (purple). Each pair of homologs associate along their length. The DNA molecules of two nonsister chromatids are broken at precisely corresponding points. The chromatin of the chromosomes is beginning to condense.

② A zipperlike protein complex, the synaptonemal complex (green), begins to form, attaching one homolog to the other. The chromatin continues to condense.

③ The synaptonemal complex is fully formed; the two homologs are said to be in synapsis. During synapsis, the DNA breaks are closed up when each broken end is joined to the corresponding segment of the nonsister chromatid, producing crossovers.

④ After the synaptonemal complex disassembles, the homologs move slightly apart from each other but remain attached because of sister chromatid cohesion, even though some of the DNA may no longer be attached to its original chromosome. The points of attachment where crossovers have occurred show up as chiasmata. The chromosomes continue to condense as they move toward the metaphase plate.

▲ **Figure 13.9 Crossing over and synapsis in prophase I: a closer look.** For simplicity, the four chromatids of the homologous pair shown here are depicted side by side, but in reality, the blue chromosome would be right on top of the red one (see the top cell in Figure 13.12).

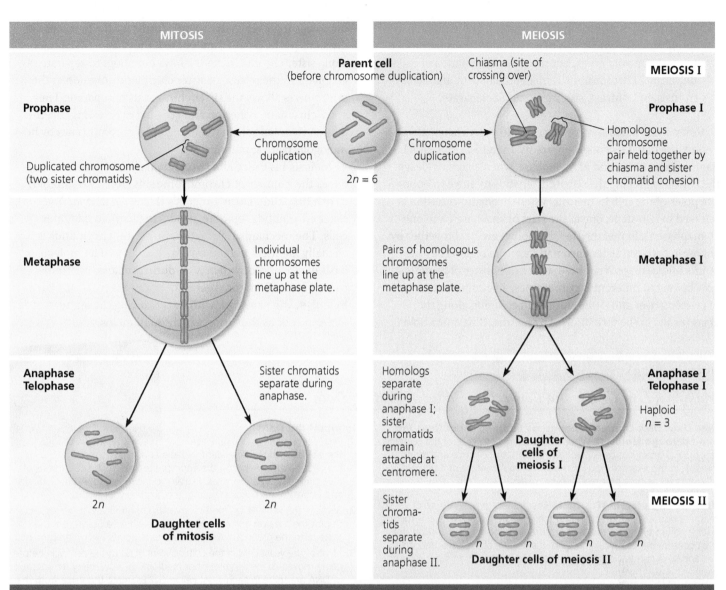

	MITOSIS	MEIOSIS

Parent cell (before chromosome duplication)

Prophase

Duplicated chromosome (two sister chromatids)

Chromosome duplication

$2n = 6$

Chromosome duplication

Chiasma (site of crossing over)

MEIOSIS I

Prophase I

Homologous chromosome pair held together by chiasma and sister chromatid cohesion

Metaphase

Individual chromosomes line up at the metaphase plate.

Pairs of homologous chromosomes line up at the metaphase plate.

Metaphase I

Anaphase Telophase

Sister chromatids separate during anaphase.

Homologs separate during anaphase I; sister chromatids remain attached at centromere.

Anaphase I Telophase I

Haploid $n = 3$

Daughter cells of meiosis I

$2n$

$2n$

Daughter cells of mitosis

Sister chromatids separate during anaphase II.

MEIOSIS II

n n n n

Daughter cells of meiosis II

SUMMARY

Property	Mitosis (occurs in both diploid and haploid cells)	Meiosis (can only occur in diploid cells)
DNA replication	Occurs during interphase before mitosis begins	Occurs during interphase before meiosis I begins
Number of divisions	One, including prophase, prometaphase, metaphase, anaphase, and telophase	Two, each including prophase, metaphase, anaphase, and telophase
Synapsis of homologous chromosomes	Does not occur	Occurs during prophase I along with crossing over between nonsister chromatids; resulting chiasmata hold pairs together due to sister chromatid cohesion
Number of daughter cells and genetic composition	Two, each genetically identical to the parent cell, with the same number of chromosomes	Four, each haploid (n); genetically different from the parent cell and from each other
Role in the animal or plant body	Enables multicellular animal or plant (gametophyte or sporophyte) to arise from a single cell; produces cells for growth, repair, and, in some species, asexual reproduction; produces gametes in the gametophyte plant	Produces gametes (in animals) or spores (in the sporophyte plant); reduces number of chromosome sets by half and introduces genetic variability among the gametes or spores

▲ **Figure 13.10 A comparison of mitosis and meiosis.**

DRAW IT *Could any other combinations of chromosomes be generated during meiosis II from the specific cells shown in telophase I? Explain. (Hint: Draw the cells as they would appear in metaphase II.)*

3. **Separation of homologs.** At anaphase I of meiosis, the duplicated chromosomes of each homologous pair move toward opposite poles, but the sister chromatids of each duplicated chromosome remain attached. In anaphase of mitosis, by contrast, sister chromatids separate.

Sister chromatids stay together due to sister chromatid cohesion, mediated by cohesin proteins. In mitosis, this attachment lasts until the end of metaphase, when enzymes cleave the cohesins, freeing the sister chromatids to move to opposite poles of the cell. In meiosis, sister chromatid cohesion is released in two steps, one at the start of anaphase I and one at anaphase II. In metaphase I, homologs are held together by cohesion between sister chromatid arms in regions beyond points of crossing over, where stretches of sister chromatids now belong to different chromosomes. The combination of crossing over and sister chromatid cohesion along the arms results in the formation of a chiasma. Chiasmata hold homologs together as the spindle forms for the first meiotic division. At the onset of anaphase I, the release of cohesion along sister chromatid *arms* allows homologs to separate. At anaphase II, the release of sister chromatid cohesion at the *centromeres* allows the sister chromatids to separate. Thus, sister chromatid cohesion and crossing over, acting together, play an essential role in the lining up of chromosomes by homologous pairs at metaphase I.

Meiosis I is called the *reductional division* because it reduces the number of chromosome sets from two (diploid) to one (haploid). During meiosis II (the *equational division*), sister chromatids separate, producing haploid daughter cells. The mechanism for separating sister chromatids is virtually identical in meiosis II and mitosis. The molecular basis of chromosome behavior during meiosis continues to be a focus of intense research. In the **Scientific Skills Exercise**, you can work with data tracking the amount of DNA in cells as they progress through meiosis.

SCIENTIFIC SKILLS EXERCISE

Making a Line Graph and Converting Between Units of Data

How Does DNA Content Change as Budding Yeast Cells Proceed Through Meiosis? When nutrients are low, cells of the budding yeast (*Saccharomyces cerevisiae*) exit the mitotic cell cycle and enter meiosis. In this exercise, you will track the DNA content of a population of yeast cells as they progress through meiosis.

How the Experiment Was Done Researchers grew a culture of yeast cells in a nutrient-rich medium and then transferred them to a nutrient-poor medium to induce meiosis. At different times after induction, the DNA content per cell was measured in a sample of the cells, and the average DNA content per cell was recorded in femtograms (fg; 1 femtogram = 1×10^{-15} gram).

Data from the Experiment

Time After Induction (hours)	Average Amount of DNA per Cell (fg)
0.0	24.0
1.0	24.0
2.0	40.0
3.0	47.0
4.0	47.5
5.0	48.0
6.0	48.0
7.0	47.5
7.5	25.0
8.0	24.0
9.0	23.5
9.5	14.0
10.0	13.0
11.0	12.5
12.0	12.0
13.0	12.5
14.0	12.0

Interpret the Data

1. First, set up your graph. (a) Place the labels for the independent variable and the dependent variable on the appropriate axes, followed by units of measurement in parentheses. Explain your choices. (b) Add tick marks and values for each axis in your graph. Explain your choices.

2. Because the variable on the *x*-axis varies continuously, it makes sense to plot the data on a line graph. (a) Plot each data point from the table onto the graph. (b) Connect the data points with line segments.

3. Most of the yeast cells in the culture were in G_1 of the cell cycle before being moved to the nutrient-poor medium. (a) How many femtograms of DNA are there in each yeast cell in G_1? Estimate this value from the data in your graph. (b) How many femtograms of DNA should be present in each cell in G_2? (See Concept 12.2 and Figure 12.6.) At the end of meiosis I (MI)? At the end of meiosis II (MII)? (See Figure 13.7.) (c) Using these values as a guideline, distinguish the different phases by inserting vertical dashed lines in the graph between phases and label each phase (G_1, S, G_2, MI, MII). You can figure out where to put the dividing lines based on what you know about the DNA content of each phase (see Figure 13.7). (d) Think carefully about the point where the line at the highest value begins to slope downward. What specific point of meiosis does this "corner" represent? What stage(s) correspond to the downward sloping line?

4. Given the fact that 1 fg of DNA = 9.78×10^5 base pairs (on average), you can convert the amount of DNA per cell to the length of DNA in numbers of base pairs. (a) Calculate the number of base pairs of DNA in the haploid yeast genome. Express your answer in millions of base pairs (Mb), a standard unit for expressing genome size. Show your work. (b) How many base pairs per minute were synthesized during the S phase of these yeast cells?

(MB) A version of this Scientific Skills Exercise can be assigned in MasteringBiology.

Further Reading G. Simchen, Commitment to meiosis: what determines the mode of division in budding yeast? *BioEssays* 31:169–177 (2009).

1. **MAKE CONNECTIONS** Compare the chromosomes in a cell at metaphase of mitosis with those in a cell at metaphase II. (See Figures 12.7 and 13.8.)

2. **WHAT IF?** After the synaptonemal complex disappears, how would the two homologs be associated if crossing over did not occur? What effect might this ultimately have on gamete formation?

CONCEPT 13.4

Genetic variation produced in sexual life cycles contributes to evolution

How do we account for the genetic variation of the family members in Figure 13.1? As you will learn in later chapters, mutations are the original source of genetic diversity. These changes in an organism's DNA create the different versions of genes known as alleles. Once these differences arise, re-shuffling of the alleles during sexual reproduction produces the variation that results in each member of a sexually re-producing population having a unique combination of traits.

Origins of Genetic Variation Among Offspring

In species that reproduce sexually, the behavior of chromosomes during meiosis and fertilization is responsible for most of the variation that arises in each generation. Three mechanisms contribute to the genetic variation arising from sexual reproduction: independent assortment of chromosomes, crossing over, and random fertilization.

Independent Assortment of Chromosomes

One aspect of sexual reproduction that generates genetic variation is the random orientation of pairs of homologous chromosomes at metaphase of meiosis I. At metaphase I, the homologous pairs, each consisting of one maternal and one paternal chromosome, are situated at the metaphase plate. (Note that the terms *maternal* and *paternal* refer, respectively, to the mother and father of the individual whose cells are undergoing meiosis.) Each pair may orient with either its maternal or paternal homolog closer to a given pole—its orientation is as random as the flip of a coin. Thus, there is a 50% chance that a particular daughter cell of meiosis I will get the maternal chromosome of a certain homologous pair and a 50% chance that it will get the pater-nal chromosome.

Because each pair of homologous chromosomes is posi-tioned independently of the other pairs at metaphase I, the first meiotic division results in each pair sorting its maternal and paternal homologs into daughter cells independently of every other pair. This is called *independent assortment*. Each daughter cell represents one outcome of all possible combi-nations of maternal and paternal chromosomes. As shown in **Figure 13.11**, the number of combinations possible for daughter cells formed by meiosis of a diploid cell with two pairs of homologous chromosomes ($n = 2$) is four: two possible arrangements for the first pair times two possible arrangements for the second pair. Note that only two of the four combinations of daughter cells shown in the figure would result from meiosis of a *single* diploid cell, because a single parent cell would have one or the other possible chro-mosomal arrangement at metaphase I, but not both. How-ever, the population of daughter cells resulting from meiosis of a large number of diploid cells contains all four types in approximately equal numbers. In the case of $n = 3$, eight combinations of chromosomes are possible for daughter cells. More generally, the number of possible combinations when chromosomes sort independently during meiosis is 2^n, where n is the haploid number of the organism.

In the case of humans ($n = 23$), the number of possible combinations of maternal and paternal chromosomes in the resulting gametes is 2^{23}, or about 8.4 million. Each gamete that you produce in your lifetime contains one of roughly 8.4 million possible combinations of chromosomes.

Crossing Over

As a consequence of the independent assortment of chro-mosomes during meiosis, each of us produces a collection of gametes differing greatly in their combinations of the chro-mosomes we inherited from our two parents. Figure 13.11

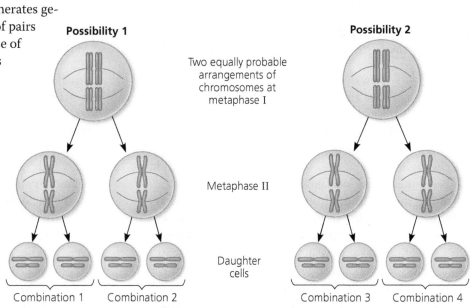

▲ **Figure 13.11** **The independent assortment of homologous chromosomes in meiosis.**

suggests that each chromosome in a gamete is exclusively maternal or paternal in origin. In fact, this is *not* the case, because crossing over produces **recombinant chromosomes**, individual chromosomes that carry genes (DNA) derived from two different parents **(Figure 13.12)**. In meiosis in humans, an average of one to three crossover events occur per chromosome pair, depending on the size of the chromosomes and the position of their centromeres.

As you learned in Figure 13.9, crossing over produces chromosomes with new combinations of maternal and paternal alleles. At metaphase II, chromosomes that contain one or more recombinant chromatids can be oriented in two alternative, nonequivalent ways with respect to other chromosomes, because their sister chromatids are no longer identical (see Figure 13.12). The different possible arrangements of nonidentical sister chromatids during meiosis II further increase the number of genetic types of daughter cells that can result from meiosis.

You will learn more about crossing over in Chapter 15. The important point for now is that crossing over, by combining DNA inherited from two parents into a single chromosome, is an important source of genetic variation in sexual life cycles.

Random Fertilization

The random nature of fertilization adds to the genetic variation arising from meiosis. In humans, each male and female gamete represents one of about 8.4 million (2^{23}) possible chromosome combinations due to independent assortment. The fusion of a male gamete with a female gamete during fertilization will produce a zygote with any of about 70 trillion ($2^{23} \times 2^{23}$) diploid combinations. If we factor in the variation brought about by crossing over, the number of possibilities is truly astronomical. It may sound trite, but you really *are* unique.

The Evolutionary Significance of Genetic Variation Within Populations

EVOLUTION Now that you've learned how new combinations of genes arise among offspring in a sexually reproducing population, let's see how the genetic variation in a population relates to evolution. Darwin recognized that a population evolves through the differential reproductive success of its variant members. On average, those individuals best suited to the local environment leave the most offspring, thereby transmitting their genes. Thus, natural selection results in the accumulation of genetic variations favored by the environment. As the environment changes, the population may survive if, in each generation, at least some of its members can cope effectively with the new conditions. Mutations are the original source of different alleles, which are then mixed and matched during meiosis. New

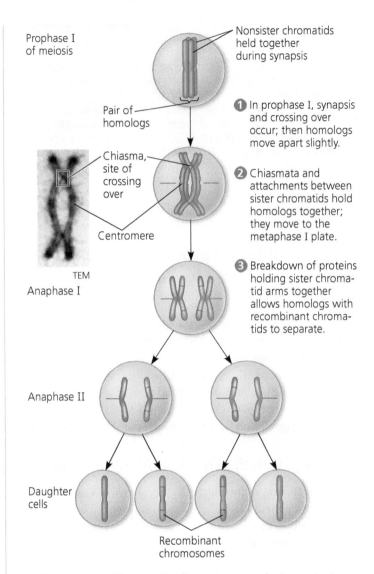

▲ **Figure 13.12 The results of crossing over during meiosis.**

and different combinations of alleles may work better than those that previously prevailed.

In a stable environment, though, sexual reproduction seems as if it would be less advantageous than asexual reproduction, which ensures perpetuation of successful combinations of alleles. Furthermore, sexual reproduction is more expensive energetically than asexual reproduction. In spite of these apparent disadvantages, sexual reproduction is almost universal among animals. Why is this?

The ability of sexual reproduction to generate genetic diversity is the most commonly proposed explanation for the evolutionary persistence of this process. Consider the rare case of the bdelloid rotifer **Figure 13.13**. This group has apparently not reproduced sexually throughout the 40 million years of its evolutionary history. Does this mean that genetic diversity is not advantageous in this species? It turns out that bdelloid rotifers are an exception that proves the rule: This group has mechanisms other than sexual reproduction for generating genetic diversity. For example, they live in environments that can dry up for long periods of time, during which they can enter a state of suspended animation. In this state, their cell membranes may crack in places, allowing entry of DNA from other rotifers and even other species. Evidence suggests that this DNA can become incorporated into the genome of the rotifer, leading to increased genetic diversity. This supports the idea that genetic diversity is advantageous, and that sexual reproduction has persisted because it generates such diversity.

▲ **Figure 13.13 A bdelloid rotifer, an animal that reproduces only asexually.**

In this chapter, we have seen how sexual reproduction greatly increases the genetic variation present in a population. Although Darwin realized that heritable variation is what makes evolution possible, he could not explain why offspring resemble—but are not identical to—their parents. Ironically, Gregor Mendel, a contemporary of Darwin, published a theory of inheritance that helps explain genetic variation, but his discoveries had no impact on biologists until 1900, more than 15 years after Darwin (1809–1882) and Mendel (1822–1884) had died. In the next chapter, you'll learn how Mendel discovered the basic rules governing the inheritance of specific traits.

CONCEPT CHECK 13.4

1. What is the original source of variation among the different alleles of a gene?
2. The diploid number for fruit flies is 8, and the diploid number for grasshoppers is 46. If no crossing over took place, would the genetic variation among offspring from a given pair of parents be greater in fruit flies or grasshoppers? Explain.
3. **WHAT IF?** If maternal and paternal chromatids have the same two alleles for every gene, will crossing over lead to genetic variation?

---

13 Chapter Review

SUMMARY OF KEY CONCEPTS

CONCEPT 13.1

Offspring acquire genes from parents by inheriting chromosomes (pp. 255–256)

- Each **gene** in an organism's DNA exists at a specific **locus** on a certain chromosome.
- In **asexual reproduction**, a single parent produces genetically identical offspring by mitosis. **Sexual reproduction** combines genes from two parents, leading to genetically diverse offspring.

? *Explain why human offspring resemble their parents but are not identical to them.*

CONCEPT 13.2

Fertilization and meiosis alternate in sexual life cycles (pp. 256–259)

- Normal human **somatic cells** are **diploid**. They have 46 chromosomes made up of two sets of 23, one set from each parent. Human diploid cells have 22 **homologous** pairs of **autosomes**, and one pair of **sex chromosomes**; the latter determines whether the person is female (XX) or male (XY).
- In humans, ovaries and testes produce **haploid gametes** by **meiosis**, each gamete containing a single set of 23 chromosomes ($n = 23$). During **fertilization**, an egg and sperm unite, forming a diploid ($2n = 46$) single-celled **zygote**, which develops into a multicellular organism by mitosis.

- Sexual life cycles differ in the timing of meiosis relative to fertilization and in the point(s) of the cycle at which a multicellular organism is produced by mitosis.

? *Compare the life cycles of animals and plants, mentioning their similarities and differences.*

CONCEPT 13.3

Meiosis reduces the number of chromosome sets from diploid to haploid (pp. 259–265)

- The two cell divisions of meiosis, **meiosis I** and **meiosis II**, produce four haploid daughter cells. The number of chromosome sets is reduced from two (diploid) to one (haploid) during meiosis I, the reductional division.
- Meiosis is distinguished from mitosis by three events of meiosis I:

Prophase I: Each homologous pair undergoes **synapsis** and **crossing over** between nonsister chromatids with the subsequent appearance of **chiasmata**.

Metaphase I: Chromosomes line up as homologous pairs on the metaphase plate.

Anaphase I: Homologs separate from each other; sister chromatids remain joined at the centromere.

Meiosis II separates the sister chromatids.

- Sister chromatid cohesion and crossing over allow chiasmata to hold homologs together until anaphase I. Cohesins are cleaved along the arms at anaphase I, allowing homologs to separate, and at the centromeres in anaphase II, releasing sister chromatids.

? *In prophase I, homologous chromosomes pair up and undergo synapsis and crossing over. Can this also occur during prophase II? Explain.*

CONCEPT 13.4

Genetic variation produced in sexual life cycles contributes to evolution (pp. 265–267)

- Three events in sexual reproduction contribute to genetic variation in a population: independent assortment of chromosomes during meiosis I, crossing over during meiosis I, and random fertilization of egg cells by sperm. During crossing over, DNA of nonsister chromatids in a homologous pair is broken and rejoined.
- Genetic variation is the raw material for evolution by natural selection. Mutations are the original source of this variation; recombination of variant genes generates additional genetic diversity.

? *Explain how three processes unique to meiosis generate a great deal of genetic variation.*

TEST YOUR UNDERSTANDING

LEVEL 1: KNOWLEDGE/COMPREHENSION

1. A human cell containing 22 autosomes and a Y chromosome is
   a. a sperm.
   b. an egg.
   c. a zygote.
   d. a somatic cell of a male.

2. Homologous chromosomes move toward opposite poles of a dividing cell during
   a. mitosis.
   b. meiosis I.
   c. meiosis II.
   d. fertilization.

LEVEL 2: APPLICATION/ANALYSIS

3. Meiosis II is similar to mitosis in that
   a. sister chromatids separate during anaphase.
   b. DNA replicates before the division.
   c. the daughter cells are diploid.
   d. homologous chromosomes synapse.

4. If the DNA content of a diploid cell in the G_1 phase of the cell cycle is x, then the DNA content of the same cell at metaphase of meiosis I would be
   a. $0.25x$. b. $0.5x$. c. x. d. $2x$.

5. If we continued to follow the cell lineage from question 4, then the DNA content of a single cell at metaphase of meiosis II would be
   a. $0.25x$. b. $0.5x$. c. x. d. $2x$.

6. **DRAW IT** The diagram at right shows a cell in meiosis.

   (a) Label the appropriate structures with these terms, drawing lines or brackets as needed: chromosome (label as duplicated or unduplicated), centromere, kinetochore, sister chromatids, nonsister chromatids, homologous pair, homologs, chiasma, sister chromatid cohesion, alleles (of the F and H genes).
   (b) Describe the makeup of a haploid set and a diploid set.
   (c) Identify the stage of meiosis shown.

LEVEL 3: SYNTHESIS/EVALUATION

7. How can you tell that the cell in question 6 is undergoing meiosis, not mitosis?

8. **EVOLUTION CONNECTION**
   Many species can reproduce either asexually or sexually. What might be the evolutionary significance of the switch from asexual to sexual reproduction that occurs in some organisms when the environment becomes unfavorable?

9. **SCIENTIFIC INQUIRY**
   The diagram in question 6 represents just a few of the chromosomes of a meiotic cell in a certain person. A previous study has shown that the freckles gene is located at the locus marked F, and the hair-color gene is located at the locus marked H, both on the long chromosome. The individual from whom this cell was taken has inherited different alleles for each gene ("freckles" and "black hair" from one parent, and "no freckles" and "blond hair" from the other). Predict allele combinations in the gametes resulting from this meiotic event. (It will help if you draw out the rest of meiosis, labeling alleles by name.) List other possible combinations of these alleles in this individual's gametes.

10. **WRITE ABOUT A THEME: INFORMATION**
    The continuity of life is based on heritable information in the form of DNA. In a short essay (100–150 words), explain how chromosome behavior during sexual reproduction in animals ensures perpetuation of parental traits in offspring and, at the same time, genetic variation among offspring.

11. **SYNTHESIZE YOUR KNOWLEDGE**

The Cavendish banana is the most popular fruit in the world, but is currently threatened by extinction due to a fungal agent (see the photo). This banana variety is "triploid" ($3n$, with three sets of chromosomes) and can only reproduce through cloning by cultivators. Given what you know about meiosis, explain how the banana's triploid number accounts for its seedless condition. Considering genetic diversity, discuss how the absence of sexual reproduction might contribute to the vulnerability of this domesticated species to infectious agents.

MasteringBiology®

Students Go to **MasteringBiology** for assignments, the eText, and the Study Area with practice tests, animations, and activities.

Instructors Go to **MasteringBiology** for automatically graded tutorials and questions that you can assign to your students, plus Instructor Resources.

14

Mendel and the Gene Idea

KEY CONCEPTS

14.1 Mendel used the scientific approach to identify two laws of inheritance

14.2 Probability laws govern Mendelian inheritance

14.3 Inheritance patterns are often more complex than predicted by simple Mendelian genetics

14.4 Many human traits follow Mendelian patterns of inheritance

▲ Figure 14.1 **What principles of inheritance did Gregor Mendel discover by breeding pea plants?**

Drawing from the Deck of Genes

The crowd at a soccer match attests to the marvelous variety and diversity of humankind. Brown, blue, or gray eyes; black, brown, or blond hair—these are just a few examples of heritable variations that we may observe. What principles account for the transmission of such traits from parents to offspring?

The explanation of heredity most widely in favor during the 1800s was the "blending" hypothesis, the idea that genetic material contributed by the two parents mixes just as blue and yellow paints blend to make green. This hypothesis predicts that over many generations, a freely mating population will give rise to a uniform population of individuals, something we don't see. The blending hypothesis also fails to explain the reappearance of traits after they've skipped a generation.

An alternative to the blending model is a "particulate" hypothesis of inheritance: the gene idea. In this model, parents pass on discrete heritable units—genes—that retain their separate identities in offspring. An organism's collection of genes is more like a deck of cards than a pail of paint. Like playing cards, genes can be shuffled and passed along, generation after generation, in undiluted form.

Modern genetics had its genesis in an abbey garden, where a monk named Gregor Mendel documented a particulate mechanism for inheritance using pea plants **(Figure 14.1)**. Mendel developed his theory of inheritance several

◀ **Mendel (third from right, holding a sprig of fuchsia) with his fellow monks.**

269

decades before chromosomes were observed under the microscope and the significance of their behavior was understood. In this chapter, we'll step into Mendel's garden to re-create his experiments and explain how he arrived at his theory of inheritance. We'll also explore inheritance patterns more complex than those observed by Mendel in garden peas. Finally, we will see how the Mendelian model applies to the inheritance of human variations, including hereditary disorders such as sickle-cell disease.

Mendel used the scientific approach to identify two laws of inheritance

Mendel discovered the basic principles of heredity by breeding garden peas in carefully planned experiments. As we retrace his work, you will recognize the key elements of the scientific process that were introduced in Chapter 1.

Mendel's Experimental, Quantitative Approach

Mendel grew up on his parents' small farm in a region of Austria that is now part of the Czech Republic. In this agricultural area, Mendel and the other children received agricultural training in school along with their basic education. As an adolescent, Mendel overcame financial hardship and illness to excel in high school and, later, at the Olmutz Philosophical Institute.

In 1843, at the age of 21, Mendel entered an Augustinian monastery, a reasonable choice at that time for someone who valued the life of the mind. He considered becoming a teacher but failed the necessary examination. In 1851, he left the monastery to pursue two years of study in physics and chemistry at the University of Vienna. These were very important years for Mendel's development as a scientist, in large part due to the strong influence of two professors. One was the physicist Christian Doppler, who encouraged his students to learn science through experimentation and trained Mendel to use mathematics to help explain natural phenomena. The other was a botanist named Franz Unger, who aroused Mendel's interest in the causes of variation in plants.

After attending the university, Mendel returned to the monastery and was assigned to teach at a local school, where several other instructors were enthusiastic about scientific research. In addition, his fellow monks shared a long-standing fascination with the breeding of plants. Around 1857, Mendel began breeding garden peas in the abbey garden to study inheritance. Although the question of heredity had long been a focus of curiosity at the monastery, Mendel's fresh approach allowed him to deduce principles that had remained elusive to others.

One reason Mendel probably chose to work with peas is that there are many varieties. For example, one variety has purple flowers, while another variety has white flowers. A heritable feature that varies among individuals, such as flower color, is called a **character**. Each variant for a character, such as purple or white color for flowers, is called a **trait**.

Other advantages of using peas are their short generation time and the large number of offspring from each mating. Furthermore, Mendel could strictly control mating between plants (**Figure 14.2**). Each pea flower has both pollen-producing organs (stamens) and an egg-bearing organ (carpel). In nature, pea plants usually self-fertilize: Pollen grains from the stamens land on the carpel of the same flower, and sperm released from the pollen grains fertilize

▼ Figure 14.2 | **Research Method**

Crossing Pea Plants

Application By crossing (mating) two true-breeding varieties of an organism, scientists can study patterns of inheritance. In this example, Mendel crossed pea plants that varied in flower color.

Technique

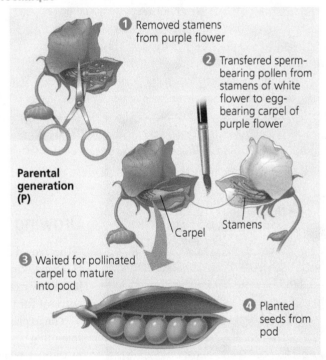

❶ Removed stamens from purple flower

❷ Transferred sperm-bearing pollen from stamens of white flower to egg-bearing carpel of purple flower

Parental generation (P)

Carpel

Stamens

❸ Waited for pollinated carpel to mature into pod

❹ Planted seeds from pod

Results When pollen from a white flower was transferred to a purple flower, the first-generation hybrids all had purple flowers. The result was the same for the reciprocal cross, which involved the transfer of pollen from purple flowers to white flowers.

First filial generation offspring (F₁)

❺ Examined offspring: all purple flowers

eggs present in the carpel.* To achieve cross-pollination of two plants, Mendel removed the immature stamens of a plant before they produced pollen and then dusted pollen from another plant onto the altered flowers (see Figure 14.2). Each resulting zygote then developed into a plant embryo encased in a seed (pea). Mendel could thus always be sure of the parentage of new seeds.

Mendel chose to track only those characters that occurred in two distinct, alternative forms, such as purple or white flower color. He also made sure that he started his experiments with varieties that, over many generations of self-pollination, had produced only the same variety as the parent plant. Such plants are said to be **true-breeding**. For example, a plant with purple flowers is true-breeding if the seeds produced by self-pollination in successive generations all give rise to plants that also have purple flowers.

In a typical breeding experiment, Mendel cross-pollinated two contrasting, true-breeding pea varieties—for example, purple-flowered plants and white-flowered plants (see Figure 14.2). This mating, or *crossing*, of two true-breeding varieties is called **hybridization**. The true-breeding parents are referred to as the **P generation** (parental generation), and their hybrid offspring are the **F_1 generation** (first filial generation, the word *filial* from the Latin word for "son"). Allowing these F_1 hybrids to self-pollinate (or to cross-pollinate with other F_1 hybrids) produces an **F_2 generation** (second filial generation). Mendel usually followed traits for at least the P, F_1, and F_2 generations. Had Mendel stopped his experiments with the F_1 generation, the basic patterns of inheritance would have eluded him. Mendel's quantitative analysis of the F_2 plants from thousands of genetic crosses like these allowed him to deduce two fundamental principles of heredity, which have come to be called the law of segregation and the law of independent assortment.

The Law of Segregation

If the blending model of inheritance were correct, the F_1 hybrids from a cross between purple-flowered and white-flowered pea plants would have pale purple flowers, a trait intermediate between those of the P generation. Notice in Figure 14.2 that the experiment produced a very different result: All the F_1 offspring had flowers just as purple as the purple-flowered parents.

What happened to the white-flowered plants' genetic contribution to the hybrids? If it were lost, then the F_1 plants could produce only purple-flowered offspring in the F_2 generation. But when Mendel allowed the F_1 plants to

self-pollinate and planted their seeds, the white-flower trait reappeared in the F_2 generation. Mendel used very large sample sizes and kept accurate records of his results: 705 of the F_2 plants had purple flowers, and 224 had white flowers. These data fit a ratio of approximately three purple to one white (Figure 14.3). Mendel reasoned that the heritable factor for white flowers did not disappear in the F_1 plants but was somehow hidden, or masked, when the purple-flower factor was present. In Mendel's terminology, purple flower color is a *dominant* trait, and white flower color is a *recessive* trait. The reappearance of white-flowered plants in the

▼ **Figure 14.3** | Inquiry

When F_1 hybrid pea plants self- or cross-pollinate, which traits appear in the F_2 generation?

Experiment Mendel crossed true-breeding purple-flowered plants and white-flowered plants (crosses are symbolized by ×). The resulting F_1 hybrids were allowed to self-pollinate or were cross-pollinated with other F_1 hybrids. The F_2 generation plants were then observed for flower color.

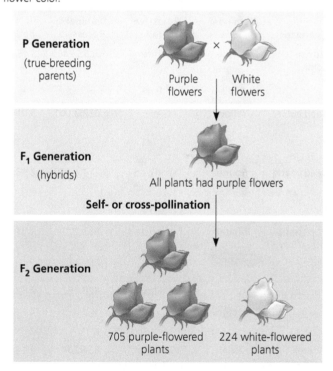

P Generation
(true-breeding parents)

Purple flowers   ×   White flowers

F_1 Generation
(hybrids)

All plants had purple flowers

Self- or cross-pollination

F_2 Generation

705 purple-flowered plants   224 white-flowered plants

Results Both purple-flowered and white-flowered plants appeared in the F_2 generation, in a ratio of approximately 3:1.

Conclusion The "heritable factor" for the recessive trait (white flowers) had not been destroyed, deleted, or "blended" in the F_1 generation but was merely masked by the presence of the factor for purple flowers, which is the dominant trait.

Source: G. Mendel, Experiments in plant hybridization, *Proceedings of the Natural History Society of Brünn* 4:3–47 (1866).

WHAT IF? *If you mated two purple-flowered plants from the P generation, what ratio of traits would you expect to observe in the offspring? Explain.*

---

*As you learned in Figure 13.6b, meiosis in plants produces spores, not gametes. In flowering plants like the pea, each spore develops into a microscopic haploid gametophyte that contains only a few cells and is located on the parent plant. The gametophyte produces sperm, in pollen grains, and eggs, in the carpel. For simplicity, we will not include the gametophyte stage in our discussion of fertilization in plants.

F_2 generation was evidence that the heritable factor causing white flowers had not been diluted or destroyed by coexisting with the purple-flower factor in the F_1 hybrids. Instead, it had been hidden when in the presence of the purple flower factor.

Mendel observed the same pattern of inheritance in six other characters, each represented by two distinctly different traits **(Table 14.1)**. For example, when Mendel crossed a true-breeding variety that produced smooth, round pea seeds with one that produced wrinkled seeds, all the F_1 hybrids produced round seeds; this is the dominant trait for seed shape. In the F_2 generation, approximately 75% of the seeds were round and 25% were wrinkled—a 3:1 ratio, as in Figure 14.3. Now let's see how Mendel deduced the law of segregation from his experimental results. In the discussion that follows, we will use modern terms instead of some of the terms used by Mendel. (For example, we'll use "gene" instead of Mendel's "heritable factor.")

Table 14.1	The Results of Mendel's F_1 Crosses for Seven Characters in Pea Plants				
Character	Dominant Trait	×	Recessive Trait	F_2 Generation Dominant: Recessive	Ratio
Flower color	Purple	×	White	705:224	3.15:1
Seed color	Yellow	×	Green	6,022:2,001	3.01:1
Seed shape	Round	×	Wrinkled	5,474:1,850	2.96:1
Pod shape	Inflated	×	Constricted	882:299	2.95:1
Pod color	Green	×	Yellow	428:152	2.82:1
Flower position	Axial	×	Terminal	651:207	3.14:1
Stem length	Tall	×	Dwarf	787:277	2.84:1

Mendel's Model

Mendel developed a model to explain the 3:1 inheritance pattern that he consistently observed among the F_2 offspring in his pea experiments. We describe four related concepts making up this model, the fourth of which is the law of segregation.

First, *alternative versions of genes account for variations in inherited characters.* The gene for flower color in pea plants, for example, exists in two versions, one for purple flowers and the other for white flowers. These alternative versions of a gene are called **alleles**. Today, we can relate this concept to chromosomes and DNA. As shown in **Figure 14.4**, each gene is a sequence of nucleotides at a specific place, or locus, along a particular chromosome. The DNA at that locus, however, can vary slightly in its nucleotide sequence. This variation in information content can affect the function of the encoded protein and thus the phenotype of the organism. The purple-flower allele and the white-flower allele are two DNA sequence variations possible at the flower-color locus on one of a pea plant's chromosomes, one that allows synthesis of purple pigment and one that does not.

Second, *for each character, an organism inherits two copies (that is, two alleles) of a gene, one from each parent.* Remarkably, Mendel made this deduction without knowing about the role, or even the existence, of chromosomes. Each somatic cell in a diploid organism has two sets of chromosomes, one set inherited from each parent (see Concept 13.2). Thus, a genetic locus is actually represented twice in a diploid cell, once on each homolog of a specific pair of chromosomes. The two alleles at a particular locus may be identical, as in the true-breeding plants of Mendel's P generation. Or the alleles may differ, as in the F_1 hybrids (see Figure 14.4).

Third, *if the two alleles at a locus differ, then one, the **dominant allele**, determines the organism's appearance; the other, the **recessive allele**, has no noticeable effect on the organism's appearance.* Accordingly, Mendel's F_1 plants had purple flowers because the allele for that trait is dominant and the allele for white flowers is recessive.

The fourth and final part of Mendel's model, the **law of segregation**, states that *the two alleles for a heritable character segregate (separate from each other) during gamete formation and end up in different gametes.* Thus, an egg or a sperm gets only one of the two alleles that are present in the somatic cells of the organism making the gamete. In terms of chromosomes, this segregation corresponds to the distribution of the two members of a pair of homologous chromosomes to different gametes in meiosis (see Figure 13.7). Note that if an organism has identical alleles for a particular character—that is, the organism is true-breeding for that character—then that allele is present in all gametes. But if different alleles are present, as in the F_1 hybrids, then 50% of the gametes receive the dominant allele and 50% receive the recessive allele.

▶ **Figure 14.4** **Alleles, alternative versions of a gene.** Shown is a pair of homologous chromosomes in an F₁ hybrid pea plant, with the DNA sequence from the flower color allele of each. The paternally inherited chromosome (blue) has an allele for purple flowers, which codes for a protein that indirectly controls synthesis of purple pigment. The maternally inherited chromosome (red) has an allele for white flowers, which results in no functional protein being made.

Allele for purple flowers

Locus for flower-color gene

Allele for white flowers

Pair of homologous chromosomes

DNA with nucleotide sequence CTAAATCGGT

DNA with nucleotide sequence ATAAATCGGT

Through a series of steps, this DNA sequence results in production of an enzyme that helps synthesize purple pigment.

Enzyme

This DNA sequence results in the absence of the enzyme.

One purple-flower allele results in sufficient pigment for purple flowers.

Does Mendel's segregation model account for the 3:1 ratio he observed in the F₂ generation of his numerous crosses? For the flower-color character, the model predicts that the two different alleles present in an F₁ individual will segregate into gametes such that half the gametes will have the purple-flower allele and half will have the white-flower allele. During self-pollination, gametes of each class unite randomly. An egg with a purple-flower allele has an equal chance of being fertilized by a sperm with a purple-flower allele or one with a white-flower allele. Since the same is true for an egg with a white-flower allele, there are four equally likely combinations of sperm and egg. **Figure 14.5** illustrates these combinations using a **Punnett square**, a handy diagrammatic device for predicting the allele composition of offspring from a cross between individuals of known genetic makeup. Notice that we use a capital letter to symbolize a dominant allele and a lowercase letter for a recessive allele. In our example, P is the purple-flower allele, and p is the white-flower allele; it is often useful as well to be able to refer to the gene itself as the P/p gene.

In the F₂ offspring, what color will the flowers be? One-fourth of the plants have inherited two purple-flower alleles; clearly, these plants will have purple flowers. One-half of the F₂ offspring

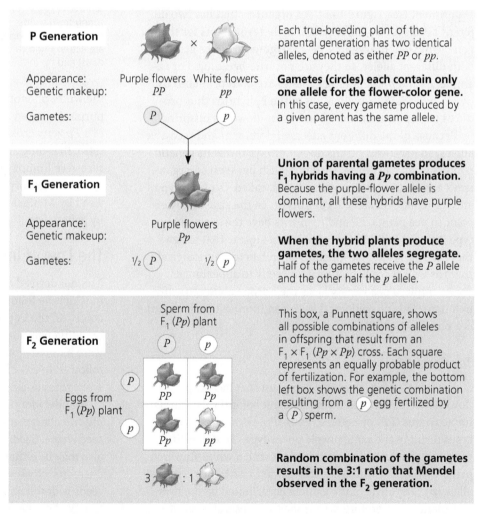

P Generation

Appearance: Purple flowers White flowers
Genetic makeup: PP pp

Gametes: P p

Each true-breeding plant of the parental generation has two identical alleles, denoted as either PP or pp.

Gametes (circles) each contain only one allele for the flower-color gene. In this case, every gamete produced by a given parent has the same allele.

F₁ Generation

Appearance: Purple flowers
Genetic makeup: Pp

Gametes: ½ P ½ p

Union of parental gametes produces F₁ hybrids having a Pp combination. Because the purple-flower allele is dominant, all these hybrids have purple flowers.

When the hybrid plants produce gametes, the two alleles segregate. Half of the gametes receive the P allele and the other half the p allele.

F₂ Generation

Sperm from F₁ (Pp) plant
P p

Eggs from F₁ (Pp) plant
P PP Pp
p Pp pp

3 : 1

This box, a Punnett square, shows all possible combinations of alleles in offspring that result from an F₁ × F₁ (Pp × Pp) cross. Each square represents an equally probable product of fertilization. For example, the bottom left box shows the genetic combination resulting from a p egg fertilized by a P sperm.

Random combination of the gametes results in the 3:1 ratio that Mendel observed in the F₂ generation.

▲ **Figure 14.5 Mendel's law of segregation.** This diagram shows the genetic makeup of the generations in Figure 14.3. It illustrates Mendel's model for inheritance of the alleles of a single gene. Each plant has two alleles for the gene controlling flower color, one allele inherited from each of the plant's parents. To construct a Punnett square that predicts the F₂ generation offspring, we list all the possible gametes from one parent (here, the F₁ female) along the left side of the square and all the possible gametes from the other parent (here, the F₁ male) along the top. The boxes represent the offspring resulting from all the possible unions of male and female gametes.

have inherited one purple-flower allele and one white-flower allele; these plants will also have purple flowers, the dominant trait. Finally, one-fourth of the F₂ plants have inherited two white-flower alleles and will express the recessive trait. Thus, Mendel's model accounts for the 3:1 ratio of traits that he observed in the F₂ generation.

Useful Genetic Vocabulary

An organism that has a pair of identical alleles for a character is said to be **homozygous** for the gene controlling that character. In the parental generation in Figure 14.5, the purple pea plant is homozygous for the dominant allele (*PP*), while the white plant is homozygous for the recessive allele (*pp*). Homozygous plants "breed true" because all of their gametes contain the same allele—either *P* or *p* in this example. If we cross dominant homozygotes with recessive homozygotes, every offspring will have two different alleles—*Pp* in the case of the F₁ hybrids of our flower-color experiment (see Figure 14.5). An organism that has two different alleles for a gene is said to be **heterozygous** for that gene. Unlike homozygotes, heterozygotes produce gametes with different alleles, so they are not true-breeding. For example, *P*- and *p*-containing gametes are both produced by our F₁ hybrids. Self-pollination of the F₁ hybrids thus produces both purple-flowered and white-flowered offspring.

Because of the different effects of dominant and recessive alleles, an organism's traits do not always reveal its genetic composition. Therefore, we distinguish between an organism's appearance or observable traits, called its **phenotype**, and its genetic makeup, its **genotype**. In the case of flower color in pea plants, *PP* and *Pp* plants have the same phenotype (purple) but different genotypes. **Figure 14.6** reviews these terms. Note that "phenotype" refers to physiological traits as well as traits that relate directly to appearance. For example, a pea variety lacks the normal ability to self-pollinate. This physiological variation (non-self-pollination) is a phenotypic trait.

The Testcross

Suppose we have a "mystery" pea plant that has purple flowers. We cannot tell from its flower color if this plant is homozygous (*PP*) or heterozygous (*Pp*) because both genotypes result in the same purple phenotype. To determine the genotype, we can cross this plant with a white-flowered plant (*pp*), which will make only gametes with the recessive allele (*p*). The allele in the gamete contributed by the mystery plant will therefore determine the appearance of the offspring (**Figure 14.7**). If all the offspring of the cross have purple flowers, then the purple-flowered mystery plant must be homozygous for the dominant allele, because a *PP* × *pp* cross produces all *Pp* offspring. But if both the purple and

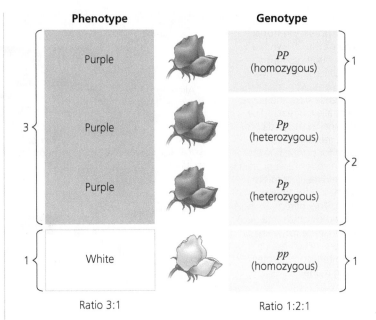

Phenotype | **Genotype**

Purple — *PP* (homozygous) — 1

Purple — *Pp* (heterozygous)

Purple — *Pp* (heterozygous) — 2

White — *pp* (homozygous) — 1

Ratio 3:1   Ratio 1:2:1

▲ **Figure 14.6 Phenotype versus genotype.** Grouping F₂ offspring from a cross for flower color according to phenotype results in the typical 3:1 phenotypic ratio. In terms of genotype, however, there are actually two categories of purple-flowered plants, *PP* (homozygous) and *Pp* (heterozygous), giving a 1:2:1 genotypic ratio.

the white phenotypes appear among the offspring, then the purple-flowered parent must be heterozygous. The offspring of a *Pp* × *pp* cross will be expected to have a 1:1 phenotypic ratio. Breeding an organism of unknown genotype with a recessive homozygote is called a **testcross** because it can reveal the genotype of that organism. The testcross was devised by Mendel and continues to be an important tool used by geneticists.

The Law of Independent Assortment

Mendel derived the law of segregation from experiments in which he followed only a *single* character, such as flower color. All the F₁ progeny produced in his crosses of true-breeding parents were **monohybrids**, meaning that they were heterozygous for the one particular character being followed in the cross. We refer to a cross between such heterozygotes as a **monohybrid cross**.

Mendel identified his second law of inheritance by following *two* characters at the same time, such as seed color and seed shape. Seeds (peas) may be either yellow or green. They also may be either round (smooth) or wrinkled. From single-character crosses, Mendel knew that the allele for yellow seeds is dominant (*Y*), and the allele for green seeds is recessive (*y*). For the seed-shape character, the allele for round is dominant (*R*), and the allele for wrinkled is recessive (*r*).

Imagine crossing two true-breeding pea varieties that differ in *both* of these characters—a cross between a plant with yellow-round seeds (*YYRR*) and a plant with green-wrinkled

Research Method

The Testcross

Application An organism that exhibits a dominant trait, such as purple flowers in pea plants, can be either homozygous for the dominant allele or heterozygous. To determine the organism's genotype, geneticists can perform a testcross.

Technique In a testcross, the individual with the unknown genotype is crossed with a homozygous individual expressing the recessive trait (white flowers in this example), and Punnett squares are used to predict the possible outcomes.

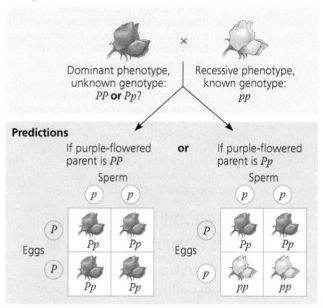

Results Matching the results to either prediction identifies the unknown parental genotype (either PP or Pp in this example). In this testcross, we transferred pollen from a white-flowered plant to the carpels of a purple-flowered plant; the opposite (reciprocal) cross would have led to the same results.

seeds ($yyrr$). The F$_1$ plants will be **dihybrids,** individuals heterozygous for the two characters being followed in the cross ($YyRr$). But are these two characters transmitted from parents to offspring as a package? That is, will the Y and R alleles always stay together, generation after generation? Or are seed color and seed shape inherited independently? **Figure 14.8** shows how a **dihybrid cross,** a cross between F$_1$ dihybrids, can determine which of these two hypotheses is correct.

The F$_1$ plants, of genotype $YyRr$, exhibit both dominant phenotypes, yellow seeds with round shapes, no matter which hypothesis is correct. The key step in the experiment is to see what happens when F$_1$ plants self-pollinate

and produce F$_2$ offspring. If the hybrids must transmit their alleles in the same combinations in which the alleles were inherited from the P generation, then the F$_1$ hybrids will produce only two classes of gametes: YR and yr. This "dependent assortment" hypothesis predicts that the phenotypic ratio of the F$_2$ generation will be 3:1, just as in a monohybrid cross (see Figure 14.8, left side).

The alternative hypothesis is that the two pairs of alleles segregate independently of each other. In other words, genes are packaged into gametes in all possible allelic combinations, as long as each gamete has one allele for each gene (see Figure 13.11). In our example, an F$_1$ plant will produce four classes of gametes in equal quantities: YR, Yr, yR, and yr. If sperm of the four classes fertilize eggs of the four classes, there will be 16 (4×4) equally probable ways in which the alleles can combine in the F$_2$ generation, as shown in Figure 14.8, right side. These combinations result in four phenotypic categories with a ratio of 9:3:3:1 (nine yellowround to three green-round to three yellow-wrinkled to one green-wrinkled). When Mendel did the experiment and classified the F$_2$ offspring, his results were close to the predicted 9:3:3:1 phenotypic ratio, supporting the hypothesis that the alleles for one gene—controlling seed color or seed shape, in this example—are sorted into gametes independently of the alleles of other genes.

Mendel tested his seven pea characters in various dihybrid combinations and always observed a 9:3:3:1 phenotypic ratio in the F$_2$ generation. Is this consistent with the 3:1 phenotypic ratio seen for the monohybrid cross shown in Figure 14.5? To investigate this question, let's consider one of the two dihybrid characters by itself: Looking only at pea color, we see that there are 416 yellow and 140 green peas—a 2.97:1 ratio, or roughly 3:1. In the dihybrid cross, the pea color alleles segregate as if this were a monohybrid cross. The results of Mendel's dihybrid experiments are the basis for what we now call the **law of independent assortment,** which states that *two or more genes assort independently—that is, each pair of alleles segregates independently of each other pair of alleles—during gamete formation.*

This law applies only to genes (allele pairs) located on different chromosomes (that is to say, on chromosomes that are not homologous) or, alternatively, to genes that are very far apart on the same chromosome. (The latter case will be explained in Chapter 15, along with the more complex inheritance patterns of genes located near each other, which tend to be inherited together.) All the pea characters Mendel chose for analysis were controlled by genes on different chromosomes or were far apart on the same chromosome; this situation greatly simplified interpretation of his multicharacter pea crosses. All the examples we consider in the rest of this chapter involve genes located on different chromosomes.

▼ Figure 14.8 · Inquiry

Do the alleles for one character assort into gametes dependently or independently of the alleles for a different character?

Experiment To follow the characters of seed color and seed shape through the F₂ generation, Mendel crossed a true-breeding plant with yellow-round seeds with a true-breeding plant with green-wrinkled seeds, producing dihybrid F₁ plants. Self-pollination of the F₁ dihybrids produced the F₂ generation. The two hypotheses (dependent and independent assortment) predict different phenotypic ratios.

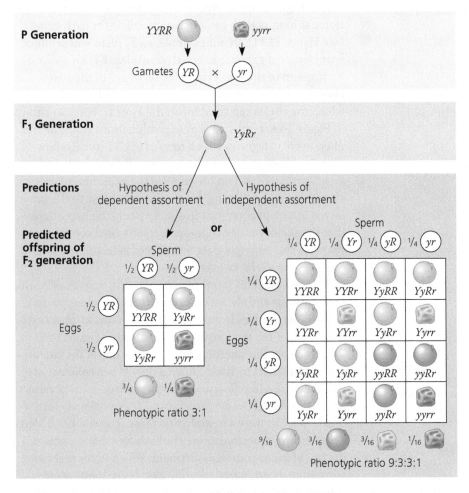

Results

315 ○ 108 ○ 101 ▨ 32 ▨   Phenotypic ratio approximately 9:3:3:1

Conclusion Only the hypothesis of independent assortment predicts two of the observed phenotypes: green-round seeds and yellow-wrinkled seeds (see the right-hand Punnett square). The alleles for each gene segregate independently of those of the other, and the two genes are said to assort independently.

Source: G. Mendel, Experiments in plant hybridization, *Proceedings of the Natural History Society of Brünn* 4:3–47 (1866).

WHAT IF? *Suppose Mendel had transferred pollen from an F₁ plant to the carpel of a plant that was homozygous recessive for both genes. Set up the cross and draw Punnett squares that predict the offspring for both hypotheses. Would this cross have supported the hypothesis of independent assortment equally well?*

CONCEPT CHECK 14.1

1. **DRAW IT** Pea plants heterozygous for flower position and stem length (*AaTt*) are allowed to self-pollinate, and 400 of the resulting seeds are planted. Draw a Punnett square for this cross. How many offspring would be predicted to have terminal flowers and be dwarf? (See Table 14.1.)

2. **WHAT IF?** List all gametes that could be made by a pea plant heterozygous for seed color, seed shape, and pod shape (*YyRrIi*; see Table 14.1). How large a Punnett square would you need to draw to predict the offspring of a self-pollination of this "trihybrid"?

3. **MAKE CONNECTIONS** In some pea plant crosses, the plants are self-pollinated. Explain whether self-pollination is considered asexual or sexual reproduction. (See Concept 13.1.)

CONCEPT 14.2

Probability laws govern Mendelian inheritance

Mendel's laws of segregation and independent assortment reflect the same rules of probability that apply to tossing coins, rolling dice, and drawing cards from a deck. The probability scale ranges from 0 to 1. An event that is certain to occur has a probability of 1, while an event that is certain *not* to occur has a probability of 0. With a coin that has heads on both sides, the probability of tossing heads is 1, and the probability of tossing tails is 0. With a normal coin, the chance of tossing heads is ½, and the chance of tossing tails is ½. The probability of drawing the ace of spades from a 52-card deck is ¹⁄₅₂. The probabilities of all possible outcomes for an event must add up to 1. With a deck of cards, the chance of picking a card other than the ace of spades is ⁵¹⁄₅₂.

Tossing a coin illustrates an important lesson about probability. For every toss, the probability of heads is ½. The outcome of any particular toss is unaffected by what has happened on previous trials. We refer to phenomena such as coin tosses as independent events. Each toss of a coin, whether done sequentially with one coin or simultaneously with many, is independent of every other toss. And like two separate coin tosses, the alleles of one gene segregate into gametes independently of another gene's alleles (the law of independent assortment). Two basic rules of probability can help us predict the outcome of the fusion of such gametes in simple monohybrid crosses and more complicated crosses as well.

The Multiplication and Addition Rules Applied to Monohybrid Crosses

How do we determine the probability that two or more independent events will occur together in some specific combination? For example, what is the chance that two coins tossed simultaneously will both land heads up? The **multiplication rule** states that to determine this probability, we multiply the probability of one event (one coin coming up heads) by the probability of the other event (the other coin coming up heads). By the multiplication rule, then, the probability that both coins will land heads up is $1/2 \times 1/2 = 1/4$.

We can apply the same reasoning to an F_1 monohybrid cross. With seed shape in pea plants as the heritable character, the genotype of F_1 plants is Rr. Segregation in a heterozygous plant is like flipping a coin in terms of calculating the probability of each outcome: Each egg produced has a $1/2$ chance of carrying the dominant allele (R) and a $1/2$ chance of carrying the recessive allele (r). The same odds apply to each sperm cell produced. For a particular F_2 plant to have wrinkled seeds, the recessive trait, both the egg and the sperm that come together must carry the r allele. The probability that an r allele will be present in both gametes at fertilization is found by multiplying $1/2$ (the probability that the egg will have an r) $\times$ $1/2$ (the probability that the sperm will have an r). Thus, the multiplication rule tells us that the probability of an F_2 plant having wrinkled seeds (rr) is $1/4$ (Figure 14.9). Likewise, the probability of an F_2 plant carrying both dominant alleles for seed shape (RR) is $1/4$.

To figure out the probability that an F_2 plant from a monohybrid cross will be heterozygous rather than homozygous, we need to invoke a second rule. Notice in Figure 14.9 that the dominant allele can come from the egg and the recessive allele from the sperm, or vice versa. That is, F_1 gametes can combine to produce Rr offspring in two *mutually exclusive* ways: For any particular heterozygous F_2 plant, the dominant allele can come from the egg *or* the sperm, but not from both. According to the **addition rule**, the probability that any one of two or more mutually exclusive events will occur is calculated by adding their individual probabilities. As we have just seen, the multiplication rule gives us the individual probabilities that we will now add together. The probability for one possible way of obtaining an F_2 heterozygote—the dominant allele from the egg and the recessive allele from the sperm—

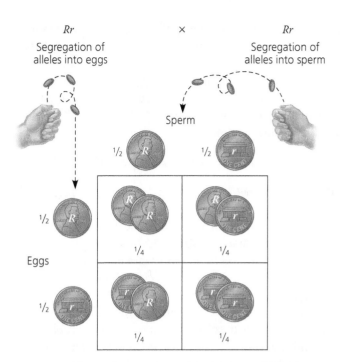

▲ **Figure 14.9 Segregation of alleles and fertilization as chance events.** When a heterozygote (Rr) forms gametes, whether a particular gamete ends up with an R or an r is like the toss of a coin. We can determine the probability for any genotype among the offspring of two heterozygotes by multiplying together the individual probabilities of an egg and sperm having a particular allele (R or r in this example).

is $1/4$. The probability for the other possible way—the recessive allele from the egg and the dominant allele from the sperm—is also $1/4$ (see Figure 14.9). Using the rule of addition, then, we can calculate the probability of an F_2 heterozygote as $1/4 + 1/4 = 1/2$.

Solving Complex Genetics Problems with the Rules of Probability

We can also apply the rules of probability to predict the outcome of crosses involving multiple characters. Recall that each allelic pair segregates independently during gamete formation (the law of independent assortment). Thus, a dihybrid or other multicharacter cross is equivalent to two or more independent monohybrid crosses occurring simultaneously. By applying what we have learned about monohybrid crosses, we can determine the probability of specific genotypes occurring in the F_2 generation without having to construct unwieldy Punnett squares.

Consider the dihybrid cross between $YyRr$ heterozygotes shown in Figure 14.8. We will focus first on the seed-color character. For a monohybrid cross of Yy plants, we can use a simple Punnett square to determine that the probabilities of the offspring genotypes are $1/4$ for YY, $1/2$ for Yy, and $1/4$ for yy. We can draw a second Punnett square to determine that the same probabilities apply to the offspring genotypes for seed shape: ¼ *RR*, ½ *Rr*, and ¼ *rr*. Knowing these probabilities, we can simply use the multiplication rule to determine the probability of each of the genotypes in the F$_2$ generation. To give two examples, the calculations for finding the probabilities of two of the possible F$_2$ genotypes (*YYRR* and *YyRR*) are shown below:

Probability of *YYRR* = ¼(probability of *YY*) × ¼ (*RR*) = ¹/₁₆

Probability of *YyRR* = ½(*Yy*)   × ¼ (*RR*) = ¹/₈

The *YYRR* genotype corresponds to the upper left box in the larger Punnett square in Figure 14.8 (one box = ¹/₁₆). Looking closely at the larger Punnett square in Figure 14.8, you will see that 2 of the 16 boxes (¹/₈) correspond to the *YyRR* genotype.

Now let's see how we can combine the multiplication and addition rules to solve even more complex problems in Mendelian genetics. Imagine a cross of two pea varieties in which we track the inheritance of three characters. Let's cross a trihybrid with purple flowers and yellow, round seeds (heterozygous for all three genes) with a plant with purple flowers and green, wrinkled seeds (heterozygous for flower color but homozygous recessive for the other two characters). Using Mendelian symbols, our cross is *PpYyRr* × *Ppyyrr*. What fraction of offspring from this cross are predicted to exhibit the recessive phenotypes for *at least two* of the three characters?

To answer this question, we can start by listing all genotypes we could get that fulfill this condition: *ppyyRr*, *ppYyrr*, *Ppyyrr*, *PPyyrr*, and *ppyyrr*. (Because the condition is *at least two* recessive traits, it includes the last genotype, which shows all three recessive traits.) Next, we calculate the probability for each of these genotypes resulting from our *PpYyRr* × *Ppyyrr* cross by multiplying together the individual probabilities for the allele pairs, just as we did in our dihybrid example. Note that in a cross involving heterozygous and homozygous allele pairs (for example, *Yy* × *yy*), the probability of heterozygous offspring is ½ and the probability of homozygous offspring is ½. Finally, we use the addition rule to add the probabilities for all the different genotypes that fulfill the condition of at least two recessive traits, as shown below:

ppyyRr	¼ (probability of *pp*) × ½ (*yy*) × ½(*Rr*)	= ¹/₁₆
ppYyrr	¼ × ½ × ½	= ¹/₁₆
Ppyyrr	½ × ½ × ½	= ²/₁₆
PPyyrr	¼ × ½ × ½	= ¹/₁₆
ppyyrr	¼ × ½ × ½	= ¹/₁₆
Chance of *at least two* recessive traits		= ⁶/₁₆ or ³/₈

In time, you'll be able to solve genetics problems faster by using the rules of probability than by filling in Punnett squares.

We cannot predict with certainty the exact numbers of progeny of different genotypes resulting from a genetic cross. But the rules of probability give us the *chance* of various outcomes. Usually, the larger the sample size, the closer the results will conform to our predictions. Mendel understood this statistical feature of inheritance and had a keen sense of the rules of chance. It was for this reason that he set up his experiments so as to generate, and then count, large numbers of offspring from his crosses.

CONCEPT CHECK 14.2

1. For any gene with a dominant allele *A* and recessive allele *a*, what proportions of the offspring from an *AA* × *Aa* cross are expected to be homozygous dominant, homozygous recessive, and heterozygous?

2. Two organisms, with genotypes *BbDD* and *BBDd*, are mated. Assuming independent assortment of the *B/b* and *D/d* genes, write the genotypes of all possible offspring from this cross and use the rules of probability to calculate the chance of each genotype occurring.

3. **WHAT IF?** Three characters (flower color, seed color, and pod shape) are considered in a cross between two pea plants: *PpYyIi* × *ppYyii*. What fraction of offspring are predicted to be homozygous recessive for at least two of the three characters?

CONCEPT 14.3

Inheritance patterns are often more complex than predicted by simple Mendelian genetics

In the 20th century, geneticists extended Mendelian principles not only to diverse organisms, but also to patterns of inheritance more complex than those described by Mendel. For the work that led to his two laws of inheritance, Mendel chose pea plant characters that turn out to have a relatively simple genetic basis: Each character is determined by one gene, for which there are only two alleles, one completely dominant and the other completely recessive. (There is one exception: Mendel's pod-shape character is actually determined by two genes.) Not all heritable characters are determined so simply, and the relationship between genotype and phenotype is rarely so straightforward. Mendel himself realized that he could not explain the more complicated patterns he observed in crosses involving other pea characters or other plant species. This does not diminish the utility of Mendelian genetics, however, because the basic principles of segregation and independent assortment apply even to more complex patterns of inheritance. In this section, we will extend Mendelian genetics to hereditary patterns that were not reported by Mendel.

Extending Mendelian Genetics for a Single Gene

The inheritance of characters determined by a single gene deviates from simple Mendelian patterns when alleles are not completely dominant or recessive, when a particular gene has more than two alleles, or when a single gene produces multiple phenotypes. We will describe examples of each of these situations in this section.

Degrees of Dominance

Alleles can show different degrees of dominance and recessiveness in relation to each other. In Mendel's classic pea crosses, the F_1 offspring always looked like one of the two parental varieties because one allele in a pair showed **complete dominance** over the other. In such situations, the phenotypes of the heterozygote and the dominant homozygote are indistinguishable.

For some genes, however, neither allele is completely dominant, and the F_1 hybrids have a phenotype somewhere between those of the two parental varieties. This phenomenon, called **incomplete dominance**, is seen when red snapdragons are crossed with white snapdragons: All the F_1 hybrids have pink flowers **(Figure 14.10)**. This third, intermediate phenotype results from flowers of the heterozygotes having less red pigment than the red homozygotes. (This is unlike the case of Mendel's pea plants, where the Pp heterozygotes make enough pigment for the flowers to be purple, indistinguishable from those of PP plants.)

At first glance, incomplete dominance of either allele seems to provide evidence for the blending hypothesis of inheritance, which would predict that the red or white trait could never reappear among offspring from the pink hybrids. In fact, interbreeding F_1 hybrids produces F_2 offspring with a phenotypic ratio of one red to two pink to one white. (Because heterozygotes have a separate phenotype, the genotypic and phenotypic ratios for the F_2 generation are the same, 1:2:1.) The segregation of the red-flower and white-flower alleles in the gametes produced by the pink-flowered plants confirms that the alleles for flower color are heritable factors that maintain their identity in the hybrids; that is, inheritance is particulate.

Another variation on dominance relationships between alleles is called **codominance**; in this variation, the two alleles each affect the phenotype in separate, distinguishable ways. For example, the human MN blood group is determined by codominant alleles for two specific molecules located on the surface of red blood cells, the M and N molecules. A single gene locus, at which two allelic variations are possible, determines the phenotype of this blood group. Individuals homozygous for the M allele (MM) have red blood cells with only M molecules; individuals homozygous for the N allele (NN) have red blood cells with only N

▲ **Figure 14.10 Incomplete dominance in snapdragon color.** When red snapdragons are crossed with white ones, the F_1 hybrids have pink flowers. Segregation of alleles into gametes of the F_1 plants results in an F_2 generation with a 1:2:1 ratio for both genotype and phenotype. Neither allele is dominant, so rather than using upper- and lowercase letters, we use the letter C with a superscript to indicate an allele for flower color: C^R for red and C^W for white.

? *Suppose a classmate argues that this figure supports the blending hypothesis for inheritance. What might your classmate say, and how would you respond?*

molecules. But *both* M and N molecules are present on the red blood cells of individuals heterozygous for the M and N alleles (MN). Note that the MN phenotype is *not* intermediate between the M and N phenotypes, which distinguishes codominance from incomplete dominance. Rather, *both* M and N phenotypes are exhibited by heterozygotes, since both molecules are present.

The Relationship Between Dominance and Phenotype We've now seen that the relative effects of two alleles range from complete dominance of one allele, through incomplete dominance of either allele, to codominance of both alleles. It is important to understand that an allele is called *dominant* because it is seen in the phenotype, not because it somehow subdues a recessive allele. Alleles are simply variations in a gene's nucleotide sequence (see Figure 14.4). When a dominant allele coexists with a recessive allele in a heterozygote, they do not actually interact at all. It is in the pathway from genotype to phenotype that dominance and recessiveness come into play.

To illustrate the relationship between dominance and phenotype, we can use one of the characters Mendel studied—round versus wrinkled pea seed shape. The dominant allele (round) codes for an enzyme that helps convert an unbranched form of starch to a branched form in the seed. The recessive allele (wrinkled) codes for a defective form of this enzyme, leading to an accumulation of unbranched starch, which causes excess water to enter the seed by osmosis. Later, when the seed dries, it wrinkles. If a dominant allele is present, no excess water enters the seed and it does not wrinkle when it dries. One dominant allele results in enough of the enzyme to synthesize adequate amounts of branched starch, which means that dominant homozygotes and heterozygotes have the same phenotype: round seeds.

A closer look at the relationship between dominance and phenotype reveals an intriguing fact: For any character, the observed dominant/recessive relationship of alleles depends on the level at which we examine phenotype. **Tay-Sachs disease**, an inherited disorder in humans, is an example. The brain cells of a child with Tay-Sachs disease cannot metabolize certain lipids because a crucial enzyme does not work properly. As these lipids accumulate in brain cells, the child begins to suffer seizures, blindness, and degeneration of motor and mental performance and dies within a few years.

Only children who inherit two copies of the Tay-Sachs allele (homozygotes) have the disease. Thus, at the *organismal* level, the Tay-Sachs allele qualifies as recessive. However, the activity level of the lipid-metabolizing enzyme in heterozygotes is intermediate between that in individuals homozygous for the normal allele and that in individuals with Tay-Sachs disease. The intermediate phenotype observed at the *biochemical* level is characteristic of incomplete dominance of either allele. Fortunately, the heterozygote condition does not lead to disease symptoms, apparently because half the normal enzyme activity is sufficient to prevent lipid accumulation in the brain. Extending our analysis to yet another level, we find that heterozygous individuals produce equal numbers of normal and dysfunctional enzyme molecules. Thus, at the *molecular* level, the normal allele and the Tay-Sachs allele are codominant. As you can see, whether alleles appear to be completely dominant, incompletely dominant, or codominant depends on the level at which the phenotype is analyzed.

Frequency of Dominant Alleles Although you might assume that the dominant allele for a particular character would be more common than the recessive allele, this is not a given. For example, about one baby out of 400 in the United States is born with extra fingers or toes, a condition known as polydactyly. Some cases are caused by the presence of a dominant allele. The low frequency of polydactyly indicates that the recessive allele, which results in five digits per appendage, is far more prevalent than the dominant allele in the population.

Multiple Alleles

Only two alleles exist for the pea characters that Mendel studied, but most genes exist in more than two allelic forms. The ABO blood groups in humans, for instance, are determined by three alleles of a single gene: I^A, I^B, and *i*. A person's blood group may be one of four types: A, B, AB, or O. These letters refer to two carbohydrates—A and B—that may be found on the surface of red blood cells. A person's blood cells may have carbohydrate A (type A blood), carbohydrate B (type B), both (type AB), or neither (type O), as shown in **Figure 14.11**. Matching compatible blood groups is critical for safe blood transfusions.

Pleiotropy

So far, we have treated Mendelian inheritance as though each gene affects only one phenotypic character. Most genes, however, have multiple phenotypic effects, a property called **pleiotropy** (from the Greek *pleion*, more). In humans, for example, pleiotropic alleles are responsible for the multiple symptoms associated with certain hereditary diseases, such as cystic fibrosis and sickle-cell disease, discussed later

(a) The three alleles for the ABO blood groups and their carbohydrates. Each allele codes for an enzyme that may add a specific carbohydrate (designated by the superscript on the allele and shown as a triangle or circle) to red blood cells.

Allele	I^A	I^B	*i*
Carbohydrate	A △	B ○	none

(b) Blood group genotypes and phenotypes. There are six possible genotypes, resulting in four different phenotypes.

Genotype	$I^A I^A$ or $I^A i$	$I^B I^B$ or $I^B i$	$I^A I^B$	*ii*
Red blood cell appearance				
Phenotype (blood group)	A	B	AB	O

▲ **Figure 14.11 Multiple alleles for the ABO blood groups.** The four blood groups result from different combinations of three alleles.

? *Based on the surface carbohydrate phenotype in (b), what are the dominance relationships among the alleles?*

in this chapter. In the garden pea, the gene that determines flower color also affects the color of the coating on the outer surface of the seed, which can be gray or white. Given the intricate molecular and cellular interactions responsible for an organism's development and physiology, it isn't surprising that a single gene can affect a number of characteristics.

Extending Mendelian Genetics for Two or More Genes

Dominance relationships, multiple alleles, and pleiotropy all have to do with the effects of the alleles of a single gene. We now consider two situations in which two or more genes are involved in determining a particular phenotype: epistasis, where one gene affects the phenotype of another because the two gene products interact; and polygenic inheritance, where multiple genes independently affect a single trait.

Epistasis

In **epistasis** (from the Greek for "standing upon"), the phenotypic expression of a gene at one locus alters that of a gene at a second locus. An example will help clarify this concept. In Labrador retrievers (commonly called "Labs"), black coat color is dominant to brown. Let's designate B and b as the two alleles for this character. For a Lab to have brown fur, its genotype must be bb; these dogs are called chocolate Labs. But there is more to the story. A second gene determines whether or not pigment will be deposited in the hair. The dominant allele, symbolized by E, results in the deposition of either black or brown pigment, depending on the genotype at the first locus. But if the Lab is homozygous recessive for the second locus (ee), then the coat is yellow, regardless of the genotype at the black/brown locus (so-called golden Labs). In this case, the gene for pigment deposition (E/e) is said to be epistatic to the gene that codes for black or brown pigment (B/b).

What happens if we mate black Labs that are heterozygous for both genes ($BbEe$)? Although the two genes affect the same phenotypic character (coat color), they follow the law of independent assortment. Thus, our breeding experiment represents an F_1 dihybrid cross, like those that produced a 9:3:3:1 ratio in Mendel's experiments. We can use a Punnett square to represent the genotypes of the F_2 offspring (Figure 14.12). As a result of epistasis, the phenotypic ratio among the F_2 offspring is 9 black to 3 chocolate to 4 golden Labs. Other types of epistatic interactions produce different ratios, but all are modified versions of 9:3:3:1.

Polygenic Inheritance

Mendel studied characters that could be classified on an either-or basis, such as purple versus white flower color. But many characters, such as human skin color and height, are not one of two discrete characters, but instead vary in the

▲ **Figure 14.12 An example of epistasis.** This Punnett square illustrates the genotypes and phenotypes predicted for offspring of matings between two black Labrador retrievers of genotype $BbEe$. The E/e gene, which is epistatic to the B/b gene coding for hair pigment, controls whether or not pigment of any color will be deposited in the hair.

? *Explain the genetic basis for the difference between the ratio (9:3:4) of phenotypes seen in this cross and that seen in Figure 14.8.*

population in gradations along a continuum. These are called **quantitative characters**. Quantitative variation usually indicates **polygenic inheritance**, an additive effect of two or more genes on a single phenotypic character. (In a way, this is the converse of pleiotropy, where a single gene affects several phenotypic characters.) Height is a good example of polygenic inheritance: A recent study using genomic methods identified at least 180 genes that affect height.

Skin pigmentation in humans is also controlled by many separately inherited genes. Here, we'll simplify the story in order to understand the concept of polygenic inheritance. Let's consider three genes, with a dark-skin allele for each gene (A, B, or C) contributing one "unit" of darkness (also a simplification) to the phenotype and being incompletely dominant to the other allele (a, b, or c). In our model, an $AABBCC$ person would be very dark, while an $aabbcc$ individual would be very light. An $AaBbCc$ person would have skin of an intermediate shade. Because the alleles have a cumulative effect, the genotypes $AaBbCc$ and $AABbcc$ would make the same genetic contribution (three units) to skin darkness. There are seven skin-color phenotypes that could result from a mating between $AaBbCc$ heterozygotes, as shown in **Figure 14.13**. In a large number of such matings, the majority of offspring would be expected to have intermediate phenotypes (skin color in the middle range). You can graph the predictions from the Punnett square in the **Scientific Skills Exercise**. Environmental factors, such as exposure to the sun, also affect the skin-color phenotype.

Nature and Nurture: The Environmental Impact on Phenotype

Another departure from simple Mendelian genetics arises when the phenotype for a character depends on environment as well as genotype. A single tree, locked into its inherited genotype, has leaves that vary in size, shape, and greenness, depending on their exposure to wind and sun. For humans, nutrition influences height, exercise alters build, sun-tanning darkens the skin, and experience improves performance on intelligence tests. Even identical twins, who are genetic equals, accumulate phenotypic differences as a result of their unique experiences.

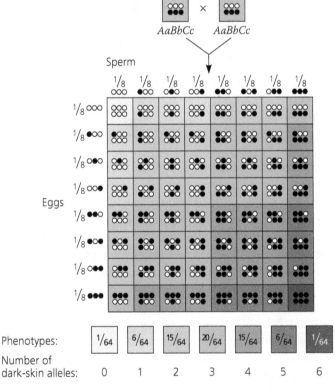

▲ **Figure 14.13 A simplified model for polygenic inheritance of skin color.** In this model, three separately inherited genes affect skin color. The heterozygous individuals (*AaBbCc*) represented by the two rectangles at the top of this figure each carry three dark-skin alleles (black circles, which represent *A*, *B*, or *C*) and three light-skin alleles (white circles, which represent *a*, *b*, or *c*). The Punnett square shows all the possible genetic combinations in gametes and offspring of many hypothetical matings between these heterozygotes. The results are summarized by the phenotypic frequencies (fractions) under the Punnett square. (The phenotypic ratio of the skin colors shown in the boxes is 1:6:15:20:15:6:1.)

▲ **Figure 14.14 The effect of environment on phenotype.** The outcome of a genotype lies within a phenotypic range that depends on the environment in which the genotype is expressed. For example, the acidity and free aluminum content of the soil affect the color range of hydrangea flowers of the same genetic variety. The color ranges from pink (basic soil) to blue-violet (acidic soil), and free aluminum is necessary for bluer colors.

Whether human characteristics are more influenced by genes or the environment—in everyday terms, nature versus nurture—is a debate that we will not attempt to settle here. We can say, however, that a genotype generally is not associated with a rigidly defined phenotype, but rather with a range of phenotypic possibilities due to environmental influences (**Figure 14.14**). For some characters, such as the ABO blood group system, the phenotypic range has no breadth whatsoever; that is, a given genotype mandates a very specific phenotype. Other characteristics, such as a person's blood count of red and white cells, vary quite a bit, depending on such factors as the altitude, the customary level of physical activity, and the presence of infectious agents.

Generally, the phenotypic range is broadest for polygenic characters. Environment contributes to the quantitative nature of these characters, as we have seen in the continuous variation of skin color. Geneticists refer to such characters as **multifactorial**, meaning that many factors, both genetic and environmental, collectively influence phenotype.

A Mendelian View of Heredity and Variation

We have now broadened our view of Mendelian inheritance by exploring degrees of dominance as well as multiple alleles, pleiotropy, epistasis, polygenic inheritance, and the phenotypic impact of the environment. How can we integrate these refinements into a comprehensive theory of Mendelian genetics? The key is to make the transition from the reductionist emphasis on single genes and phenotypic characters to the emergent properties of the organism as a whole, one of the themes of this book.

The term *phenotype* can refer not only to specific characters, such as flower color and blood group, but also to an organism in its entirety—*all* aspects of its physical appearance, internal anatomy, physiology, and behavior. Similarly, the term *genotype* can refer to an organism's entire genetic makeup, not just its alleles for a single genetic locus. In most

Making a Histogram and Analyzing a Distribution Pattern

What Is the Distribution of Phenotypes Among Offspring of Two Parents Who Are Both Heterozygous for Three Additive Genes? Human skin color is a polygenic trait that is determined by the additive effects of many different genes. In this exercise, you will work with a simplified model of skin-color genetics where only three genes are assumed to affect the darkness of skin color and where each gene has two alleles—dark or light (see Figure 14.13). In this model, each dark allele contributes equally to the darkness of skin color, and each pair of alleles segregates independently of each other pair. Using a type of graph called a histogram, you will determine the distribution of phenotypes of offspring with different numbers of dark-skin alleles.

How This Model Is Analyzed To predict the phenotypes of the offspring of parents heterozygous for the three genes in our simplified model, we can use the Punnett square in Figure 14.13. The heterozygous individuals (*AaBbCc*) represented by the two rectangles at the top of this figure each carry three dark-skin alleles (black circles, which represent *A*, *B*, or *C*) and three light-skin alleles (white circles, which represent *a*, *b*, or *c*). The Punnett square shows all the possible genetic combinations in gametes and in offspring of a large number of hypothetical matings between these heterozygotes.

Predictions from the Punnett Square If we assume that each square in the Punnett square represents one offspring of the heterozygous *AaBbCc* parents, then the squares below show the frequencies of all seven possible phenotypes of offspring, with each phenotype having a specific number of dark-skin alleles.

Phenotypes:	$\frac{1}{64}$	$\frac{6}{64}$	$\frac{15}{64}$	$\frac{20}{64}$	$\frac{15}{64}$	$\frac{6}{64}$	$\frac{1}{64}$
Number of dark-skin alleles:	0	1	2	3	4	5	6

Interpret the Data

1. A histogram is a bar graph that shows the distribution of numeric data (here, the number of dark-skin alleles). To make a histogram of the allele distribution, put skin color (as the number of dark-skin alleles) along the *x*-axis and number of offspring (out of 64) with each phenotype on the *y*-axis. There are no gaps in our allele data, so draw the bars next to each other with no space in between.

2. You can see that the skin-color phenotypes are not distributed uniformly. (a) Which phenotype has the highest frequency? Draw a vertical dashed line through that bar. (b) Distributions of values like this one tend to show one of several common patterns. Sketch a rough curve that approximates the values and look at its shape. Is it symmetrically distributed around a central peak value (a "normal distribution," sometimes called a bell curve); is it skewed to one end of the *x*-axis or the other (a "skewed distribution"); or does it show two apparent groups of frequencies (a "bimodal distribution")? Explain the reason for the curve's shape. (It will help to read the text description that supports Figure 14.13.)

3. If one of the three genes were lethal when homozygous recessive, what would happen to the distribution of phenotype frequencies? To determine this, use *bb* as an example of a lethal genotype. Using Figure 14.13, identify offspring where the center circle (the *B/b* gene) in both the top and bottom rows of the square is white, representing the homozygous state *bb*. Because *bb* individuals would not survive, cross out those squares, then count the phenotype frequencies of the surviving offspring according to the number of dark-skin alleles (0–6) and graph the new data. What happens to the shape of the curve compared with the curve in question 2? What does this indicate about the distribution of phenotype frequencies?

(MB) A version of this Scientific Skills Exercise can be assigned in MasteringBiology.

Further Reading R. A. Sturm, A golden age of human pigmentation genetics, *Trends in Genetics* 22:464–468 (2006).

---

cases, a gene's impact on phenotype is affected by other genes and by the environment. In this integrated view of heredity and variation, an organism's phenotype reflects its overall genotype and unique environmental history.

Considering all that can occur in the pathway from genotype to phenotype, it is indeed impressive that Mendel could uncover the fundamental principles governing the transmission of individual genes from parents to offspring. Mendel's two laws, of segregation and of independent assortment, explain heritable variations in terms of alternative forms of genes (hereditary "particles," now known as the alleles of genes) that are passed along, generation after generation, according to simple rules of probability. This theory of inheritance is equally valid for peas, flies, fishes, birds, and human beings—indeed, for any organism with a sexual life cycle. Furthermore, by extending the principles of segregation and independent assortment to help explain such hereditary patterns as epistasis and quantitative characters, we begin to see how broadly Mendelian genetics applies. From Mendel's

abbey garden came a theory of particulate inheritance that anchors modern genetics. In the last section of this chapter, we will apply Mendelian genetics to human inheritance, with emphasis on the transmission of hereditary diseases.

CONCEPT CHECK 14.3

1. *Incomplete dominance* and *epistasis* are both terms that define genetic relationships. What is the most basic distinction between these terms?

2. If a man with type AB blood marries a woman with type O, what blood types would you expect in their children? What fraction would you expect of each type?

3. **WHAT IF?** A rooster with gray feathers and a hen of the same phenotype produce 15 gray, 6 black, and 8 white chicks. What is the simplest explanation for the inheritance of these colors in chickens? What phenotypes would you expect in the offspring of a cross between a gray rooster and a black hen?

Many human traits follow Mendelian patterns of inheritance

Peas are convenient subjects for genetic research, but humans are not. The human generation span is long—about 20 years—and human parents produce many fewer offspring than peas and most other species. Even more important, it wouldn't be ethical to ask pairs of humans to breed so that the phenotypes of their offspring could be analyzed! In spite of these constraints, the study of human genetics continues, spurred on by our desire to understand our own inheritance. New molecular biological techniques have led to many breakthrough discoveries.

Pedigree Analysis

Unable to manipulate the mating patterns of people, geneticists instead analyze the results of matings that have already occurred. They do so by collecting information about a family's history for a particular trait and assembling this information into a family tree describing the traits of parents and children across the generations—the family **pedigree**.

Figure 14.15a shows a three-generation pedigree that traces the occurrence of a pointed contour of the hairline on the forehead. This trait, called a widow's peak, is due to a dominant allele, *W*. Because the widow's-peak allele is dominant, all individuals who lack a widow's peak must be homozygous recessive (*ww*). The two grandparents with widow's peaks must have the *Ww* genotype, since some of their offspring are homozygous recessive. The offspring in the second generation who *do* have widow's peaks must also be heterozygous, because they are the products of *Ww* × *ww* matings. The third generation in this pedigree consists of two sisters. The one who has a widow's peak could be either homozygous (*WW*) or heterozygous (*Ww*), given what we know about the genotypes of her parents (both *Ww*).

Figure 14.15b is a pedigree of the same family, but this time we focus on a recessive trait, attached earlobes. We'll use *f* for the recessive allele and *F* for the dominant allele, which results in free earlobes. As you work your way through the pedigree, notice once again that you can apply what you have learned about Mendelian inheritance to understand the genotypes shown for the family members.

An important application of a pedigree is to help us calculate the probability that a future child will have a particular genotype and phenotype. Suppose that the couple represented in the second generation of Figure 14.15 decides to have one more child. What is the probability that the child will have a widow's peak? This is equivalent to a

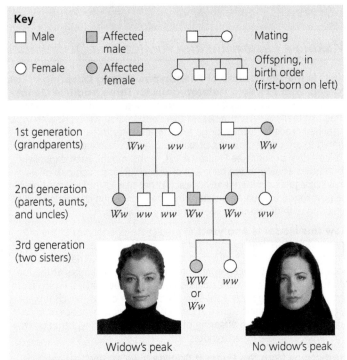

(a) Is a widow's peak a dominant or recessive trait?

Tips for pedigree analysis: Notice in the third generation that the second-born daughter lacks a widow's peak, although both of her parents had the trait. Such a pattern of inheritance supports the hypothesis that the trait is due to a dominant allele. If the trait were due to a *recessive* allele, and both parents had the recessive phenotype, then *all* of their offspring would also have the recessive phenotype.

(b) Is an attached earlobe a dominant or recessive trait?

Tips for pedigree analysis: Notice that the first-born daughter in the third generation has attached earlobes, although both of her parents lack that trait (they have free earlobes). Such a pattern is easily explained if the attached-lobe phenotype is due to a recessive allele. If it were due to a *dominant* allele, then at least one parent would also have had the trait.

▲ **Figure 14.15 Pedigree analysis.** Each of these pedigrees traces a trait through three generations of the same family. The two traits have different inheritance patterns, as shown by the pedigrees.

Mendelian F_1 monohybrid cross ($Ww \times Ww$), and thus the probability that a child will inherit a dominant allele and have a widow's peak is ¾ (¼ WW + ½ Ww). What is the probability that the child will have attached earlobes? Again, we can treat this as a monohybrid cross ($Ff \times Ff$), but this time we want to know the chance that the offspring will be homozygous recessive (ff). That probability is ¼. Finally, what is the chance that the child will have a widow's peak *and* attached earlobes? Assuming that the genes for these two characters are on different chromosomes, the two pairs of alleles will assort independently in this dihybrid cross ($WwFf \times WwFf$). Thus, we can use the multiplication rule: ¾ (chance of widow's peak) × ¼ (chance of attached earlobes) = ³⁄₁₆ (chance of widow's peak and attached earlobes).

Pedigrees are a more serious matter when the alleles in question cause disabling or deadly diseases instead of innocuous human variations such as hairline or earlobe configuration. However, for disorders inherited as simple Mendelian traits, the same techniques of pedigree analysis apply.

Recessively Inherited Disorders

Thousands of genetic disorders are known to be inherited as simple recessive traits. These disorders range in severity from relatively mild, such as albinism (lack of pigmentation, which results in susceptibility to skin cancers and vision problems), to life-threatening, such as cystic fibrosis.

The Behavior of Recessive Alleles

How can we account for the behavior of alleles that cause recessively inherited disorders? Recall that genes code for proteins of specific function. An allele that causes a genetic disorder (let's call it allele *a*) codes for either a malfunctioning protein or no protein at all. In the case of disorders classified as recessive, heterozygotes (Aa) are typically normal in phenotype because one copy of the normal allele (A) produces a sufficient amount of the specific protein. Thus, a recessively inherited disorder shows up only in the homozygous individuals (aa) who inherit one recessive allele from each parent. Although phenotypically normal with regard to the disorder, heterozygotes may transmit the recessive allele to their offspring and thus are called **carriers**. **Figure 14.16** illustrates these ideas using albinism as an example.

Most people who have recessive disorders are born to parents who are carriers of the disorder but have a normal phenotype, as is the case shown in the Punnett square in Figure 14.16. A mating between two carriers corresponds to a Mendelian F_1 monohybrid cross, so the predicted genotypic ratio for the offspring is 1 AA : 2 Aa : 1 aa. Thus, each child has a ¼ chance of inheriting a double dose of the recessive allele; in the case of albinism, such a child will be albino. From the genotypic ratio, we also can see that out of three offspring with the *normal* phenotype (one AA plus

▲ **Figure 14.16 Albinism: a recessive trait.** One of the two sisters shown here has normal coloration; the other is albino. Most recessive homozygotes are born to parents who are carriers of the disorder but themselves have a normal phenotype, the case shown in the Punnett square.

[?] *What is the probability that the sister with normal coloration is a carrier of the albinism allele?*

two Aa), two are predicted to be heterozygous carriers, a ⅔ chance. Recessive homozygotes could also result from $Aa \times aa$ and $aa \times aa$ matings, but if the disorder is lethal before reproductive age or results in sterility (neither of which is true for albinism), no aa individuals will reproduce. Even if recessive homozygotes are able to reproduce, this will occur relatively rarely, since such individuals account for a much smaller percentage of the population than heterozygous carriers.

In general, genetic disorders are not evenly distributed among all groups of people. For example, the incidence of Tay-Sachs disease, which we described earlier in this chapter, is disproportionately high among Ashkenazic Jews, Jewish people whose ancestors lived in central Europe. In that population, Tay-Sachs disease occurs in one out of 3,600 births, an incidence about 100 times greater than that among non-Jews or Mediterranean (Sephardic) Jews. This uneven distribution results from the different genetic histories of the world's peoples during less technological times, when populations were more geographically (and hence genetically) isolated.

When a disease-causing recessive allele is rare, it is relatively unlikely that two carriers of the same harmful allele will meet and mate. The probability of passing on recessive traits increases greatly, however, if the man and woman are close relatives (for example, siblings or first cousins). This is because people with recent common ancestors are more likely to carry the same recessive alleles than are unrelated people. Thus, these consanguineous ("same blood") matings, indicated in pedigrees by double lines, are more likely to produce offspring homozygous for recessive traits—including harmful ones. Such effects can be observed in many types of domesticated and zoo animals that have become inbred.

There is debate among geneticists about the extent to which human consanguinity increases the risk of inherited diseases. Many deleterious alleles have such severe effects that a homozygous embryo spontaneously aborts long before birth. Still, most societies and cultures have laws or taboos forbidding marriages between close relatives. These rules may have evolved out of empirical observation that in most populations, stillbirths and birth defects are more common when parents are closely related. Social and economic factors have also influenced the development of customs and laws against consanguineous marriages.

Cystic Fibrosis

The most common lethal genetic disease in the United States is **cystic fibrosis**, which strikes one out of every 2,500 people of European descent but is much rarer in other groups. Among people of European descent, one out of 25 (4%) are carriers of the cystic fibrosis allele. The normal allele for this gene codes for a membrane protein that functions in the transport of chloride ions between certain cells and the extracellular fluid. These chloride transport channels are defective or absent in the plasma membranes of children who inherit two recessive alleles for cystic fibrosis. The result is an abnormally high concentration of extracellular chloride, which causes the mucus that coats certain cells to become thicker and stickier than normal. The mucus builds up in the pancreas, lungs, digestive tract, and other organs, leading to multiple (pleiotropic) effects, including poor absorption of nutrients from the intestines, chronic bronchitis, and recurrent bacterial infections.

Untreated, cystic fibrosis can cause death by the age of 5. Daily doses of antibiotics to stop infection, gentle pounding on the chest to clear mucus from clogged airways, and other therapies can prolong life. In the United States, more than half of those with cystic fibrosis now survive into their 30s and beyond.

Sickle-Cell Disease: A Genetic Disorder with Evolutionary Implications

EVOLUTION   The most common inherited disorder among people of African descent is **sickle-cell disease**, which affects one out of 400 African-Americans. Sickle-cell disease is caused by the substitution of a single amino acid in the hemoglobin protein of red blood cells; in homozygous individuals, all hemoglobin is of the sickle-cell (abnormal) variety. When the oxygen content of an affected individual's blood is low (at high altitudes or under physical stress, for instance), the sickle-cell hemoglobin proteins aggregate into long fibers that deform the red cells into a sickle shape (see Figure 5.19). Sickled cells may clump and clog small blood vessels, often leading to other symptoms throughout the body, including physical weakness, pain, organ damage, and even paralysis. Regular blood transfusions can ward off brain damage in children with sickle-cell disease, and new drugs can help prevent or treat other problems, but there is currently no widely available cure.

Although two sickle-cell alleles are necessary for an individual to manifest full-blown sickle-cell disease, the presence of one sickle-cell allele can affect the phenotype. Thus, at the organismal level, the normal allele is incompletely dominant to the sickle-cell allele (Figure 14.17). At the molecular level, the two alleles are codominant; both normal and abnormal (sickle-cell) hemoglobins are made in heterozygotes (carriers), who are said to have *sickle-cell trait*. Heterozygotes are usually healthy but may suffer some symptoms during long periods of reduced blood oxygen.

About one out of ten African-Americans have sickle-cell trait, an unusually high frequency of heterozygotes for an allele with severe detrimental effects in homozygotes. Why haven't evolutionary processes resulted in the disappearance of this allele among this population? One explanation is that having a single copy of the sickle-cell allele reduces the frequency and severity of malaria attacks, especially among young children. The malaria parasite spends part of its life cycle in red blood cells, and the presence of even heterozygous amounts of sickle-cell hemoglobin results in lower parasite densities and hence reduced malaria symptoms. Thus, in tropical Africa, where infection with the

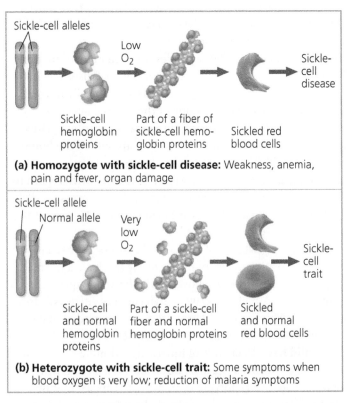

(a) Homozygote with sickle-cell disease: Weakness, anemia, pain and fever, organ damage

Sickle-cell alleles
Low O₂
Sickle-cell hemoglobin proteins
Part of a fiber of sickle-cell hemoglobin proteins
Sickled red blood cells
Sickle-cell disease

(b) Heterozygote with sickle-cell trait: Some symptoms when blood oxygen is very low; reduction of malaria symptoms

Sickle-cell allele
Normal allele
Very low O₂
Sickle-cell and normal hemoglobin proteins
Part of a sickle-cell fiber and normal hemoglobin proteins
Sickled and normal red blood cells
Sickle-cell trait

▲ Figure 14.17 **Sickle-cell disease and sickle-cell trait.**

malaria parasite is common, the sickle-cell allele confers an advantage to heterozygotes even though it is harmful in the homozygous state. The relatively high frequency of African-Americans with sickle-cell trait is a vestige of their African roots.

Dominantly Inherited Disorders

Although many harmful alleles are recessive, a number of human disorders are due to dominant alleles. One example is *achondroplasia*, a form of dwarfism that occurs in one of every 25,000 people. Heterozygous individuals have the dwarf phenotype (Figure 14.18). Therefore, all people who are not achondroplastic dwarfs—99.99% of the population— are homozygous for the recessive allele. Like the presence of extra fingers or toes mentioned earlier, achondroplasia is a trait for which the recessive allele is much more prevalent than the corresponding dominant allele.

Dominant alleles that cause a lethal disease are much less common than recessive alleles that have lethal effects. All lethal alleles arise by mutations (changes to the DNA) in cells that produce sperm or eggs; presumably, such mutations are equally likely to be recessive or dominant. A lethal recessive allele can be passed from one generation to the next by heterozygous carriers because the carriers themselves have normal phenotypes. A lethal dominant allele, however, often causes the death of afflicted individuals before they can mature and reproduce, so the allele is not passed on to future generations.

In cases of late-onset diseases, however, a lethal dominant allele may be passed on. If symptoms first appear after reproductive age, the individual may already have transmitted the allele to his or her children. For example,

a degenerative disease of the nervous system, called **Huntington's disease**, is caused by a lethal dominant allele that has no obvious phenotypic effect until the individual is about 35 to 45 years old. Once the deterioration of the nervous system begins, it is irreversible and inevitably fatal. As with other dominant traits, a child born to a parent with the Huntington's disease allele has a 50% chance of inheriting the allele and the disorder (see the Punnett square in Figure 14.18). In the United States, this disease afflicts about one in 10,000 people.

At one time, the onset of symptoms was the only way to know if a person had inherited the Huntington's allele, but this is no longer the case. By analyzing DNA samples from a large family with a high incidence of the disorder, geneticists tracked the Huntington's allele to a locus near the tip of chromosome 4, and the gene was sequenced in 1993. This information led to the development of a test that could detect the presence of the Huntington's allele in an individual's genome. The availability of this test poses an agonizing dilemma for those with a family history of Huntington's disease. Some individuals may want to be tested for this disease, whereas others may decide it would be too stressful to find out whether they carry the allele.

Multifactorial Disorders

The hereditary diseases we have discussed so far are sometimes described as simple Mendelian disorders because they result from abnormality of one or both alleles at a single genetic locus. Many more people are susceptible to diseases that have a multifactorial basis—a genetic component plus a significant environmental influence. Heart disease, diabetes, cancer, alcoholism, certain mental illnesses such as schizophrenia and bipolar disorder, and many other diseases are multifactorial. In these cases, the hereditary component is polygenic. For example, many genes affect cardiovascular health, making some of us more prone than others to heart attacks and strokes. No matter what our genotype, however, our lifestyle has a tremendous effect on phenotype for cardiovascular health and other multifactorial characters. Exercise, a healthful diet, abstinence from smoking, and an ability to handle stressful situations all reduce our risk of heart disease and some types of cancer.

Genetic Testing and Counseling

Avoiding simple Mendelian disorders is possible when the risk of a particular genetic disorder can be assessed before a child is conceived or during the early stages of the pregnancy. Many hospitals have genetic counselors who can provide information to prospective parents concerned about a family history for a specific disease. Fetal and newborn testing can also reveal genetic disorders.

▲ Figure 14.18 **Achondroplasia: a dominant trait.** Dr. Michael C. Ain has achondroplasia, a form of dwarfism caused by a dominant allele. This has inspired his work: He is a specialist in the repair of bone defects caused by achondroplasia and other disorders. The dominant allele (*D*) might have arisen as a mutation in the egg or sperm of a parent or could have been inherited from an affected parent, as shown for an affected father in the Punnett square.

Counseling Based on Mendelian Genetics and Probability Rules

Consider the case of a hypothetical couple, John and Carol. Each had a brother who died from the same recessively inherited lethal disease. Before conceiving their first child, John and Carol seek genetic counseling to determine the risk of having a child with the disease. From the information about their brothers, we know that both parents of John and both parents of Carol must have been carriers of the recessive allele. Thus, John and Carol are both products of $Aa \times Aa$ crosses, where a symbolizes the allele that causes this particular disease. We also know that John and Carol are not homozygous recessive (aa), because they do not have the disease. Therefore, their genotypes are either AA or Aa.

Given a genotypic ratio of $1 \, AA : 2 \, Aa : 1 \, aa$ for offspring of an $Aa \times Aa$ cross, John and Carol each have a $\frac{2}{3}$ chance of being carriers (Aa). According to the rule of multiplication, the overall probability of their firstborn having the disorder is $\frac{2}{3}$ (the chance that John is a carrier) times $\frac{2}{3}$ (the chance that Carol is a carrier) times $\frac{1}{4}$ (the chance of two carriers having a child with the disease), which equals $\frac{1}{9}$. Suppose that Carol and John decide to have a child—after all, there is an $\frac{8}{9}$ chance that their baby will not have the disorder. If, despite these odds, their child is born with the disease, then we would know that *both* John and Carol are, in fact, carriers (Aa genotype). If both John and Carol are carriers, there is a $\frac{1}{4}$ chance that any subsequent child this couple has will have the disease. The probability is higher for subsequent children because the diagnosis of the disease in the first child established that both parents are carriers, not because the genotype of the first child affects in any way that of future children.

When we use Mendel's laws to predict possible outcomes of matings, it is important to remember that each child represents an independent event in the sense that its genotype is unaffected by the genotypes of older siblings. Suppose that John and Carol have three more children, and *all three* have the hypothetical hereditary disease. There is only one chance in 64 ($\frac{1}{4} \times \frac{1}{4} \times \frac{1}{4}$) that such an outcome will occur. Despite this run of misfortune, the chance that still another child of this couple will have the disease remains $\frac{1}{4}$.

Tests for Identifying Carriers

Most children with recessive disorders are born to parents with normal phenotypes. The key to accurately assessing the genetic risk for a particular disease is therefore to find out whether the prospective parents are heterozygous carriers of the recessive allele. For an increasing number of heritable disorders, tests are available that can distinguish individuals of normal phenotype who are dominant homozygotes from those who are heterozygous carriers. There are now tests that can identify carriers of the alleles for Tay-Sachs disease, sickle-cell disease, and the most common form of cystic fibrosis.

These tests for identifying carriers enable people with family histories of genetic disorders to make informed decisions about having children, but raise other issues. Could carriers be denied health or life insurance or lose the jobs providing those benefits, even though they themselves are healthy? The Genetic Information Nondiscrimination Act, signed into law in the United States in 2008, allays these concerns by prohibiting discrimination in employment or insurance coverage based on genetic test results. A question that remains is whether sufficient genetic counseling is available to help large numbers of individuals understand their genetic test results. Even when test results are clearly understood, affected individuals may still face difficult decisions. Advances in biotechnology offer the potential to reduce human suffering, but along with them come ethical issues that require conscientious deliberation.

Fetal Testing

Suppose a couple expecting a child learns that they are both carriers of the Tay-Sachs allele. In the 14th–16th week of pregnancy, tests performed along with a technique called **amniocentesis** can determine whether the developing fetus has Tay-Sachs disease **(Figure 14.19a)**. In this procedure, a physician inserts a needle into the uterus and extracts about 10 mL of amniotic fluid, the liquid that bathes the fetus. Some genetic disorders can be detected from the presence of certain molecules in the amniotic fluid itself. Tests for other disorders, including Tay-Sachs disease, are performed on the DNA of cells cultured in the laboratory, descendants of fetal cells sloughed off into the amniotic fluid. A karyotype of these cultured cells can also identify certain chromosomal defects (see Figure 13.3).

In an alternative technique called **chorionic villus sampling (CVS)**, a physician inserts a narrow tube through the cervix into the uterus and suctions out a tiny sample of tissue from the placenta, the organ that transmits nutrients and fetal wastes between the fetus and the mother **(Figure 14.19b)**. The cells of the chorionic villi of the placenta, the portion sampled, are derived from the fetus and have the same genotype and DNA sequence as the new individual. These cells are proliferating rapidly enough to allow karyotyping to be carried out immediately. This rapid analysis represents an advantage over amniocentesis, in which the cells must be cultured for several weeks before karyotyping. Another advantage of CVS is that it can be performed as early as the 8th–10th week of pregnancy.

Medical scientists have also developed methods for isolating fetal cells, or even fetal DNA, that have escaped into the mother's blood. Although very few are present,

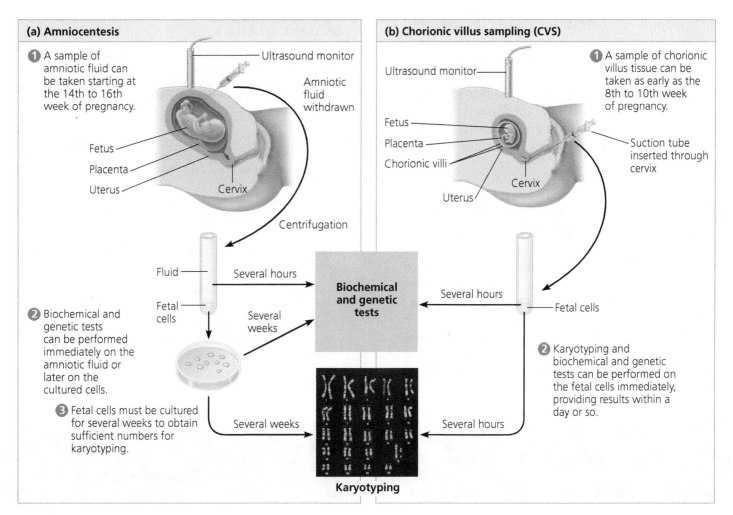

(a) Amniocentesis

① A sample of amniotic fluid can be taken starting at the 14th to 16th week of pregnancy.

Ultrasound monitor

Amniotic fluid withdrawn

Fetus

Placenta

Uterus

Cervix

Centrifugation

Fluid

Several hours

Fetal cells

Several weeks

② Biochemical and genetic tests can be performed immediately on the amniotic fluid or later on the cultured cells.

③ Fetal cells must be cultured for several weeks to obtain sufficient numbers for karyotyping.

Several weeks

Biochemical and genetic tests

(b) Chorionic villus sampling (CVS)

Ultrasound monitor

① A sample of chorionic villus tissue can be taken as early as the 8th to 10th week of pregnancy.

Fetus

Placenta

Chorionic villi

Cervix

Uterus

Suction tube inserted through cervix

Several hours

Fetal cells

② Karyotyping and biochemical and genetic tests can be performed on the fetal cells immediately, providing results within a day or so.

Several hours

Several hours

Karyotyping

▲ **Figure 14.19 Testing a fetus for genetic disorders.** Biochemical tests may detect substances associated with particular disorders, and genetic testing can detect many genetic abnormalities. Karyotyping shows whether the chromosomes of the fetus are normal in number and appearance.

the cells can be cultured and tested, and the fetal DNA can be analyzed. In 2012, researchers were able to analyze the entire genome of a fetus, comparing sequences of samples obtained from both parents and fetal DNA found in the mother's blood. This noninvasive method will likely become the method of choice in diagnosing most genetically based disorders.

Imaging techniques allow a physician to examine a fetus directly for major anatomical abnormalities that might not show up in genetic tests. In the *ultrasound* technique, reflected sound waves are used to produce an image of the fetus by a simple noninvasive procedure. In *fetoscopy*, a needle-thin tube containing a viewing scope and fiber optics (to transmit light) is inserted into the uterus.

Ultrasound and isolation of fetal cells or DNA from maternal blood pose no known risk to either mother or fetus, while the other procedures can cause complications in a small percentage of cases. Amniocentesis or CVS for

diagnostic testing is generally offered to women over age 35, due to their increased risk of bearing a child with Down syndrome, and may also be offered to younger women if there are known concerns. If the fetal tests reveal a serious disorder like Tay-Sachs, the parents face the difficult choice of either terminating the pregnancy or preparing to care for a child with a genetic disorder, one that might even be fatal. Parental and fetal screening for Tay-Sachs alleles done since 1980 has reduced the number of children born with this incurable disease by 90%.

Newborn Screening

Some genetic disorders can be detected at birth by simple biochemical tests that are now routinely performed in most hospitals in the United States. One common screening program is for phenylketonuria (PKU), a recessively inherited disorder that occurs in about one out of every 10,000–15,000 births in the United States. Children with this disease cannot properly metabolize the amino acid phenylalanine. This compound and its by-product, phenylpyruvate, can accumulate to toxic levels in the blood, causing severe intellectual disability (mental retardation). However, if PKU is detected in the newborn, a special diet low in phenylalanine will usually allow normal development. (Among many other substances, this diet excludes the artificial sweetener aspartame, which contains phenylalanine.) Unfortunately, few other genetic disorders are treatable at present.

Fetal and newborn screening for serious inherited diseases, tests for identifying carriers, and genetic counseling all rely on the Mendelian model of inheritance. We owe the "gene idea"—the concept of heritable factors transmitted according to simple rules of chance—to the elegant quantitative experiments of Gregor Mendel. The importance of his discoveries was overlooked by most biologists until early in the 20th century, decades after he reported his findings. In the next chapter, you will learn how Mendel's laws have their physical basis in the behavior of chromosomes during sexual life cycles and how the synthesis of Mendelian genetics and a chromosome theory of inheritance catalyzed progress in genetics.

CONCEPT CHECK 14.4

1. Beth and Tom each have a sibling with cystic fibrosis, but neither Beth nor Tom nor any of their parents have the disease. Calculate the probability that if this couple has a child, the child will have cystic fibrosis. What would be the probability if a test revealed that Tom is a carrier but Beth is not? Explain your answers.

2. **MAKE CONNECTIONS** Explain how the change of a single amino acid in hemoglobin leads to the aggregation of hemoglobin into long fibers. (Review Figures 5.14, 5.18, and 5.19.)

3. Joan was born with six toes on each foot, a dominant trait called polydactyly. Two of her five siblings and her mother, but not her father, also have extra digits. What is Joan's genotype for the number-of-digits character? Explain your answer. Use D and d to symbolize the alleles for this character.

4. **MAKE CONNECTIONS** In Table 14.1, note the phenotypic ratio of the dominant to recessive trait in the F_2 generation for the monohybrid cross involving flower color. Then determine the phenotypic ratio for the offspring of the second-generation couple in Figure 14.15b. What accounts for the difference in the two ratios?

14 Chapter Review

SUMMARY OF KEY CONCEPTS

CONCEPT 14.1

Mendel used the scientific approach to identify two laws of inheritance (pp. 270–276)

- Gregor Mendel formulated a theory of inheritance based on experiments with garden peas, proposing that parents pass on to their offspring discrete genes that retain their identity through generations. This theory includes two "laws."
- The **law of segregation** states that genes have alternative forms, or **alleles**. In a diploid organism, the two alleles of a gene segregate (separate) during meiosis and gamete formation; each sperm or egg carries only one allele of each pair. This law explains the 3:1 ratio of F_2 phenotypes observed when **monohybrids** self-pollinate. Each organism inherits one allele for each gene from each parent. In **heterozygotes**, the two alleles are different; expression of the **dominant allele** masks the phenotypic effect of the **recessive allele**. **Homozygotes** have identical alleles of a given gene and are **true-breeding**.
- The **law of independent assortment** states that the pair of alleles for a given gene segregates into gametes independently of the pair of alleles for any other gene. In a cross between **dihybrids** (individuals heterozygous for two genes), the offspring have four phenotypes in a 9:3:3:1 ratio.

? *When Mendel did crosses of true-breeding purple- and white-flowered pea plants, the white-flowered trait disappeared from the F_1 generation but reappeared in the F_2 generation. Use genetic terms to explain why that happened.*

CONCEPT 14.2

Probability laws govern Mendelian inheritance (pp. 276–278)

Rr
Segregation of alleles into sperm

Sperm

$1/2$ $1/2$

- The **multiplication rule** states that the probability of two or more events occurring together is equal to the product of the individual probabilities of the independent single events. The **addition rule** states that the probability of an event that can occur in two or more independent, mutually exclusive ways is the sum of the individual probabilities.
- The rules of probability can be used to solve complex genetics problems. A dihybrid or other multicharacter cross is equivalent to two or more independent monohybrid crosses occurring simultaneously. In calculating the chances of the various offspring genotypes from such crosses, each character is first considered separately and then the individual probabilities are multiplied.

DRAW IT *Redraw the Punnett square on the right side of Figure 14.8 as two smaller monohybrid Punnett squares, one for each gene. Below each square, list the fractions of each phenotype produced. Use the rule of multiplication to compute the overall fraction of each possible dihybrid phenotype. What is the phenotypic ratio?*

Inheritance patterns are often more complex than predicted by simple Mendelian genetics (pp. 278–283)

- Extensions of Mendelian genetics for a single gene:

Relationship among alleles of a single gene	Description	Example
Complete dominance of one allele	Heterozygous phenotype same as that of homozygous dominant	PP Pp
Incomplete dominance of either allele	Heterozygous phenotype intermediate between the two homozygous phenotypes	$C^R C^R$ $C^R C^W$ $C^W C^W$
Codominance	Both phenotypes expressed in heterozygotes	$I^A I^B$
Multiple alleles	In the population, some genes have more than two alleles	ABO blood group alleles I^A, I^B, i
Pleiotropy	One gene affects multiple phenotypic characters	Sickle-cell disease

- Extensions of Mendelian genetics for two or more genes:

Relationship among two or more genes	Description	Example
Epistasis	The phenotypic expression of one gene affects the expression of another gene	$BbEe \times BbEe$ $9 : 3 : 4$
Polygenic inheritance	A single phenotypic character is affected by two or more genes	$AaBbCc \times AaBbCc$

- The expression of a genotype can be affected by environmental influences, resulting in a range of phenotypes. Polygenic characters that are also influenced by the environment are called **multifactorial** characters.
- An organism's overall phenotype, including its physical appearance, internal anatomy, physiology, and behavior, reflects its overall genotype and unique environmental history. Even in more complex inheritance patterns, Mendel's fundamental laws of segregation and independent assortment still apply.

  ?   *Which of the following are demonstrated by the inheritance patterns of the ABO blood group alleles: complete dominance, incomplete dominance, codominance, multiple alleles, pleiotropy, epistasis, and/or polygenic inheritance? Explain each of your answers.*

Many human traits follow Mendelian patterns of inheritance (pp. 284–290)

- Analysis of family **pedigrees** can be used to deduce the possible genotypes of individuals and make predictions about future offspring. Such predictions are statistical probabilities rather than certainties.

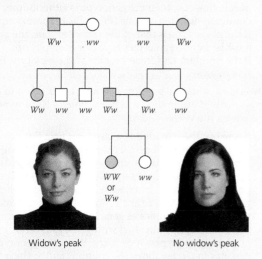

Widow's peak   No widow's peak

- Many genetic disorders are inherited as simple recessive traits. Most affected (homozygous recessive) individuals are children of phenotypically normal, heterozygous **carriers**.
- The sickle-cell allele has probably persisted for evolutionary reasons: Heterozygotes have an advantage because one copy of the sickle-cell allele reduces both the frequency and severity of malaria attacks.

Sickle-cell alleles

Sickle-cell hemoglobin proteins   Low O_2 Part of a fiber of sickle-cell hemoglobin proteins   Sickled red blood cells   Sickle-cell disease

- Lethal dominant alleles are eliminated from the population if affected people die before reproducing. Nonlethal dominant alleles and lethal ones that strike relatively late in life can be inherited in a Mendelian way.
- Many human diseases are multifactorial—that is, they have both genetic and environmental components and do not follow simple Mendelian inheritance patterns.
- Using family histories, genetic counselors help couples determine the probability that their children will have genetic disorders. Genetic testing of prospective parents to reveal whether they are carriers of recessive alleles associated with specific disorders has become widely available. **Amniocentesis** and **chorionic villus sampling** can indicate whether a suspected genetic disorder is present in a fetus. Other genetic tests can be performed after birth.

  ?   *Both members of a couple know that they are carriers of the cystic fibrosis allele. None of their three children has cystic fibrosis, but any one of them might be a carrier. They would like to have a fourth child but are worried that he or she would very likely have the disease, since the first three do not. What would you tell the couple? Would it remove some uncertainty from their prediction if they could find out from genetic tests whether the three children are carriers?*

1. Write down symbols for the alleles. (These may be given in the problem.) When represented by single letters, the dominant allele is uppercase and the recessive is lowercase.

2. Write down the possible genotypes, as determined by the phenotype.
   a. If the phenotype is that of the dominant trait (for example, purple flowers), then the genotype is either homozygous dominant or heterozygous (*PP* or *Pp*, in this example).
   b. If the phenotype is that of the recessive trait, the genotype must be homozygous recessive (for example, *pp*).
   c. If the problem says "true-breeding," the genotype is homozygous.

3. Determine what the problem is asking for. If asked to do a cross, write it out in the form [Genotype] × [Genotype], using the alleles you've decided on.

4. To figure out the outcome of a cross, set up a Punnett square.
   a. Put the gametes of one parent at the top and those of the other on the left. To determine the allele(s) in each gamete for a given genotype, set up a systematic way to list all the possibilities. (Remember, each gamete has one allele of each gene.) Note that there are 2^n possible types of gametes, where n is the number of gene loci that are heterozygous. For example, an individual with genotype *AaBbCc* would produce $2^3 = 8$ types of gametes. Write the genotypes of the gametes in circles above the columns and to the left of the rows.
   b. Fill in the Punnett square as if each possible sperm were fertilizing each possible egg, making all of the possible offspring. In a cross of *AaBbCc* × *AaBbCc*, for example, the Punnett square would have 8 columns and 8 rows, so there are 64 different offspring; you would know the genotype of each and thus the phenotype. Count genotypes and phenotypes to obtain the genotypic and phenotypic ratios. Because the Punnett square is so large, this method is not the most efficient. See tip 5.

5. You can use the rules of probability if the Punnett square would be too big. (For example, see the question at the end of the summary for Concept 14.2 and question 7 below.) You can consider each gene separately (see Concept 14.2).

6. If, instead, the problem gives you the phenotypic ratios of offspring but not the genotypes of the parents in a given cross, the phenotypes can help you deduce the parents' unknown genotypes.
   a. For example, if ½ of the offspring have the recessive phenotype and ½ the dominant, you know that the cross was between a heterozygote and a homozygous recessive.
   b. If the ratio is 3:1, the cross was between two heterozygotes.
   c. If two genes are involved and you see a 9:3:3:1 ratio in the offspring, you know that each parent is heterozygous for both genes. Caution: Don't assume that the reported numbers will exactly equal the predicted ratios. For example, if there are 13 offspring with the dominant trait and 11 with the recessive, assume that the ratio is one dominant to one recessive.

7. For pedigree problems, use the tips in Figure 14.15 and below to determine what kind of trait is involved.
   a. If parents without the trait have offspring with the trait, the trait must be recessive and the parents both carriers.
   b. If the trait is seen in every generation, it is most likely dominant (see the next possibility, though).
   c. If both parents have the trait and the trait is recessive, all offspring will show the trait.
   d. To determine the likely genotype of a certain individual in a pedigree, first label the genotypes of all the family members you can. Even if some of the genotypes are incomplete, label what you do know. For example, if an individual has the dominant phenotype, the genotype must be *AA* or *Aa*; you can write this as *A–*. Try different possibilities to see which fits the results. Use the rules of probability to calculate the probability of each possible genotype being the correct one.

TEST YOUR UNDERSTANDING

LEVEL 1: KNOWLEDGE/COMPREHENSION

1. **DRAW IT** Two pea plants heterozygous for the characters of pod color and pod shape are crossed. Draw a Punnett square to determine the phenotypic ratios of the offspring.

2. A man with type A blood marries a woman with type B blood. Their child has type O blood. What are the genotypes of these three individuals? What genotypes, and in what frequencies, would you expect in future offspring from this marriage?

3. A man has six fingers on each hand and six toes on each foot. His wife and their daughter have the normal number of digits. Remember that extra digits is a dominant trait. What fraction of this couple's children would be expected to have extra digits?

4. **DRAW IT** A pea plant heterozygous for inflated pods (*Ii*) is crossed with a plant homozygous for constricted pods (*ii*). Draw a Punnett square for this cross to predict genotypic and phenotypic ratios. Assume that pollen comes from the *ii* plant.

LEVEL 2: APPLICATION/ANALYSIS

5. Flower position, stem length, and seed shape are three characters that Mendel studied. Each is controlled by an independently assorting gene and has dominant and recessive expression as indicated in Table 14.1. If a plant that is heterozygous for all three characters is allowed to self-fertilize, what proportion of the offspring would you expect to be as follows? (*Note*: Use the rules of probability instead of a huge Punnett square.)
   (a) homozygous for the three dominant traits
   (b) homozygous for the three recessive traits
   (c) heterozygous for all three characters
   (d) homozygous for axial and tall, heterozygous for seed shape

6. Phenylketonuria (PKU) is an inherited disease caused by a recessive allele. If a woman and her husband, who are both carriers, have three children, what is the probability of each of the following?
   (a) All three children are of normal phenotype.
   (b) One or more of the three children have the disease.
   (c) All three children have the disease.
   (d) At least one child is phenotypically normal.

   (*Note:* It will help to remember that the probabilities of all possible outcomes always add up to 1.)

7. The genotype of F_1 individuals in a tetrahybrid cross is *AaBbCcDd*. Assuming independent assortment of these four genes, what are the probabilities that F_2 offspring will have the following genotypes?
   (a) *aabbccdd*   (d) *AaBBccDd*
   (b) *AaBbCcDd*   (e) *AaBBCCdd*
   (c) *AABBCCDD*

8. What is the probability that each of the following pairs of parents will produce the indicated offspring? (Assume independent assortment of all gene pairs.)
   (a) $AABBCC \times aabbcc \rightarrow AaBbCc$
   (b) $AABbCc \times AaBbCc \rightarrow AAbbCC$
   (c) $AaBbCc \times AaBbCc \rightarrow AaBbCc$
   (d) $aaBbCC \times AABbcc \rightarrow AaBbCc$

9. Karen and Steve each have a sibling with sickle-cell disease. Neither Karen nor Steve nor any of their parents have the disease, and none of them have been tested to see if they have the sickle-cell trait. Based on this incomplete information, calculate the probability that if this couple has a child, the child will have sickle-cell disease.

10. In 1981, a stray black cat with unusual rounded, curled-back ears was adopted by a family in California. Hundreds of descendants of the cat have since been born, and cat fanciers hope to develop the curl cat into a show breed. Suppose you owned the first curl cat and wanted to develop a true-breeding variety. How would you determine whether the curl allele is dominant or recessive? How would you obtain true-breeding curl cats? How could you be sure they are true-breeding?

11. In tigers, a recessive allele of a particular gene causes both an absence of fur pigmentation (a white tiger) and a cross-eyed condition. If two phenotypically normal tigers that are heterozygous at this locus are mated, what percentage of their offspring will be cross-eyed? What percentage of cross-eyed tigers will be white?

12. In maize (corn) plants, a dominant allele I inhibits kernel color, while the recessive allele i permits color when homozygous. At a different locus, the dominant allele P causes purple kernel color, while the homozygous recessive genotype pp causes red kernels. If plants heterozygous at both loci are crossed, what will be the phenotypic ratio of the offspring?

13. The pedigree below traces the inheritance of alkaptonuria, a biochemical disorder. Affected individuals, indicated here by the colored circles and squares, are unable to metabolize a substance called alkapton, which colors the urine and stains body tissues. Does alkaptonuria appear to be caused by a dominant allele or by a recessive allele? Fill in the genotypes of the individuals whose genotypes can be deduced. What genotypes are possible for each of the other individuals?

14. Imagine that you are a genetic counselor, and a couple planning to start a family comes to you for information. Charles was married once before, and he and his first wife had a child with cystic fibrosis. The brother of his current wife, Elaine, died of cystic fibrosis. What is the probability that Charles and Elaine will have a baby with cystic fibrosis? (Neither Charles, Elaine, nor their parents have cystic fibrosis.)

LEVEL 3: SYNTHESIS/EVALUATION

15. **EVOLUTION CONNECTION**
    Over the past half century, there has been a trend in the United States and other developed countries for people to marry and start families later in life than did their parents and grandparents. What effects might this trend have on the incidence (frequency) of late-acting dominant lethal alleles in the population?

16. **SCIENTIFIC INQUIRY**
    You are handed a mystery pea plant with tall stems and axial flowers and asked to determine its genotype as quickly as possible. You know that the allele for tall stems (T) is dominant to that for dwarf stems (t) and that the allele for axial flowers (A) is dominant to that for terminal flowers (a).
    (a) What are *all* the possible genotypes for your mystery plant?
    (b) Describe the *one* cross you would do, out in your garden, to determine the exact genotype of your mystery plant.
    (c) While waiting for the results of your cross, you predict the results for each possible genotype listed in part a. How do you do this? Why is this not called "performing a cross"?
    (d) Explain how the results of your cross and your predictions will help you learn the genotype of your mystery plant.

17. **WRITE ABOUT A THEME: INFORMATION**
    The continuity of life is based on heritable information in the form of DNA. In a short essay (100–150 words), explain how the passage of genes from parents to offspring, in the form of particular alleles, ensures perpetuation of parental traits in offspring and, at the same time, genetic variation among offspring. Use genetic terms in your explanation.

18. **SYNTHESIZE YOUR KNOWLEDGE**

Just for fun, imagine that "shirt-striping" is a phenotypic character caused by a single gene. Make up a genetic explanation for the appearance of the family in the above photograph, consistent with their "shirt phenotypes." Include in your answer the presumed allele combinations for "shirt-striping" in each family member. What is the inheritance pattern shown by the child?

MasteringBiology®

Students Go to **MasteringBiology** for assignments, the eText, and the Study Area with practice tests, animations, and activities.

Instructors Go to **MasteringBiology** for automatically graded tutorials and questions that you can assign to your students, plus Instructor Resources.

15

The Chromosomal Basis of Inheritance

▲ Figure 15.1 **Where are Mendel's hereditary factors located in the cell?**

Locating Genes Along Chromosomes

Today, we know that genes—Mendel's "factors"—are segments of DNA located along chromosomes. We can see the location of a particular gene by tagging chromosomes with a fluorescent dye that highlights that gene. For example, the two yellow spots in **Figure 15.1** mark a specific gene on human chromosome 6. (The chromosome has duplicated, so the allele on that chromosome is present as two copies, one per sister chromatid.) However, Gregor Mendel's "hereditary factors" were purely an abstract concept when he proposed their existence in 1860. At that time, no cellular structures had been identified that could house these imaginary units, and most biologists were skeptical about Mendel's proposed laws of inheritance.

Using improved techniques of microscopy, cytologists worked out the process of mitosis in 1875 (see the drawing at the lower left) and meiosis in the 1890s. Cytology and genetics converged as biologists began to see parallels between the behavior of Mendel's proposed hereditary factors during sexual life cycles and the behavior of chromosomes: As shown in **Figure 15.2**, chromosomes and genes are both present in pairs in diploid cells, and homologous chromosomes separate and alleles segregate during the process of meiosis. Furthermore, after meiosis, fertilization restores the paired condition for both chromosomes and genes.

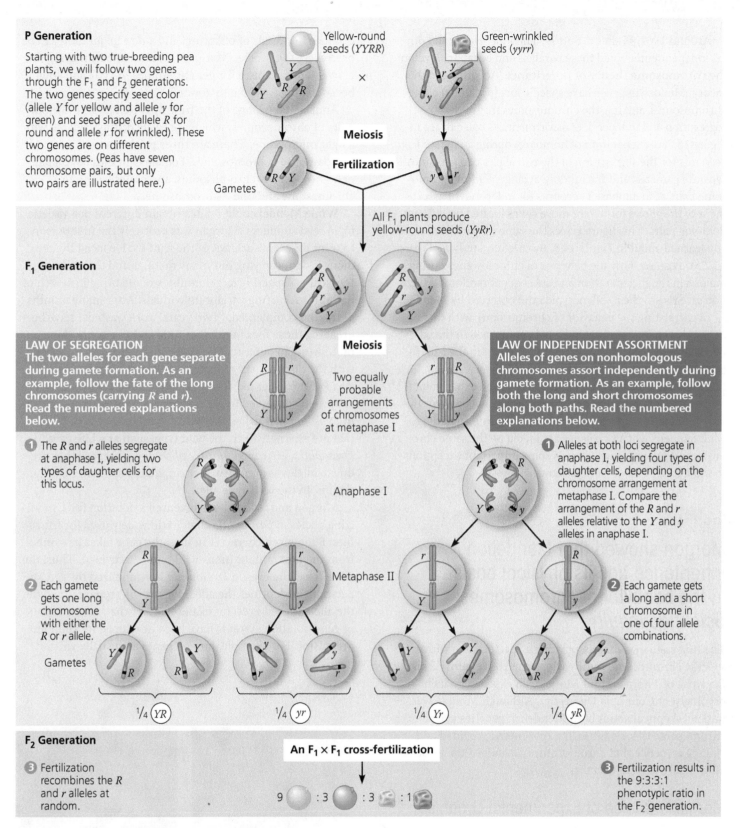

P Generation

Starting with two true-breeding pea plants, we will follow two genes through the F_1 and F_2 generations. The two genes specify seed color (allele *Y* for yellow and allele *y* for green) and seed shape (allele *R* for round and allele *r* for wrinkled). These two genes are on different chromosomes. (Peas have seven chromosome pairs, but only two pairs are illustrated here.)

Yellow-round seeds (*YYRR*)

×

Green-wrinkled seeds (*yyrr*)

Meiosis

Fertilization

Gametes

All F_1 plants produce yellow-round seeds (*YyRr*).

F_1 Generation

LAW OF SEGREGATION
The two alleles for each gene separate during gamete formation. As an example, follow the fate of the long chromosomes (carrying *R* and *r*). Read the numbered explanations below.

Meiosis

Two equally probable arrangements of chromosomes at metaphase I

LAW OF INDEPENDENT ASSORTMENT
Alleles of genes on nonhomologous chromosomes assort independently during gamete formation. As an example, follow both the long and short chromosomes along both paths. Read the numbered explanations below.

1 The *R* and *r* alleles segregate at anaphase I, yielding two types of daughter cells for this locus.

Anaphase I

1 Alleles at both loci segregate in anaphase I, yielding four types of daughter cells, depending on the chromosome arrangement at metaphase I. Compare the arrangement of the *R* and *r* alleles relative to the *Y* and *y* alleles in anaphase I.

Metaphase II

2 Each gamete gets one long chromosome with either the *R* or *r* allele.

2 Each gamete gets a long and a short chromosome in one of four allele combinations.

Gametes

$^1/_4$ (YR) $^1/_4$ (yr) $^1/_4$ (Yr) $^1/_4$ (yR)

F_2 Generation

An F_1 × F_1 cross-fertilization

3 Fertilization recombines the *R* and *r* alleles at random.

9 : 3 : 3 : 1

3 Fertilization results in the 9:3:3:1 phenotypic ratio in the F_2 generation.

▲ **Figure 15.2 The chromosomal basis of Mendel's laws.** Here we correlate the results of one of Mendel's dihybrid crosses (see Figure 14.8) with the behavior of chromosomes during meiosis (see Figure 13.8). The arrangement of chromosomes at metaphase I of meiosis and their movement during anaphase I account, respectively, for the independent assortment and segregation of the alleles for seed color and shape. Each cell that undergoes meiosis in an F_1 plant produces two kinds of gametes. If we count the results for all cells, however, each F_1 plant produces equal numbers of all four kinds of gametes because the alternative chromosome arrangements at metaphase I are equally likely.

? *If you crossed an F_1 plant with a plant that was homozygous recessive for both genes (yyrr), how would the phenotypic ratio of the offspring compare with the 9:3:3:1 ratio seen here?*

Around 1902, Walter S. Sutton, Theodor Boveri, and others independently noted these parallels and began to develop the **chromosome theory of inheritance**. According to this theory, Mendelian genes have specific loci (positions) along chromosomes, and it is the chromosomes that undergo segregation and independent assortment. As you can see in Figure 15.2, the separation of homologs during anaphase I accounts for the segregation of the two alleles of a gene into separate gametes, and the random arrangement of chromosome pairs at metaphase I accounts for independent assortment of the alleles for two or more genes located on different homolog pairs. This figure traces the same dihybrid pea cross you learned about in Figure 14.8. By carefully studying Figure 15.2, you can see how the behavior of chromosomes during meiosis in the F_1 generation and subsequent random fertilization give rise to the F_2 phenotypic ratio observed by Mendel.

In correlating the behavior of chromosomes with that of genes, this chapter will extend what you learned in the past two chapters. First, we'll describe evidence from the fruit fly that strongly supported the chromosome theory. (Although this theory made a lot of sense, it still required experimental evidence.) Next, we'll explore the chromosomal basis for the transmission of genes from parents to offspring, including what happens when two genes are linked on the same chromosome. Finally, we will discuss some important exceptions to the standard mode of inheritance.

CONCEPT 15.1

Morgan showed that Mendelian inheritance has its physical basis in the behavior of chromosomes: *Scientific inquiry*

The first solid evidence associating a specific gene with a specific chromosome came early in the 20th century from the work of Thomas Hunt Morgan, an experimental embryologist at Columbia University. Although Morgan was initially skeptical about both Mendelian genetics and the chromosome theory, his early experiments provided convincing evidence that chromosomes are indeed the location of Mendel's heritable factors.

Morgan's Choice of Experimental Organism

Many times in the history of biology, important discoveries have come to those insightful or lucky enough to choose an experimental organism suitable for the research problem being tackled. Mendel chose the garden pea because a number of distinct varieties were available. For his work, Morgan selected a species of fruit fly, *Drosophila melanogaster*, a common insect that feeds on the fungi growing on fruit. Fruit flies are prolific breeders; a single mating will

produce hundreds of offspring, and a new generation can be bred every two weeks. Morgan's laboratory began using this convenient organism for genetic studies in 1907 and soon became known as "the fly room."

Another advantage of the fruit fly is that it has only four pairs of chromosomes, which are easily distinguishable with a light microscope. There are three pairs of autosomes and one pair of sex chromosomes. Female fruit flies have a pair of homologous X chromosomes, and males have one X chromosome and one Y chromosome.

While Mendel could readily obtain different pea varieties from seed suppliers, Morgan was probably the first person to want different varieties of the fruit fly. He faced the tedious task of carrying out many matings and then microscopically inspecting large numbers of offspring in search of naturally occurring variant individuals. After many months of this, he complained, "Two years' work wasted. I have been breeding those flies for all that time and I've got nothing out of it." Morgan persisted, however, and was finally rewarded with the discovery of a single male fly with white eyes instead of the usual red. The phenotype for a character most commonly observed in natural populations, such as red eyes in *Drosophila*, is called the **wild type (Figure 15.3)**. Traits that are alternatives to the wild type, such as white eyes in *Drosophila*, are called *mutant phenotypes* because they are due to alleles assumed to have originated as changes, or mutations, in the wild-type allele.

Morgan and his students invented a notation for symbolizing alleles in *Drosophila* that is still widely used for fruit flies. For a given character in flies, the gene takes its symbol from the first mutant (non–wild type) discovered. Thus, the allele for white eyes in *Drosophila* is symbolized by *w*. A superscript $+$ identifies the allele for the wild-type trait: w^+ for the allele for red eyes, for example. Over the years, a variety of gene notation systems have been developed for different organisms. For example, human genes are usually written

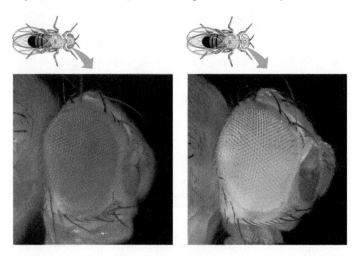

▲ Figure 15.3 **Morgan's first mutant.** Wild-type *Drosophila* flies have red eyes (left). Among his flies, Morgan discovered a mutant male with white eyes (right). This variation made it possible for Morgan to trace a gene for eye color to a specific chromosome (LMs).

in all capitals, such as *HD* for the allele for Huntington's disease.

Correlating Behavior of a Gene's Alleles with Behavior of a Chromosome Pair

Morgan mated his white-eyed male fly with a red-eyed female. All the F_1 offspring had red eyes, suggesting that the wild-type allele is dominant. When Morgan bred the F_1 flies to each other, he observed the classical 3:1 phenotypic ratio among the F_2 offspring. However, there was a surprising additional result: The white-eye trait showed up only in males. All the F_2 females had red eyes, while half the males had red eyes and half had white eyes. Therefore, Morgan concluded that somehow a fly's eye color was linked to its sex. (If the eye-color gene were unrelated to sex, half of the white-eyed flies would have been male and half female.)

Recall that a female fly has two X chromosomes (XX), while a male fly has an X and a Y (XY). The correlation between the trait of white eye color and the male sex of the affected F_2 flies suggested to Morgan that the gene involved in his white-eyed mutant was located exclusively on the X chromosome, with no corresponding allele present on the Y chromosome. His reasoning can be followed in **Figure 15.4**. For a male, a single copy of the mutant allele would confer white eyes; since a male has only one X chromosome, there can be no wild-type allele (w^+) present to mask the recessive allele. However, a female could have white eyes only if both her X chromosomes carried the recessive mutant allele (w). This was impossible for the F_2 females in Morgan's experiment because all the F_1 fathers had red eyes, so each F_2 female received a w^+ allele on the X chromosome inherited from her father.

Morgan's finding of the correlation between a particular trait and an individual's sex provided support for the chromosome theory of inheritance: namely, that a specific gene is carried on a specific chromosome (in this case, an eye-color gene on the X chromosome). In addition, Morgan's work indicated that genes located on a sex chromosome exhibit unique inheritance patterns, which we will discuss in the next section. Recognizing the importance of Morgan's early work, many bright students were attracted to his fly room.

CONCEPT CHECK 15.1

1. Which one of Mendel's laws relates to the inheritance of alleles for a single character? Which law relates to the inheritance of alleles for two characters in a dihybrid cross?

2. **MAKE CONNECTIONS** Review the description of meiosis (see Figure 13.8) and Mendel's laws of segregation and independent assortment (see Concept 14.1). What is the physical basis for each of Mendel's laws?

3. **WHAT IF?** Propose a possible reason that the first naturally occurring mutant fruit fly Morgan saw involved a gene on a sex chromosome.

▼ Figure 15.4 | Inquiry

In a cross between a wild-type female fruit fly and a mutant white-eyed male, what color eyes will the F_1 and F_2 offspring have?

Experiment Thomas Hunt Morgan wanted to analyze the behavior of two alleles of a fruit fly eye-color gene. In crosses similar to those done by Mendel with pea plants, Morgan and his colleagues mated a wild-type (red-eyed) female with a mutant white-eyed male.

Morgan then bred an F_1 red-eyed female to an F_1 red-eyed male to produce the F_2 generation.

Results The F_2 generation showed a typical Mendelian ratio of 3 red-eyed flies : 1 white-eyed fly. However, all white-eyed flies were males; no females displayed the white-eye trait.

Conclusion All F_1 offspring had red eyes, so the mutant white-eye trait (w) must be recessive to the wild-type red-eye trait (w^+). Since the recessive trait—white eyes—was expressed only in males in the F_2 generation, Morgan deduced that this eye-color gene is located on the X chromosome and that there is no corresponding locus on the Y chromosome.

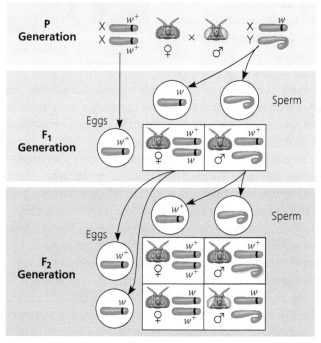

Source: T. H. Morgan, Sex-limited inheritance in *Drosophila, Science* 32:120–122 (1910).

(MB) A related Experimental Inquiry Tutorial can be assigned in MasteringBiology.

WHAT IF? *Suppose this eye-color gene were located on an autosome. Predict the phenotypes (including gender) of the F_2 flies in this hypothetical cross. (Hint: Draw a Punnett square.)*

CONCEPT 15.2

Sex-linked genes exhibit unique patterns of inheritance

As you just learned, Morgan's discovery of a trait (white eyes) that correlated with the sex of flies was a key episode in the development of the chromosome theory of inheritance. Because the identity of the sex chromosomes in an individual could be inferred by observing the sex of the fly, the behavior of the two members of the pair of sex chromosomes could be correlated with the behavior of the two alleles of the eye-color gene. In this section, we'll take a closer look at the role of sex chromosomes in inheritance.

The Chromosomal Basis of Sex

Although the anatomical and physiological differences between women and men are numerous, the chromosomal basis for determining sex is rather simple. Humans and other

mammals have two types of sex chromosomes, designated X and Y. The Y chromosome is much smaller than the X chromosome (Figure 15.5). A person who inherits two X chromosomes, one from each parent, usually develops as a female; a male inherits one X chromosome and one Y chromosome (Figure 15.6a). Short segments at either end

▲ **Figure 15.5 Human sex chromosomes.**

of the Y chromosome are the only regions that are homologous with regions of the X. These homologous regions allow the X and Y chromosomes in males to pair and behave like homologs during meiosis in the testes.

In mammalian testes and ovaries, the two sex chromosomes segregate during meiosis. Each egg receives one X chromosome. In contrast, sperm fall into two categories: Half the sperm cells a male produces receive an X chromosome, and half receive a Y chromosome. We can trace the sex of each offspring to the events of conception: If a sperm cell bearing an X chromosome fertilizes an egg, the zygote is XX, a female; if a sperm cell containing a Y chromosome fertilizes an egg, the zygote is XY, a male (see Figure 15.6a). Thus, sex determination is a matter of chance—a fifty-fifty chance. Note that the mammalian X-Y system isn't the only chromosomal system for determining sex. Figure 15.6b–d illustrates three other systems.

In humans, the anatomical signs of sex begin to emerge when the embryo is about 2 months old. Before then, the rudiments of the gonads are generic—they can develop into either testes or ovaries, depending on whether or not a Y chromosome is present. In 1990, a British research team

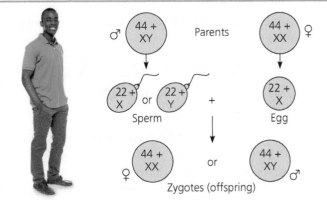

(a) The X-Y system. In mammals, the sex of an offspring depends on whether the sperm cell contains an X chromosome or a Y.

(b) The X-0 system. In grasshoppers, cockroaches, and some other insects, there is only one type of sex chromosome, the X. Females are XX; males have only one sex chromosome (X0). Sex of the offspring is determined by whether the sperm cell contains an X chromosome or no sex chromosome.

(c) The Z-W system. In birds, some fishes, and some insects, the sex chromosomes present in the egg (not the sperm) determine the sex of offspring. The sex chromosomes are designated Z and W. Females are ZW and males are ZZ.

(d) The haplo-diploid system. There are no sex chromosomes in most species of bees and ants. Females develop from fertilized eggs and are thus diploid. Males develop from unfertilized eggs and are haploid; they have no fathers.

▲ **Figure 15.6 Some chromosomal systems of sex determination.** Numerals indicate the number of autosomes in the species pictured. In *Drosophila*, males are XY, but sex depends on the ratio between the number of X chromosomes and the number of autosome sets, not simply on the presence of a Y chromosome.

identified a gene on the Y chromosome required for the development of testes. They named the gene *SRY*, for <u>s</u>ex-determining <u>r</u>egion of <u>Y</u>. In the absence of *SRY*, the gonads develop into ovaries. The biochemical, physiological, and anatomical features that distinguish males and females are complex, and many genes are involved in their development. In fact, *SRY* codes for a protein that regulates other genes.

Researchers have sequenced the human Y chromosome and have identified 78 genes that code for about 25 proteins (some genes are duplicates). About half of these genes are expressed only in the testis, and some are required for normal testicular functioning and the production of normal sperm. A gene located on either sex chromosome is called a **sex-linked gene**; those located on the Y chromosome are called *Y-linked genes*. The Y chromosome is passed along virtually intact from a father to all his sons. Because there are so few Y-linked genes, very few disorders are transferred from father to son on the Y chromosome. A rare example is that in the absence of certain Y-linked genes, an XY individual is male but does not produce normal sperm.

The human X chromosome contains approximately 1,100 genes, which are called **X-linked genes**. The fact that males and females inherit a different number of X chromosomes leads to a pattern of inheritance different from that produced by genes located on autosomes.

Inheritance of X-Linked Genes

While most Y-linked genes help determine sex, the X chromosomes have genes for many characters unrelated to sex. X-linked genes in humans follow the same pattern of inheritance that Morgan observed for the eye-color locus he studied in *Drosophila* (see Figure 15.4). Fathers pass X-linked alleles to all of their daughters but to none of their sons. In contrast, mothers can pass X-linked alleles to both sons and daughters, as shown in **Figure 15.7** for the inheritance of a mild X-linked disorder, red-green color blindness.

If an X-linked trait is due to a recessive allele, a female will express the phenotype only if she is homozygous for that allele. Because males have only one locus, the terms *homozygous* and *heterozygous* lack meaning for describing their X-linked genes; the term *hemizygous* is used in such cases. Any male receiving the recessive allele from his mother will express the trait. For this reason, far more males than females have X-linked recessive disorders. However, even though the chance of a female inheriting a double dose of the mutant allele is much less than the probability of a male inheriting a single dose, there *are* females with X-linked disorders. For instance, color blindness is almost always inherited as an X-linked trait. A color-blind daughter may be born to a color-blind father whose mate is a carrier (see Figure 15.7c). Because the X-linked allele for color blindness is relatively rare, though, the probability that such a man and woman will mate is low.

A number of human X-linked disorders are much more serious than color blindness, such as **Duchenne muscular dystrophy**, which affects about one out of 3,500 males born in the United States. The disease is characterized by a progressive weakening of the muscles and loss of coordination. Affected individuals rarely live past their early 20s. Researchers have traced the disorder to the absence of a key muscle protein called dystrophin and have mapped the gene for this protein to a specific locus on the X chromosome.

Hemophilia is an X-linked recessive disorder defined by the absence of one or more of the proteins required for blood clotting. When a person with hemophilia is injured, bleeding is prolonged because a firm clot is slow to form. Small cuts in the skin are usually not a problem, but bleeding in the muscles or joints can be painful and can lead to serious damage. In the 1800s, hemophilia was widespread among the royal families of Europe. Queen Victoria of

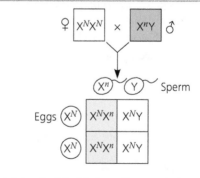

(a) A color-blind father will transmit the mutant allele to all daughters but to no sons. When the mother is a dominant homozygote, the daughters will have the normal phenotype but will be carriers of the mutation.

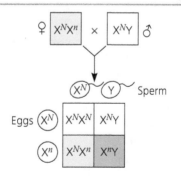

(b) If a carrier mates with a male who has normal color vision, there is a 50% chance that each daughter will be a carrier like her mother and a 50% chance that each son will have the disorder.

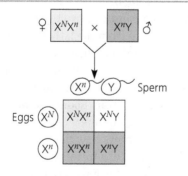

(c) If a carrier mates with a color-blind male, there is a 50% chance that each child born to them will have the disorder, regardless of sex. Daughters who have normal color vision will be carriers, whereas males who have normal color vision will be free of the recessive allele.

▲ **Figure 15.7 The transmission of X-linked recessive traits.** In this diagram, red-green color blindness is used as an example. The superscript N represents the dominant allele for normal color vision carried on the X chromosome, while n represents the recessive allele, which has a mutation for color blindness. White boxes indicate unaffected individuals, light orange boxes indicate carriers, and dark orange boxes indicate color-blind individuals.

? *If a color-blind woman married a man who had normal color vision, what would be the probable phenotypes of their children?*

England is known to have passed the allele to several of her descendants. Subsequent intermarriage with royal family members of other nations, such as Spain and Russia, further spread this X-linked trait, and its incidence is well documented in royal pedigrees. A few years ago, new genomic techniques allowed sequencing of DNA from tiny amounts isolated from the buried remains of royal family members. The genetic basis of the mutation, and how it resulted in a nonfunctional blood-clotting factor, is now understood. Today, people with hemophilia are treated as needed with intravenous injections of the protein that is missing.

X Inactivation in Female Mammals

Female mammals, including human females, inherit two X chromosomes—twice the number inherited by males—so you may wonder whether females make twice as much as males of the proteins encoded by X-linked genes. In fact, almost all of one X chromosome in each cell in female mammals becomes inactivated during early embryonic development. As a result, the cells of females and males have the same effective dose (one copy) of most X-linked genes. The inactive X in each cell of a female condenses into a compact object called a **Barr body** (discovered by Canadian anatomist Murray Barr), which lies along the inside of the nuclear envelope. Most of the genes of the X chromosome that forms the Barr body are not expressed. In the ovaries, however, Barr-body chromosomes are reactivated in the cells that give rise to eggs, such that following meiosis, every female gamete (egg) has an active X.

British geneticist Mary Lyon demonstrated that the selection of which X chromosome will form the Barr body occurs randomly and independently in each embryonic cell present at the time of X inactivation. As a consequence, females consist of a *mosaic* of two types of cells: those with the active X derived from the father and those with the active X derived from the mother. After an X chromosome is inactivated in a particular cell, all mitotic descendants of that cell have the same inactive X. Thus, if a female is heterozygous for a sex-linked trait, about half her cells will express one allele, while the others will express the alternate allele. **Figure 15.8** shows how this mosaicism results in the mottled coloration of a tortoiseshell cat. In humans, mosaicism can be observed in a recessive X-linked mutation that prevents the development of sweat glands. A woman who is heterozygous for this trait has patches of normal skin and patches of skin lacking sweat glands.

Inactivation of an X chromosome involves modification of the DNA and proteins bound to it, called histones, including attachment of methyl groups ($-CH_3$) to DNA nucleotides. A particular region of each X chromosome contains several genes involved in the inactivation process. The two regions, one on each X chromosome, associate briefly with each other in each cell at an early stage of embryonic

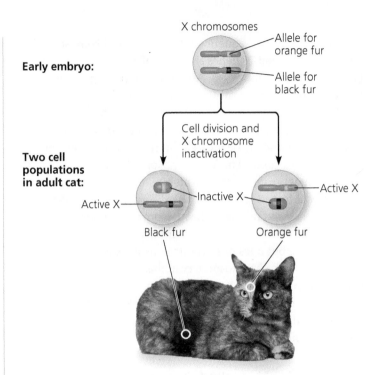

▲ **Figure 15.8 X inactivation and the tortoiseshell cat.** The tortoiseshell gene is on the X chromosome, and the tortoiseshell phenotype requires the presence of two different alleles, one for orange fur and one for black fur. Normally, only females can have both alleles, because only they have two X chromosomes. If a female cat is heterozygous for the tortoiseshell gene, she is tortoiseshell. Orange patches are formed by populations of cells in which the X chromosome with the orange allele is active; black patches have cells in which the X chromosome with the black allele is active. ("Calico" cats also have white areas, which are determined by another gene.)

development. Then one of the genes, called *XIST* (for <u>X</u>-<u>i</u>nactive <u>s</u>pecific <u>t</u>ranscript) becomes active *only* on the chromosome that will become the Barr body. Multiple copies of the RNA product of this gene apparently attach to the X chromosome on which they are made, eventually almost covering it. Interaction of this RNA with the chromosome initiates X inactivation, and the RNA products of other nearby genes help to regulate the process.

CONCEPT CHECK 15.2

1. A white-eyed female *Drosophila* is mated with a red-eyed (wild-type) male, the reciprocal cross of the one shown in Figure 15.4. What phenotypes and genotypes do you predict for the offspring?

2. Neither Tim nor Rhoda has Duchenne muscular dystrophy, but their firstborn son does. What is the probability that a second child will have the disease? What is the probability if the second child is a boy? A girl?

3. MAKE CONNECTIONS Consider what you learned about dominant and recessive alleles in Concept 14.1. If a disorder were caused by a dominant X-linked allele, how would the inheritance pattern differ from what we see for recessive X-linked disorders?

Linked genes tend to be inherited together because they are located near each other on the same chromosome

The number of genes in a cell is far greater than the number of chromosomes; in fact, each chromosome (except the Y) has hundreds or thousands of genes. Genes located near each other on the same chromosome tend to be inherited together in genetic crosses; such genes are said to be genetically linked and are called **linked genes**. When geneticists follow linked genes in breeding experiments, the results deviate from those expected from Mendel's law of independent assortment.

How Linkage Affects Inheritance

To see how linkage between genes affects the inheritance of two different characters, let's examine another of Morgan's *Drosophila* experiments. In this case, the characters are body color and wing size, each with two different phenotypes. Wild-type flies have gray bodies and normal-sized wings. In addition to these flies, Morgan had managed to obtain, through breeding, doubly mutant flies with black bodies and wings much smaller than normal, called vestigial wings. The mutant alleles are recessive to the wild-type alleles, and neither gene is on a sex chromosome. In his investigation of these two genes, Morgan carried out the crosses shown in **Figure 15.9**. The first was a P generation cross to generate F_1 dihybrid flies, and the second was a testcross.

▼ **Figure 15.9** | Inquiry

How does linkage between two genes affect inheritance of characters?

Experiment Morgan wanted to know whether the genes for body color and wing size are genetically linked, and if so, how this affects their inheritance. The alleles for body color are b^+ (gray) and b (black), and those for wing size are vg^+ (normal) and vg (vestigial).

Morgan mated true-breeding P (parental) generation flies—wild-type flies with black, vestigial-winged flies—to produce heterozygous F_1 dihybrids ($b^+ b\ vg^+ vg$), all of which are wild-type in appearance.

He then mated wild-type F_1 dihybrid females with homozygous recessive males. This testcross will reveal the genotype of the eggs made by the dihybrid female.

The testcross male's sperm contributes only recessive alleles, so the phenotype of the offspring reflects the genotype of the female's eggs.

Note: Although only females (with pointed abdomens) are shown, half the offspring in each class would be males (with rounded abdomens).

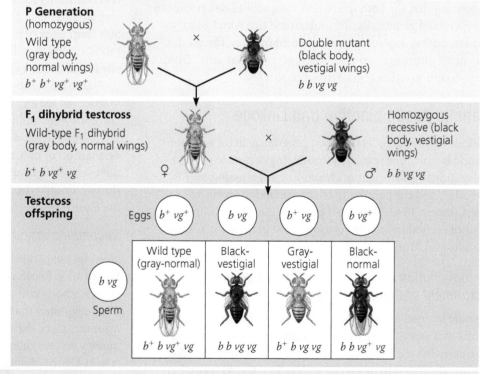

PREDICTED RATIOS

Predicted ratio if genes are located on different chromosomes:	1	:	1	:	1	:	1
Predicted ratio if genes are located on the same chromosome *and* parental alleles are always inherited together:	1	:	1	:	0	:	0
Results Data from Morgan's experiment:	965	:	944	:	206	:	185

Conclusion Since most offspring had a parental (P generation) phenotype, Morgan concluded that the genes for body color and wing size are genetically linked on the same chromosome. However, the production of a relatively small number of offspring with nonparental phenotypes indicated that some mechanism occasionally breaks the linkage between specific alleles of genes on the same chromosome.

Source: T. H. Morgan and C. J. Lynch, The linkage of two factors in *Drosophila* that are not sex-linked, *Biological Bulletin* 23:174–182 (1912).

WHAT IF? *If the parental (P generation) flies had been true-breeding for gray body with vestigial wings and black body with normal wings, which phenotypic class(es) would be largest among the testcross offspring?*

The resulting flies had a much higher proportion of the combinations of traits seen in the P generation flies (called parental phenotypes) than would be expected if the two genes assorted independently. Morgan thus concluded that body color and wing size are usually inherited together in specific (parental) combinations because the genes for these characters are near each other on the same chromosome:

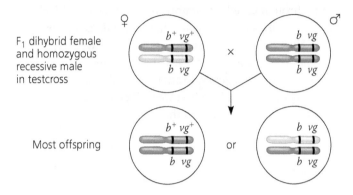

F₁ dihybrid female and homozygous recessive male in testcross

Most offspring

However, as Figure 15.9 shows, both of the combinations of traits not seen in the P generation (called nonparental phenotypes) were also produced in Morgan's experiments, suggesting that the body-color and wing-size alleles are not always linked genetically. To understand this conclusion, we need to further explore **genetic recombination**, the production of offspring with combinations of traits that differ from those found in either P generation parent.*

Genetic Recombination and Linkage

Meiosis and random fertilization generate genetic variation among offspring of sexually reproducing organisms due to independent assortment of chromosomes, crossing over in meiosis I, and the possibility of any sperm fertilizing any egg (see Concept 13.4). Here we'll examine the chromosomal basis of recombination in relation to the genetic findings of Mendel and Morgan.

Recombination of Unlinked Genes: Independent Assortment of Chromosomes

Mendel learned from crosses in which he followed two characters that some offspring have combinations of traits that do not match those of either parent. For example, consider a cross of a dihybrid pea plant with yellow-round seeds, heterozygous for both seed color and seed shape (*YyRr*), with a plant homozygous for both recessive alleles (with green-wrinkled seeds, *yyrr*). (This acts as a testcross because the results will reveal the genotype of the gametes made in the

dihybrid *YyRr* plant.) Let's represent the cross by the following Punnett square:

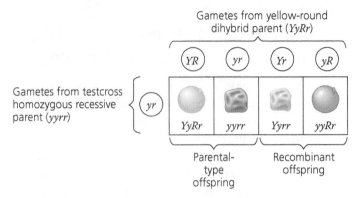

Notice in this Punnett square that one-half of the offspring are expected to inherit a phenotype that matches either of the phenotypes of the P (parental) generation originally crossed to produce the F₁ dihybrid (see Figure 15.2). These matching offspring are called **parental types**. But two nonparental phenotypes are also found among the offspring. Because these offspring have new combinations of seed shape and color, they are called **recombinant types**, or **recombinants** for short. When 50% of all offspring are recombinants, as in this example, geneticists say that there is a 50% frequency of recombination. The predicted phenotypic ratios among the offspring are similar to what Mendel actually found in his *YyRr* × *yyrr* crosses.

A 50% frequency of recombination in such testcrosses is observed for any two genes that are located on different chromosomes and thus cannot be linked. The physical basis of recombination between unlinked genes is the random orientation of homologous chromosomes at metaphase I of meiosis, which leads to the independent assortment of the two unlinked genes (see Figure 13.11 and the question in the Figure 15.2 legend).

Recombination of Linked Genes: Crossing Over

Now, let's explain the results of the *Drosophila* testcross in Figure 15.9. Recall that most of the offspring from the testcross for body color and wing size had parental phenotypes. That suggested that the two genes were on the same chromosome, since the occurrence of parental types with a frequency greater than 50% indicates that the genes are linked. About 17% of offspring, however, were recombinants.

Seeing these results, Morgan proposed that some process must occasionally break the physical connection between specific alleles of genes on the same chromosome. Later experiments showed that this process, now called **crossing over**, accounts for the recombination of linked genes. In crossing over, which occurs while replicated homologous chromosomes are paired during prophase of meiosis I, a set of proteins orchestrates an exchange of corresponding segments of one maternal and one paternal chromatid (see

---

* As you proceed, be sure to keep in mind the distinction between the terms *linked genes* (two or more genes on the same chromosome that tend to be inherited together) and *sex-linked gene* (a single gene on a sex chromosome).

▶ **Figure 15.10 Chromosomal basis for recombination of linked genes.** In these diagrams re-creating the testcross in Figure 15.9, we track chromosomes as well as genes. The maternal chromosomes (present in the wild-type F_1 dihybrid) are color-coded red and pink to distinguish one homolog from the other before any meiotic crossing over has occurred. Because crossing over between the b^+/b and vg^+/vg loci occurs in some, but not all, egg-producing cells, more eggs with parental-type chromosomes than with recombinant ones are produced in the mating females. Fertilization of the eggs by sperm of genotype $b\ vg$ gives rise to some recombinant offspring. The recombination frequency is the percentage of recombinant flies in the total pool of offspring.

DRAW IT *Suppose, as in the question at the bottom of Figure 15.9, the parental (P generation) flies were true-breeding for gray body with vestigial wings and black body with normal wings. Draw the chromosomes in each of the four possible kinds of eggs from an F_1 female, and label each chromosome as "parental" or "recombinant."*

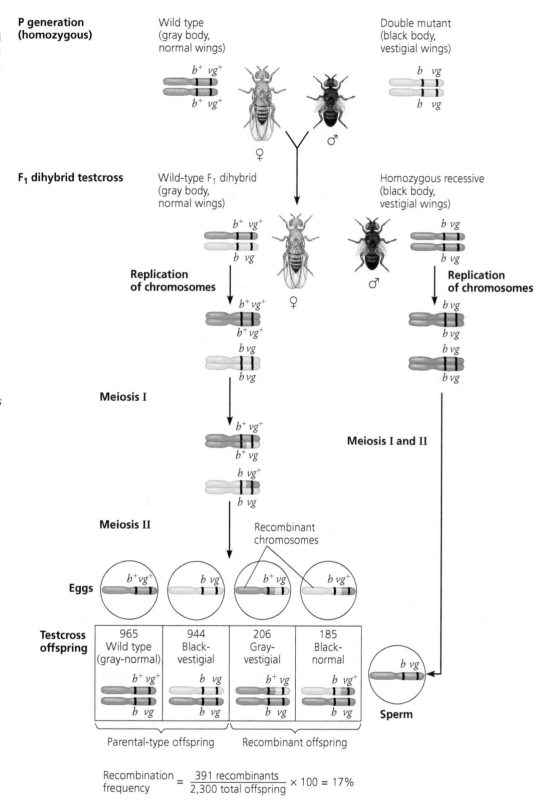

Figure 13.9). In effect, when a single crossover occurs, end portions of two nonsister chromatids trade places.

Figure 15.10 shows how crossing over in a dihybrid female fly resulted in recombinant eggs and ultimately recombinant offspring in Morgan's testcross. Most eggs had a chromosome with either the $b^+\ vg^+$ or $b\ vg$ parental genotype, but some had a recombinant chromosome ($b^+\ vg$ or $b\ vg^+$). Fertilization of

all classes of eggs by homozygous recessive sperm ($b\ vg$) produced an offspring population in which 17% exhibited a nonparental, recombinant phenotype, reflecting combinations of alleles not seen before in either P generation parent. In the Scientific Skills Exercise, you can use a statistical test to analyze the results from an F_1 dihybrid testcross and see whether the two genes assort independently or are linked.

Using the Chi-Square (χ^2) Test

Are Two Genes Linked or Unlinked? Genes that are in close proximity on the same chromosome will result in the linked alleles being inherited together more often than not. But how can you tell if certain alleles are inherited together due to linkage or whether they just happen to assort together? In this exercise, you will use a simple statistical test, the chi-square (χ^2) test, to analyze phenotypes of F_1 testcross progeny in order to see whether two genes are linked or unlinked.

How These Experiments Are Done If genes are unlinked and assorting independently, the phenotypic ratio of offspring from an F_1 testcross is expected to be 1:1:1:1 (see Figure 15.9). If the two genes are linked, however, the observed phenotypic ratio of the offspring will not match that ratio. Given that random fluctuations in the data do occur, how much must the observed numbers deviate from the expected numbers for us to conclude that the genes are not assorting independently but may instead be linked? To answer this question, scientists use a statistical test. This test, called a chi-square (χ^2) test, compares an observed data set to an expected data set predicted by a hypothesis (here, that the genes are unlinked) and measures the discrepancy between the two, thus determining the "goodness of fit." If the discrepancy between the observed and expected data sets is so large that it is unlikely to have occurred by random fluctuation, we say there is statistically significant evidence against the hypothesis (or, more specifically, evidence for the genes being linked). If the discrepancy is small, then our observations are well explained by random variation alone. In this case, we say the observed data are consistent with our hypothesis, or that the discrepancy is statistically insignificant. Note, however, that consistency with our hypothesis is not the same as proof of our hypothesis. Also, the size of the experimental data set is important: With small data sets like this one, even if the genes are linked, discrepancies might be small by chance alone if the linkage is weak. For simplicity, we overlook the effect of sample size here.

Data from the Simulated Experiment In cosmos plants, purple stem (A) is dominant to green stem (a), and short petals (B) is dominant to long petals (b). In a simulated cross, $AABB$ plants were crossed with $aabb$ plants to generate F_1 dihybrids ($AaBb$), which were then test-crossed ($AaBb \times aabb$). A total of 900 offspring plants were scored for stem color and flower petal length.

Offspring from test-cross of $AaBb$ (F_1) $\times$ $aabb$	Purple stem/short petals ($A–B–$)	Green stem/short petals ($aaB–$)	Purple stem/long petals ($A–bb$)	Green stem/long petals ($aabb$)
Expected ratio if the genes are unlinked	1	1	1	1
Expected number of offspring (of 900)				
Observed number of offspring (of 900)	220	210	231	239

Interpret the Data

1. The results in the data table are from a simulated F_1 dihybrid testcross. The hypothesis that the two genes are unlinked predicts the offspring phenotypic ratio will be 1:1:1:1. Using this ratio, calculate the expected number of each phenotype out of the 900 total offspring, and enter the values in the data table.

2. The goodness of fit is measured by χ^2. This statistic measures the amounts by which the observed values differ from their respective predictions to indicate how closely the two sets of values match. The formula for calculating this value is

▲ **Cosmos plants**

where o = observed and e = expected. Calculate the χ^2 value for the data using the table below. Fill out the table, carrying out the operations indicated in the top row. Then add up the entries in the last column to find the χ^2 value.

Testcross Offspring	Expected (e)	Observed (o)	Deviation (o−e)	(o−e)²	(o−e)²/e
($A–B–$)		220			
($aaB–$)		210			
($A–bb$)		231			
($aabb$)		239			
				χ^2 = Sum	

3. The χ^2 value means nothing on its own—it is used to find the probability that, assuming the hypothesis is true, the observed data set could have resulted from random fluctuations. A low probability suggests that the observed data are not consistent with the hypothesis, and thus the hypothesis should be rejected. A standard cutoff point used by biologists is a probability of 0.05 (5%). If the probability corresponding to the χ^2 value is 0.05 or less, the differences between observed and expected values are considered statistically significant and the hypothesis (that the genes are unlinked) should be rejected. If the probability is above 0.05, the results are not statistically significant; the observed data are consistent with the hypothesis. The "degrees of freedom" (df) of your data set is the number of categories (here, 4 phenotypes) minus 1, so df = 3. (a) Determine which values on the df = 3 line of the table your calculated χ^2 value lies between. (b) The column headings for these values show the probability range for your χ^2 number. Based on whether there are nonsignificant ($p > 0.05$) or significant ($p \leq 0.05$) differences between the observed and expected values, are the data consistent with the hypothesis that the two genes are unlinked and assorting independently, or is there enough evidence to reject this hypothesis?

(MB) A version of this Scientific Skills Exercise can be assigned in MasteringBiology.

New Combinations of Alleles: Variation for Natural Selection

EVOLUTION The physical behavior of chromosomes during meiosis contributes to the generation of variation in offspring (see Concept 13.4). Each pair of homologous chromosomes lines up independently of other pairs during metaphase I, and crossing over prior to that, during prophase I, can mix and match parts of maternal and paternal homologs. Mendel's elegant experiments show that the behavior of the abstract entities known as genes—or, more concretely, alleles of genes—also leads to variation in offspring (see Concept 14.1). Now, putting these different ideas together, you can see that the recombinant chromosomes resulting from crossing over may bring alleles together in new combinations, and the subsequent events of meiosis distribute to gametes the recombinant chromosomes in a multitude of combinations, such as the new variants seen in Figures 15.9 and 15.10. Random fertilization then increases even further the number of variant allele combinations that can be created.

This abundance of genetic variation provides the raw material on which natural selection works. If the traits conferred by particular combinations of alleles are better suited for a given environment, organisms possessing those genotypes will be expected to thrive and leave more offspring, ensuring the continuation of their genetic complement. In the next generation, of course, the alleles will be shuffled anew. Ultimately, the interplay between environment and genotype will determine which genetic combinations persist over time.

Mapping the Distance Between Genes Using Recombination Data: *Scientific Inquiry*

The discovery of linked genes and recombination due to crossing over motivated one of Morgan's students, Alfred H. Sturtevant, to work out a method for constructing a **genetic map**, an ordered list of the genetic loci along a particular chromosome.

Sturtevant hypothesized that the percentage of recombinant offspring, the *recombination frequency*, calculated from experiments like the one in Figures 15.9 and 15.10, depends on the distance between genes on a chromosome. He assumed that crossing over is a random event, with the chance of crossing over approximately equal at all points along a chromosome. Based on these assumptions, Sturtevant predicted that *the farther apart two genes are, the higher the probability that a crossover will occur between them and therefore the higher the recombination frequency.* His reasoning was simple: The greater the distance between two genes, the more points there are between them where crossing over can occur. Using recombination data from various fruit fly crosses, Sturtevant proceeded to assign relative positions to genes on the same chromosomes—that is, to *map* genes.

A genetic map based on recombination frequencies is called a **linkage map**. **Figure 15.11** shows Sturtevant's linkage map of three genes: the body-color (*b*) and wing-size (*vg*) genes depicted in Figure 15.10 and a third gene, called cinnabar (*cn*). Cinnabar is one of many *Drosophila* genes affecting eye color. Cinnabar eyes, a mutant phenotype, are a brighter red than the wild-type color. The recombination frequency between *cn* and *b* is 9%; that between *cn* and *vg*, 9.5%; and that between *b* and *vg*, 17%. In other words, crossovers between *cn* and *b* and between *cn* and *vg* are about half as frequent as crossovers between *b* and *vg*. Only a map that locates *cn* about midway between *b* and *vg* is consistent with these data, as you can prove to yourself by drawing alternative maps. Sturtevant expressed the distances between genes in **map units**, defining one map unit as equivalent to a 1% recombination frequency.

In practice, the interpretation of recombination data is more complicated than this example suggests. Some genes on a chromosome are so far from each other that a crossover between them is virtually certain. The observed frequency of recombination in crosses involving two such

▼ **Figure 15.11** | **Research Method**

Constructing a Linkage Map

Application A linkage map shows the relative locations of genes along a chromosome.

Technique A linkage map is based on the assumption that the probability of a crossover between two genetic loci is proportional to the distance separating the loci. The recombination frequencies used to construct a linkage map for a particular chromosome are obtained from experimental crosses, such as the cross depicted in Figures 15.9 and 15.10. The distances between genes are expressed as map units, with one map unit equivalent to a 1% recombination frequency. Genes are arranged on the chromosome in the order that best fits the data.

Results In this example, the observed recombination frequencies between three *Drosophila* gene pairs (*b–cn* 9%, *cn–vg* 9.5%, and *b–vg* 17%) best fit a linear order in which *cn* is positioned about halfway between the other two genes:

The *b–vg* recombination frequency (17%) is slightly less than the sum of the *b–cn* and *cn–vg* frequencies (9 + 9.5 = 18.5%) because of the few times that one crossover occurs between *b* and *cn* and another crossover occurs between *cn* and *vg*. The second crossover would "cancel out" the first, reducing the observed *b–vg* recombination frequency while contributing to the frequency between each of the closer pairs of genes. The value of 18.5% (18.5 map units) is closer to the actual distance between the genes. In practice, a geneticist would add the smaller distances in constructing a map.

genes can have a maximum value of 50%, a result indistinguishable from that for genes on different chromosomes. In this case, the physical connection between genes on the same chromosome is not reflected in the results of genetic crosses. Despite being on the same chromosome and thus being *physically connected*, the genes are *genetically unlinked*; alleles of such genes assort independently, as if they were on different chromosomes. In fact, at least two of the genes for pea characters that Mendel studied are now known to be on the same chromosome, but the distance between them is so great that linkage is not observed in genetic crosses. Consequently, the two genes behaved as if they were on different chromosomes in Mendel's experiments. Genes located far apart on a chromosome are mapped by adding the recombination frequencies from crosses involving closer pairs of genes lying between the two distant genes.

Using recombination data, Sturtevant and his colleagues were able to map numerous *Drosophila* genes in linear arrays. They found that the genes clustered into four groups of linked genes (*linkage groups*). Light microscopy had revealed four pairs of chromosomes in *Drosophila*, so the linkage map provided additional evidence that genes are located on chromosomes. Each chromosome has a linear array of specific genes, each gene with its own locus (Figure 15.12).

Because a linkage map is based strictly on recombination frequencies, it gives only an approximate picture of a chromosome. The frequency of crossing over is not actually uniform over the length of a chromosome, as Sturtevant assumed, and therefore map units do not correspond to actual physical distances (in nanometers, for instance). A linkage map does portray the order of genes along a chromosome, but it does not accurately portray the precise locations of those genes. Other methods enable geneticists to construct *cytogenetic maps* of chromosomes, which locate genes with respect to chromosomal features, such as stained bands, that can be seen in the microscope. Technical advances over the last two decades have enormously increased the rate and affordability of DNA sequencing. Today, most researchers sequence whole genomes to map the locations of genes of a given species. The entire nucleotide sequence is the ultimate physical map of a chromosome, revealing the physical distances between gene loci in DNA nucleotides. Comparing a linkage map with such a physical map or with a cytogenetic map of the same chromosome, we find that the linear order of genes is identical in all the maps, but the spacing between genes is not.

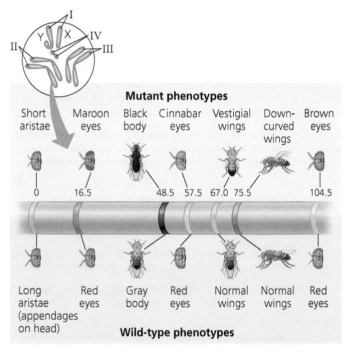

▲ **Figure 15.12 A partial genetic (linkage) map of a *Drosophila* chromosome.** This simplified map shows just seven of the genes that have been mapped on *Drosophila* chromosome II. (DNA sequencing has revealed over 9,000 genes on that chromosome.) The number at each gene locus indicates the number of map units between that locus and the locus for arista length (left). Notice that more than one gene can affect a given phenotypic characteristic, such as eye color.

Mutant phenotypes

Short aristae | Maroon eyes | Black body | Cinnabar eyes | Vestigial wings | Down-curved wings | Brown eyes

0 | 16.5 | 48.5 | 57.5 | 67.0 | 75.5 | 104.5

Long aristae (appendages on head) | Red eyes | Gray body | Red eyes | Normal wings | Normal wings | Red eyes

Wild-type phenotypes

CONCEPT CHECK 15.3

1. When two genes are located on the same chromosome, what is the physical basis for the production of recombinant offspring in a testcross between a dihybrid parent and a double-mutant (recessive) parent?

2. For each type of offspring of the testcross in Figure 15.9, explain the relationship between its phenotype and the alleles contributed by the female parent. (It will be useful to draw out the chromosomes of each fly and follow the alleles throughout the cross.)

3. **WHAT IF?** Genes *A*, *B*, and *C* are located on the same chromosome. Testcrosses show that the recombination frequency between *A* and *B* is 28% and between *A* and *C* is 12%. Can you determine the linear order of these genes? Explain.

CONCEPT 15.4

Alterations of chromosome number or structure cause some genetic disorders

As you have learned so far in this chapter, the phenotype of an organism can be affected by small-scale changes involving individual genes. Random mutations are the source of all new alleles, which can lead to new phenotypic traits.

Large-scale chromosomal changes can also affect an organism's phenotype. Physical and chemical disturbances, as well as errors during meiosis, can damage chromosomes in major ways or alter their number in a cell. Large-scale chromosomal alterations in humans and other mammals often lead to spontaneous abortion (miscarriage) of a fetus, and individuals born with these types of genetic defects commonly exhibit various developmental disorders. Plants may tolerate such genetic defects better than animals do.

Abnormal Chromosome Number

Ideally, the meiotic spindle distributes chromosomes to daughter cells without error. But there is an occasional mishap, called a **nondisjunction**, in which the members of a pair of homologous chromosomes do not move apart properly during meiosis I or sister chromatids fail to separate during meiosis II (**Figure 15.13**). In nondisjunction, one gamete receives two of the same type of chromosome and another gamete receives no copy. The other chromosomes are usually distributed normally.

If either of the aberrant gametes unites with a normal one at fertilization, the zygote will also have an abnormal number of a particular chromosome, a condition known as **aneuploidy**. Fertilization involving a gamete that has no copy of a particular chromosome will lead to a missing chromosome in the zygote (so that the cell has $2n - 1$ chromosomes); the aneuploid zygote is said to be **monosomic** for that chromosome. If a chromosome is present in triplicate in the zygote (so that the cell has $2n + 1$ chromosomes), the aneuploid cell is **trisomic** for that chromosome. Mitosis will subsequently transmit the anomaly to all embryonic cells. Monosomy and trisomy are estimated to occur in between 10 and 25% of human conceptions, and is the main reason for pregnancy loss. If the organism survives, it usually has a set of traits caused by the abnormal dose of the genes associated with the extra or missing chromosome. Down syndrome is an example of trisomy in humans that

will be discussed later. Nondisjunction can also occur during mitosis. If such an error takes place early in embryonic development, then the aneuploid condition is passed along by mitosis to a large number of cells and is likely to have a substantial effect on the organism.

Some organisms have more than two complete chromosome sets in all somatic cells. The general term for this chromosomal alteration is **polyploidy**; the specific terms *triploidy* ($3n$) and *tetraploidy* ($4n$) indicate three or four chromosomal sets, respectively. One way a triploid cell may arise is by the fertilization of an abnormal diploid egg produced by nondisjunction of all its chromosomes. Tetraploidy could result from the failure of a $2n$ zygote to divide after replicating its chromosomes. Subsequent normal mitotic divisions would then produce a $4n$ embryo.

Polyploidy is fairly common in the plant kingdom. The spontaneous origin of polyploid individuals plays an important role in plant evolution. Many species we eat are polyploid: Bananas are triploid, wheat hexaploid ($6n$), and strawberries octoploid ($8n$). Polyploid animal species are much less common, but there are a few fishes and amphibians known to be polyploid. In general, polyploids are more nearly normal in appearance than aneuploids. One extra (or missing) chromosome apparently disrupts genetic balance more than does an entire extra set of chromosomes.

Alterations of Chromosome Structure

Errors in meiosis or damaging agents such as radiation can cause breakage of a chromosome, which can lead to four types of changes in chromosome structure (**Figure 15.14**). A **deletion** occurs when a chromosomal fragment is lost. The affected chromosome is then missing certain genes. The "deleted" fragment may become attached as an extra segment to a sister chromatid, producing a **duplication**. Alternatively, a detached fragment could attach to a nonsister chromatid of a homologous chromosome. In that case, though, the "duplicated" segments might not be identical because the homologs could carry different alleles of certain genes. A chromosomal fragment may also reattach to the original chromosome but in the reverse orientation, producing an **inversion**. A fourth possible result of chromosomal breakage is for the fragment to join a nonhomologous chromosome, a rearrangement called a **translocation**.

Deletions and duplications are especially likely to occur during meiosis. In crossing over, nonsister chromatids sometimes exchange unequal-sized segments of DNA, so that one partner gives up more genes than it receives. The products of such an unequal crossover are one chromosome with a deletion and one chromosome with a duplication.

A diploid embryo that is homozygous for a large deletion (or has a single X chromosome with a large deletion, in a male) is usually missing a number of essential genes, a condition typically lethal. Duplications and translocations also tend

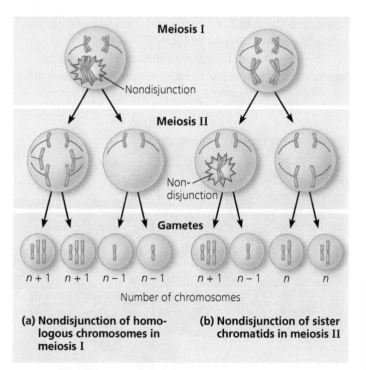

▲ **Figure 15.13 Meiotic nondisjunction.** Gametes with an abnormal chromosome number can arise by nondisjunction in either meiosis I or meiosis II. For simplicity, the figure does not show the spores formed by meiosis in plants. Ultimately, spores form gametes that have the defects shown. (See Figure 13.6.)

(a) Deletion

A **deletion** removes a chromosomal segment.

(b) Duplication

A **duplication** repeats a segment.

(c) Inversion

An **inversion** reverses a segment within a chromosome.

(d) Translocation

A **translocation** moves a segment from one chromosome to a nonhomologous chromosome. In a reciprocal translocation, the most common type, nonhomologous chromosomes exchange fragments.

Less often, a nonreciprocal translocation occurs: A chromosome transfers a fragment but receives none in return (not shown).

Human Disorders Due to Chromosomal Alterations

Alterations of chromosome number and structure are associated with a number of serious human disorders. As described earlier, nondisjunction in meiosis results in aneuploidy in gametes and any resulting zygotes. Although

the frequency of aneuploid zygotes may be quite high in humans, most of these chromosomal alterations are so disastrous to development that the affected embryos are spontaneously aborted long before birth. However, some types of aneuploidy appear to upset the genetic balance less than others, where individuals with certain aneuploid conditions can survive to birth and beyond. These individuals have a set of traits—a *syndrome*—characteristic of the type of aneuploidy. Genetic disorders caused by aneuploidy can be diagnosed before birth by fetal testing (see Figure 14.19).

Down Syndrome (Trisomy 21)

One aneuploid condition, **Down syndrome**, affects approximately one out of every 830 children born in the United States (**Figure 15.15**). Down syndrome is usually the result of an extra chromosome 21, so that each body cell has a total of 47 chromosomes. Because the cells are trisomic for chromosome 21, Down syndrome is often called *trisomy 21*. Down syndrome includes characteristic facial features, short stature, correctable heart defects, and developmental delays. Individuals with Down syndrome have an increased chance of developing leukemia and Alzheimer's disease but have a lower rate of high blood pressure, atherosclerosis (hardening of the arteries), stroke, and many types of solid tumors. Although people with Down syndrome, on average, have a life span shorter than normal, most, with proper medical treatment, live to middle age and beyond. Many live independently or at home with their families, are employed, and are valuable contributors to their communities. Almost all males and about half of females with Down syndrome are sexually underdeveloped and sterile.

The frequency of Down syndrome increases with the age of the mother. While the disorder occurs in just 0.04% of children born to women under age 30, the risk climbs

to be harmful. In reciprocal translocations, in which segments are exchanged between nonhomologous chromosomes, and in inversions, the balance of genes is not abnormal—all genes are present in their normal doses. Nevertheless, translocations and inversions can alter phenotype because a gene's expression can be influenced by its location among neighboring genes, which can have devastating effects.

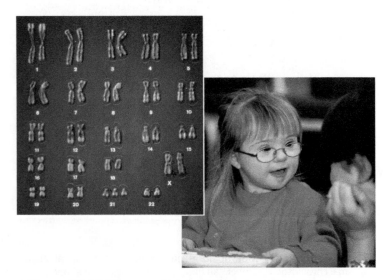

▲ Figure 15.15 **Down syndrome.** The karyotype shows trisomy 21, the most common cause of Down syndrome. The child exhibits the facial features characteristic of this disorder.

to 0.92% for mothers at age 40 and is even higher for older mothers. The correlation of Down syndrome with maternal age has not yet been explained. Most cases result from nondisjunction during meiosis I, and some research points to an age-dependent abnormality in meiosis. Trisomies of some other chromosomes also increase in incidence with maternal age, although infants with other autosomal trisomies rarely survive for long. Due to its low risk and its potential for providing useful information, prenatal screening for trisomies in the embryo is now offered to all pregnant women. In 2008, the Prenatally and Postnatally Diagnosed Conditions Awareness Act was signed into law in the United States. This law stipulates that medical practitioners give accurate, up-to-date information about any prenatal or postnatal diagnosis received by parents and that they connect parents with appropriate support services.

Aneuploidy of Sex Chromosomes

Aneuploid conditions involving sex chromosomes appear to upset the genetic balance less than those involving autosomes. This may be because the Y chromosome carries relatively few genes. Also, extra copies of the X chromosome simply become inactivated as Barr bodies.

An extra X chromosome in a male, producing XXY, occurs approximately once in every 500 to 1,000 live male births. People with this disorder, called *Klinefelter syndrome*, have male sex organs, but the testes are abnormally small and the man is sterile. Even though the extra X is inactivated, some breast enlargement and other female body characteristics are common. Affected individuals may have subnormal intelligence. About 1 of every 1,000 males is born with an extra Y chromosome (XYY). These males undergo normal sexual development and do not exhibit any well-defined syndrome, but tend to be taller than average.

Females with trisomy X (XXX), which occurs once in approximately 1,000 live female births, are healthy and have no unusual physical features other than being slightly taller than average. Triple-X females are at risk for learning disabilities but are fertile. Monosomy X, which is called *Turner syndrome*, occurs about once in every 2,500 female births and is the only known viable monosomy in humans. Although these X0 individuals are phenotypically female, they are sterile because their sex organs do not mature. When provided with estrogen replacement therapy, girls with Turner syndrome do develop secondary sex characteristics. Most have normal intelligence.

Disorders Caused by Structurally Altered Chromosomes

Many deletions in human chromosomes, even in a heterozygous state, cause severe problems. One such syndrome, known as *cri du chat* ("cry of the cat"), results from a specific deletion in chromosome 5. A child born with this deletion is severely intellectually disabled, has a small head with

▲ **Figure 15.16 Translocation associated with chronic myelogenous leukemia (CML).** The cancerous cells in nearly all CML patients contain an abnormally short chromosome 22, the so-called Philadelphia chromosome, and an abnormally long chromosome 9. These altered chromosomes result from the reciprocal translocation shown here, which presumably occurred in a single white blood cell precursor undergoing mitosis and was then passed along to all descendant cells.

unusual facial features, and has a cry that sounds like the mewing of a distressed cat. Such individuals usually die in infancy or early childhood.

Chromosomal translocations have been implicated in certain cancers, including *chronic myelogenous leukemia* (*CML*). This disease occurs when a reciprocal translocation happens during mitosis of cells that will become white blood cells. In these cells, the exchange of a large portion of chromosome 22 with a small fragment from a tip of chromosome 9 produces a much shortened, easily recognized chromosome 22, called the *Philadelphia chromosome* (**Figure 15.16**). Such an exchange causes cancer by activating a gene that leads to uncontrolled cell cycle progression.

CONCEPT CHECK 15.4

1. About 5% of individuals with Down syndrome have a chromosomal translocation in which a third copy of chromosome 21 is attached to chromosome 14. If this translocation occurred in a parent's gonad, how could it lead to Down syndrome in a child?

2. **WHAT IF?** The ABO blood type locus has been mapped on chromosome 9. A father who has type AB blood and a mother who has type O blood have a child with trisomy 9 and type A blood. Using this information, can you tell in which parent the nondisjunction occurred? Explain your answer. (See Figure 14.11.)

3. **MAKE CONNECTIONS** The gene that is activated on the Philadelphia chromosome codes for an intracellular tyrosine kinase. Review the discussion of cell cycle control in Concept 12.3, and explain how the activation of this gene could contribute to the development of cancer.

CONCEPT 15.5

Some inheritance patterns are exceptions to standard Mendelian inheritance

In the previous section, you learned about deviations from the usual patterns of chromosomal inheritance due to abnormal events in meiosis and mitosis. We conclude this chapter by describing two normally occurring exceptions to Mendelian genetics, one involving genes located in the nucleus and the other involving genes located outside the nucleus. In both cases, the sex of the parent contributing an allele is a factor in the pattern of inheritance.

Genomic Imprinting

Throughout our discussions of Mendelian genetics and the chromosomal basis of inheritance, we have assumed that a given allele will have the same effect whether it was inherited from the mother or the father. This is probably a safe assumption most of the time. For example, when Mendel crossed purple-flowered pea plants with white-flowered pea plants, he observed the same results regardless of whether the purple-flowered parent supplied the eggs or the sperm. In recent years, however, geneticists have identified a number of traits in mammals that depend on which parent passed along the alleles for those traits. Such variation in phenotype depending on whether an allele is inherited from the male or female parent is called **genomic imprinting**. (Note that unlike sex-linked genes, most imprinted genes are on autosomes.) Using newer DNA sequence-based methods, over 60 imprinted genes have been identified, with hundreds more suspected.

Genomic imprinting occurs during gamete formation and results in the silencing of a particular allele of certain genes. Because these genes are imprinted differently in sperm and eggs, the offspring expresses only one allele of an imprinted gene, the one that has been inherited from either the female or the male parent. The imprints are then transmitted to all body cells during development. In each generation, the old imprints are "erased" in gamete-producing cells, and the chromosomes of the developing gametes are newly imprinted according to the sex of the individual forming the gametes. In a given species, the imprinted genes are always imprinted in the same way. For instance, a gene imprinted for maternal allele expression is always imprinted this way, generation after generation.

Consider, for example, the mouse gene for insulin-like growth factor 2 (*Igf2*), one of the first imprinted genes to be identified. Although this growth factor is required for normal prenatal growth, only the paternal allele is expressed **(Figure 15.17a)**. Evidence that the *Igf2* gene is imprinted

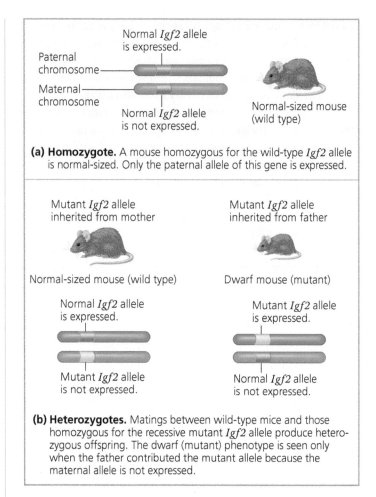

(a) Homozygote. A mouse homozygous for the wild-type *Igf2* allele is normal-sized. Only the paternal allele of this gene is expressed.

(b) Heterozygotes. Matings between wild-type mice and those homozygous for the recessive mutant *Igf2* allele produce heterozygous offspring. The dwarf (mutant) phenotype is seen only when the father contributed the mutant allele because the maternal allele is not expressed.

▲ **Figure 15.17 Genomic imprinting of the mouse *Igf2* gene.**

came initially from crosses between normal-sized (wild-type) mice and dwarf (mutant) mice homozygous for a recessive mutation in the *Igf2* gene. The phenotypes of heterozygous offspring (with one normal allele and one mutant) differed depending on whether the mutant allele came from the mother or the father **(Figure 15.17b)**.

What exactly is a genomic imprint? In many cases, it seems to consist of methyl ($-CH_3$) groups that are added to cytosine nucleotides of one of the alleles. Such methylation may silence the allele, an effect consistent with evidence that heavily methylated genes are usually inactive. However, for a few genes, methylation has been shown to *activate* expression of the allele. This is the case for the *Igf2* gene: Methylation of certain cytosines on the paternal chromosome leads to expression of the paternal *Igf2* allele, by an indirect mechanism involving chromatin condensation.

Genomic imprinting is thought to affect only a small fraction of the genes in mammalian genomes, but most of the known imprinted genes are critical for embryonic development. In experiments with mice, embryos engineered to inherit both copies of certain chromosomes from the same parent usually die before birth, whether that parent is male or female. A few years ago, however, scientists in Japan combined the genetic material from two eggs in a zygote while allowing expression of the *Igf2* gene from only one of the egg nuclei. The zygote developed into an apparently healthy mouse. Normal development seems to require that embryonic cells have exactly one active copy—not zero, not two—of certain genes. The association of improper imprinting with abnormal development and certain cancers has stimulated ongoing studies of how different genes are imprinted.

Inheritance of Organelle Genes

Although our focus in this chapter has been on the chromosomal basis of inheritance, we end with an important amendment: Not all of a eukaryotic cell's genes are located on nuclear chromosomes, or even in the nucleus; some genes are located in organelles in the cytoplasm. Because they are outside the nucleus, these genes are sometimes called *extranuclear genes* or *cytoplasmic genes*. Mitochondria, as well as chloroplasts and other plastids in plants, contain small circular DNA molecules that carry a number of genes. These organelles reproduce themselves and transmit their genes to daughter organelles. Organelle genes are not distributed to offspring according to the same rules that direct the distribution of nuclear chromosomes during meiosis, so they do not display Mendelian inheritance.

The first hint that extranuclear genes exist came from studies by the German scientist Carl Correns on the inheritance of yellow or white patches on the leaves of an otherwise green plant. In 1909, he observed that the coloration of the offspring was determined only by the maternal parent (the source of eggs) and not by the paternal parent (the source of sperm). Subsequent research showed that such coloration patterns, or variegation, are due to mutations in plastid genes that control pigmentation (Figure 15.18). In most plants, a zygote receives all its plastids from the cytoplasm of the egg and none from the sperm, which contributes little more than a haploid set of chromosomes. An egg may contain plastids with different alleles for a pigmentation gene. As the zygote develops, plastids containing wild-type or mutant pigmentation genes are distributed randomly to daughter cells. The pattern of leaf coloration exhibited by a plant depends on the ratio of wild-type to mutant plastids in its various tissues.

Similar maternal inheritance is also the rule for mitochondrial genes in most animals and plants, because almost all the mitochondria passed on to a zygote come from the cytoplasm of the egg. (The few mitochondria contributed by the sperm appear to be destroyed in the egg by autophagy; see Figure 6.13.) The products of most mitochondrial genes help make up the protein complexes of the electron transport chain and ATP synthase (see Figure 10.15). Defects in one or more of these proteins, therefore, reduce the amount of ATP the cell can make and have been shown to cause a number of rare human disorders. Because the parts of the body most susceptible to energy deprivation are the nervous system and the muscles, most mitochondrial diseases primarily affect these systems. For example, *mitochondrial myopathy* causes weakness, intolerance of exercise, and muscle deterioration. Another mitochondrial disorder is *Leber's hereditary optic neuropathy*, which can produce sudden blindness in people as young as their 20s or 30s. The four mutations found thus far to cause this disorder affect oxidative phosphorylation during cellular respiration, a crucial function for the cell (see Concept 10.4).

In addition to the rare diseases clearly caused by defects in mitochondrial DNA, mitochondrial mutations inherited from a person's mother may contribute to at least some types of diabetes and heart disease, as well as to other disorders that commonly debilitate the elderly, such as Alzheimer's disease. In the course of a lifetime, new mutations gradually accumulate in our mitochondrial DNA, and some researchers think that these mutations play a role in the normal aging process.

Wherever genes are located in the cell—in the nucleus or in cytoplasmic organelles—their inheritance depends on the precise replication of DNA. In the next chapter, you will learn how this molecular reproduction occurs.

▼ Figure 15.18 **A painted nettle coleus plant.** The variegated (patterned) leaves on this coleus plant (*Solenostemon scutellarioides*) result from mutations that affect expression of pigment genes located in plastids, which generally are inherited from the maternal parent.

CONCEPT CHECK 15.5

1. Gene dosage—the number of copies of a gene that are actively being expressed—is important to proper development. Identify and describe two processes that establish the proper dosage of certain genes.

2. Reciprocal crosses between two primrose varieties, A and B, produced the following results: A female × B male → offspring with all green (nonvariegated) leaves; B female × A male → offspring with patterned (variegated) leaves. Explain these results.

3. **WHAT IF?** Mitochondrial genes are critical to the energy metabolism of cells, but mitochondrial disorders caused by mutations in these genes are generally not lethal. Why not?

SUMMARY OF KEY CONCEPTS

CONCEPT 15.1

Morgan showed that Mendelian inheritance has its physical basis in the behavior of chromosomes: *scientific inquiry* (pp. 296–297)

- Morgan's work with an eye color gene in *Drosophila* led to the **chromosome theory of inheritance**, which states that genes are located on chromosomes and that the behavior of chromosomes during meiosis accounts for Mendel's laws.

? *What characteristic of the sex chromosomes allowed Morgan to correlate their behavior with that of the alleles of the eye-color gene?*

CONCEPT 15.2

Sex-linked genes exhibit unique patterns of inheritance (pp. 298–300)

- Sex is often chromosomally based. Humans and other mammals have an X-Y system in which sex is determined by whether a Y chromosome is present. Other systems are found in birds, fishes, and insects.
- The sex chromosomes carry **sex-linked genes**, virtually all of which are on the X chromosome (X-linked). Any male who inherits a recessive X-linked allele (from his mother) will express the trait, such as color blindness.
- In mammalian females, one of the two X chromosomes in each cell is randomly inactivated during early embryonic development, becoming highly condensed into a **Barr body**.

? *Why are males affected much more often than females by X-linked disorders?*

CONCEPT 15.3

Linked genes tend to be inherited together because they are located near each other on the same chromosome (pp. 301–306)

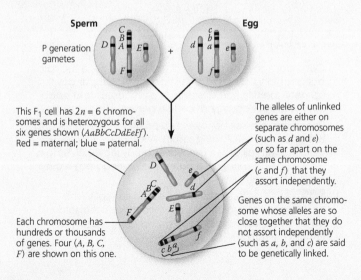

P generation gametes

Sperm + **Egg**

This F_1 cell has $2n = 6$ chromosomes and is heterozygous for all six genes shown (*AaBbCcDdEeFf*). Red = maternal; blue = paternal.

Each chromosome has hundreds or thousands of genes. Four (*A, B, C, F*) are shown on this one.

The alleles of unlinked genes are either on separate chromosomes (such as *d* and *e*) or so far apart on the same chromosome (*c* and *f*) that they assort independently.

Genes on the same chromosome whose alleles are so close together that they do not assort independently (such as *a, b,* and *c*) are said to be genetically linked.

- Among offspring from an F_1 dihybrid testcross, **parental types** have the same combination of traits as those in the P generation parents. **Recombinant types (recombinants)** exhibit new combinations of traits not seen in either P generation parent. Because of the independent assortment of chromosomes, unlinked genes exhibit a 50% frequency of recombination in the gametes. For genetically **linked genes, crossing over** between nonsister chromatids during meiosis I accounts for the observed recombinants, always less than 50% of the total.
- The order of genes on a chromosome and the relative distances between them can be deduced from recombination frequencies observed in genetic crosses. These data allow construction of a **linkage map** (a type of **genetic map**). The farther apart genes are, the more likely their allele combinations will be recombined during crossing over.

? *Why are specific alleles of two distant genes more likely to show recombination than those of two closer genes?*

CONCEPT 15.4

Alterations of chromosome number or structure cause some genetic disorders (pp. 306–309)

- **Aneuploidy**, an abnormal chromosome number, can result from **nondisjunction** during meiosis. When a normal gamete unites with one containing two copies or no copies of a particular chromosome, the resulting zygote and its descendant cells either have one extra copy of that chromosome (**trisomy**, $2n + 1$) or are missing a copy (**monosomy**, $2n - 1$). **Polyploidy** (more than two complete sets of chromosomes) can result from complete nondisjunction during gamete formation.
- Chromosome breakage can result in alterations of chromosome structure: **deletions, duplications, inversions,** and **translocations**. Translocations can be reciprocal or nonreciprocal.
- Changes in the number of chromosomes per cell or in the structure of individual chromosomes can affect the phenotype and, in some cases, lead to disorders. Such alterations cause **Down syndrome** (usually due to trisomy of chromosome 21), certain cancers associated with chromosomal translocations, and various other human disorders.

? *Why are inversions and reciprocal translocations less likely to be lethal than are aneuploidy, duplications, deletions, and nonreciprocal translocations?*

CONCEPT 15.5

Some inheritance patterns are exceptions to standard Mendelian inheritance (pp. 310–311)

- In mammals, the phenotypic effects of a small number of particular genes depend on which allele is inherited from each parent, a phenomenon called **genomic imprinting**. Imprints are formed during gamete production, with the result that one allele (either maternal or paternal) is not expressed in offspring.
- The inheritance of traits controlled by the genes present in mitochondria and plastids depends solely on the maternal parent because the zygote's cytoplasm containing these organelles comes from the egg. Some diseases affecting the nervous and muscular systems are caused by defects in mitochondrial genes that prevent cells from making enough ATP.

? *Explain how genomic imprinting and inheritance of mitochondrial and chloroplast DNA are exceptions to standard Mendelian inheritance.*

LEVEL 1: KNOWLEDGE/COMPREHENSION

1. A man with hemophilia (a recessive, sex-linked condition) has a daughter of normal phenotype. She marries a man who is normal for the trait. What is the probability that a daughter of this mating will have hemophilia? That a son will have hemophilia? If the couple has four sons, what is the probability that all four will be born with hemophilia?

2. Pseudohypertrophic muscular dystrophy is an inherited disorder that causes gradual deterioration of the muscles. It is seen almost exclusively in boys born to apparently normal parents and usually results in death in the early teens. Is this disorder caused by a dominant or a recessive allele? Is its inheritance sex-linked or autosomal? How do you know? Explain why this disorder is almost never seen in girls.

3. A wild-type fruit fly (heterozygous for gray body color and normal wings) is mated with a black fly with vestigial wings. The offspring have the following phenotypic distribution: wild-type, 778; black-vestigial, 785; black-normal, 158; gray-vestigial, 162. What is the recombination frequency between these genes for body color and wing size? Is this consistent with the results of the experiment in Figure 15.9?

4. A planet is inhabited by creatures that reproduce with the same hereditary patterns seen in humans. Three phenotypic characters are height (T = tall, t = dwarf), head appendages (A = antennae, a = no antennae), and nose morphology (S = upturned snout, s = downturned snout). Since the creatures are not "intelligent," Earth scientists are able to do some controlled breeding experiments using various heterozygotes in testcrosses. For tall heterozygotes with antennae, the offspring are tall-antennae, 46; dwarf-antennae, 7; dwarf-no antennae, 42; tall-no antennae, 5. For heterozygotes with antennae and an upturned snout, the offspring are antennae-upturned snout, 47; antennae-downturned snout, 2; no antennae-downturned snout, 48; no antennae-upturned snout, 3. Calculate the recombination frequencies for both experiments.

LEVEL 2: APPLICATION/ANALYSIS

5. Using the information from problem 4, scientists do a further testcross using a heterozygote for height and nose morphology. The offspring are tall-upturned snout, 40; dwarf-upturned snout, 9; dwarf-downturned snout, 42; tall-downturned snout, 9. Calculate the recombination frequency from these data, and then use your answer from problem 4 to determine the correct order of the three linked genes.

6. A wild-type fruit fly (heterozygous for gray body color and red eyes) is mated with a black fruit fly with purple eyes. The offspring are wild-type, 721; black-purple, 751; gray-purple, 49; black-red, 45. What is the recombination frequency between these genes for body color and eye color? Using information from problem 3, what fruit flies (genotypes and phenotypes) would you mate to determine the order of the body-color, wing-size, and eye-color genes on the chromosome?

7. Assume that genes A and B are on the same chromosome and are 50 map units apart. An animal heterozygous at both loci is crossed with one that is homozygous recessive at both loci. What percentage of the offspring will show recombinant phenotypes resulting from crossovers? Without knowing these genes are on the same chromosome, how would you interpret the results of this cross?

8. Two genes of a flower, one controlling blue (B) versus white (b) petals and the other controlling round (R) versus oval (r) stamens, are linked and are 10 map units apart. You cross a homozygous blue-oval plant with a homozygous white-round plant. The resulting F_1 progeny are crossed with homozygous white-oval plants, and 1,000 F_2 progeny are obtained. How many F_2 plants of each of the four phenotypes do you expect?

9. You design *Drosophila* crosses to provide recombination data for gene a, which is located on the chromosome shown in Figure 15.12. Gene a has recombination frequencies of 14% with the vestigial-wing locus and 26% with the brown-eye locus. Approximately where is a located along the chromosome?

LEVEL 3: SYNTHESIS/EVALUATION

10. Banana plants, which are triploid, are seedless and therefore sterile. Propose a possible explanation.

11. **EVOLUTION CONNECTION**
Crossing over is thought to be evolutionarily advantageous because it continually shuffles genetic alleles into novel combinations. Until recently, it was thought that the genes on the Y chromosome might degenerate because they lack homologous genes on the X chromosome with which to pair up prior to crossing over. However, when the Y chromosome was sequenced, eight large regions were found to be internally homologous to each other, and quite a few of the 78 genes represent duplicates. (Y chromosome researcher David Page has called it a "hall of mirrors.") What might be a benefit of these regions?

12. **SCIENTIFIC INQUIRY**
DRAW IT Assume you are mapping genes A, B, C, and D in *Drosophila*. You know that these genes are linked on the same chromosome, and you determine the recombination frequencies between each pair of genes to be as follows: A–B, 8%; A–C, 28%; A–D, 25%; B–C, 20%; B–D, 33%.
(a) Describe how you determined the recombination frequencies for each pair of genes.
(b) Draw a chromosome map based on your data.

13. **WRITE ABOUT A THEME: INFORMATION**
The continuity of life is based on heritable information in the form of DNA. In a short essay (100–150 words), relate the structure and behavior of chromosomes to inheritance in both asexually and sexually reproducing species.

14. **SYNTHESIZE YOUR KNOWLEDGE**

Butterflies have an X-Y sex determination system that is different from that of flies or humans. Female butterflies may be either XY or XO, while butterflies with two or more X chromosomes are males. This photograph shows a tiger swallowtail *gynandromorph*, which is half male (left side) and half female (right side). Given that the first division of the zygote divides the embryo into the future right and left halves of the butterfly, propose a hypothesis that explains how nondisjunction during the first mitosis might have produced this unusual-looking butterfly.

MasteringBiology®

Students Go to **MasteringBiology** for assignments, the eText, and the Study Area with practice tests, animations, and activities.

Instructors Go to **MasteringBiology** for automatically graded tutorials and questions that you can assign to your students, plus Instructor Resources.

16

The Molecular Basis of Inheritance

▲ Figure 16.1 **What is the structure of DNA?**

▲ James Watson (left) and Francis Crick with their DNA model.

Life's Operating Instructions

In April 1953, James Watson and Francis Crick shook the scientific world by proposing an elegant double-helical model for the structure of deoxyribonucleic acid, or DNA **(Figure 16.1).** The photo at the lower left shows the DNA model they constructed from sheet metal and wire. Over the past 60 years, their model has become an icon of modern biology. Gregor Mendel's heritable factors and Thomas Hunt Morgan's genes on chromosomes are, in fact, composed of DNA. Chemically speaking, your genetic endowment is the DNA you inherited from your parents. DNA, the substance of inheritance, is the most celebrated molecule of our time.

Of all nature's molecules, nucleic acids are unique in their ability to direct their own replication from monomers. Indeed, the resemblance of offspring to their parents has its basis in the accurate replication of DNA and its transmission from one generation to the next. Hereditary information in DNA directs the development of your biochemical, anatomical, physiological, and, to some extent, behavioral traits. In this chapter, you will discover how biologists deduced that DNA is the genetic material and how Watson and Crick worked out its structure. You will also learn how a molecule of DNA is copied during **DNA replication** and how cells repair their DNA. Finally, you will explore how a molecule of DNA is packaged together with proteins in a chromosome.

CONCEPT 16.1

DNA is the genetic material

Today, even schoolchildren have heard of DNA, and scientists routinely manipulate DNA in the laboratory, often to change the heritable traits of cells in their experiments. Early in the 20th century, however, identifying the molecules of inheritance loomed as a major challenge to biologists.

The Search for the Genetic Material: *Scientific Inquiry*

Once T. H. Morgan's group showed that genes exist as parts of chromosomes (described in Chapter 15), the two chemical components of chromosomes—DNA and protein—emerged as the leading candidates for the genetic material. Until the 1940s, the case for proteins seemed stronger: Biochemists had identified proteins as a class of macromolecules with great heterogeneity and specificity of function, essential requirements for the hereditary material. Moreover, little was known about nucleic acids, whose physical and chemical properties seemed far too uniform to account for the multitude of specific inherited traits exhibited by every organism. This view gradually changed as the role of DNA in heredity was worked out in studies of bacteria and the viruses that infect them, systems far simpler than fruit flies or humans. Let's trace the search for the genetic material as a case study in scientific inquiry.

Evidence That DNA Can Transform Bacteria

In 1928, a British medical officer named Frederick Griffith was trying to develop a vaccine against pneumonia. He was studying *Streptococcus pneumoniae*, a bacterium that causes pneumonia in mammals. Griffith had two strains (varieties) of the bacterium, one pathogenic (disease-causing) and one nonpathogenic (harmless). He was surprised to find that when he killed the pathogenic bacteria with heat and then mixed the cell remains with living bacteria of the nonpathogenic strain, some of the living cells became pathogenic (**Figure 16.2**). Furthermore, this newly acquired trait of pathogenicity was inherited by all the descendants of the transformed bacteria. Apparently, some chemical component of the dead pathogenic cells caused this heritable change, although the identity of the substance was not known. Griffith called the phenomenon **transformation**, now defined as a change in genotype and phenotype due to the assimilation of external DNA by a cell. Later work by Oswald Avery, Maclyn McCarty, and Colin MacLeod identified the transforming substance as DNA.

Scientists remained skeptical, however, many still viewing proteins as better candidates for the genetic material. Also, many biologists were not convinced that bacterial genes would be similar in composition and function to those of

▼ **Figure 16.2** | Inquiry

Can a genetic trait be transferred between different bacterial strains?

Experiment Frederick Griffith studied two strains of the bacterium *Streptococcus pneumoniae*. The S (smooth) strain can cause pneumonia in mice; it is pathogenic because the cells have an outer capsule that protects them from an animal's immune system. Cells of the R (rough) strain lack a capsule and are nonpathogenic. To test for the trait of pathogenicity, Griffith injected mice with the two strains:

Living S cells (pathogenic control)	Living R cells (nonpathogenic control)	Heat-killed S cells (nonpathogenic control)	Mixture of heat-killed S cells and living R cells

Results

Mouse dies	Mouse healthy	Mouse healthy	Mouse dies

In blood sample, living S cells were found. They could reproduce, yielding more S cells.

Conclusion The living R bacteria had been transformed into pathogenic S bacteria by an unknown, heritable substance from the dead S cells that enabled the R cells to make capsules.

Source: F. Griffith, The significance of pneumococcal types, *Journal of Hygiene* 27:113–159 (1928).

WHAT IF? *How did this experiment rule out the possibility that the R cells simply used the dead S cells' capsules to become pathogenic?*

more complex organisms. But the major reason for the continued doubt was that so little was known about DNA.

Evidence That Viral DNA Can Program Cells

Additional evidence that DNA was the genetic material came from studies of viruses that infect bacteria (**Figure 16.3**). These viruses are called **bacteriophages** (meaning "bacteria-eaters"), or **phages** for short. Viruses are much simpler than

▶ **Figure 16.3 A virus infecting a bacterial cell.** A phage called T2 attaches to a host cell and injects its genetic material through the plasma membrane, while the head and tail parts remain on the outer bacterial surface (color-ized TEM).

Phage head
DNA
Tail sheath
Tail fiber
Genetic material
Bacterial cell

100 nm

cells. A **virus** is little more than DNA (or sometimes RNA) enclosed by a protective coat, which is often simply protein. To produce more viruses, a virus must infect a cell and take over the cell's metabolic machinery.

Phages have been widely used as tools by researchers in molecular genetics. In 1952, Alfred Hershey and Martha Chase performed experiments showing that DNA is the genetic material of a phage known as T2. This is one of many phages that infect *Escherichia coli* (*E. coli*), a bacterium that normally lives in the intestines of mammals and is a model organism for molecular biologists. At that time,

biologists already knew that T2, like many other phages, was composed almost entirely of DNA and protein. They also knew that the T2 phage could quickly turn an *E. coli* cell into a T2-producing factory that released many copies of new phages when the cell ruptured. Somehow, T2 could reprogram its host cell to produce viruses. But which viral component—protein or DNA—was responsible?

Hershey and Chase answered this question by devising an experiment showing that only one of the two components of T2 actually enters the *E. coli* cell during infection (Figure 16.4). In their experiment, they used a radioactive

▼ **Figure 16.4** | Inquiry

Is protein or DNA the genetic material of phage T2?

Experiment Alfred Hershey and Martha Chase used radioactive sulfur and phosphorus to trace the fates of protein and DNA, respectively, of T2 phages that infected bacterial cells. They wanted to see which of these molecules entered the cells and could reprogram them to make more phages.

1. Mixed radioactively labeled phages with bacteria. The phages infected the bacterial cells.

2. Agitated the mixture in a blender to free phage parts outside the bacteria from the cells.

3. Centrifuged the mixture so that bacteria formed a pellet at the bottom of the test tube; free phages and phage parts, which are lighter, remained suspended in the liquid.

4. Measured the radioactivity in the pellet and the liquid.

Phage
Radioactive protein
Bacterial cell
DNA

Batch 1: Phages were grown with radioactive sulfur (^{35}S), which was incorporated into phage protein (pink).

Empty protein shell
Phage DNA
Centrifuge

Radioactivity (phage protein) found in liquid

Pellet (bacterial cells and contents)

Radioactive DNA

Batch 2: Phages were grown with radioactive phosphorus (^{32}P), which was incorporated into phage DNA (blue).

Centrifuge

Pellet

Radioactivity (phage DNA) found in pellet

Results When proteins were labeled (batch 1), radioactivity remained outside the cells, but when DNA was labeled (batch 2), radioactivity was found inside the cells. Bacterial cells containing radioactive phage DNA released new phages with some radioactive phosphorus.

Conclusion Phage DNA entered bacterial cells, but phage proteins did not. Hershey and Chase concluded that DNA, not protein, functions as the genetic material of phage T2.

Source: A. D. Hershey and M. Chase, Independent functions of viral protein and nucleic acid in growth of bacteriophage, *Journal of General Physiology* 36:39–56 (1952).

WHAT IF? *How would the results have differed if proteins carried the genetic information?*

isotope of sulfur to tag protein in one batch of T2 and a radioactive isotope of phosphorus to tag DNA in a second batch. Because protein, but not DNA, contains sulfur, radioactive sulfur atoms were incorporated only into the protein of the phage. In a similar way, the atoms of radioactive phosphorus labeled only the DNA, not the protein, because nearly all the phage's phosphorus is in its DNA. In the experiment, separate samples of nonradioactive *E. coli* cells were infected with the protein-labeled and DNA-labeled batches of T2. The researchers then tested the two samples shortly after the onset of infection to see which type of molecule—protein or DNA—had entered the bacterial cells and would therefore be capable of reprogramming them.

Hershey and Chase found that the phage DNA entered the host cells but the phage protein did not. Moreover, when these bacteria were returned to a culture medium, and the infection ran its course, the *E. coli* released phages that contained some radioactive phosphorus. This result further showed that the DNA inside the cell played an ongoing role during the infection process.

Hershey and Chase concluded that the DNA injected by the phage must be the molecule carrying the genetic information that makes the cells produce new viral DNA and proteins. The Hershey-Chase experiment was a landmark study because it provided powerful evidence that nucleic acids, rather than proteins, are the hereditary material, at least for certain viruses.

Additional Evidence That DNA Is the Genetic Material

Further evidence that DNA is the genetic material came from the laboratory of biochemist Erwin Chargaff. It was already known that DNA is a polymer of nucleotides, each consisting of three components: a nitrogenous (nitrogen-containing) base, a pentose sugar called deoxyribose, and a phosphate group (Figure 16.5). The base can be adenine (A), thymine (T), guanine (G), or cytosine (C). Chargaff analyzed the base composition of DNA from a number of different organisms. In 1950, he reported that the base composition of DNA varies from one species to another. For example, he found that 32.8% of sea urchin DNA nucleotides have the base A, whereas only 30.4% of human DNA nucleotides have the base A and only 24.7% of the DNA nucleotides from the bacterium *E. coli* have the base A. Chargaff's evidence of molecular diversity among species, which most scientists had presumed to be absent from DNA, made DNA a more credible candidate for the genetic material.

Chargaff also noticed a peculiar regularity in the ratios of nucleotide bases. In the DNA of each species he studied, the number of adenines approximately equaled the number

▲ Figure 16.5 **The structure of a DNA strand.** Each of the four DNA nucleotide monomers consists of a nitrogenous base (T, A, C, or G), the sugar deoxyribose (blue), and a phosphate group (yellow). The phosphate group of one nucleotide is attached to the sugar of the next, forming a "backbone" of alternating phosphates and sugars from which the bases project. The polynucleotide strand has directionality, from the 5′ end (with the phosphate group) to the 3′ end (with the —OH group of the sugar). 5′ and 3′ refer to the numbers assigned to the carbons in the sugar ring.

of thymines, and the number of guanines approximately equaled the number of cytosines. In sea urchin DNA, for example, Chargaff's analysis found the four bases in these percentages: A = 32.8% and T = 32.1%; G = 17.7% and C = 17.3%. (The percentages are not exactly the same because of limitations in Chargaff's techniques.)

These two findings became known as *Chargaff's rules*: (1) the base composition v of DNA aries between species, and (2) for each species, the percentages of A and T bases are roughly equal and the percentages of G and C bases are roughly equal. In the Scientific Skills Exercise, you can use Chargaff's rules to predict unknown percentages of nucleotide bases. The basis for these rules remained unexplained until the discovery of the double helix.

Working with Data in a Table

Given the Percentage Composition of One Nucleotide in a Genome, Can We Predict the Percentages of the Other Three Nucleotides? Even before the structure of DNA was elucidated, Erwin Chargaff and his coworkers noticed a pattern in the base composition of nucleotides from different organisms: The percentage of adenine (A) bases roughly equaled that of thymine (T) bases, and the percentage of cytosine (C) bases roughly equaled that of guanine (G) bases. Further, the percentage of each pair (A/T or C/G) varied from species to species. We now know that the 1:1 A/T and C/G ratios are due to complementary base pairing between A and T and between C and G in the DNA double helix, and interspecies differences are due to the unique sequences of bases along a DNA strand. In this exercise, you will apply Chargaff's rules to predict the composition of bases in a genome.

How the Experiments Were Done In Chargaff's experiments, DNA was extracted from the given organism, hydrolyzed to break apart the individual nucleotides, and then analyzed chemically. (These experiments provided approximate values for each type of nucleotide. Today, whole-genome sequencing allows base composition analysis to be done more precisely directly from the sequence data.)

Data from the Experiments Tables are useful for organizing sets of data representing a common set of values (here, percentages of A, G, C, and T) for a number of different samples (in this case, from different species). You can apply the patterns that you see in the known data to predict unknown values. In the table at the upper right, complete base distribution data are given for sea urchin DNA and salmon DNA; you will use Chargaff's rules to fill in the rest of the table with predicted values.

Source of DNA	Base Percentage			
	Adenine	Guanine	Cytosine	Thymine
Sea urchin	32.8	17.7	17.3	32.1
Salmon	29.7	20.8	20.4	29.1
Wheat	28.1	21.8	22.7	
E. coli	24.7	26.0		
Human	30.4			30.1
Ox	29.0			

Interpret the Data

1. Explain how the sea urchin and salmon data demonstrate both of Chargaff's rules.

2. Using Chargaff's rules, fill in the table with your predictions of the missing percentages of bases, starting with the wheat genome and proceeding through *E. coli*, human, and ox. Show how you arrived at your answers.

3. If Chargaff's rule—that the amount of A equals the amount of T and the amount of C equals the amount of G—is valid, then hypothetically we could extrapolate this to the combined DNA of all species on Earth (like one huge Earth genome). To see whether the data in the table support this hypothesis, calculate the average percentage for each base in your completed table by averaging the values in each column. Does Chargaff's equivalence rule still hold true?

(MB) A version of this Scientific Skills Exercise can be assigned in MasteringBiology.

Data from several papers by Chargaff: for example, E. Chargaff et al., Composition of the desoxypentose nucleic acids of four genera of sea-urchin, Journal of Biological Chemistry 195:155–160 (1952).

Building a Structural Model of DNA: *Scientific Inquiry*

Once most biologists were convinced that DNA was the genetic material, the challenge was to determine how the structure of DNA could account for its role in inheritance. By the early 1950s, the arrangement of covalent bonds in a nucleic acid polymer was well established (see Figure 16.5), and researchers focused on discovering the three-dimensional structure of DNA. Among the scientists working on the problem were Linus Pauling, at the California Institute of Technology, and Maurice Wilkins and Rosalind Franklin, at King's College in London. First to come up with the correct answer, however, were two scientists who were relatively unknown at the time—the American James Watson and the Englishman Francis Crick.

The brief but celebrated partnership that solved the puzzle of DNA structure began soon after Watson journeyed to Cambridge University, where Crick was studying protein structure with a technique called X-ray crystallography (see Figure 5.22). While visiting the laboratory of Maurice Wilkins, Watson saw an X-ray diffraction image of DNA produced by Wilkins's accomplished colleague Rosalind Franklin (**Figure 16.6a**). Images produced by X-ray crystallography are not actually pictures of molecules. The spots

and smudges in **Figure 16.6b** were produced by X-rays that were diffracted (deflected) as they passed through aligned fibers of purified DNA. Watson was familiar with the type of X-ray diffraction pattern that helical molecules produce, and an examination of the photo that Wilkins showed him confirmed that DNA was helical in shape. It also augmented earlier data obtained by Franklin and others suggesting the

(a) Rosalind Franklin (b) Franklin's X-ray diffraction photograph of DNA

▲ **Figure 16.6 Rosalind Franklin and her X-ray diffraction photo of DNA.** Franklin, a very accomplished X-ray crystallographer, conducted critical experiments resulting in the photo that allowed Watson and Crick to deduce the double-helical structure of DNA.

width of the helix and the spacing of the nitrogenous bases along it. The pattern in this photo implied that the helix was made up of two strands, contrary to a three-stranded model that Linus Pauling had proposed a short time earlier. The presence of two strands accounts for the now-familiar term **double helix (Figure 16.7)**.

Watson and Crick began building models of a double helix that would conform to the X-ray measurements and what was then known about the chemistry of DNA, including Chargaff's rule of base equivalences. Having also read an unpublished annual report summarizing Franklin's work, they knew she had concluded that the sugar-phosphate backbones were on the outside of the DNA molecule, contrary to their working model. Franklin's arrangement was appealing because it put the relatively hydrophobic nitrogenous bases in the molecule's interior, away from the surrounding aqueous solution, and the negatively charged phosphate groups wouldn't be forced together in the interior. Watson constructed such a model, shown in the lower photo on the first page of this chapter.

In this model, the two sugar-phosphate backbones are **antiparallel**—that is, their subunits run in opposite directions (see Figure 16.7b). You can imagine the overall

arrangement as a rope ladder with rigid rungs. The side ropes represent the sugar-phosphate backbones, and the rungs represent pairs of nitrogenous bases. Now imagine twisting the ladder to form a helix. Franklin's X-ray data indicated that the helix makes one full turn every 3.4 nm along its length. With the bases stacked just 0.34 nm apart, there are ten layers of base pairs, or rungs of the ladder, in each full turn of the helix.

The nitrogenous bases of the double helix are paired in specific combinations: adenine (A) with thymine (T), and guanine (G) with cytosine (C). It was mainly by trial and error that Watson and Crick arrived at this key feature of DNA. At first, Watson imagined that the bases paired like with like—for example, A with A and C with C. But this model did not fit the X-ray data, which suggested that the double helix had a uniform diameter. Why is this requirement inconsistent with like-with-like pairing of bases? Adenine and guanine are purines, nitrogenous bases with two organic rings, while cytosine and thymine are nitrogenous bases called pyrimidines, which have a single ring. Thus, purines (A and G) are about twice as wide as pyrimidines (C and T). A purine-purine pair is too wide and a pyrimidine-pyrimidine pair too narrow to account for the 2-nm

(a) Key features of DNA structure. The "ribbons" in this diagram represent the sugar-phosphate backbones of the two DNA strands. The helix is "right-handed," curving up to the right. The two strands are held together by hydrogen bonds (dotted lines) between the nitrogenous bases, which are paired in the interior of the double helix.

(b) Partial chemical structure. For clarity, the two DNA strands are shown untwisted in this partial chemical structure. Strong covalent bonds link the units of each strand, while weaker hydrogen bonds between the bases hold one strand to the other. Notice that the strands are antiparallel, meaning that they are oriented in opposite directions, like the lanes of a divided highway.

(c) Space-filling model. The tight stacking of the base pairs is clear in this computer-generated, space-filling model. Van der Waals interactions between the stacked pairs play a major role in holding the molecule together.

▲ Figure 16.7 **The structure of the double helix.**

diameter of the double helix. Always pairing a purine with a pyrimidine, however, results in a uniform diameter:

Purine + purine: too wide

Pyrimidine + pyrimidine: too narrow

Purine + pyrimidine: width consistent with X-ray data

Watson and Crick reasoned that there must be additional specificity of pairing dictated by the structure of the bases. Each base has chemical side groups that can form hydrogen bonds with its appropriate partner: Adenine can form two hydrogen bonds with thymine and only thymine; guanine forms three hydrogen bonds with cytosine and only cytosine. In shorthand, A pairs with T, and G pairs with C (Figure 16.8).

The Watson-Crick model took into account Chargaff's ratios and ultimately explained them. Wherever one strand of a DNA molecule has an A, the partner strand has a T. Similarly, a G in one strand is always paired with a C in the complementary strand. Therefore, in the DNA of any organism, the amount of adenine equals the amount of thymine, and the amount of guanine equals the amount of cytosine. (Modern DNA sequencing techniques have confirmed that the amounts are exactly equal.) Although the base-pairing rules dictate the combinations of nitrogenous bases that form the "rungs" of the double helix, they do not restrict the sequence of nucleotides *along* each DNA strand. The linear sequence of the four bases can be varied in countless ways, and each gene has a unique base sequence.

▲ **Figure 16.8 Base pairing in DNA.** The pairs of nitrogenous bases in a DNA double helix are held together by hydrogen bonds, shown here as black dotted lines.

Adenine (A)   **Thymine (T)**

Guanine (G)   **Cytosine (C)**

In April 1953, Watson and Crick surprised the scientific world with a succinct, one-page paper that reported their molecular model for DNA: the double helix, which has since become the symbol of molecular biology. Watson and Crick, along with Maurice Wilkins, were awarded the Nobel Prize in 1962 for this work. (Sadly, Rosalind Franklin had died at the age of 38 in 1958 and was thus ineligible for the prize.) The beauty of the double helix model was that the structure of DNA suggested the basic mechanism of its replication.

CONCEPT 16.2

Many proteins work together in DNA replication and repair

The relationship between structure and function is manifest in the double helix. The idea that there is specific pairing of nitrogenous bases in DNA was the flash of inspiration that led Watson and Crick to the double helix. At the same time, they saw the functional significance of the base-pairing rules. They ended their classic paper with this wry statement: "It has not escaped our notice that the specific pairing we have postulated immediately suggests a possible copying mechanism for the genetic material."* In this section, you will learn about the basic principle of DNA replication, as well as some important details of the process.

The Basic Principle: Base Pairing to a Template Strand

In a second paper, Watson and Crick stated their hypothesis for how DNA replicates:

Now our model for deoxyribonucleic acid is, in effect, a pair of templates, each of which is complementary to the other. We imagine that prior to duplication the hydrogen bonds are broken, and the two chains unwind and separate. Each chain then acts as a template for the formation on to itself of a new companion chain, so that eventually we shall have two pairs of chains, where we only had one before. Moreover, the sequence of the pairs of bases will have been duplicated exactly.†

*J. D. Watson and F. H. C. Crick, Molecular structure of nucleic acids: a structure for deoxyribose nucleic acids, *Nature* 171:737–738 (1953).

†J. D. Watson and F. H. C. Crick, Genetical implications of the structure of deoxyribonucleic acid, *Nature* 171:964–967 (1953).

(a) The parental molecule has two complementary strands of DNA. Each base is paired by hydrogen bonding with its specific partner, A with T and G with C.

(b) First, the two DNA strands are separated. Each parental strand can now serve as a template for a new, complementary strand.

(c) Nucleotides complementary to the parental (dark blue) strand are connected to form the sugar-phosphate backbones of the new "daughter" (light blue) strands.

▲ **Figure 16.9 A model for DNA replication: the basic concept.** In this simplified illustration, a short segment of DNA has been untwisted. Simple shapes symbolize the four kinds of bases. Dark blue represents DNA strands present in the parental molecule; light blue represents newly synthesized DNA.

Figure 16.9 illustrates Watson and Crick's basic idea. To make it easier to follow, we show only a short section of double helix in untwisted form. Notice that if you cover one of the two DNA strands of Figure 16.9a, you can still determine its linear sequence of nucleotides by referring to the uncovered strand and applying the base-pairing rules. The two strands are complementary; each stores the information necessary to reconstruct the other. When a cell copies a DNA molecule, each strand serves as a template for ordering nucleotides into a new, complementary strand. Nucleotides line up along the template strand according to the base-pairing rules and are linked to form the new strands. Where there was one double-stranded DNA molecule at the beginning of the process, there are soon two, each an exact replica of the "parental" molecule. The copying mechanism is analogous to using a photographic negative to make a positive image, which can in turn be used to make another negative, and so on.

This model of DNA replication remained untested for several years following publication of the DNA structure. The requisite experiments were simple in concept but difficult to perform. Watson and Crick's model predicts that when a double helix replicates, each of the two daughter molecules will have one old strand, from the parental molecule, and one newly made strand. This **semiconservative model** can be distinguished from a conservative model of replication, in which the two parental strands somehow come back together after the process (that is, the parental molecule is conserved). In yet a third model, called the dispersive model, all four strands of DNA following replication have a mixture of old and new DNA. These three models are shown in **Figure 16.10**. Although mechanisms for conservative or dispersive DNA replication are not easy to devise, these models remained possibilities until they could be

	Parent cell	First replication	Second replication

(a) Conservative model. The two parental strands reassociate after acting as templates for new strands, thus restoring the parental double helix.

(b) Semiconservative model. The two strands of the parental molecule separate, and each functions as a template for synthesis of a new, complementary strand.

(c) Dispersive model. Each strand of *both* daughter molecules contains a mixture of old and newly synthesized DNA.

▲ **Figure 16.10 Three alternative models of DNA replication.** Each short segment of double helix symbolizes the DNA within a cell. Beginning with a parent cell, we follow the DNA for two more generations of cells—two rounds of DNA replication. Parental DNA is dark blue; newly made DNA is light blue.

ruled out. After two years of preliminary work at the California Institute of Technology in the late 1950s, Matthew Meselson and Franklin Stahl devised a clever experiment that distinguished between the three models, described in Figure 16.11. The results of their experiment supported the semiconservative model of DNA replication, as predicted by Watson and Crick, and is widely acknowledged among biologists to be a classic example of elegant experimental design.

The basic principle of DNA replication is conceptually simple. However, the actual process involves some complicated biochemical gymnastics, as we will now see.

DNA Replication: *A Closer Look*

The bacterium *E. coli* has a single chromosome of about 4.6 million nucleotide pairs. In a favorable environment, an *E. coli* cell can copy all this DNA and divide to form two genetically identical daughter cells in less than an hour. Each of *your* cells has 46 DNA molecules in its nucleus, one long double-helical molecule per chromosome. In all, that represents about 6 billion nucleotide pairs, or over a thousand times more DNA than is found in a bacterial cell. If we were to print the one-letter symbols for these bases (A, G, C, and T) the size of the type you are now reading, the 6 billion nucleotide pairs of information in a diploid human cell would fill about 1,400 biology textbooks. Yet it takes one of your cells just a few hours to copy all of this DNA. This replication of an enormous amount of genetic information is achieved with very few errors—only about one per 10 billion nucleotides. The copying of DNA is remarkable in its speed and accuracy.

More than a dozen enzymes and other proteins participate in DNA replication. Much more is known about how this "replication machine" works in bacteria (such as *E. coli*) than in eukaryotes, and we will describe the basic steps of the process for *E. coli*, except where otherwise noted. What scientists have learned about eukaryotic DNA replication suggests, however, that most of the process is fundamentally similar for prokaryotes and eukaryotes.

Getting Started

The replication of a chromosome begins at particular sites called **origins of replication**, short stretches of DNA having a specific sequence of nucleotides. The *E. coli* chromosome, like many other bacterial chromosomes, is circular and has a single origin. Proteins that initiate DNA replication recognize this sequence and attach to the DNA, separating the two strands and opening up a replication "bubble." Replication of DNA then proceeds in both directions until the entire molecule is copied (**Figure 16.12a**). In contrast to a bacterial chromosome, a eukaryotic chromosome may have hundreds or even a few thousand replication origins. Multiple replication bubbles form and eventually fuse, thus speeding up the copying of the very long DNA molecules

▼ Figure 16.11 Inquiry

Does DNA replication follow the conservative, semiconservative, or dispersive model?

Experiment Matthew Meselson and Franklin Stahl cultured *E. coli* for several generations in a medium containing nucleotide precursors labeled with a heavy isotope of nitrogen, ^{15}N. They then transferred the bacteria to a medium with only ^{14}N, a lighter isotope. A sample was taken after the first DNA replication; another sample was taken after the second replication. They extracted DNA from the bacteria in the samples and then centrifuged each DNA sample to separate DNA of different densities.

❶ Bacteria cultured in medium with ^{15}N (heavy isotope)

❷ Bacteria transferred to medium with ^{14}N (lighter isotope)

Results

❸ DNA sample centrifuged after first replication

❹ DNA sample centrifuged after second replication

Less dense

More dense

Conclusion Meselson and Stahl compared their results to those predicted by each of the three models in Figure 16.10, as shown below. The first replication in the ^{14}N medium produced a band of hybrid (^{15}N-^{14}N) DNA. This result eliminated the conservative model. The second replication produced both light and hybrid DNA, a result that refuted the dispersive model and supported the semiconservative model. They therefore concluded that DNA replication is semiconservative.

Predictions:	**First replication**	**Second replication**
Conservative model		
Semiconservative model		
Dispersive model		

Source: M. Meselson and F. W. Stahl, The replication of DNA in *Escherichia coli, Proceedings of the National Academy of Sciences USA* 44:671–682 (1958).

Inquiry in Action Read and analyze the original paper in *Inquiry in Action: Interpreting Scientific Papers.*

(MB) A related Experimental Inquiry Tutorial can be assigned in MasteringBiology.

WHAT IF? *If Meselson and Stahl had first grown the cells in ^{14}N-containing medium and then moved them into ^{15}N-containing medium before taking samples, what would have been the result?*

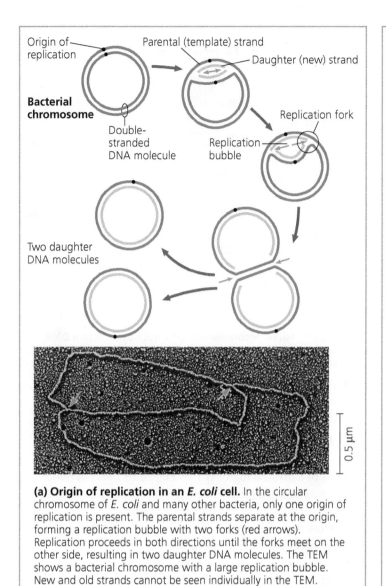

(a) **Origin of replication in an *E. coli* cell.** In the circular chromosome of *E. coli* and many other bacteria, only one origin of replication is present. The parental strands separate at the origin, forming a replication bubble with two forks (red arrows). Replication proceeds in both directions until the forks meet on the other side, resulting in two daughter DNA molecules. The TEM shows a bacterial chromosome with a large replication bubble. New and old strands cannot be seen individually in the TEM.

(b) **Origins of replication in a eukaryotic cell.** In each linear chromosome of a eukaryote, DNA replication begins when replication bubbles form at many sites along the giant DNA molecule. The bubbles expand as replication proceeds in both directions (red arrows). Eventually, the bubbles fuse and synthesis of the daughter strands is complete. The TEM shows three replication bubbles along the DNA of a cultured Chinese hamster cell.

DRAW IT *In the TEM, add arrows in the forks of the third bubble.*

▲ **Figure 16.12 Origins of replication in *E. coli* and eukaryotes.** The red arrows indicate the movement of the replication forks and thus the overall directions of DNA replication within each bubble.

(Figure 16.12b). As in bacteria, eukaryotic DNA replication proceeds in both directions from each origin.

At each end of a replication bubble is a **replication fork**, a Y-shaped region where the parental strands of DNA are being unwound. Several kinds of proteins participate in the unwinding **(Figure 16.13)**. **Helicases** are enzymes that untwist the double helix at the replication forks, separating the two parental strands and making them available as template strands. After the parental strands separate, **single-strand binding proteins** bind to the unpaired DNA strands, keeping them from re-pairing. The untwisting of the double helix causes tighter twisting and strain ahead of the replication fork. **Topoisomerase** helps relieve this strain by breaking, swiveling, and rejoining DNA strands.

The unwound sections of parental DNA strands are now available to serve as templates for the synthesis of new

▲ **Figure 16.13 Some of the proteins involved in the initiation of DNA replication.** The same proteins function at both replication forks in a replication bubble. For simplicity, only the left-hand fork is shown, and the DNA bases are drawn much larger in relation to the proteins than they are in reality.

complementary DNA strands. However, the enzymes that synthesize DNA cannot *initiate* the synthesis of a polynucleotide; they can only add DNA nucleotides to the end of an already existing chain that is base-paired with the template strand. The initial nucleotide chain that is produced during DNA synthesis is actually a short stretch of RNA, not DNA. This RNA chain is called a **primer** and is synthesized by the enzyme **primase** (see Figure 16.13). Primase starts a complementary RNA chain from a single RNA nucleotide, adding more RNA nucleotides one at a time, using the parental DNA strand as a template. The completed primer, generally 5–10 nucleotides long, is thus base-paired to the template strand. The new DNA strand will start from the 3′ end of the RNA primer.

Synthesizing a New DNA Strand

Enzymes called **DNA polymerases** catalyze the synthesis of new DNA by adding nucleotides to a preexisting chain. In *E. coli*, there are several different DNA polymerases, but two appear to play the major roles in DNA replication: DNA polymerase III and DNA polymerase I. The situation in eukaryotes is more complicated, with at least 11 different DNA polymerases discovered so far; however, the general principles are the same.

Most DNA polymerases require a primer and a DNA template strand, along which complementary DNA nucleotides are lined up. In *E. coli*, DNA polymerase III (abbreviated DNA pol III) adds a DNA nucleotide to the RNA primer and then continues adding DNA nucleotides, complementary to the parental DNA template strand, to the growing end of the new DNA strand. The rate of elongation is about 500 nucleotides per second in bacteria and 50 per second in human cells.

Each nucleotide to be added to a growing DNA strand consists of a sugar attached to a base and to three phosphate groups. You have already encountered such a molecule—ATP (adenosine triphosphate; see Figure 9.9). The only difference between the ATP of energy metabolism and dATP, the adenine nucleotide used to make DNA, is the sugar component, which is deoxyribose in the building block of DNA but ribose in ATP. Like ATP, the nucleotides used for DNA synthesis are chemically reactive, partly because their triphosphate tails have an unstable cluster of negative charge. As each monomer joins the growing end of a DNA strand, two phosphate groups are lost as a molecule of pyrophosphate (P—P_i). Subsequent hydrolysis of the pyrophosphate to two molecules of inorganic phosphate (P_i) is a coupled exergonic reaction that helps drive the polymerization reaction **(Figure 16.14)**.

Antiparallel Elongation

As we have noted previously, the two ends of a DNA strand are different, giving each strand directionality, like a one-way street (see Figure 16.5). In addition, the two strands of

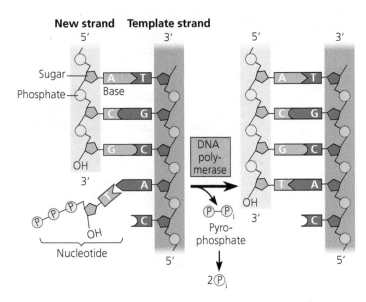

▲ **Figure 16.14 Incorporation of a nucleotide into a DNA strand.** DNA polymerase catalyzes the addition of a nucleotide to the 3′ end of a growing DNA strand, with the release of two phosphates.

? *Use this diagram to explain what we mean when we say that each DNA strand has directionality.*

DNA in a double helix are antiparallel, meaning that they are oriented in opposite directions to each other, like the lanes of a divided highway (see Figure 16.14). Therefore, the two new strands formed during DNA replication must also be antiparallel to their template strands.

How does the antiparallel arrangement of the double helix affect replication? Because of their structure, DNA polymerases can add nucleotides only to the free 3′ end of a primer or growing DNA strand, never to the 5′ end (see Figure 16.14). Thus, a new DNA strand can elongate only in the 5′ → 3′ direction. With this in mind, let's examine one of the two replication forks in a bubble **(Figure 16.15)**. Along one template strand, DNA polymerase III can synthesize a complementary strand continuously by elongating the new DNA in the mandatory 5′ → 3′ direction. DNA pol III remains in the replication fork on that template strand and continuously adds nucleotides to the new complementary strand as the fork progresses. The DNA strand made by this mechanism is called the **leading strand**. Only one primer is required for DNA pol III to synthesize the entire leading strand (see Figure 16.15).

To elongate the other new strand of DNA in the mandatory 5′ → 3′ direction, DNA pol III must work along the other template strand in the direction *away from* the replication fork. The DNA strand elongating in this direction is called the **lagging strand**.* In contrast to the leading strand,

---

*Synthesis of the leading strand and synthesis of the lagging strand occur concurrently and at the same rate. The lagging strand is so named because its synthesis is delayed slightly relative to synthesis of the leading strand; each new fragment of the lagging strand cannot be started until enough template has been exposed at the replication fork.

Overview

Leading strand — Origin of replication — Lagging strand

Primer

Lagging strand — Leading strand

Overall directions of replication

❶ After RNA primer is made, DNA pol III starts to synthesize the leading strand.

Origin of replication

3′
5′

RNA primer

Sliding clamp

DNA pol III

5′
3′

Parental DNA

5′

3′
5′

5′
3′

3′

5′

❷ The leading strand is elongated continuously in the 5′→ 3′ direction as the fork progresses.

▲ **Figure 16.15 Synthesis of the leading strand during DNA replication.** This diagram focuses on the left replication fork shown in the overview box. DNA polymerase III (DNA pol III), shaped like a cupped hand, is shown closely associated with a protein called the "sliding clamp" that encircles the newly synthesized double helix like a doughnut. The sliding clamp moves DNA pol III along the DNA template strand.

which elongates continuously, the lagging strand is synthesized discontinuously, as a series of segments. These segments of the lagging strand are called **Okazaki fragments**, after the Japanese scientist who discovered them. The fragments are about 1,000–2,000 nucleotides long in *E. coli* and 100–200 nucleotides long in eukaryotes.

Figure 16.16 illustrates the steps in the synthesis of the lagging strand at one fork. Whereas only one primer is required on the leading strand, each Okazaki fragment on the lagging strand must be primed separately (steps and ❹). After DNA pol III forms an Okazaki fragment (steps ❷–❹), another DNA polymerase, DNA polymerase I (DNA pol I), replaces the RNA nucleotides of the adjacent primer with DNA nucleotides (step ❺). But DNA pol I cannot join the final nucleotide of this replacement DNA segment to the first DNA nucleotide of the adjacent Okazaki fragment. Another enzyme, **DNA ligase**, accomplishes this task, joining the sugar-phosphate backbones of all the Okazaki fragments into a continuous DNA strand (step ❻).

Overview

Leading strand — Origin of replication — Lagging strand

Lagging strand

2 1

Leading strand

Overall directions of replication

❶ Primase joins RNA nucleotides into a primer.

Template strand

Origin of replication

3′
5′   3′
5′

❷ DNA pol III adds DNA nucleotides to the primer, forming Okazaki fragment 1.

RNA primer for fragment 1

3′
5′   1   3′   5′   3′   5′

❸ After reaching the next RNA primer to the right, DNA pol III detaches.

Okazaki fragment 1

3′
5′   1   3′   5′

RNA primer for fragment 2

5′
3′   Okazaki fragment 2

❹ Fragment 2 is primed. Then DNA pol III adds DNA nucleotides, detaching when it reaches the fragment 1 primer.

2   1   3′   5′

5′
3′

❺ DNA pol I replaces the RNA with DNA, adding nucleotides to the 3′ end of fragment 2 (and, earlier, of fragment 1).

2   1   3′   5′

❻ DNA ligase forms a bond between the newest DNA and the DNA of fragment 1.

5′
3′

❼ The lagging strand in this region is now complete.

2   1   3′   5′

Overall direction of replication

▲ **Figure 16.16 Synthesis of the lagging strand.**

Figure 16.17 and **Table 16.1** summarize DNA replication. Please study them carefully before proceeding.

The DNA Replication Complex

It is traditional—and convenient—to represent DNA polymerase molecules as locomotives moving along a DNA railroad track, but such a model is inaccurate in two important ways. First, the various proteins that participate in DNA replication actually form a single large complex, a "DNA replication machine." Many protein-protein interactions facilitate the efficiency of this complex. For example, by interacting with other proteins at the fork, primase apparently acts as a molecular brake, slowing progress of the replication fork and coordinating the placement of primers and

the rates of replication on the leading and lagging strands. Second, the DNA replication complex may not move along the DNA; rather, the DNA may move through the complex during the replication process. In eukaryotic cells, multiple copies of the complex, perhaps grouped into "factories," may be anchored to the nuclear matrix, a framework of fibers extending through the interior of the nucleus. Experimental evidence supports a model in which two DNA polymerase molecules, one on each template strand, "reel in" the parental DNA and extrude newly made daughter DNA molecules. In this so-called trombone model, the lagging strand is also looped back through the complex (**Figure 16.18**).

❶ Helicase unwinds the parental double helix.

❷ Molecules of single-strand binding protein stabilize the unwound template strands.

❸ The leading strand is synthesized continuously in the 5′ to 3′ direction by DNA pol III.

❹ Primase begins synthesis of the RNA primer for the fifth Okazaki fragment.

❺ DNA pol III is completing synthesis of fragment 4. When it reaches the RNA primer on fragment 3, it will detach and begin adding DNA nucleotides to the 3′ end of the fragment 5 primer in the replication fork.

❻ DNA pol I removes the primer from the 5′ end of fragment 2, replacing it with DNA nucleotides added one by one to the 3′ end of fragment 3. After the last addition, the backbone is left with a free 3′ end.

❼ DNA ligase joins the 3′ end of fragment 2 to the 5′ end of fragment 1.

Overview

Origin of replication

Leading strand · Lagging strand · Lagging strand · Leading strand

Overall directions of replication

Leading strand template · Leading strand · Parental DNA · DNA pol III · Primer · Primase · DNA pol III · Lagging strand · Lagging strand template · DNA pol I · DNA ligase

▲ **Figure 16.17 A summary of bacterial DNA replication.** The detailed diagram shows the left-hand replication fork of the replication bubble shown in the overview (upper right). Viewing each daughter strand in its entirety in the overview, you can see that half of it is made continuously as the leading strand, while the other half (on the other side of the origin) is synthesized in fragments as the lagging strand.

DRAW IT *Draw a similar diagram showing the right-hand fork of this bubble, numbering the Okazaki fragments appropriately. Label all 5′ and 3′ ends.*

Table 16.1 Bacterial DNA Replication Proteins and Their Functions

Protein	Function
Helicase 	Unwinds parental double helix at replication forks
Single-strand binding protein 	Binds to and stabilizes single-stranded DNA until it is used as a template
Topoisomerase 	Relieves overwinding strain ahead of replication forks by breaking, swiveling, and rejoining DNA strands
Primase 	Synthesizes an RNA primer at 5′ end of leading strand and at 5′ end of each Okazaki fragment of lagging strand
DNA pol III 	Using parental DNA as a template, synthesizes new DNA strand by adding nucleotides to an RNA primer or a pre-existing DNA strand
DNA pol I 	Removes RNA nucleotides of primer from 5′ end and replaces them with DNA nucleotides
DNA ligase 	Joins Okazaki fragments of lagging strand; on leading strand, joins 3′ end of DNA that replaces primer to rest of leading strand DNA

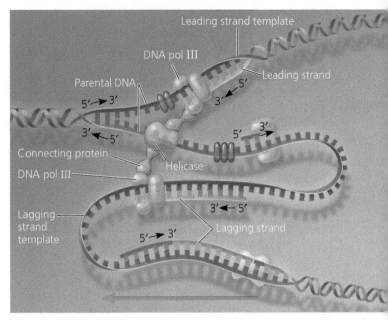

▲ **Figure 16.18 A current model of the DNA replication complex.** Two DNA polymerase III molecules work together in a complex with helicase and other proteins. One DNA polymerase acts on each template strand. The lagging strand template DNA loops through the complex, resembling the slide of a trombone. (This is often called the trombone model.)

DRAW IT *Draw a line tracing the lagging strand template along the entire stretch of DNA shown here.*

ANIMATION *BioFlix* Visit the Study Area in **MasteringBiology** for the BioFlix® 3-D Animation on DNA Replication. BioFlix Tutorials can also be assigned in MasteringBiology.

Proofreading and Repairing DNA

We cannot attribute the accuracy of DNA replication solely to the specificity of base pairing. Initial pairing errors between incoming nucleotides and those in the template strand occur at a rate of one in 10^5 nucleotides. However, errors in the completed DNA molecule amount to only one in 10^{10} (10 billion) nucleotides, an error rate that is 100,000 times lower. This is because during DNA replication, DNA polymerases proofread each nucleotide against its template as soon as it is covalently bonded to the growing strand. Upon finding an incorrectly paired nucleotide, the polymerase removes the nucleotide and then resumes synthesis. (This action is similar to fixing a word processing error by deleting the wrong letter and then entering the correct letter.)

Mismatched nucleotides sometimes evade proofreading by a DNA polymerase. In **mismatch repair**, other enzymes remove and replace incorrectly paired nucleotides that have resulted from replication errors. Researchers spotlighted the importance of such repair enzymes when they found that a hereditary defect in one of them is associated with a form of colon cancer. Apparently, this defect allows cancer-causing errors to accumulate in the DNA faster than normal.

Incorrectly paired or altered nucleotides can also arise after replication. In fact, maintenance of the genetic

information encoded in DNA requires frequent repair of various kinds of damage to existing DNA. DNA molecules are constantly subjected to potentially harmful chemical and physical agents, such as X-rays, as we'll discuss in Chapter 17. In addition, DNA bases often undergo spontaneous chemical changes under normal cellular conditions. However, these changes in DNA are usually corrected before they become permanent changes—*mutations*—perpetuated through successive replications. Each cell continuously monitors and repairs its genetic material. Because repair of damaged DNA is so important to the survival of an organism, it is no surprise that many different DNA repair enzymes have evolved. Almost 100 are known in *E. coli*, and about 130 have been identified so far in humans.

Most cellular systems for repairing incorrectly paired nucleotides, whether they are due to DNA damage or to replication errors, use a mechanism that takes advantage of the base-paired structure of DNA. In many cases, a segment of the strand containing the damage is cut out (excised) by a DNA-cutting enzyme—a **nuclease**—and the resulting gap is then filled in with nucleotides, using the undamaged strand as a template. The enzymes involved in filling the gap are

① Teams of enzymes detect and repair damaged DNA, such as this thymine dimer (often caused by ultraviolet radiation), which distorts the DNA molecule.

② A nuclease enzyme cuts the damaged DNA strand at two points, and the damaged section is removed.

③ Repair synthesis by a DNA polymerase fills in the missing nucleotides.

④ DNA ligase seals the free end of the new DNA to the old DNA, making the strand complete.

▲ Figure 16.19 **Nucleotide excision repair of DNA damage.**

a DNA polymerase and DNA ligase. One such DNA repair system is called **nucleotide excision repair** (Figure 16.19).

An important function of the DNA repair enzymes in our skin cells is to repair genetic damage caused by the ultraviolet rays of sunlight. One type of damage, shown in Figure 16.19, is the covalent linking of thymine bases that are adjacent on a DNA strand. Such *thymine dimers* cause the DNA to buckle and interfere with DNA replication. The importance of repairing this kind of damage is underscored by a disorder called xeroderma pigmentosum, which in most cases is caused by an inherited defect in a nucleotide excision repair enzyme. Individuals with this disorder are hypersensitive to sunlight; mutations in their skin cells caused by ultraviolet light are left uncorrected, resulting in skin cancer.

Evolutionary Significance of Altered DNA Nucleotides

EVOLUTION Faithful replication of the genome and repair of DNA damage are important for the functioning of the organism and for passing on a complete, accurate genome to the next generation. The error rate after proofreading and repair is extremely low, but rare mistakes do slip through. Once a mismatched nucleotide pair is replicated, the sequence change is permanent in the daughter molecule that has the incorrect nucleotide as well as in any subsequent copies. As we mentioned earlier, a permanent change in the DNA sequence is called a mutation.

Mutations can change the phenotype of an organism (as you'll learn in Chapter 17). And if they occur in germ cells, which give rise to gametes, mutations can be passed on from generation to generation. The vast majority of such changes either have no effect or are harmful, but a very small percentage can be beneficial. In either case, mutations are the original source of the variation on which natural selection operates during evolution and are ultimately responsible for the appearance of new species. The balance between complete fidelity of DNA replication or repair and a low mutation rate has, over long periods of time, allowed the evolution of the rich diversity of species we see on Earth today.

Replicating the Ends of DNA Molecules

For linear DNA, such as the DNA of eukaryotic chromosomes, the usual replication machinery cannot complete the 5′ ends of daughter DNA strands. This is a consequence of the fact that a DNA polymerase can add nucleotides only to the 3′ end of a preexisting polynucleotide. Even if an Okazaki fragment can be started with an RNA primer bound to the very end of the template strand, once that primer is removed, it cannot be replaced with DNA because there is no 3′ end available for nucleotide addition (Figure 16.20). As a result, repeated rounds of replication produce shorter and shorter DNA molecules with uneven ("staggered") ends.

Most prokaryotes have a circular chromosome, with no ends, so the shortening of DNA does not occur. But what protects the genes of linear eukaryotic chromosomes from being eroded away during successive rounds of DNA replication? Eukaryotic chromosomal DNA molecules have special nucleotide sequences called **telomeres** at their ends (Figure 16.21). Telomeres do not contain genes; instead, the DNA typically consists of multiple repetitions of one short nucleotide sequence. In each human telomere, for example, the six-nucleotide sequence TTAGGG is repeated between 100 and 1,000 times. Telomeres have two protective functions.

First, specific proteins associated with telomeric DNA prevent the staggered ends of the daughter molecule from activating the cell's systems for monitoring DNA damage. (Staggered ends of a DNA molecule, which often result from double-strand breaks, can trigger signal transduction pathways leading to cell cycle arrest or cell death.) Second, telomeric DNA acts as a kind of buffer zone that provides some protection against the organism's genes shortening, somewhat like how the plastic-wrapped ends of a shoelace slow its unraveling. However, telomeres do not prevent the erosion of genes near the ends of chromosomes; they merely postpone it.

As shown in Figure 16.20, telomeres become shorter during every round of replication. Thus, as expected, telomeric DNA tends to be shorter in dividing somatic cells of older

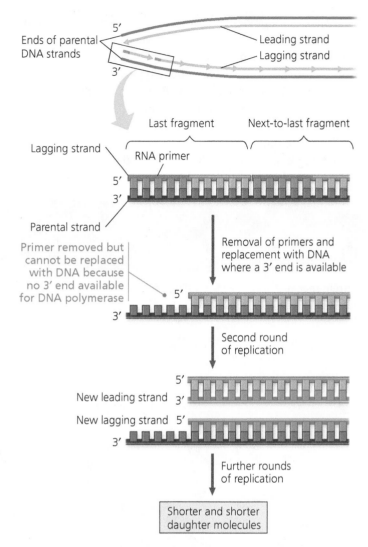

▲ **Figure 16.20 Shortening of the ends of linear DNA molecules.** Here we follow the end of one strand of a DNA molecule through two rounds of replication. After the first round, the new lagging strand is shorter than its template. After a second round, both the leading and lagging strands have become shorter than the original parental DNA. Although not shown here, the other ends of these DNA molecules also become shorter.

individuals and in cultured cells that have divided many times. It has been proposed that shortening of telomeres is somehow connected to the aging process of certain tissues and even to aging of the organism as a whole.

But what about cells whose genome must persist virtually unchanged from an organism to its offspring over many generations? If the chromosomes of germ cells became shorter in every cell cycle, essential genes would eventually be missing from the gametes they produce. However, this does not occur: An enzyme called *telomerase* catalyzes the lengthening of telomeres in eukaryotic germ cells, thus restoring their original length and compensating for the shortening that occurs during DNA replication. Telomerase is not active in most human somatic cells, but its activity varies from tissue to tissue. The activity of telomerase in germ cells results in telomeres of maximum length in the zygote.

▲ **Figure 16.21 Telomeres.** Eukaryotes have repetitive, noncoding sequences called telomeres at the ends of their DNA. Telomeres are stained orange in these mouse chromosomes (LM).

Normal shortening of telomeres may protect organisms from cancer by limiting the number of divisions that somatic cells can undergo. Cells from large tumors often have unusually short telomeres, as we would expect for cells that have undergone many cell divisions. Further shortening would presumably lead to self-destruction of the tumor cells. Telomerase activity is abnormally high in cancerous somatic cells, suggesting that its ability to stabilize telomere length may allow these cancer cells to persist. Many cancer cells do seem capable of unlimited cell division, as do immortal strains of cultured cells (see Chapter 12). For several years, researchers have studied inhibition of telomerase as a possible cancer therapy. Thus far, while studies that inhibited telomerase in mice with tumors have led to the death of cancer cells, eventually the cells have restored the length of their telomeres by an alternative pathway. This is an area of ongoing research that may eventually yield useful cancer treatments.

Thus far in this chapter, you have learned about the structure and replication of a DNA molecule. In the next section, we'll take a step back and examine how DNA is packaged into chromosomes, the structures that carry the genetic information.

CONCEPT CHECK 16.2

1. What role does complementary base pairing play in the replication of DNA?

2. Identify two major functions of DNA pol III in DNA replication.

3. **MAKE CONNECTIONS** What is the relationship between DNA replication and the S phase of the cell cycle? See Figure 12.6.

4. **WHAT IF?** If the DNA pol I in a given cell were nonfunctional, how would that affect the synthesis of a *leading* strand? In the overview box in Figure 16.17, point out where DNA pol I would normally function on the top leading strand.

A chromosome consists of a DNA molecule packed together with proteins

The main component of the genome in most bacteria is one double-stranded, circular DNA molecule that is associated with a small amount of protein. Although we refer to this structure as the bacterial chromosome, it is very different from a eukaryotic chromosome, which consists of one linear DNA molecule associated with a large amount of protein. In *E. coli*, the chromosomal DNA consists of about 4.6 million nucleotide pairs, representing about 4,400 genes. This is 100 times more DNA than is found in a typical virus, but only about one-thousandth as much DNA as in a human somatic cell. Still, that is a tremendous amount of DNA to be packaged in such a small container.

Stretched out, the DNA of an *E. coli* cell would measure about a millimeter in length, which is 500 times longer than the cell. Within a bacterium, however, certain proteins

▼ **Figure 16.22**

Exploring Chromatin Packing in a Eukaryotic Chromosome

This series of diagrams and transmission electron micrographs depicts a current model for the progressive levels of DNA coiling and folding. The illustration zooms out from a single molecule of DNA to a metaphase chromosome, which is large enough to be seen with a light microscope.

Nucleosome
(10 nm in diameter)

DNA
double helix
(2 nm in diameter)

Histones

Histone tail

H1

DNA, the double helix

Shown here is a ribbon model of DNA, with each ribbon representing one of the sugar-phosphate backbones. Recall that the phosphate groups along the backbone contribute a negative charge along the outside of each strand. The TEM shows a molecule of naked (protein-free) DNA; the double helix alone is 2 nm across.

Histones

Proteins called **histones** are responsible for the first level of DNA packing in chromatin. Although each histone is small—containing only about 100 amino acids—the total mass of histone in chromatin roughly equals the mass of DNA. More than a fifth of a histone's amino acids are positively charged (lysine or arginine) and therefore bind tightly to the negatively charged DNA.

Four types of histones are most common in chromatin: H2A, H2B, H3, and H4. The histones are very similar among eukaryotes; for example, all but two of the amino acids in cow H4 are identical to those in pea H4. The apparent conservation of histone genes during evolution probably reflects the important role of histones in organizing DNA within cells.

These four types of histones are critical to the next level of DNA packing. (A fifth type of histone, called H1, is involved in a further stage of packing.)

Nucleosomes, or "beads on a string" (10-nm fiber)

In electron micrographs, unfolded chromatin is 10 nm in diameter (the *10-nm fiber*). Such chromatin resembles beads on a string (see the TEM). Each "bead" is a **nucleosome**, the basic unit of DNA packing; the "string" between beads is called *linker DNA*.

A nucleosome consists of DNA wound twice around a protein core of eight histones, two each of the main histone types (H2A, H2B, H3, and H4). The amino end (N-terminus) of each histone (the *histone tail*) extends outward from the nucleosome.

In the cell cycle, the histones leave the DNA only briefly during DNA replication. Generally, they do the same during transcription, another process that requires access to the DNA by the cell's molecular machinery. Nucleosomes, and in particular their histone tails, are involved in the regulation of gene expression.

cause the chromosome to coil and "supercoil," densely packing it so that it fills only part of the cell. Unlike the nucleus of a eukaryotic cell, this dense region of DNA in a bacterium, called the nucleoid, is not bounded by membrane (see Figure 6.5).

Each eukaryotic chromosome contains a single linear DNA double helix that, in humans, averages about 1.5×10^8 nucleotide pairs. This is an enormous amount of DNA relative to a chromosome's condensed length. If completely stretched out, such a DNA molecule would be about 4 cm long, thousands of times the diameter of a cell nucleus—and that's not even considering the DNA of the other 45 human chromosomes!

In the cell, eukaryotic DNA is precisely combined with a large amount of protein. Together, this complex of DNA and protein, called **chromatin**, fits into the nucleus through an elaborate, multilevel system of packing. Our current view of the successive levels of DNA packing in a chromosome is outlined in **Figure 16.22**. Study this figure carefully before reading further.

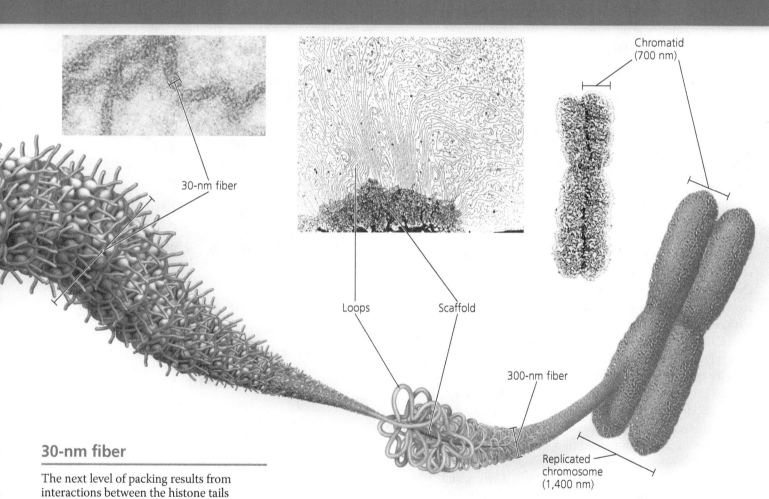

30-nm fiber

Chromatid (700 nm)

Loops Scaffold

300-nm fiber

Replicated chromosome (1,400 nm)

30-nm fiber

The next level of packing results from interactions between the histone tails of one nucleosome and the linker DNA and nucleosomes on either side. The fifth histone, H1, is involved at this level. These interactions cause the extended 10-nm fiber to coil or fold, forming a chromatin fiber roughly 30 nm in thickness, the *30-nm fiber*. Although the 30-nm fiber is quite prevalent in the interphase nucleus, the packing arrangement of nucleosomes in this form of chromatin is still a matter of some debate.

Looped domains (300-nm fiber)

The 30-nm fiber, in turn, forms loops called *looped domains* attached to a chromosome scaffold composed of proteins, thus making up a *300-nm fiber*. The scaffold is rich in one type of topoisomerase, and H1 molecules also appear to be present.

Metaphase chromosome

In a mitotic chromosome, the looped domains themselves coil and fold in a manner not yet fully understood, further compacting all the chromatin to produce the characteristic metaphase chromosome (also shown in the micrograph above). The width of one chromatid is 700 nm. Particular genes always end up located at the same places in metaphase chromosomes, indicating that the packing steps are highly specific and precise.

Chromatin undergoes striking changes in its degree of packing during the course of the cell cycle (see Figure 12.7). In interphase cells stained for light microscopy, the chromatin usually appears as a diffuse mass within the nucleus, suggesting that the chromatin is highly extended. As a cell prepares for mitosis, its chromatin coils and folds up (condenses), eventually forming a characteristic number of short, thick metaphase chromosomes that are distinguishable from each other with the light microscope (Figure 16.23a).

Though interphase chromatin is generally much less condensed than the chromatin of mitotic chromosomes, it shows several of the same levels of higher-order packing. Some of the chromatin comprising a chromosome seems to be present as a 10-nm fiber, but much is compacted into a 30-nm fiber, which in some regions is further folded into looped domains. Early on, biologists assumed that interphase chromatin was a tangled mass in the nucleus, like a bowl of spaghetti, but this is far from the case. Although an interphase chromosome lacks an obvious scaffold, its looped domains appear to be attached to the nuclear lamina, on the inside of the nuclear envelope, and perhaps also to fibers of the nuclear matrix. These attachments may help organize regions of chromatin where genes are active. The chromatin of each chromosome occupies a specific restricted area within the interphase nucleus, and the chromatin fibers of different chromosomes do not appear to be entangled (Figure 16.23b).

Even during interphase, the centromeres and telomeres of chromosomes, as well as other chromosomal regions in some cells, exist in a highly condensed state similar to that seen in a metaphase chromosome. This type of interphase chromatin, visible as irregular clumps with a light microscope, is called **heterochromatin**, to distinguish it from the less compacted, more dispersed **euchromatin** ("true chromatin"). Because of its compaction, heterochromatic DNA is largely inaccessible to the machinery in the cell responsible for transcribing the genetic information coded in the DNA, a crucial early step in gene expression. In contrast, the looser packing of euchromatin makes its DNA accessible to this machinery, so the genes present in euchromatin can be transcribed. The chromosome is a dynamic structure that is condensed, loosened, modified, and remodeled as necessary for various cell processes, including mitosis, meiosis, and gene activity. Chemical modifications of histones affect the state of chromatin condensation and also have multiple effects on gene activity, as you'll see in Chapter 18.

In this chapter, you have learned how DNA molecules are arranged in chromosomes and how DNA replication provides the copies of genes that parents pass to offspring. However, it is not enough that genes be copied and transmitted; the information they carry must be used by the cell. In other words, genes must also be expressed. In the next chapter, we will examine how the cell expresses the genetic information encoded in DNA.

(a) These metaphase chromosomes have been "painted" so that the two homologs of a pair are the same color. Above is a spread of treated chromosomes; on the right, they have been organized into a karyotype.

(b) The ability to visually distinguish among chromosomes makes it possible to see how the chromosomes are arranged in the interphase nucleus. Each chromosome appears to occupy a specific territory during interphase. In general, the two homologs of a pair are not located together.

▲ **Figure 16.23 "Painting" chromosomes.** Researchers can treat ("paint") human chromosomes with molecular tags that cause each chromosome pair to appear a different color.

MAKE CONNECTIONS *If you arrested a human cell in metaphase I of meiosis and applied this technique, what would you observe? How would this differ from what you would see in metaphase of mitosis? Review Figure 13.8 and Figure 12.7.*

CONCEPT CHECK 16.3

1. Describe the structure of a nucleosome, the basic unit of DNA packing in eukaryotic cells.

2. What two properties, one structural and one functional, distinguish heterochromatin from euchromatin?

3. MAKE CONNECTIONS Interphase chromosomes appear to be attached to the nuclear lamina and perhaps also the nuclear matrix. Describe these two structures. See Figure 6.9 and the associated text.

16 Chapter Review

SUMMARY OF KEY CONCEPTS

CONCEPT 16.1

DNA is the genetic material (pp. 315–320)

- Experiments with bacteria and with **phages** provided the first strong evidence that the genetic material is DNA.
- Watson and Crick deduced that DNA is a **double helix** and built a structural model. Two **antiparallel** sugar-phosphate chains wind around the outside of the molecule; the nitrogenous bases project into the interior, where they hydrogen-bond in specific pairs, A with T, G with C.

Sugar-phosphate backbone

Nitrogenous bases

Hydrogen bond

? *What does it mean when we say that the two DNA strands in the double helix are antiparallel? What would an end of the double helix look like if the strands were parallel?*

CONCEPT 16.2

Many proteins work together in DNA replication and repair (pp. 320–329)

- The Meselson-Stahl experiment showed that **DNA replication** is **semiconservative**: The parental molecule unwinds, and each strand then serves as a template for the synthesis of a new strand according to base-pairing rules.
- DNA replication at one **replication fork** is summarized here:

DNA pol III synthesizes **leading strand** continuously

Parental DNA

Helicase

Primase synthesizes a short RNA **primer**

DNA pol III starts DNA synthesis at 3′ end of primer, continues in 5′ → 3′ direction

Lagging strand synthesized in short **Okazaki fragments**, later joined by **DNA ligase**

DNA pol I replaces the RNA primer with DNA nucleotides

Origin of replication

- DNA polymerases proofread new DNA, replacing incorrect nucleotides. In **mismatch repair**, enzymes correct errors that persist. **Nucleotide excision repair** is a process by which **nucleases** cut out and other enzymes replace damaged stretches of DNA.
- The ends of eukaryotic chromosomal DNA get shorter with each round of replication. The presence of **telomeres**, repetitive sequences at the ends of linear DNA molecules, postpones the erosion of genes. Telomerase catalyzes the lengthening of telomeres in germ cells.

? *Compare DNA replication on the leading and lagging strands, including both similarities and differences.*

CONCEPT 16.3

A chromosome consists of a DNA molecule packed together with proteins (pp. 330–332)

- The chromosome of most bacterial species is a circular DNA molecule with some associated proteins, making up the nucleoid. The **chromatin** making up a eukaryotic chromosome is composed of DNA, **histones**, and other proteins. The histones bind to each other and to the DNA to form **nucleosomes**, the most basic units of DNA packing. Histone tails extend outward from each bead-like nucleosome core. Additional coiling and folding lead ultimately to the highly condensed chromatin of the metaphase chromosome. Chromosomes occupy restricted areas in the interphase nucleus. In interphase cells, most chromatin is less compacted (**euchromatin**), but some remains highly condensed (**heterochromatin**). Euchromatin, but not heterochromatin, is generally accessible for transcription of genes.

? *Describe the levels of chromatin packing you'd expect to see in an interphase nucleus.*

TEST YOUR UNDERSTANDING

LEVEL 1: KNOWLEDGE/COMPREHENSION

1. In his work with pneumonia-causing bacteria and mice, Griffith found that
   a. the protein coat from pathogenic cells was able to transform nonpathogenic cells.
   b. heat-killed pathogenic cells caused pneumonia.
   c. some substance from pathogenic cells was transferred to nonpathogenic cells, making them pathogenic.
   d. the polysaccharide coat of bacteria caused pneumonia.

2. What is the basis for the difference in how the leading and lagging strands of DNA molecules are synthesized?
   a. The origins of replication occur only at the 5′ end.
   b. Helicases and single-strand binding proteins work at the 5′ end.
   c. DNA polymerase can join new nucleotides only to the 3′ end of a pre-existing strand.
   d. DNA ligase works only in the 3′ → 5′ direction.

3. In analyzing the number of different bases in a DNA sample, which result would be consistent with the base-pairing rules?
   a. A = G
   b. A + G = C + T
   c. A + T = G + C
   d. A = C

4. The elongation of the leading strand during DNA synthesis
   a. progresses away from the replication fork.
   b. occurs in the 3′ → 5′ direction.
   c. does not require a template strand.
   d. depends on the action of DNA polymerase.

5. In a nucleosome, the DNA is wrapped around
   a. histones.
   b. ribosomes.
   c. polymerase molecules.
   d. a thymine dimer.

6. *E. coli* cells grown on ^{15}N medium are transferred to ^{14}N medium and allowed to grow for two more generations (two rounds of DNA replication). DNA extracted from these cells is centrifuged. What density distribution of DNA would you expect in this experiment?
   a. one high-density and one low-density band
   b. one intermediate-density band
   c. one high-density and one intermediate-density band
   d. one low-density and one intermediate-density band

7. A biochemist isolates, purifies, and combines in a test tube a variety of molecules needed for DNA replication. When she adds some DNA to the mixture, replication occurs, but each DNA molecule consists of a normal strand paired with numerous segments of DNA a few hundred nucleotides long. What has she probably left out of the mixture?
   a. DNA polymerase
   b. DNA ligase
   c. Okazaki fragments
   d. primase

8. The spontaneous loss of amino groups from adenine in DNA results in hypoxanthine, an uncommon base, opposite thymine. What combination of proteins could repair such damage?
   a. nuclease, DNA polymerase, DNA ligase
   b. telomerase, primase, DNA polymerase
   c. telomerase, helicase, single-strand binding protein
   d. DNA ligase, replication fork proteins, adenylyl cyclase

9. **MAKE CONNECTIONS** Although the proteins that cause the *E. coli* chromosome to coil are not histones, what property would you expect them to share with histones, given their ability to bind to DNA (see Figure 5.14)?

LEVEL 3: SYNTHESIS/EVALUATION

10. **EVOLUTION CONNECTION**
    Some bacteria may be able to respond to environmental stress by increasing the rate at which mutations occur during cell division. How might this be accomplished? Might there be an evolutionary advantage of this ability? Explain.

11. **SCIENTIFIC INQUIRY**

DRAW IT Model building can be an important part of the scientific process. The illustration shown above is a computer-generated model of a DNA replication complex. The parental and newly synthesized DNA strands are color-coded differently, as are each of the following three proteins: DNA pol III, the sliding clamp, and single-strand binding protein. Use what you've learned in this chapter to clarify this model by labeling each DNA strand and each protein and indicating the overall direction of DNA replication.

12. **WRITE ABOUT A THEME: INFORMATION**
    The continuity of life is based on heritable information in the form of DNA, and structure and function are correlated at all levels of biological organization. In a short essay (100–150 words), describe how the structure of DNA is correlated with its role as the molecular basis of inheritance.

13. **SYNTHESIZE YOUR KNOWLEDGE**

This image shows DNA interacting with a computer-generated model of a TAL protein, one of a family of proteins found only in a species of the bacterium *Xanthomonas*. The bacterium uses proteins like this one to find particular gene sequences in cells of the organisms it infects, such as tomatoes, rice, and citrus fruits. Researchers are excited about working with this family of proteins. Their goal is to generate modified versions that can home in on specific gene sequences. Such proteins could then be used in an approach called gene therapy to "fix" mutated genes in individuals with genetic diseases. Given what you know about DNA structure and considering the image above, discuss how the TAL protein's structure suggests that it functions.

MasteringBiology®

Students Go to **MasteringBiology** for assignments, the eText, and the Study Area with practice tests, animations, and activities.

Instructors Go to **MasteringBiology** for automatically graded tutorials and questions that you can assign to your students, plus Instructor Resources.

17

Gene Expression: From Gene to Protein

▲ **Figure 17.1 How does a single faulty gene result in the dramatic appearance of an albino animal?**

The Flow of Genetic Information

In 2006, a young albino deer seen frolicking with several brown deer in the mountains of eastern Germany elicited a public outcry (Figure 17.1). A local hunting organization announced that the albino deer suffered from a "genetic disorder" and should be shot. Some argued that the deer should merely be prevented from mating with other deer to safeguard the population's gene pool. Others favored relocating the albino deer to a nature reserve because they worried that it might be more noticeable to predators if left in the wild. A German rock star even held a benefit concert to raise funds for the relocation. What led to the striking phenotype of this deer, the cause of this lively debate?

You learned in Chapter 14 that inherited traits are determined by genes, and that the trait of albinism is caused by a recessive allele of a pigmentation gene. The information content of genes is in the form of specific sequences of nucleotides along strands of DNA, the genetic material. But how does this information determine an organism's traits? Put another way, what does a gene actually say? And how is its message translated by cells into a specific trait, such as brown hair, type A blood, or, in the case of an albino deer, a total lack of pigment? The albino deer has a faulty version of a key protein, an enzyme required for pigment synthesis, and this protein is faulty because the gene that codes for it contains incorrect information.

◄ **An albino raccoon.**

This example illustrates the main point of this chapter: The DNA inherited by an organism leads to specific traits by dictating the synthesis of proteins and of RNA molecules involved in protein synthesis. In other words, proteins are the link between genotype and phenotype. **Gene expression** is the process by which DNA directs the synthesis of proteins (or, in some cases, just RNAs). The expression of genes that code for proteins includes two stages: transcription and translation. This chapter describes the flow of information from gene to protein and explains how genetic mutations affect organisms through their proteins. Understanding the processes of gene expression, which are similar in all three domains of life, will allow us to revisit the concept of the gene in more detail at the end of the chapter.

CONCEPT 17.1

Genes specify proteins via transcription and translation

Before going into the details of how genes direct protein synthesis, let's step back and examine how the fundamental relationship between genes and proteins was discovered.

Evidence from the Study of Metabolic Defects

In 1902, British physician Archibald Garrod was the first to suggest that genes dictate phenotypes through enzymes that catalyze specific chemical reactions in the cell. Garrod postulated that the symptoms of an inherited disease reflect a person's inability to make a particular enzyme. He later referred to such diseases as "inborn errors of metabolism." Garrod gave as one example the hereditary condition called alkaptonuria. In this disorder, the urine is black because it contains the chemical alkapton, which darkens upon exposure to air. Garrod reasoned that most people have an enzyme that metabolizes alkapton, whereas people with alkaptonuria have inherited an inability to make that metabolic enzyme.

Garrod may have been the first to recognize that Mendel's principles of heredity apply to humans as well as peas. Garrod's realization was ahead of its time, but research several decades later supported his hypothesis that a gene dictates the production of a specific enzyme, later named the *one gene–one enzyme hypothesis*. Biochemists accumulated much evidence that cells synthesize and degrade most organic molecules via metabolic pathways, in which each chemical reaction in a sequence is catalyzed by a specific enzyme (see Concept 9.1). Such metabolic pathways lead, for instance, to the synthesis of the pigments that give the brown deer in Figure 17.1 their fur color or fruit flies (*Drosophila*) their eye color (see Figure 15.3). In the 1930s, the American biochemist and geneticist George Beadle and his French colleague Boris Ephrussi speculated that in *Drosophila*, each of the various mutations affecting eye color blocks pigment synthesis at a specific step by preventing production of the enzyme that catalyzes that step. But neither the chemical reactions nor the enzymes that catalyze them were known at the time.

Nutritional Mutants in Neurospora: Scientific Inquiry

A breakthrough in demonstrating the relationship between genes and enzymes came a few years later at Stanford University, where Beadle and Edward Tatum began working with a bread mold, *Neurospora crassa*. They bombarded *Neurospora* with X-rays, shown in the 1920s to cause genetic changes, and then looked among the survivors for mutants that differed in their nutritional needs from the wild-type bread mold. Wild-type *Neurospora* has modest food requirements. It can grow in the laboratory on a simple solution of inorganic salts, glucose, and the vitamin biotin, incorporated into agar, a support medium. From this minimal medium, the mold cells use their metabolic pathways to produce all the other molecules they need. Beadle and Tatum identified mutants that could not survive on minimal medium, apparently because they were unable to synthesize certain essential molecules from the minimal ingredients. To ensure survival of these nutritional mutants, Beadle and Tatum allowed them to grow on a complete growth medium, which consisted of minimal medium supplemented with all 20 amino acids and a few other nutrients. The complete growth medium could support any mutant that couldn't synthesize one of the supplements.

To characterize the metabolic defect in each nutritional mutant, Beadle and Tatum took samples from the mutant growing on complete medium and distributed them to a number of different vials. Each vial contained minimal medium plus a single additional nutrient. The particular supplement that allowed growth indicated the metabolic defect. For example, if the only supplemented vial that supported growth of the mutant was the one fortified with the amino acid arginine, the researchers could conclude that the mutant was defective in the biochemical pathway that wild-type cells use to synthesize arginine.

In fact, such arginine-requiring mutants were obtained and studied by two colleagues of Beadle and Tatum, Adrian Srb and Norman Horowitz, who wanted to investigate the biochemical pathway for arginine synthesis in *Neurospora* **(Figure 17.2)**. Srb and Horowitz pinned down each mutant's defect more specifically, using additional tests to distinguish among three classes of arginine-requiring mutants. Mutants in each class required a different set of compounds along the arginine-synthesizing pathway, which has three steps. These results, and those of many similar experiments done by Beadle and Tatum, suggested that each class was blocked at a different step in this pathway because mutants in that class lacked the enzyme that catalyzes the blocked step.

Do individual genes specify the enzymes that function in a biochemical pathway?

Experiment Working with the mold *Neurospora crassa*, Adrian Srb and Norman Horowitz, then at Stanford University, used Beadle and Tatum's experimental approach to isolate mutants that required arginine in their growth medium. The researchers showed that these mutants fell into three classes, each defective in a different gene. From studies by others on mammalian liver cells, they suspected that the metabolic pathway of arginine biosynthesis involved a precursor nutrient and the intermediate molecules ornithine and citrulline, as shown in the diagram on the right.

Their most famous experiment, shown here, tested both the *one gene–one enzyme hypothesis* and their postulated arginine-synthesizing pathway. In this experiment, they grew their three classes of mutants under the four different conditions shown in the Results Table below. They included minimal medium (MM) as a control, knowing that wild-type cells could grow on MM but mutant cells could not. (See test tubes below.)

Precursor
↓ Enzyme A
Ornithine
↓ Enzyme B
Citrulline
↓ Enzyme C
Arginine

Growth: Wild-type cells growing and dividing — No growth: Mutant cells cannot grow and divide

Control: Minimal medium

Results As shown in the table on the right, the wild-type strain was capable of growth under all experimental conditions, requiring only the minimal medium. The three classes of mutants each had a specific set of growth requirements. For example, class II mutants could not grow when ornithine alone was added but could grow when either citrulline or arginine was added.

Results Table	Classes of *Neurospora crassa*			
Condition	**Wild type**	**Class I mutants**	**Class II mutants**	**Class III mutants**
Minimal medium (MM) (control)	growth	no growth	no growth	no growth
MM + ornithine	growth	growth	no growth	no growth
MM + citrulline	growth	growth	growth	no growth
MM + arginine (control)	growth	growth	growth	growth
Summary of results	Can grow with or without any supplements	Can grow on ornithine, citrulline, or arginine	Can grow only on citrulline or arginine	Require arginine to grow

Conclusion From the growth requirements of the mutants, Srb and Horowitz deduced that each class of mutant was unable to carry out one step in the pathway for synthesizing arginine, presumably because it lacked the necessary enzyme, as shown in the table on the right. Because each of their mutants was mutated in a single gene, they concluded that each mutated gene must normally dictate the production of one enzyme. Their results supported the one gene–one enzyme hypothesis, proposed by Beadle and Tatum, and also confirmed that the arginine pathway described in the mammalian liver also operates in *Neurospora*. (Notice in the Results Table that a mutant can grow only if supplied with a compound made *after* the defective step because this bypasses the defect.)

Source: A. M. Srb and N. H. Horowitz, The ornithine cycle in *Neurospora* and its genetic control, *Journal of Biological Chemistry* 154:129–139 (1944).

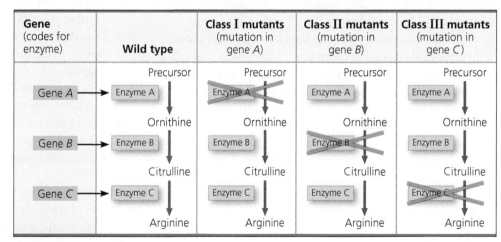

Gene (codes for enzyme)	Wild type	Class I mutants (mutation in gene A)	Class II mutants (mutation in gene B)	Class III mutants (mutation in gene C)
Gene A → Enzyme A, Gene B → Enzyme B, Gene C → Enzyme C	Precursor → Ornithine → Citrulline → Arginine	Enzyme A blocked	Enzyme B blocked	Enzyme C blocked

WHAT IF? *Suppose the experiment had shown that class I mutants could grow only in MM supplemented by ornithine or arginine and that class II mutants could grow in MM supplemented by citrulline, ornithine, or arginine. What conclusions would the researchers have drawn from those results regarding the biochemical pathway and the defect in class I and class II mutants?*

Because each mutant was defective in a single gene, Beadle and Tatum saw that, taken together, the collected results provided strong support for a working hypothesis they had proposed earlier. The one gene–one enzyme hypothesis, as they dubbed it, states that the function of a gene is to dictate the production of a specific enzyme. Further support for this hypothesis came from experiments that identified the specific enzymes lacking in the mutants. Beadle and Tatum shared a Nobel Prize in 1958 for "their discovery that genes act by regulating definite chemical events" (in the words of the Nobel committee).

Today, we know of countless examples in which a mutation in a gene causes a faulty enzyme that in turn leads to an identifiable condition. The albino deer in Figure 17.1 lacks a key enzyme called tyrosinase in the metabolic pathway that produces melanin, a dark pigment. The absence of melanin causes white fur and other effects throughout the deer's body. Its nose, ears, and hooves, as well as its eyes, are pink because no melanin is present to mask the reddish color of the blood vessels that run through those structures.

The Products of Gene Expression: A Developing Story

As researchers learned more about proteins, they made revisions to the one gene–one enzyme hypothesis. First of all, not all proteins are enzymes. Keratin, the structural protein of animal hair, and the hormone insulin are two examples of nonenzyme proteins. Because proteins that are not enzymes are nevertheless gene products, molecular biologists began to think in terms of one gene–one protein. However, many proteins are constructed from two or more different polypeptide chains, and each polypeptide is specified by its own gene. For example, hemoglobin, the oxygen-transporting protein of vertebrate red blood cells, contains two kinds of polypeptides, and thus two genes code for this protein (see Figure 5.18). Beadle and Tatum's idea was therefore restated as the one gene–one polypeptide hypothesis. Even this description is not entirely accurate, though. First, in many cases, a eukaryotic gene can code for a set of closely related polypeptides via a process called alternative splicing, which you will learn about later in this chapter. Second, quite a few genes code for RNA molecules that have important functions in cells even though they are never translated into protein. For now, we will focus on genes that do code for polypeptides. (Note that it is common to refer to these gene products as proteins—a practice you will encounter in this book—rather than more precisely as polypeptides.)

Basic Principles of Transcription and Translation

Genes provide the instructions for making specific proteins. But a gene does not build a protein directly. The bridge between DNA and protein synthesis is the nucleic acid RNA.

RNA is chemically similar to DNA except that it contains ribose instead of deoxyribose as its sugar and has the nitrogenous base uracil rather than thymine (see Figure 5.24). Thus, each nucleotide along a DNA strand has A, G, C, or T as its base, and each nucleotide along an RNA strand has A, G, C, or U as its base. An RNA molecule usually consists of a single strand.

It is customary to describe the flow of information from gene to protein in linguistic terms because both nucleic acids and proteins are polymers with specific sequences of monomers that convey information, much as specific sequences of letters communicate information in a language like English. In DNA or RNA, the monomers are the four types of nucleotides, which differ in their nitrogenous bases. Genes are typically hundreds or thousands of nucleotides long, each gene having a specific sequence of nucleotides. Each polypeptide of a protein also has monomers arranged in a particular linear order (the protein's primary structure), but its monomers are amino acids. Thus, nucleic acids and proteins contain information written in two different chemical languages. Getting from DNA to protein requires two major stages: transcription and translation.

Transcription is the synthesis of RNA using information in the DNA. The two nucleic acids are written in different forms of the same language, and the information is simply transcribed, or "rewritten," from DNA to RNA. Just as a DNA strand provides a template for making a new complementary strand during DNA replication, it also can serve as a template for assembling a complementary sequence of RNA nucleotides. For a protein-coding gene, the resulting RNA molecule is a faithful transcript of the gene's protein-building instructions. This type of RNA molecule is called **messenger RNA (mRNA)** because it carries a genetic message from the DNA to the protein-synthesizing machinery of the cell. (Transcription is the general term for the synthesis of *any* kind of RNA on a DNA template. Later, you will learn about some other types of RNA produced by transcription.)

Translation is the synthesis of a polypeptide using the information in the mRNA. During this stage, there is a change in language: The cell must translate the nucleotide sequence of an mRNA molecule into the amino acid sequence of a polypeptide. The sites of translation are **ribosomes**, molecular complexes that facilitate the orderly linking of amino acids into polypeptide chains.

Transcription and translation occur in all organisms—those that lack a membrane-bounded nucleus (bacteria and archaea) and those that have one (eukaryotes). Because most studies of transcription and translation have used bacteria and eukaryotic cells, they are our main focus in this chapter. Our understanding of transcription and translation in archaea lags behind, but we do know that archaeal cells share some features of gene expression with bacteria and others with eukaryotes.

The basic mechanics of transcription and translation are similar for bacteria and eukaryotes, but there is an important difference in the flow of genetic information within the cells. Because bacteria do not have nuclei, their DNA is not separated by nuclear membranes from ribosomes and the other protein-synthesizing equipment (**Figure 17.3a**). As you will see later, this lack of compartmentalization allows translation of an mRNA to begin while its transcription is still in progress. In a eukaryotic cell, by contrast, the nuclear envelope separates transcription from translation in space and time (**Figure 17.3b**). Transcription occurs in the nucleus, and mRNA is then transported to the cytoplasm, where translation occurs. But before eukaryotic RNA transcripts from protein-coding genes can leave the nucleus, they are modified in various ways to produce the final, functional mRNA. The transcription of a protein-coding eukaryotic gene results in *pre-mRNA*, and further processing yields the finished mRNA. The initial RNA transcript from any gene, including those specifying RNA that is not translated into protein, is more generally called a **primary transcript**.

To summarize: Genes program protein synthesis via genetic messages in the form of messenger RNA. Put another way, cells are governed by a molecular chain of command with a directional flow of genetic information, shown here by arrows:

This concept was dubbed the *central dogma* by Francis Crick in 1956. How has the concept held up over time? In the 1970s, scientists were surprised to discover that some enzymes exist that use RNA molecules as templates for DNA synthesis. However, these exceptions do not invalidate the idea that, in general, genetic information flows from DNA to RNA to protein. In the next section, we discuss how the instructions for assembling amino acids into a specific order are encoded in nucleic acids.

The Genetic Code

When biologists began to suspect that the instructions for protein synthesis were encoded in DNA, they recognized a problem: There are only four nucleotide bases to specify 20 amino acids. Thus, the genetic code cannot be a language like Chinese, where each written symbol corresponds to a word. How many nucleotides, then, correspond to an amino acid?

Codons: Triplets of Nucleotides

If each kind of nucleotide base were translated into an amino acid, only four amino acids could be specified, one per nucleotide base. Would a language of two-letter code

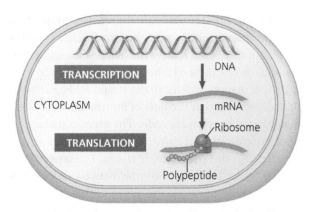

(a) Bacterial cell. In a bacterial cell, which lacks a nucleus, mRNA produced by transcription is immediately translated without additional processing.

(b) Eukaryotic cell. The nucleus provides a separate compartment for transcription. The original RNA transcript, called pre-mRNA, is processed in various ways before leaving the nucleus as mRNA.

▲ **Figure 17.3 Overview: the roles of transcription and translation in the flow of genetic information.** In a cell, inherited information flows from DNA to RNA to protein. The two main stages of information flow are transcription and translation. A miniature version of part (a) or (b) accompanies several figures later in the chapter as an orientation diagram to help you see where a particular figure fits into the overall scheme.

words suffice? The two-nucleotide sequence AG, for example, could specify one amino acid, and GT could specify another. Since there are four possible nucleotide bases in each position, this would give us 16 (that is, 4×4, or 4^2) possible arrangements—still not enough to code for all 20 amino acids.

Triplets of nucleotide bases are the smallest units of uniform length that can code for all the amino acids. If each arrangement of three consecutive nucleotide bases specifies an amino acid, there can be 64 (that is, 4^3) possible code words—more than enough to specify all the amino acids. Experiments have verified that the flow of information from gene to protein is based on a **triplet code**: The genetic instructions for a polypeptide chain are written in the DNA as a series of nonoverlapping, three-nucleotide words. The series of words in a gene is transcribed into a complementary series of non-overlapping, three-nucleotide words in mRNA, which is then translated into a chain of amino acids (**Figure 17.4**).

During transcription, the gene determines the sequence of nucleotide bases along the length of the RNA molecule that is being synthesized. For each gene, only one of the two DNA strands is transcribed. This strand is called the **template strand** because it provides the pattern, or template, for the sequence of nucleotides in an RNA transcript. For any given gene, the same strand is used as the template every time the gene is transcribed. For other genes on the same DNA molecule, however, the opposite strand may be the one that always functions as the template.

▲ **Figure 17.4 The triplet code.** For each gene, one DNA strand functions as a template for transcription of RNAs, such as mRNA. The base-pairing rules for DNA synthesis also guide transcription, except that uracil (U) takes the place of thymine (T) in RNA. During translation, the mRNA is read as a sequence of nucleotide triplets, called codons. Each codon specifies an amino acid to be added to the growing polypeptide chain. The mRNA is read in the 5' → 3' direction.

? *Write the sequence of the mRNA strand and the nontemplate DNA strand—in both cases reading from 5' to 3'—and compare them.*

An mRNA molecule is complementary rather than identical to its DNA template because RNA nucleotides are assembled on the template according to base-pairing rules (see Figure 17.4). The pairs are similar to those that form during DNA replication, except that U (the RNA substitute for T) pairs with A and the mRNA nucleotides contain ribose instead of deoxyribose. Like a new strand of DNA, the RNA molecule is synthesized in an antiparallel direction to the template strand of DNA. (To review what is meant by "antiparallel" and the 5' and 3' ends of a nucleic acid chain, see Figure 16.7.) In the example in Figure 17.4, the nucleotide triplet ACC along the DNA (written as 3'-ACC-5') provides a template for 5'-UGG-3' in the mRNA molecule. The mRNA nucleotide triplets are called **codons**, and they are customarily written in the 5' → 3' direction. In our example, UGG is the codon for the amino acid tryptophan (abbreviated Trp). The term *codon* is also used for the DNA nucleotide triplets along the *nontemplate* strand. These codons are complementary to the template strand and thus identical in sequence to the mRNA, except that they have a T wherever there is a U in the mRNA. (For this reason, the nontemplate DNA strand is often called the *coding strand*.)

During translation, the sequence of codons along an mRNA molecule is decoded, or translated, into a sequence of amino acids making up a polypeptide chain. The codons are read by the translation machinery in the 5' → 3' direction along the mRNA. Each codon specifies which one of the 20 amino acids will be incorporated at the corresponding position along a polypeptide. Because codons are nucleotide triplets, the number of nucleotides making up a genetic message must be three times the number of amino acids in the protein product. For example, it takes 300 nucleotides along an mRNA strand to code for the amino acids in a polypeptide that is 100 amino acids long.

Cracking the Code

Molecular biologists cracked the genetic code of life in the early 1960s when a series of elegant experiments disclosed the amino acid translations of each of the RNA codons. The first codon was deciphered in 1961 by Marshall Nirenberg, of the National Institutes of Health, along with his colleagues. Nirenberg synthesized an artificial mRNA by linking identical RNA nucleotides containing uracil as their base. No matter where this message started or stopped, it could contain only one codon in repetition: UUU. Nirenberg added this "poly-U" to a test-tube mixture containing amino acids, ribosomes, and the other components required for protein synthesis. His artificial system translated the poly-U into a polypeptide containing many units of the amino acid phenylalanine (Phe), strung together as a long polyphenylalanine chain. Thus, Nirenberg determined that the mRNA codon UUU specifies the amino acid phenylalanine. Soon, the amino acids specified by the codons AAA, GGG, and CCC were also determined.

Although more elaborate techniques were required to decode mixed triplets such as AUA and CGA, all 64 codons were deciphered by the mid-1960s. As **Figure 17.5** shows, 61 of the 64 triplets code for amino acids. The three codons that do not designate amino acids are "stop" signals, or termination codons, marking the end of translation. Notice that the codon AUG has a dual function: It codes for the amino acid methionine (Met) and also functions as a "start" signal, or initiation codon. Genetic messages usually begin with the mRNA codon AUG, which signals the protein-synthesizing machinery to begin translating the mRNA at that location. (Because AUG also stands for methionine, polypeptide chains begin with methionine when they are synthesized. However, an enzyme may subsequently remove this starter amino acid from the chain.)

Notice in Figure 17.5 that there is redundancy in the genetic code, but no ambiguity. For example, although codons GAA and GAG both specify glutamic acid (redundancy), neither of them ever specifies any other amino acid (no ambiguity). The redundancy in the code is not altogether random. In many cases, codons that are synonyms for a particular amino acid differ only in the third nucleotide base of

the triplet. We will consider the significance of this redundancy later in the chapter.

Our ability to extract the intended message from a written language depends on reading the symbols in the correct groupings—that is, in the correct **reading frame**. Consider this statement: "The red dog ate the bug." Group the letters incorrectly by starting at the wrong point, and the result will probably be gibberish: for example, "her edd oga tet heb ug." The reading frame is also important in the molecular language of cells. The short stretch of polypeptide shown in Figure 17.4, for instance, will be made correctly only if the mRNA nucleotides are read from left to right (5′ → 3′) in the groups of three shown in the figure: <u>UGG</u> <u>UUU</u> <u>GGC</u> <u>UCA</u>. Although a genetic message is written with no spaces between the codons, the cell's protein-synthesizing machinery reads the message as a series of nonoverlapping three-letter words. The message is *not* read as a series of overlapping words—<u>UGGUUU</u>, and so on—which would convey a very different message.

Evolution of the Genetic Code

EVOLUTION   The genetic code is nearly universal, shared by organisms from the simplest bacteria to the most complex plants and animals. The RNA codon CCG, for instance, is translated as the amino acid proline in all organisms whose genetic code has been examined. In laboratory experiments, genes can be transcribed and translated after being transplanted from one species to another, sometimes with quite striking results, as shown in **Figure 17.6**. Bacteria can

Second mRNA base

First mRNA base (5′ end of codon)	U	C	A	G	Third mRNA base (3′ end of codon)
U	UUU ⎫ Phe UUC ⎭ UUA ⎫ Leu UUG ⎭	UCU ⎫ UCC ⎪ Ser UCA ⎪ UCG ⎭	UAU ⎫ Tyr UAC ⎭ UAA Stop UAG Stop	UGU ⎫ Cys UGC ⎭ UGA Stop UGG Trp	U C A G
C	CUU ⎫ CUC ⎪ Leu CUA ⎪ CUG ⎭	CCU ⎫ CCC ⎪ Pro CCA ⎪ CCG ⎭	CAU ⎫ His CAC ⎭ CAA ⎫ Gln CAG ⎭	CGU ⎫ CGC ⎪ Arg CGA ⎪ CGG ⎭	U C A G
A	AUU ⎫ AUC ⎪ Ile AUA ⎭ AUG Met or start	ACU ⎫ ACC ⎪ Thr ACA ⎪ ACG ⎭	AAU ⎫ Asn AAC ⎭ AAA ⎫ Lys AAG ⎭	AGU ⎫ Ser AGC ⎭ AGA ⎫ Arg AGG ⎭	U C A G
G	GUU ⎫ GUC ⎪ Val GUA ⎪ GUG ⎭	GCU ⎫ GCC ⎪ Ala GCA ⎪ GCG ⎭	GAU ⎫ Asp GAC ⎭ GAA ⎫ Glu GAG ⎭	GGU ⎫ GGC ⎪ Gly GGA ⎪ GGG ⎭	U C A G

▲ **Figure 17.5 The codon table for mRNA.** The three nucleotide bases of an mRNA codon are designated here as the first, second, and third bases, reading in the 5′ → 3′ direction along the mRNA. (Practice using this table by finding the codons in Figure 17.4.) The codon AUG not only stands for the amino acid methionine (Met) but also functions as a "start" signal for ribosomes to begin translating the mRNA at that point. Three of the 64 codons function as "stop" signals, marking where ribosomes end translation. See Figure 5.14 for a list of the full names of all the amino acids.

(a) Tobacco plant expressing a firefly gene. The yellow glow is produced by a chemical reaction catalyzed by the protein product of the firefly gene.

(b) Pig expressing a jellyfish gene. Researchers injected a jellyfish gene for a fluorescent protein into fertilized pig eggs. One developed into this fluorescent pig.

▲ **Figure 17.6 Expression of genes from different species.** Because diverse forms of life share a common genetic code, one species can be programmed to produce proteins characteristic of a second species by introducing DNA from the second species into the first.

be programmed by the insertion of human genes to synthesize certain human proteins for medical use, such as insulin. Such applications have produced many exciting developments in the area of biotechnology.

Despite a small number of exceptions in which a few codons differ from the standard ones, the evolutionary significance of the code's near universality is clear. A language shared by all living things must have been operating very early in the history of life—early enough to be present in the common ancestor of all present-day organisms. A shared genetic vocabulary is a reminder of the kinship that bonds all life on Earth.

CONCEPT CHECK 17.1

1. **MAKE CONNECTIONS** In a research article about alkaptonuria published in 1902, Garrod suggested that humans inherit two "characters" (alleles) for a particular enzyme and that both parents must contribute a faulty version for the offspring to have the disorder. Today, would this disorder be called dominant or recessive? (See Concept 14.4.)

2. What polypeptide product would you expect from a poly-G mRNA that is 30 nucleotides long?

3. **DRAW IT** The template strand of a gene contains the sequence 3'-TTCAGTCGT-5'. Draw the nontemplate sequence and mRNA sequence, indicating the 5' and 3' ends of each. Compare the two sequences.

4. **DRAW IT** Imagine that the nontemplate sequence in question 3 had been transcribed instead of the template sequence. Draw the mRNA sequence and translate it using Figure 17.5. (Be sure to pay attention to the 5' and 3' ends.) Predict how well the protein synthesized from the nontemplate strand would function, if at all.

CONCEPT 17.2

Transcription is the DNA-directed synthesis of RNA: *A closer look*

Now that we have considered the linguistic logic and evolutionary significance of the genetic code, we are ready to reexamine transcription, the first stage of gene expression, in more detail.

Molecular Components of Transcription

Messenger RNA, the carrier of information from DNA to the cell's protein-synthesizing machinery, is transcribed from the template strand of a gene. An enzyme called an **RNA polymerase** pries the two strands of DNA apart and joins together RNA nucleotides complementary to the DNA template strand, thus elongating the RNA polynucleotide **(Figure 17.7)**. Like the DNA polymerases that function in

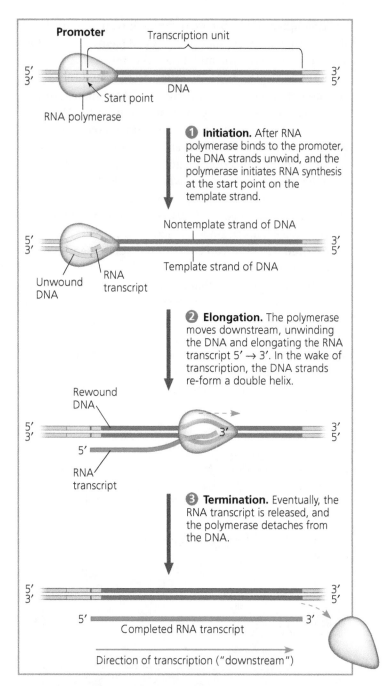

▲ **Figure 17.7 The stages of transcription: initiation, elongation, and termination.** This general depiction of transcription applies to both bacteria and eukaryotes, but the details of termination differ, as described in the text. Also, in a bacterium, the RNA transcript is immediately usable as mRNA; in a eukaryote, the RNA transcript must first undergo processing.

MAKE CONNECTIONS *Compare the use of a template strand during transcription and replication. See Figure 16.17.*

DNA replication, RNA polymerases can assemble a polynucleotide only in its 5' → 3' direction. Unlike DNA polymerases, however, RNA polymerases are able to start a chain from scratch; they don't need a primer.

Specific sequences of nucleotides along the DNA mark where transcription of a gene begins and ends. The DNA sequence where RNA polymerase attaches and initiates transcription is known as the **promoter**; in bacteria, the sequence that signals the end of transcription is called the **terminator**. (The termination mechanism is different in eukaryotes; we'll describe it later.) Molecular biologists refer to the direction of transcription as "downstream" and the other direction as "upstream." These terms are also used to describe the positions of nucleotide sequences within the DNA or RNA. Thus, the promoter sequence in DNA is said to be upstream from the terminator. The stretch of DNA downstream from the promoter that is transcribed into an RNA molecule is called a **transcription unit**.

Bacteria have a single type of RNA polymerase that synthesizes not only mRNA but also other types of RNA that function in protein synthesis, such as ribosomal RNA. In contrast, eukaryotes have at least three types of RNA polymerase in their nuclei; the one used for pre-mRNA synthesis is called RNA polymerase II. The other RNA polymerases transcribe RNA molecules that are not translated into protein. In the discussion that follows, we start with the features of mRNA synthesis common to both bacteria and eukaryotes and then describe some key differences.

Synthesis of an RNA Transcript

The three stages of transcription, as shown in Figure 17.7 and described next, are initiation, elongation, and termination of the RNA chain. Study Figure 17.7 to familiarize yourself with the stages and the terms used to describe them.

RNA Polymerase Binding and Initiation of Transcription

The promoter of a gene includes within it the transcription **start point** (the nucleotide where RNA synthesis actually begins) and typically extends several dozen or more nucleotide pairs upstream from the start point. RNA polymerase binds in a precise location and orientation on the promoter, therefore determining where transcription starts and which of the two strands of the DNA helix is used as the template.

Certain sections of a promoter are especially important for binding RNA polymerase. In bacteria, part of the RNA polymerase itself specifically recognizes and binds to the promoter. In eukaryotes, a collection of proteins called **transcription factors** mediate the binding of RNA polymerase and the initiation of transcription. Only after transcription factors are attached to the promoter does RNA polymerase II bind to it. The whole complex of transcription factors and RNA polymerase II bound to the promoter is called a **transcription initiation complex**. **Figure 17.8** shows the role of transcription factors and a crucial promoter DNA sequence called a **TATA box** in forming the initiation complex at a eukaryotic promoter.

The interaction between eukaryotic RNA polymerase II and transcription factors is an example of the importance

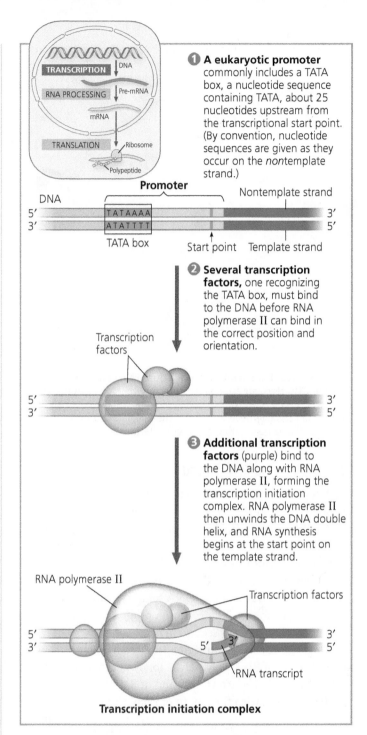

1 **A eukaryotic promoter** commonly includes a TATA box, a nucleotide sequence containing TATA, about 25 nucleotides upstream from the transcriptional start point. (By convention, nucleotide sequences are given as they occur on the *non*template strand.)

2 **Several transcription factors,** one recognizing the TATA box, must bind to the DNA before RNA polymerase II can bind in the correct position and orientation.

3 **Additional transcription factors** (purple) bind to the DNA along with RNA polymerase II, forming the transcription initiation complex. RNA polymerase II then unwinds the DNA double helix, and RNA synthesis begins at the start point on the template strand.

Transcription initiation complex

▲ **Figure 17.8 The initiation of transcription at a eukaryotic promoter.** In eukaryotic cells, proteins called transcription factors mediate the initiation of transcription by RNA polymerase II.

? *Explain how the interaction of RNA polymerase with the promoter would differ if the figure showed transcription initiation for bacteria.*

of protein-protein interactions in controlling eukaryotic transcription. Once the appropriate transcription factors are firmly attached to the promoter DNA and the polymerase is bound in the correct orientation, the enzyme unwinds the two DNA strands and begins transcribing the template strand at the start point.

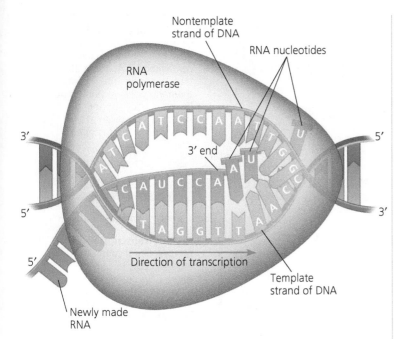

Nontemplate
strand of DNA

RNA nucleotides

RNA
polymerase

3′ end

3′

5′

5′

3′

5′

Direction of transcription

Template
strand of DNA

Newly made
RNA

▲ **Figure 17.9 Transcription elongation.** RNA polymerase moves along the DNA template strand, joining complementary RNA nucleotides to the 3′ end of the growing RNA transcript. Behind the polymerase, the new RNA peels away from the template strand, which re-forms a double helix with the nontemplate strand.

Elongation of the RNA Strand

As RNA polymerase moves along the DNA, it untwists the double helix, exposing about 10–20 DNA nucleotides at a time for pairing with RNA nucleotides **(Figure 17.9)**. The enzyme adds nucleotides to the 3′ end of the growing RNA molecule as it continues along the double helix. In the wake of this advancing wave of RNA synthesis, the new RNA molecule peels away from its DNA template, and the DNA double helix re-forms. Transcription progresses at a rate of about 40 nucleotides per second in eukaryotes.

A single gene can be transcribed simultaneously by several molecules of RNA polymerase following each other like trucks in a convoy. A growing strand of RNA trails off from each polymerase, with the length of each new strand reflecting how far along the template the enzyme has traveled from the start point (see the mRNA molecules in Figure 17.22). The congregation of many polymerase molecules simultaneously transcribing a single gene increases the amount of mRNA transcribed from it, which helps the cell make the encoded protein in large amounts.

Termination of Transcription

The mechanism of termination differs between bacteria and eukaryotes. In bacteria, transcription proceeds through a terminator sequence in the DNA. The transcribed terminator (an RNA sequence) functions as the termination signal, causing the polymerase to detach from the DNA and release the transcript, which requires no further modification before translation. In eukaryotes, RNA polymerase II

transcribes a sequence on the DNA called the polyadenylation signal sequence, which specifies a polyadenylation signal (AAUAAA) in the pre-mRNA. This is called a "signal" because once this stretch of six RNA nucleotides appears, it is immediately bound by certain proteins in the nucleus. Then, at a point about 10–35 nucleotides downstream from the AAUAAA, these proteins cut it free from the polymerase, releasing the pre-mRNA. The pre-mRNA then undergoes processing, the topic of the next section. Although that cleavage marks the end of the mRNA, the RNA polymerase II continues to transcribe. Since the new 5′ end isn't protected by a cap, however, enzymes degrade the RNA from the 5′ end. The polymerase continues transcribing, pursued by the enzymes, until they catch up to the polymerase and it dissociates from the DNA.

CONCEPT 17.3

Eukaryotic cells modify RNA after transcription

Enzymes in the eukaryotic nucleus modify pre-mRNA in specific ways before the genetic message is dispatched to the cytoplasm. During this **RNA processing**, both ends of the primary transcript are altered. Also, in most cases, certain interior sections of the RNA molecule are cut out and the remaining parts spliced together. These modifications produce an mRNA molecule ready for translation.

Alteration of mRNA Ends

Each end of a pre-mRNA molecule is modified in a particular way **(Figure 17.10)**. The 5′ end, which is synthesized first, receives a **5′ cap**, a modified form of a guanine (G) nucleotide added onto the 5′ end after transcription of the first 20–40 nucleotides. The 3′ end of the pre-mRNA molecule is also modified before the mRNA exits the nucleus. Recall that the pre-mRNA is released soon after the polyadenylation signal, AAUAAA, is transcribed. At the 3′ end, an enzyme then adds 50–250 more adenine (A) nucleotides, forming a **poly-A tail**. The 5′ cap and poly-A tail share several important functions. First, they seem to facilitate the

A modified guanine nucleotide added to the 5' end

50–250 adenine nucleotides added to the 3' end

Region that includes protein-coding segments

Polyadenylation signal

5' Cap | 5' UTR | Start codon | Stop codon | 3' UTR | Poly-A tail

▲ **Figure 17.10 RNA processing: Addition of the 5' cap and poly-A tail.** Enzymes modify the two ends of a eukaryotic pre-mRNA molecule. The modified ends may promote the export of mRNA from the nucleus, and they help protect the mRNA from degradation. When the mRNA reaches the cytoplasm, the modified ends, in conjunction with certain cytoplasmic proteins, facilitate ribosome attachment. The 5' cap and poly-A tail are not translated into protein, nor are the regions called the 5' untranslated region (5' UTR) and 3' untranslated region (3' UTR). The pink segments will be described shortly (see Figure 17.11).

export of the mature mRNA from the nucleus. Second, they help protect the mRNA from degradation by hydrolytic enzymes. And third, they help ribosomes attach to the 5' end of the mRNA once the mRNA reaches the cytoplasm. Figure 17.10 shows a diagram of a eukaryotic mRNA molecule with cap and tail. The figure also shows the untranslated regions (UTRs) at the 5' and 3' ends of the mRNA (referred to as the 5' UTR and 3' UTR). The UTRs are parts of the mRNA that will not be translated into protein, but they have other functions, such as ribosome binding.

Split Genes and RNA Splicing

A remarkable stage of RNA processing in the eukaryotic nucleus is the removal of large portions of the RNA molecule that is initially synthesized. This cut-and-paste job, called **RNA splicing**, is similar to editing a video **(Figure 17.11)**. The average length of a transcription unit along a human DNA molecule is about 27,000 nucleotide pairs, so the primary RNA transcript is also that long. However, the average-sized protein of 400 amino acids requires only 1,200 nucleotides in RNA to code for it. (Remember, each amino acid is encoded by a *triplet* of nucleotides.) This means that most eukaryotic genes and their RNA transcripts have long noncoding stretches of nucleotides, regions that are not translated. Even more surprising is that most of these noncoding sequences are interspersed between coding segments of the gene and thus between coding segments of the pre-mRNA. In other words, the sequence of DNA nucleotides that codes for a eukaryotic polypeptide is usually not continuous; it is split into segments. The noncoding segments of nucleic acid that lie between coding regions are called *int*ervening sequences, or **introns**. The other regions are called **exons**, because they are eventually *ex*pressed, usually by being translated into amino acid sequences. (Exceptions include the UTRs of the exons at the ends of the RNA, which make up part of the mRNA but are not translated into protein. Because of these exceptions, you may prefer to think of exons as sequences of RNA that *ex*it the nucleus.) The terms *intron* and *exon* are used for both RNA sequences and the DNA sequences that encode them.

In making a primary transcript from a gene, RNA polymerase II transcribes both introns and exons from the DNA, but the mRNA molecule that enters the cytoplasm is an abridged version. The introns are cut out from the molecule

Pre-mRNA

5' Exon | Intron | Exon | Intron | Exon | 3'

5' Cap | Poly-A tail

Codon numbers: 1–30 | 31–104 | 105–146

Introns cut out and exons spliced together

mRNA

5' Cap | Poly-A tail

5' UTR | 1–146 | 3' UTR

Coding segment

© Pearson Education, Inc.

▲ **Figure 17.11 RNA processing: RNA splicing.** The RNA molecule shown here codes for β-globin, one of the polypeptides of hemoglobin. The numbers under the RNA refer to codons; β-globin is 146 amino acids long. The β-globin gene and its pre-mRNA transcript have three exons, corresponding to sequences that will leave the nucleus as mRNA. (The 5' UTR and 3' UTR are parts of exons because they are included in the mRNA; however, they do not code for protein.) During RNA processing, the introns are cut out and the exons spliced together. In many genes, the introns are much longer than the exons.

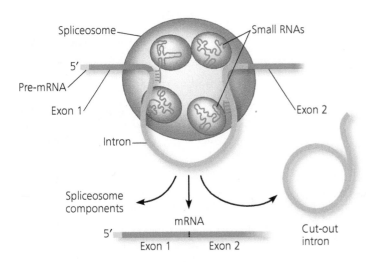

▲ **Figure 17.12 A spliceosome splicing a pre-mRNA.** The diagram shows a portion of a pre-mRNA transcript, with an intron (pink) flanked by two exons (red). Small RNAs within the spliceosome base-pair with nucleotides at specific sites along the intron. Next, the spliceosome catalyzes cutting of the pre-mRNA and the splicing together of the exons, releasing the intron for rapid degradation.

and the exons joined together, forming an mRNA molecule with a continuous coding sequence. This is the process of RNA splicing.

How is pre-mRNA splicing carried out? The removal of introns is accomplished by a large complex made of proteins and small RNAs called a **spliceosome**. This complex binds to several short nucleotide sequences along an intron, including key sequences at each end (**Figure 17.12**). The intron is then released (and rapidly degraded), and the spliceosome joins together the two exons that flanked the intron. It turns out that the small RNAs in the spliceosome not only participate in spliceosome assembly and splice site recognition, but also catalyze the splicing reaction.

Ribozymes

The idea of a catalytic role for the RNAs in the spliceosome arose from the discovery of **ribozymes**, RNA molecules that function as enzymes. In some organisms, RNA splicing can occur without proteins or even additional RNA molecules: The intron RNA functions as a ribozyme and catalyzes its own excision! For example, in the ciliate protist *Tetrahymena*, self-splicing occurs in the production of ribosomal RNA (rRNA), a component of the organism's ribosomes. The pre-rRNA actually removes its own introns. The discovery of ribozymes rendered obsolete the idea that all biological catalysts are proteins.

Three properties of RNA enable some RNA molecules to function as enzymes. First, because RNA is single-stranded, a region of an RNA molecule may base-pair, in an antiparallel arrangement, with a complementary region elsewhere in the same molecule; this gives the molecule a particular three-dimensional structure. A specific structure is essential to the catalytic function of ribozymes, just as it is

for enzymatic proteins. Second, like certain amino acids in an enzymatic protein, some of the bases in RNA contain functional groups that can participate in catalysis. Third, the ability of RNA to hydrogen-bond with other nucleic acid molecules (either RNA or DNA) adds specificity to its catalytic activity. For example, complementary base pairing between the RNA of the spliceosome and the RNA of a primary RNA transcript precisely locates the region where the ribozyme catalyzes splicing. Later in this chapter, you will see how these properties of RNA also allow it to perform important noncatalytic roles in the cell, such as recognition of the three-nucleotide codons on mRNA.

The Functional and Evolutionary Importance of Introns

EVOLUTION Whether or not RNA splicing and the presence of introns have provided selective advantages during evolutionary history is a matter of some debate. In any case, it is informative to consider their possible adaptive benefits. Specific functions have not been identified for most introns, but at least some contain sequences that regulate gene expression, and many affect gene products.

One important consequence of the presence of introns in genes is that a single gene can encode more than one kind of polypeptide. Many genes are known to give rise to two or more different polypeptides, depending on which segments are treated as exons during RNA processing; this is called **alternative RNA splicing**. For example, sex differences in fruit flies are largely due to differences in how males and females splice the RNA transcribed from certain genes. Results from the Human Genome Project suggest that alternative RNA splicing is one reason humans can get along with about the same number of genes as a nematode (roundworm). Because of alternative splicing, the number of different protein products an organism produces can be much greater than its number of genes.

Proteins often have a modular architecture consisting of discrete structural and functional regions called **domains**. One domain of an enzyme, for example, might include the active site, while another might allow the enzyme to bind to a cellular membrane. In quite a few cases, different exons code for the different domains of a protein (**Figure 17.13**).

The presence of introns in a gene may facilitate the evolution of new and potentially beneficial proteins as a result of a process known as *exon shuffling*. Introns increase the probability of crossing over between the exons of alleles of a gene—simply by providing more terrain for crossovers without interrupting coding sequences. This might result in new combinations of exons and proteins with altered structure and function. We can also imagine the occasional mixing and matching of exons between completely different (nonallelic) genes. Exon shuffling of either sort could lead to new proteins with novel combinations of functions. While most of the shuffling would result in nonbeneficial changes, occasionally a beneficial variant might arise.

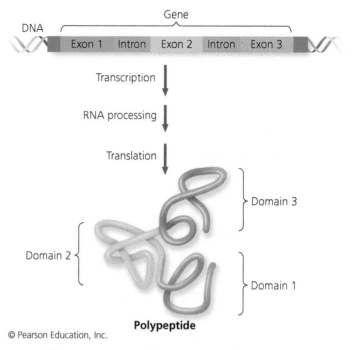

DNA

Gene

Exon 1 | Intron | Exon 2 | Intron | Exon 3

Transcription

RNA processing

Translation

Domain 3

Domain 2

Domain 1

Polypeptide

© Pearson Education, Inc.

▲ **Figure 17.13 Correspondence between exons and protein domains.**

CONCEPT CHECK 17.3

1. There are fewer than 21,000 human genes. How, then, can human cells make 75,000–100,000 different proteins?

2. How is RNA splicing similar to how you would watch a television show recorded earlier using a DVR? What would introns correspond to in this analogy?

3. **WHAT IF?** What would be the effect of treating cells with an agent that removed the cap from mRNAs?

CONCEPT 17.4

Translation is the RNA-directed synthesis of a polypeptide: *A closer look*

We will now examine in greater detail how genetic information flows from mRNA to protein—the process of translation. As we did for transcription, we'll concentrate on the basic steps of translation that occur in both bacteria and eukaryotes, while pointing out key differences.

Molecular Components of Translation

In the process of translation, a cell "reads" a genetic message and builds a polypeptide accordingly. The message is a series of codons along an mRNA molecule, and the translator is called **transfer RNA (tRNA)**. The function of tRNA is to transfer amino acids from the cytoplasmic pool of amino acids to a growing polypeptide in a ribosome. A cell keeps its cytoplasm stocked with all 20 amino acids, either by synthesizing them from other compounds or by taking them up

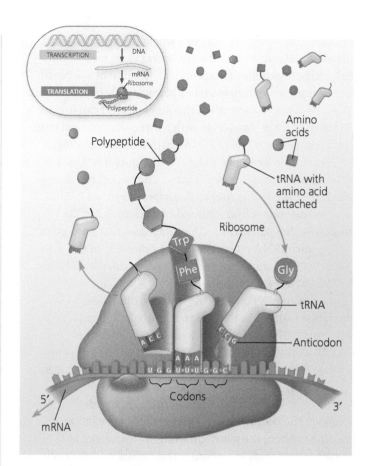

Polypeptide

Amino acids

tRNA with amino acid attached

Ribosome

Trp

Phe

Gly

tRNA

Anticodon

A C C

A A A

U G G U U U G G C

Codons

5′

mRNA

3′

▲ **Figure 17.14 Translation: the basic concept.** As a molecule of mRNA is moved through a ribosome, codons are translated into amino acids, one by one. The interpreters are tRNA molecules, each type with a specific nucleotide triplet called an anticodon at one end and a corresponding amino acid at the other end. A tRNA adds its amino acid cargo to a growing polypeptide chain when the anticodon hydrogen-bonds to the complementary codon on the mRNA. The figures that follow show some of the details of translation in a bacterial cell.

ANIMATION **BioFlix** Visit the Study Area in **MasteringBiology** for the BioFlix® 3-D Animation on Protein Synthesis. BioFlix Tutorials can also be assigned in MasteringBiology.

from the surrounding solution. The ribosome, a structure made of proteins and RNAs, adds each amino acid brought to it by tRNA to the growing end of a polypeptide chain **(Figure 17.14)**.

Translation is simple in principle but complex in its biochemistry and mechanics, especially in the eukaryotic cell. In dissecting translation, we'll focus on the slightly less complicated version of the process that occurs in bacteria. We'll first look at the major players in this process and then see how they act together in making a polypeptide.

The Structure and Function of Transfer RNA

The key to translating a genetic message into a specific amino acid sequence is the fact that each tRNA molecule translates a given mRNA codon into a certain amino acid. This is possible because a tRNA bears a specific amino acid at one end, while at the other end is a nucleotide triplet that can base-pair with the complementary codon on mRNA.

A tRNA molecule consists of a single RNA strand that is only about 80 nucleotides long (whereas most mRNA molecules have hundreds of nucleotides). Because of the presence of complementary stretches of nucleotide bases that can hydrogen-bond to each other, this single strand can fold back on itself and form a molecule with a three-dimensional structure. Flattened into one plane to clarify this base pairing, a tRNA molecule looks like a cloverleaf (Figure 17.15a). The tRNA actually twists and folds into a compact three-dimensional structure that is roughly L-shaped (Figure 17.15b). The loop extending from one end of the L includes the **anticodon**, the particular nucleotide triplet that base-pairs to a specific mRNA codon. From the other end of the L-shaped tRNA molecule protrudes its 3′ end, which is the attachment site for an amino acid.

As an example, consider the mRNA codon 5′-GGC-3′, which is translated as the amino acid glycine. The tRNA that base-pairs with this codon by hydrogen bonding has 3′-CCG-5′ as its anticodon and carries glycine at its other end (see the incoming tRNA approaching the ribosome in Figure 17.14). As an mRNA molecule is moved through a ribosome, glycine will be added to the polypeptide chain whenever the codon GGC is presented for translation. Codon by codon, the genetic message is translated as tRNAs deposit amino acids in the order prescribed, and the ribosome joins the amino acids into a chain. The tRNA molecule is a translator in the sense that it can read a nucleic acid word (the mRNA codon) and interpret it as a protein word (the amino acid).

Like mRNA and other types of cellular RNA, transfer RNA molecules are transcribed from DNA templates. In a eukaryotic cell, tRNA, like mRNA, is made in the nucleus and then travels from the nucleus to the cytoplasm, where it will participate in the process of translation. In both bacterial and eukaryotic cells, each tRNA molecule is used repeatedly, picking up its designated amino acid in the cytosol, depositing this cargo onto a polypeptide chain at the ribosome, and then leaving the ribosome, ready to pick up another of the same amino acid.

The accurate translation of a genetic message requires two instances of molecular recognition. First, a tRNA that binds to an mRNA codon specifying a particular amino acid must carry that amino acid, and no other, to the ribosome. The correct matching up of tRNA and amino acid is carried out by a family of related enzymes called **aminoacyl-tRNA synthetases (Figure 17.16)**. The active site of each type of aminoacyl-tRNA synthetase fits only a specific combination of amino acid and tRNA. There are 20 different synthetases, one for each amino acid; each synthetase is able to bind to all the different tRNAs that code for its particular amino acid. The synthetase catalyzes the covalent attachment of the amino acid to its tRNA in a process driven by the hydrolysis of ATP. The resulting aminoacyl tRNA, also called a charged tRNA, is released from the enzyme and is then

(a) **Two-dimensional structure.** The four base-paired regions and three loops are characteristic of all tRNAs, as is the base sequence of the amino acid attachment site at the 3′ end. The anticodon triplet is unique to each tRNA type, as are some sequences in the other two loops. (The asterisks mark bases that have been chemically modified, a characteristic of tRNA. The modified bases contribute to tRNA function in a way that is not yet understood.)

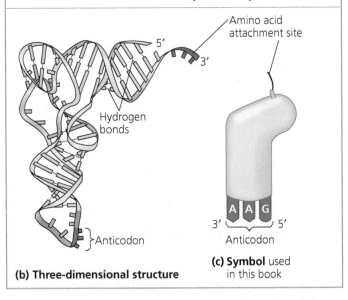

(b) **Three-dimensional structure**

(c) **Symbol** used in this book

▲ Figure 17.15 **The structure of transfer RNA (tRNA).** Anticodons are conventionally written 3′ → 5′ to align properly with codons written 5′ → 3′ (see Figure 17.14). For base pairing, RNA strands must be antiparallel, like DNA. For example, anticodon 3′-AAG-5′ pairs with mRNA codon 5′-UUC-3′.

available to deliver its amino acid to a growing polypeptide chain on a ribosome.

The second instance of molecular recognition is the pairing of the tRNA anticodon with the appropriate mRNA codon. If one tRNA variety existed for each mRNA codon specifying an amino acid, there would be 61 tRNAs (see Figure 17.5). In fact, there are only about 45, signifying that some tRNAs must be able to bind to more than one codon.

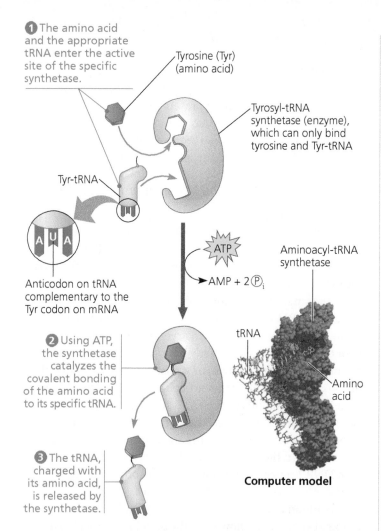

1 The amino acid and the appropriate tRNA enter the active site of the specific synthetase.

Tyrosine (Tyr) (amino acid)

Tyrosyl-tRNA synthetase (enzyme), which can only bind tyrosine and Tyr-tRNA

Tyr-tRNA

Anticodon on tRNA complementary to the Tyr codon on mRNA

ATP

AMP + 2 P$_i$

Aminoacyl-tRNA synthetase

2 Using ATP, the synthetase catalyzes the covalent bonding of the amino acid to its specific tRNA.

tRNA

Amino acid

3 The tRNA, charged with its amino acid, is released by the synthetase.

Computer model

▲ **Figure 17.16 Aminoacyl-tRNA synthetases provide specificity in joining amino acids to their tRNAs.** Linkage of a tRNA to its amino acid is an endergonic process that occurs at the expense of ATP, which loses two phosphate groups, becoming AMP (adenosine monophosphate).

Such versatility is possible because the rules for base pairing between the third nucleotide base of a codon and the corresponding base of a tRNA anticodon are relaxed compared to those at other codon positions. For example, the nucleotide base U at the 5′ end of a tRNA anticodon can pair with either A or G in the third position (at the 3′ end) of an mRNA codon. The flexible base pairing at this codon position is called **wobble**. Wobble explains why the synonymous codons for a given amino acid most often differ in their third nucleotide base, but not in the other bases. A case in point is that a tRNA with the anticodon 3′-UCU-5′ can base-pair with either the mRNA codon 5′-AGA-3′ or 5′-AGG-3′, both of which code for arginine (see Figure 17.5).

Ribosomes

Ribosomes facilitate the specific coupling of tRNA anticodons with mRNA codons during protein synthesis. A ribosome consists of a large subunit and a small subunit, each made up of proteins and one or more **ribosomal RNAs (rRNAs)** (Figure 17.17). In eukaryotes, the subunits are

Growing polypeptide

Exit tunnel

tRNA molecules

Large subunit

Small subunit

5′

3′

mRNA

(a) Computer model of functioning ribosome. This is a model of a bacterial ribosome, showing its overall shape. The eukaryotic ribosome is roughly similar. A ribosomal subunit is a complex of ribosomal RNA molecules and proteins.

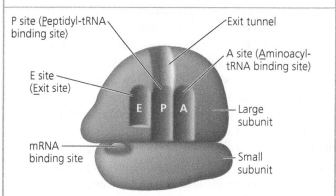

P site (Peptidyl-tRNA binding site)

Exit tunnel

E site (Exit site)

A site (Aminoacyl-tRNA binding site)

Large subunit

mRNA binding site

Small subunit

(b) Schematic model showing binding sites. A ribosome has an mRNA binding site and three tRNA binding sites, known as the A, P, and E sites. This schematic ribosome will appear in later diagrams.

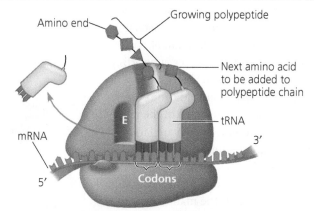

Growing polypeptide

Amino end

Next amino acid to be added to polypeptide chain

tRNA

mRNA

3′

5′

Codons

(c) Schematic model with mRNA and tRNA. A tRNA fits into a binding site when its anticodon base-pairs with an mRNA codon. The P site holds the tRNA attached to the growing polypeptide. The A site holds the tRNA carrying the next amino acid to be added to the polypeptide chain. Discharged tRNAs leave from the E site. The polypeptide grows at its carboxyl end.

▲ **Figure 17.17 The anatomy of a functioning ribosome.**

made in the nucleolus. Ribosomal RNA genes are transcribed, and the RNA is processed and assembled with proteins imported from the cytoplasm. Completed ribosomal subunits are then exported via nuclear pores to the cytoplasm. In both bacteria and eukaryotes, a large and a small subunit join to form a functional ribosome only when attached to an mRNA molecule. About one-third of the mass of a ribosome is made up of proteins; the rest consists of rRNAs, either three molecules (in bacteria) or four (in eukaryotes). Because most cells contain thousands of ribosomes, rRNA is the most abundant type of cellular RNA.

Although the ribosomes of bacteria and eukaryotes are very similar in structure and function, eukaryotic ribosomes are slightly larger, as well as differing somewhat from bacterial ribosomes in their molecular composition. The differences are medically significant. Certain antibiotic drugs can inactivate bacterial ribosomes without affecting eukaryotic ribosomes. These drugs, including tetracycline and streptomycin, are used to combat bacterial infections.

The structure of the bacterial ribosome has been determined to the atomic level. This structure clearly reflects its function of bringing mRNA together with tRNAs carrying amino acids. In addition to a binding site for mRNA, each ribosome has three binding sites for tRNA, as described in Figure 17.17. The **P site** (peptidyl-tRNA binding site) holds the tRNA carrying the growing polypeptide chain, while the **A site** (aminoacyl-tRNA binding site) holds the tRNA carrying the next amino acid to be added to the chain. Discharged tRNAs leave the ribosome from the **E site** (exit site). The ribosome holds the tRNA and mRNA in close proximity and positions the new amino acid so that it can be added to the carboxyl end of the growing polypeptide. It then catalyzes the formation of the peptide bond. As the polypeptide becomes longer, it passes through an *exit tunnel* in the ribosome's large subunit. When the polypeptide is complete, it is released through the exit tunnel.

There is strong evidence supporting the hypothesis that rRNA, not protein, is primarily responsible for both the structure and the function of the ribosome. The proteins, which are largely on the exterior, support the shape changes of the rRNA molecules as they carry out catalysis during translation. Ribosomal RNA is the main constituent of the A and P sites and of the interface between the two subunits; it also acts as the catalyst of peptide bond formation. Thus, a ribosome can be regarded as one colossal ribozyme!

Building a Polypeptide

We can divide translation, the synthesis of a polypeptide chain, into three stages: initiation, elongation, and termination. All three stages require protein "factors" that aid in the translation process. For certain aspects of chain initiation and elongation, energy is also required. It is provided by the hydrolysis of guanosine triphosphate (GTP).

Ribosome Association and Initiation of Translation

The initiation stage of translation brings together mRNA, a tRNA bearing the first amino acid of the polypeptide, and the two subunits of a ribosome (Figure 17.18). First, a small ribosomal subunit binds to both mRNA and a specific initiator tRNA, which carries the amino acid methionine. In bacteria, the small subunit can bind these two in either order; it binds the mRNA at a specific RNA sequence, just upstream of the start codon, AUG. In eukaryotes, the small subunit, with the initiator tRNA already bound, binds to the 5' cap of the mRNA and then moves, or *scans*, downstream along the mRNA until it reaches the start codon; the initiator tRNA then hydrogen-bonds to the AUG start codon. In either case, the start codon signals the start of translation; this is important because it establishes the codon reading frame for the mRNA. In the Scientific Skills Exercise, you can work with DNA sequences encoding the ribosomal binding sites on the mRNAs of a group of *E. coli* genes.

The union of mRNA, initiator tRNA, and a small ribosomal subunit is followed by the attachment of a large ribosomal subunit, completing the *translation initiation complex*. Proteins called *initiation factors* are required to

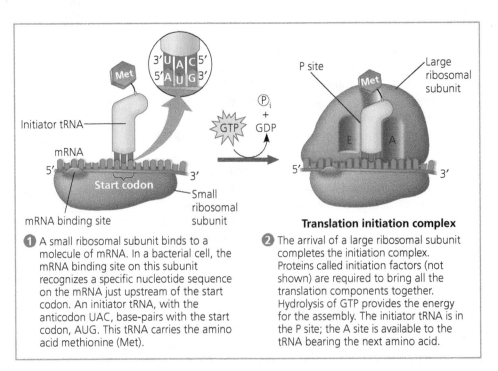

① A small ribosomal subunit binds to a molecule of mRNA. In a bacterial cell, the mRNA binding site on this subunit recognizes a specific nucleotide sequence on the mRNA just upstream of the start codon. An initiator tRNA, with the anticodon UAC, base-pairs with the start codon, AUG. This tRNA carries the amino acid methionine (Met).

② The arrival of a large ribosomal subunit completes the initiation complex. Proteins called initiation factors (not shown) are required to bring all the translation components together. Hydrolysis of GTP provides the energy for the assembly. The initiator tRNA is in the P site; the A site is available to the tRNA bearing the next amino acid.

▲ Figure 17.18 The initiation of translation.

Interpreting a Sequence Logo

How Can a Sequence Logo Be Used to Identify Ribosome Binding Sites? When initiating translation, ribosomes bind to an mRNA at a ribosome binding site upstream of the AUG start codon. Because mRNAs from different genes all bind to a ribosome, the genes encoding these mRNAs are likely to have a similar base sequence where the ribosomes bind. Therefore, candidate ribosome binding sites on mRNA can be identified by comparing DNA sequences (and thus the mRNA sequences) of multiple genes in a species, searching the region upstream of the start codon for shared ("conserved") stretches of bases. In this exercise, you will analyze DNA sequences from multiple such genes, represented by a visual graphic called a sequence logo.

How the Experiment Was Done The DNA sequences of 149 genes from the *E. coli* genome were aligned using computer software. The aim was to identify similar base sequences—at the appropriate location in each gene—as potential ribosome binding sites. Rather than presenting the data as a series of 149 sequences aligned in a column (a sequence alignment), the researchers used a sequence logo.

Data from the Experiment To show how sequence logos are made, the potential ribosome binding regions from 10 *E. coli* genes are shown in a sequence alignment, followed by the sequence logo derived from the aligned sequences. Note that the DNA shown is the nontemplate (coding) strand, which is how DNA sequences are typically presented.

thrA	G G T A A C G A G G T A A C A A C C A T G C G A G T G
lacA	C A T A A C G G A G T G A T C G C A T T G A A C A T G
lacY	C G C G T A A G G A A A T C C A T T A T G T A C T A T
lacZ	T T C A C A C A G G A A A C A G C T A T G A C C A T G
lacI	C A A T T C A G G G T G G T G A A T G T G A A A C C A
recA	G G C A T G A C A G G A G T A A A A A T G G C T A T C
galR	A C C C A C T A A G G T A T T T T C A T G G C G A C C
metJ	A A G A G G A T T A A G T A T C T C A T G G C T G A A
lexA	A T A C A C C C A G G G G G G C G G A A T G A A A G C G
trpR	T A A C A A T G G C G A C A T A T T A T G G C C C A A

▲ Sequence alignment

▲ Sequence logo

Interpret the Data

1. In the sequence logo (bottom, left), the horizontal axis shows the primary sequence of the DNA by nucleotide position. Letters for each base are stacked on top of each other according to their relative frequency at that position among the aligned sequences, with the most common base as the largest letter at the top of the stack. The height of each letter represents the relative frequency of that base *at that position*. (a) In the sequence alignment, count the number of each base at position –9 and order them from most to least frequent. Compare this to the size and placement of each base at –9 in the logo. (b) Do the same for positions 0 and 1.

2. The height of a stack of letters in a logo indicates the predictive power of that stack (determined statistically). If the stack is tall, we can be more confident in predicting what base will be in that position if a new sequence is added to the logo. For example, at position 2, all 10 sequences have a G; the probability of finding a G there in a new sequence is very high, as is the stack. For short stacks, the bases all have about the same frequency, so it's hard to predict a base at those positions. (a) Which two positions have the most predictable bases? What bases do you predict would be at those positions in a newly sequenced gene? (b) Which 12 positions have the least predictable bases? How do you know? How does this reflect the relative frequencies of the bases shown in the 10 sequences? Use the two leftmost positions of the 12 as examples in your answer.

3. In the actual experiment, the researchers used 149 sequences to build their sequence logo, which is shown below. There is a stack at each position, even if short, because the sequence logo includes more data. (a) Which three positions in this sequence logo have the most predictable bases? Name the most frequent base at each. (b) Which positions have the least predictable bases? How can you tell?

4. A consensus sequence identifies the base occurring most often at each position in the set of sequences. (a) Write out the consensus sequence of this (the nontemplate) strand. In any position where the base can't be determined, put a dash. (b) Which provides more information—the consensus sequence or the sequence logo? What is lost in the less informative method?

5. (a) Based on the logo, what five adjacent base positions in the 5′ UTR region are most likely to be involved in ribosome binding? Explain. (b) What is represented by the bases in positions 0–2?

(MB) A version of this Scientific Skills Exercise can be assigned in MasteringBiology.

Further Reading T. D. Schneider and R. M. Stephens, Sequence logos: A new way to display consensus sequences, *Nucleic Acids Research* 18:6097–6100 (1990).

bring all these components together. The cell also expends energy obtained by hydrolysis of a GTP molecule to form the initiation complex. At the completion of the initiation process, the initiator tRNA sits in the P site of the ribosome, and the vacant A site is ready for the next aminoacyl tRNA. Note that a polypeptide is always synthesized in one direction, from the initial methionine at the amino end, also called the N-terminus, toward the final amino acid at the carboxyl end, also called the C-terminus (see Figure 5.15).

Elongation of the Polypeptide Chain

In the elongation stage of translation, amino acids are added one by one to the previous amino acid at the C-terminus of the growing chain. Each addition involves the participation of several proteins called *elongation factors* and occurs in a three-step cycle described in **Figure 17.19.** Energy expenditure occurs in the first and third steps. Codon recognition requires hydrolysis of one molecule of GTP, which increases the accuracy and efficiency of this step. One more GTP is hydrolyzed to provide energy for the translocation step.

The mRNA is moved through the ribosome in one direction only, 5′ end first; this is equivalent to the ribosome moving 5′ → 3′ on the mRNA. The important point is that the ribosome and the mRNA move relative to each other, unidirectionally, codon by codon. The elongation cycle takes less than a tenth of a second in bacteria and is repeated as each amino acid is added to the chain until the polypeptide is completed. The empty tRNAs that are released from the E site return to the cytoplasm, where they will be reloaded with the appropriate amino acid (see Figure 17.16).

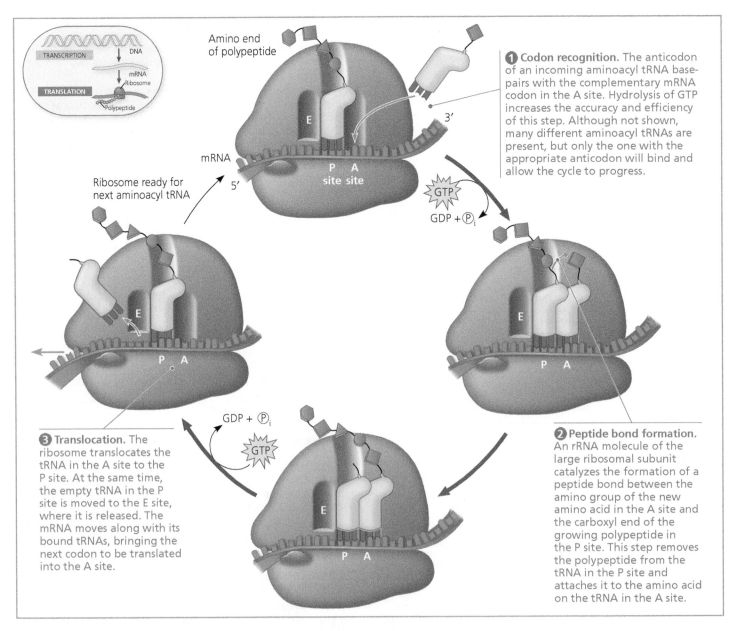

1 Codon recognition. The anticodon of an incoming aminoacyl tRNA base-pairs with the complementary mRNA codon in the A site. Hydrolysis of GTP increases the accuracy and efficiency of this step. Although not shown, many different aminoacyl tRNAs are present, but only the one with the appropriate anticodon will bind and allow the cycle to progress.

2 Peptide bond formation. An rRNA molecule of the large ribosomal subunit catalyzes the formation of a peptide bond between the amino group of the new amino acid in the A site and the carboxyl end of the growing polypeptide in the P site. This step removes the polypeptide from the tRNA in the P site and attaches it to the amino acid on the tRNA in the A site.

3 Translocation. The ribosome translocates the tRNA in the A site to the P site. At the same time, the empty tRNA in the P site is moved to the E site, where it is released. The mRNA moves along with its bound tRNAs, bringing the next codon to be translated into the A site.

▲ **Figure 17.19 The elongation cycle of translation.** The hydrolysis of GTP plays an important role in the elongation process. Not shown are the proteins called elongation factors.

Release factor

Stop codon
(UAG, UAA, or UGA)

Free polypeptide

5'

3'

5'

3'

2 GTP

2 GDP + 2 (P)ᵢ

5'

3'

1 When a ribosome reaches a stop codon on mRNA, the A site of the ribosome accepts a "release factor," a protein shaped like a tRNA, instead of an aminoacyl tRNA.

2 The release factor promotes hydrolysis of the bond between the tRNA in the P site and the last amino acid of the polypeptide, thus freeing the polypeptide from the ribosome.

3 The two ribosomal subunits and the other components of the assembly dissociate.

▲ **Figure 17.20 The termination of translation.** Like elongation, termination requires GTP hydrolysis as well as additional protein factors, which are not shown here.

Termination of Translation

The final stage of translation is termination (**Figure 17.20**). Elongation continues until a stop codon in the mRNA reaches the A site of the ribosome. The nucleotide base triplets UAG, UAA, and UGA do not code for amino acids but instead act as signals to stop translation. A *release factor*, a protein shaped like an aminoacyl tRNA, binds directly to the stop codon in the A site. The release factor causes the addition of a water molecule instead of an amino acid to the polypeptide chain. (There are plenty of water molecules available in the aqueous cellular environment.) This reaction breaks (hydrolyzes) the bond between the completed polypeptide and the tRNA in the P site, releasing the polypeptide through the exit tunnel of the ribosome's large subunit. The remainder of the translation assembly then comes apart in a multistep process, aided by other protein factors. Breakdown of the translation assembly requires the hydrolysis of two more GTP molecules.

Completing and Targeting the Functional Protein

The process of translation is often not sufficient to make a functional protein. In this section, you will learn about modifications that polypeptide chains undergo after the translation process as well as some of the mechanisms used to target completed proteins to specific sites in the cell.

Protein Folding and Post-Translational Modifications

During its synthesis, a polypeptide chain begins to coil and fold spontaneously as a consequence of its amino acid sequence (primary structure), forming a protein with a specific shape: a three-dimensional molecule with secondary and tertiary structure (see Figure 5.18). Thus, a gene determines primary structure, and primary structure in turn determines shape. In many cases, a chaperone protein (chaperonin) helps the polypeptide fold correctly (see Figure 5.21).

Additional steps—*post-translational modifications*—may be required before the protein can begin doing its particular job in the cell. Certain amino acids may be chemically modified by the attachment of sugars, lipids, phosphate groups, or other additions. Enzymes may remove one or more amino acids from the leading (amino) end of the polypeptide chain. In some cases, a polypeptide chain may be enzymatically cleaved into two or more pieces. For example, the protein insulin is first synthesized as a single polypeptide chain but becomes active only after an enzyme cuts out a central part of the chain, leaving a protein made up of two polypeptide chains connected by disulfide bridges. In other cases, two or more polypeptides that are synthesized separately may come together, becoming the subunits of a protein that has quaternary structure. A familiar example is hemoglobin (see Figure 5.18).

Targeting Polypeptides to Specific Locations

In electron micrographs of eukaryotic cells active in protein synthesis, two populations of ribosomes are evident: free and bound (see Figure 6.10). Free ribosomes are suspended in the cytosol and mostly synthesize proteins that stay in the cytosol and function there. In contrast, bound ribosomes are attached to the cytosolic side of the endoplasmic reticulum (ER) or to the nuclear envelope. Bound ribosomes make proteins of the endomembrane system (the nuclear envelope, ER, Golgi apparatus, lysosomes, vacuoles, and plasma membrane) as well as proteins secreted from the cell, such as insulin. It is important to note that the ribosomes themselves are identical and can alternate between being free one time they are used and bound the next.

What determines whether a ribosome is free in the cytosol or bound to rough ER? Polypeptide synthesis always begins in the cytosol as a free ribosome starts to translate an mRNA molecule. There the process continues to completion—*unless* the growing polypeptide itself cues the ribosome to attach to the ER. The polypeptides of proteins destined for the endomembrane system or for secretion are marked by a **signal peptide**, which targets the protein to the ER **(Figure 17.21)**. The signal peptide, a sequence of about 20 amino acids at or near the leading end (N-terminus) of the polypeptide, is recognized as it emerges from the ribosome by a protein-RNA complex called a **signal-recognition particle (SRP)**. This particle functions as an escort that brings the ribosome to a receptor protein built into the ER membrane. The receptor is part of a multiprotein translocation complex. Polypeptide synthesis continues there, and the growing polypeptide snakes across the membrane into the ER lumen via a protein pore. The signal peptide is usually removed by an enzyme. The rest of the completed polypeptide, if it is to be secreted from the cell, is released into solution within the ER lumen (as in Figure 17.21). Alternatively, if the polypeptide is to be a

membrane protein, it remains partially embedded in the ER membrane. In either case, it travels in a transport vesicle to its destination (see, for example, Figure 7.9).

Other kinds of signal peptides are used to target polypeptides to mitochondria, chloroplasts, the interior of the nucleus, and other organelles that are not part of the endomembrane system. The critical difference in these cases is that translation is completed in the cytosol before the polypeptide is imported into the organelle. Translocation mechanisms also vary, but in all cases studied to date, the "postal zip codes" that address proteins for secretion or to cellular locations are signal peptides of some sort. Bacteria also employ signal peptides to target proteins to the plasma membrane for secretion.

Making Multiple Polypeptides in Bacteria and Eukaryotes

In previous sections, you learned how a single polypeptide is synthesized using the information encoded in an mRNA molecule. When a polypeptide is required in a cell, though, the need is for many copies, not just one.

A single ribosome can make an average-sized polypeptide in less than a minute. In both bacteria and eukaryotes,

1 Polypeptide synthesis begins on a free ribosome in the cytosol.

2 An SRP binds to the signal peptide, halting synthesis momentarily.

3 The SRP binds to a receptor protein in the ER membrane, part of a protein complex that forms a pore and has a signal-cleaving enzyme.

4 The SRP leaves, and polypeptide synthesis resumes, with simultaneous translocation across the membrane.

5 The signal-cleaving enzyme cuts off the signal peptide.

6 The rest of the completed polypeptide leaves the ribosome and folds into its final conformation.

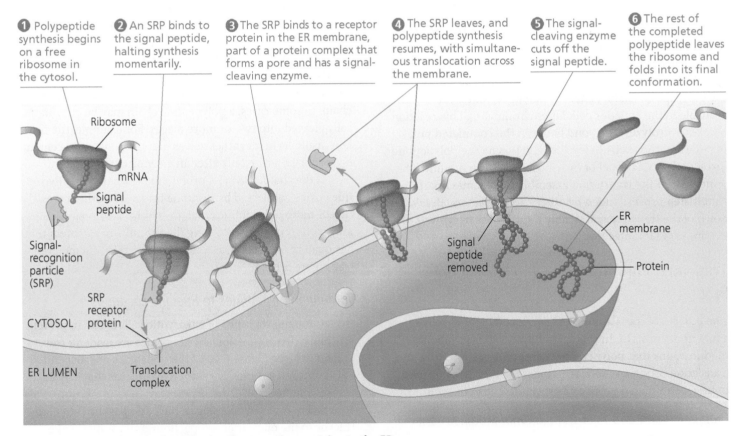

▲ **Figure 17.21 The signal mechanism for targeting proteins to the ER.**

MAKE CONNECTIONS *If this protein were destined for secretion, what would happen to it after its synthesis was completed? See Figure 7.9.*

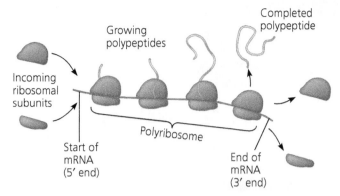

(a) An mRNA molecule is generally translated simultaneously by several ribosomes in clusters called polyribosomes.

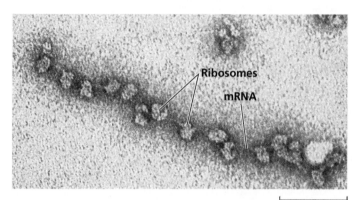

(b) This micrograph shows a large polyribosome in a bacterial cell. Growing polypeptides are not visible here (TEM).

0.1 μm

▲ Figure 17.22 **Polyribosomes.**

0.25 μm

▲ Figure 17.23 **Coupled transcription and translation in bacteria.** In bacterial cells, the translation of mRNA can begin as soon as the leading (5') end of the mRNA molecule peels away from the DNA template. The micrograph (TEM) shows a strand of *E. coli* DNA being transcribed by RNA polymerase molecules. Attached to each RNA polymerase molecule is a growing strand of mRNA, which is already being translated by ribosomes. The newly synthesized polypeptides are not visible in the micrograph but are shown in the diagram.

? *Which one of the mRNA molecules started being transcribed first? On that mRNA, which ribosome started translating the mRNA first?*

however, multiple ribosomes translate an mRNA at the same time (Figure 17.22); that is, a single mRNA is used to make many copies of a polypeptide simultaneously. Once a ribosome is far enough past the start codon, a second ribosome can attach to the mRNA, eventually resulting in a number of ribosomes trailing along the mRNA. Such strings of ribosomes, called **polyribosomes** (or **polysomes**), can be seen with an electron microscope (see Figure 17.22). They enable a cell to make many copies of a polypeptide very quickly.

Another way both bacteria and eukaryotes augment the number of copies of a polypeptide is by transcribing multiple mRNAs from the same gene, as we mentioned earlier. However, the coordination of the two processes—transcription and translation—differ in the two groups. The most important differences between bacteria and eukaryotes arise from the bacterial cell's lack of compartmental organization. Like a one-room workshop, a bacterial cell ensures a streamlined operation by coupling the two processes. In the absence of a nucleus, it can simultaneously transcribe and translate the same gene (Figure 17.23), and the newly made protein can quickly diffuse to its site of function.

In contrast, the eukaryotic cell's nuclear envelope segregates transcription from translation and provides a compartment for extensive RNA processing. This processing stage includes additional steps, discussed earlier, the regulation of which can help coordinate the eukaryotic cell's elaborate activities. **Figure 17.24** summarizes the path from gene to polypeptide in a eukaryotic cell.

CONCEPT CHECK 17.4

1. What two processes ensure that the correct amino acid is added to a growing polypeptide chain?

2. Discuss the ways in which rRNA structure likely contributes to ribosomal function.

3. Describe how a polypeptide to be secreted reaches the endomembrane system.

4. **WHAT IF?** **DRAW IT** Draw a tRNA with the anticodon 3'-CGU-5'. What two different codons could it bind to? Draw each codon on an mRNA, labeling all 5' and 3' ends, the tRNA, and the amino acid it carries.

5. **WHAT IF?** In eukaryotic cells, mRNAs have been found to have a circular arrangement in which proteins hold the poly-A tail near the 5' cap. How might this increase translation efficiency?

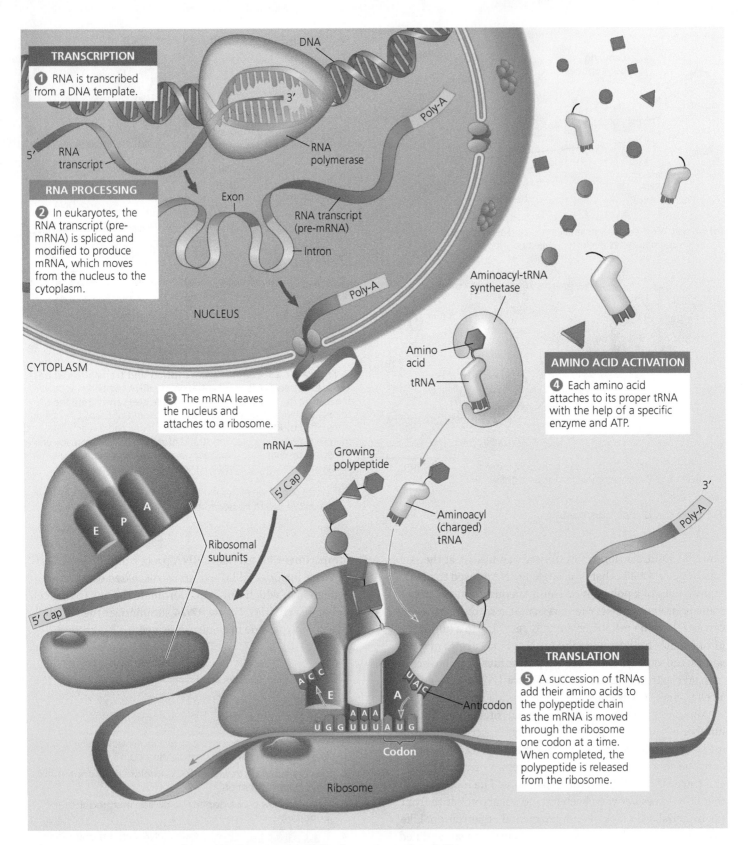

TRANSCRIPTION

❶ RNA is transcribed from a DNA template.

DNA

3′

5′

RNA transcript

RNA polymerase

Poly-A

RNA PROCESSING

❷ In eukaryotes, the RNA transcript (pre-mRNA) is spliced and modified to produce mRNA, which moves from the nucleus to the cytoplasm.

Exon

Intron

RNA transcript (pre-mRNA)

Poly-A

NUCLEUS

CYTOPLASM

❸ The mRNA leaves the nucleus and attaches to a ribosome.

mRNA

Growing polypeptide

5′ Cap

Ribosomal subunits

E P A

5′ Cap

Aminoacyl-tRNA synthetase

Amino acid

tRNA

AMINO ACID ACTIVATION

❹ Each amino acid attaches to its proper tRNA with the help of a specific enzyme and ATP.

Aminoacyl (charged) tRNA

3′

Poly-A

A C C

E

U A C

A

Anticodon

A A A

U G G U U U A U G

Codon

Ribosome

TRANSLATION

❺ A succession of tRNAs add their amino acids to the polypeptide chain as the mRNA is moved through the ribosome one codon at a time. When completed, the polypeptide is released from the ribosome.

▲ **Figure 17.24 A summary of transcription and translation in a eukaryotic cell.** This diagram shows the path from one gene to one polypeptide. Keep in mind that each gene in the DNA can be transcribed repeatedly into many identical RNA molecules and that each mRNA can be translated repeatedly to yield many identical polypeptide molecules. (Also, remember that the final products of some genes are not polypeptides but RNA molecules, including tRNA and rRNA.) In general, the steps of transcription and translation are similar in bacterial, archaeal, and eukaryotic cells. The major difference is the occurrence of RNA processing in the eukaryotic nucleus. Other significant differences are found in the initiation stages of both transcription and translation and in the termination of transcription.

Mutations of one or a few nucleotides can affect protein structure and function

Now that you have explored the process of gene expression, you are ready to understand the effects of changes to the genetic information of a cell. These changes, called **mutations**, are responsible for the huge diversity of genes found among organisms because mutations are the ultimate source of new genes. Earlier, we considered chromosomal rearrangements that affect long segments of DNA (see Figure 15.14); these are considered large-scale mutations. Here we examine small-scale mutations of one or a few nucleotide pairs, including **point mutations**, changes in a single nucleotide pair of a gene.

If a point mutation occurs in a gamete or in a cell that gives rise to gametes, it may be transmitted to offspring and to future generations. If the mutation has an adverse effect on the phenotype of a person, the mutant condition is referred to as a genetic disorder or hereditary disease. For example, we can trace the genetic basis of sickle-cell disease to the mutation of a single nucleotide pair in the gene that encodes the β-globin polypeptide of hemoglobin. The change of a single nucleotide in the DNA's template strand leads to the production of an abnormal protein (**Figure 17.25**; also see Figure 5.19). In individuals who are homozygous for the mutant allele, the sickling of red blood cells caused by the altered hemoglobin produces the multiple symptoms associated with sickle-cell disease (see Concept 14.4). Another disorder caused by a point mutation is a heart condition called familial cardiomyopathy that is responsible for some incidents of sudden death in young athletes. Point mutations in several genes that encode muscle proteins have been identified, any of which can lead to this disorder.

Types of Small-Scale Mutations

Let's now consider how small-scale mutations affect proteins. Point mutations within a gene can be divided into two general categories: (1) single nucleotide-pair substitutions and (2) nucleotide-pair insertions or deletions. Insertions and deletions can involve one or more nucleotide pairs.

Substitutions

A **nucleotide-pair substitution** is the replacement of one nucleotide and its partner with another pair of nucleotides (**Figure 17.26a**). Some substitutions have no effect on the encoded protein, owing to the redundancy of the genetic code. For example, if 3'-CCG-5' on the template strand mutated to 3'-CCA-5', the mRNA codon that used to be GGC would become GGU, but a glycine would still be inserted at the proper location in the protein (see Figure 17.5). In other words, a change in a nucleotide pair may transform one codon into another that is translated into the same amino acid. Such a change is an example of a **silent mutation**, which has no observable effect on the phenotype. (Silent mutations can occur outside genes as well.) Substitutions that change one amino acid to another one are called **missense mutations**. Such a mutation may have little effect on the protein: The new amino acid may have properties similar to those of the amino acid it replaces, or it may be in a region of the protein where the exact sequence of amino acids is not essential to the protein's function.

However, the nucleotide-pair substitutions of greatest interest are those that cause a major change in a protein.

The alteration of a single amino acid in a crucial area of a protein—such as in the part of the β-globin subunit of hemoglobin shown in Figure 17.25 or in the active site of an enzyme as shown in Figure 9.19—can significantly alter protein activity. Occasionally, such a mutation leads to an improved protein or one with novel capabilities, but much more often such mutations are neutral or detrimental, leading to a useless or less active protein that impairs cellular function.

Substitution mutations are usually missense mutations; that is, the altered codon still codes for an amino acid and thus makes sense, although not necessarily the *right* sense. But a point mutation can also change a codon for an amino acid into a stop codon. This is called a **nonsense mutation**,

Wild-type β-globin	Sickle-cell β-globin	
Wild-type β-globin DNA	Mutant β-globin DNA	In the DNA, the mutant (sickle-cell) template strand (top) has an A where the wild-type template has a T.
3' C T C 5' 5' G A G 3'	3' C A C 5' 5' G T G 3'	
mRNA	mRNA	The mutant mRNA has a U instead of an A in one codon.
5' G A G 3'	5' G U G 3'	
Normal hemoglobin	Sickle-cell hemoglobin	The mutant β-globin has a valine (Val) instead of a glutamic acid (Glu).
Glu	Val	

▲ **Figure 17.25 The molecular basis of sickle-cell disease: a point mutation.** The allele that causes sickle-cell disease differs from the wild-type (normal) allele by a single DNA nucleotide pair. The micrographs are SEMs of a normal red blood cell (on the left) and a sickled red blood cell (right) from individuals homozygous for either wild-type or mutant alleles, respectively.

▼ **Figure 17.26 Types of small-scale mutations that affect mRNA sequence.** All but one of the types shown here also affect the amino acid sequence of the encoded polypeptide.

Wild type

DNA template strand 3′ `T A C T T C A A A C C G A T T` 5′
5′ `A T G A A G T T T G G C T A A` 3′

mRNA 5′ `A U G A A G U U U G G C U A A` 3′

Protein [Met]—[Lys]—[Phe]—[Gly] Stop

Amino end / Carboxyl end

(a) Nucleotide-pair substitution

A instead of G
3′ `T A C T T C A A A C C A A T T` 5′
5′ `A T G A A G T T T G G T T A A` 3′

U instead of C
5′ `A U G A A G U U U G G U U A A` 3′
[Met]—[Lys]—[Phe]—[Gly] Stop

Silent: No effect on the amino acid sequence

T instead of C
3′ `T A C T T C A A A T C G A T T` 5′
5′ `A T G A A G T T T A G C T A A` 3′

A instead of G
5′ `A U G A A G U U U A G C U A A` 3′
[Met]—[Lys]—[Phe]—[Ser] Stop

Missense: A range of effects depending on the location within the protein and the identity of the new amino acid

A instead of T
3′ `T A C A T C A A A C C G A T T` 5′
5′ `A T G T A G T T T G G C T A A` 3′

U instead of A
5′ `A U G U A G U U U G G U U A A` 3′
[Met] Stop

Nonsense: Effect depends on how close the mutation is to the wild-type stop codon

(b) Nucleotide-pair insertion or deletion

Extra A
3′ `T A C A T T C A A A C C G A T T` 5′
5′ `A T G T A A G T T T G G C T A A` 3′

Extra U
5′ `A U G U A A G U U U G G C U A A` 3′
[Met] Stop

Frameshift causing immediate nonsense (1 nucleotide-pair insertion)

`A` missing
3′ `T A C T T C A A C C G A T T` 5′
5′ `A T G A A G T T G G C T A A` 3′

`U` missing
5′ `A U G A A G U U G G C U A A` ⋯ 3′
[Met]—[Lys]—[Leu]—[Ala] ⋯

Frameshift causing extensive missense (1 nucleotide-pair deletion)

`T T C` missing
3′ `T A C A A A C C G A T T` 5′
5′ `A T G T T T G G C T A A` 3′

`A A G` missing
5′ `A U G U U U G G C U A A` 3′
[Met]—[Phe]—[Gly] Stop

3 nucleotide-pair deletion: No frameshift, but one amino acid is missing. A 3 nucleotide-pair insertion (not shown) would lead to an extra amino acid.

---

and it causes translation to be terminated prematurely; the resulting polypeptide will be shorter than the polypeptide encoded by the normal gene. Nearly all nonsense mutations lead to nonfunctional proteins.

Insertions and Deletions

Insertions and **deletions** are additions or losses of nucleotide pairs in a gene **(Figure 17.26b)**. These mutations have a disastrous effect on the resulting protein more often than substitutions do. Insertion or deletion of nucleotides may

alter the reading frame of the genetic message, the triplet grouping of nucleotides on the mRNA that is read during translation. Such a mutation, called a **frameshift mutation**, occurs whenever the number of nucleotides inserted or deleted is not a multiple of three. All nucleotides downstream of the deletion or insertion will be improperly grouped into codons; the result will be extensive missense, usually ending sooner or later in nonsense and premature termination. Unless the frameshift is very near the end of the gene, the protein is almost certain to be nonfunctional.

New Mutations and Mutagens

Mutations can arise in a number of ways. Errors during DNA replication or recombination can lead to nucleotide-pair substitutions, insertions, or deletions, as well as to mutations affecting longer stretches of DNA. If an incorrect nucleotide is added to a growing chain during replication, for example, the base on that nucleotide will then be mismatched with the nucleotide base on the other strand. In many cases, the error will be corrected by DNA proofreading and repair systems (see Concept 16.2). Otherwise, the incorrect base will be used as a template in the next round of replication, resulting in a mutation. Such mutations are called *spontaneous mutations*. It is difficult to calculate the rate at which such mutations occur. Rough estimates have been made of the rate of mutation during DNA replication for both *E. coli* and eukaryotes, and the numbers are similar: About one nucleotide in every 10^{10} is altered, and the change is passed on to the next generation of cells.

A number of physical and chemical agents, called **mutagens**, interact with DNA in ways that cause mutations. In the 1920s, Hermann Muller discovered that X-rays caused genetic changes in fruit flies, and he used X-rays to make *Drosophila* mutants for his genetic studies. But he also recognized an alarming implication of his discovery: X-rays and other forms of high-energy radiation pose hazards to the genetic material of people as well as laboratory organisms. Mutagenic radiation, a physical mutagen, includes ultraviolet (UV) light, which can cause disruptive thymine dimers in DNA (see Figure 16.19).

Chemical mutagens fall into several categories. Nucleotide analogs are chemicals similar to normal DNA nucleotides but that pair incorrectly during DNA replication. Other chemical mutagens interfere with correct DNA replication by inserting themselves into the DNA and distorting the double helix. Still other mutagens cause chemical changes in bases that change their pairing properties.

Researchers have developed a variety of methods to test the mutagenic activity of chemicals. A major application of these tests is the preliminary screening of chemicals to identify those that may cause cancer. This approach makes sense because most carcinogens (cancer-causing chemicals) are mutagenic, and conversely, most mutagens are carcinogenic.

What Is a Gene? *Revisiting the Question*

Our definition of a gene has evolved over the past few chapters, as it has through the history of genetics. We began with the Mendelian concept of a gene as a discrete unit of inheritance that affects a phenotypic character (Chapter 14). We saw that Morgan and his colleagues assigned such genes to specific loci on chromosomes (Chapter 15). We went on to view a gene as a region of specific nucleotide sequence along the length of the DNA molecule of a chromosome (Chapter 16). Finally, in this chapter, we have considered a functional definition of a gene as a DNA sequence that codes for a specific polypeptide chain. All these definitions are useful, depending on the context in which genes are being studied.

We now realize that saying a gene codes for a polypeptide is an oversimplification. Most eukaryotic genes contain non-coding segments (such as introns), so large portions of these genes have no corresponding segments in polypeptides. Molecular biologists also often include promoters and certain other regulatory regions of DNA within the boundaries of a gene. These DNA sequences are not transcribed, but they can be considered part of the functional gene because they must be present for transcription to occur. Our definition of a gene must also be broad enough to include the DNA that is transcribed into rRNA, tRNA, and other RNAs that are not translated. These genes have no polypeptide products but play crucial roles in the cell. Thus, we arrive at the following definition: *A gene is a region of DNA that can be expressed to produce a final functional product that is either a polypeptide or an RNA molecule.*

When considering phenotypes, however, it is often useful to start by focusing on genes that code for polypeptides. In this chapter, you have learned in molecular terms how a typical gene is expressed—by transcription into RNA and then translation into a polypeptide that forms a protein of specific structure and function. Proteins, in turn, bring about an organism's observable phenotype.

A given type of cell expresses only a subset of its genes. This is an essential feature in multicellular organisms: You'd be in trouble if the lens cells in your eyes started expressing the genes for hair proteins, which are normally expressed only in hair follicle cells! Gene expression is precisely regulated, which we'll explore in the next chapter, beginning with the simpler case of bacteria and continuing with eukaryotes.

CONCEPT CHECK 17.5

1. What happens when one nucleotide pair is lost from the middle of the coding sequence of a gene?

2. **MAKE CONNECTIONS** Individuals heterozygous for the sickle-cell allele are generally healthy but show phenotypic effects of the allele under some circumstances (see Figure 14.17). Explain in terms of gene expression.

3. **WHAT IF?** **DRAW IT** The template strand of a gene includes this sequence:

   3'-TACTTGTCCGATATC-5'. It is mutated to

   3'-TACTTGTCCAATATC-5'. For both normal and mutant sequences, draw the double-stranded DNA, the resulting mRNA, and the amino acid sequence each encodes. What is the effect of the mutation on the amino acid sequence?

CONCEPT 17.1

Genes specify proteins via transcription and translation (pp. 336–342)

- Beadle and Tatum's studies of mutant strains of *Neurospora* led to the one gene–one polypeptide hypothesis. During **gene expression**, the information encoded in genes is used to make specific polypeptide chains (enzymes and other proteins) or RNA molecules.
- **Transcription** is the synthesis of RNA complementary to a **template strand** of DNA. **Translation** is the synthesis of a polypeptide whose amino acid sequence is specified by the nucleotide sequence in **mRNA**.
- Genetic information is encoded as a sequence of nonoverlapping nucleotide triplets, or **codons**. A codon in messenger RNA (mRNA) either is translated into an amino acid (61 of the 64 codons) or serves as a stop signal (3 codons). Codons must be read in the correct **reading frame**.

? *Describe the process of gene expression, by which a gene affects the phenotype of an organism.*

CONCEPT 17.2

Transcription is the DNA-directed synthesis of RNA: A closer look (pp. 342–344)

- RNA synthesis is catalyzed by **RNA polymerase**, which links together RNA nucleotides complementary to a DNA template strand. This process follows the same base-pairing rules as DNA replication, except that in RNA, uracil substitutes for thymine.

- The three stages of transcription are initiation, elongation, and termination. A **promoter**, often including a **TATA box** in eukaryotes, establishes where RNA synthesis is initiated. **Transcription factors** help eukaryotic RNA polymerase recognize promoter sequences, forming a **transcription initiation complex**. Termination differs in bacteria and eukaryotes.

? *What are the similarities and differences in the initiation of gene transcription in bacteria and eukaryotes?*

CONCEPT 17.3

Eukaryotic cells modify RNA after transcription (pp. 344–347)

- Eukaryotic mRNAs undergo **RNA processing**, which includes RNA splicing, the addition of a modified nucleotide **5′ cap** to the 5′ end, and the addition of a **poly-A tail** to the 3′ end.

- Most eukaryotic genes are split into segments: They have **introns** interspersed among the **exons** (the regions included in the mRNA). In **RNA splicing**, introns are removed and exons joined. RNA splicing is typically carried out by **spliceosomes**, but in some cases, RNA alone catalyzes its own splicing. The catalytic ability of some RNA molecules, called **ribozymes**, derives from the inherent properties of RNA. The presence of introns allows for **alternative RNA splicing**.

? *What function do the 5′ cap and the poly-A tail serve on a eukaryotic mRNA?*

CONCEPT 17.4

Translation is the RNA-directed synthesis of a polypeptide: A closer look (pp. 347–356)

- A cell translates an mRNA message into protein using **transfer RNAs (tRNAs)**. After being bound to a specific amino acid by an **aminoacyl-tRNA synthetase**, a tRNA lines up via its **anticodon** at the complementary codon on mRNA. A **ribosome**, made up of **ribosomal RNAs (rRNAs)** and proteins, facilitates this coupling with binding sites for mRNA and tRNA.
- Ribosomes coordinate the three stages of translation: initiation, elongation, and termination. The formation of peptide bonds between amino acids is catalyzed by rRNA as tRNAs move through the **A and P sites** and exit through the **E site**.

- After translation, modifications to proteins can affect their shape. Free ribosomes in the cytosol initiate synthesis of all proteins, but proteins with a **signal peptide** are synthesized on the ER.
- A gene can be transcribed by multiple RNA polymerases simultaneously. A single mRNA molecule can be translated simultaneously by a number of ribosomes, forming a **polyribosome**. In bacteria, these processes are coupled, but in eukaryotes they are separated in space and time by the nuclear membrane.

? *What function do tRNAs serve in the process of translation?*

CONCEPT 17.5

Mutations of one or a few nucleotides can affect protein structure and function (pp. 357–359)

- Small-scale **mutations** include **point mutations**, changes in one DNA nucleotide pair, which may lead to production of nonfunctional proteins. **Nucleotide-pair substitutions** can cause **missense** or **nonsense mutations**. Nucleotide-pair **insertions** or **deletions** may produce **frameshift mutations**.
- Spontaneous mutations can occur during DNA replication, recombination, or repair. Chemical and physical **mutagens** cause DNA damage that can alter genes.

? *What will be the results of chemically modifying one nucleotide base of a gene? What role is played by DNA repair systems in the cell?*

TEST YOUR UNDERSTANDING

LEVEL 1: KNOWLEDGE/COMPREHENSION

1. In eukaryotic cells, transcription cannot begin until
   a. the two DNA strands have completely separated and exposed the promoter.
   b. several transcription factors have bound to the promoter.
   c. the 5' caps are removed from the mRNA.
   d. the DNA introns are removed from the template.

2. Which of the following is *not* true of a codon?
   a. It may code for the same amino acid as another codon.
   b. It never codes for more than one amino acid.
   c. It extends from one end of a tRNA molecule.
   d. It is the basic unit of the genetic code.

3. The anticodon of a particular tRNA molecule is
   a. complementary to the corresponding mRNA codon.
   b. complementary to the corresponding triplet in rRNA.
   c. the part of tRNA that bonds to a specific amino acid.
   d. catalytic, making the tRNA a ribozyme.

4. Which of the following is *not* true of RNA processing?
   a. Exons are cut out before mRNA leaves the nucleus.
   b. Nucleotides may be added at both ends of the RNA.
   c. Ribozymes may function in RNA splicing.
   d. RNA splicing can be catalyzed by spliceosomes.

5. Which component is *not* directly involved in translation?
   a. GTP
   b. DNA
   c. tRNA
   d. ribosomes

LEVEL 2: APPLICATION/ANALYSIS

6. Using Figure 17.5, identify a 5' → 3' sequence of nucleotides in the DNA template strand for an mRNA coding for the polypeptide sequence Phe-Pro-Lys.
   a. 5'-UUUGGGAAA-3'
   b. 5'-GAACCCCTT-3'
   c. 5'-CTTCGGGAA-3'
   d. 5'-AAACCCUUU-3'

7. Which of the following mutations would be *most* likely to have a harmful effect on an organism?
   a. a deletion of three nucleotides near the middle of a gene
   b. a single nucleotide deletion in the middle of an intron
   c. a single nucleotide deletion near the end of the coding sequence
   d. a single nucleotide insertion downstream of, and close to, the start of the coding sequence

8. Would the coupling of the processes shown in Figure 17.23 be found in a eukaryotic cell? Explain why or why not.

9. **DRAW IT** Fill in the following table:

Type of RNA	Functions
Messenger RNA (mRNA)	
Transfer RNA (tRNA)	
	Plays catalytic (ribozyme) roles and structural roles in ribosomes
Primary transcript	
Small RNAs in the spliceosome	

LEVEL 3: SYNTHESIS/EVALUATION

10. **EVOLUTION CONNECTION**
    Most amino acids are coded for by a set of similar codons (see Figure 17.5). What evolutionary explanations can you give for this pattern? (*Hint*: There is one explanation relating to ancestry, and some less obvious ones of a "form-fits-function" type.)

11. **SCIENTIFIC INQUIRY**
    Knowing that the genetic code is almost universal, a scientist uses molecular biological methods to insert the human β-globin gene (shown in Figure 17.11) into bacterial cells, hoping the cells will express it and synthesize functional β-globin protein. Instead, the protein produced is nonfunctional and is found to contain many fewer amino acids than does β-globin made by a eukaryotic cell. Explain why.

12. **WRITE ABOUT A THEME: INFORMATION**
    Evolution accounts for the unity and diversity of life, and the continuity of life is based on heritable information in the form of DNA. In a short essay (100–150 words), discuss how the fidelity with which DNA is inherited is related to the processes of evolution. (Review the discussion of proofreading and DNA repair in Concept 16.2.)

13. **SYNTHESIZE YOUR KNOWLEDGE**

Some mutations result in proteins that function well at one temperature but are nonfunctional at a different (usually higher) temperature. Siamese cats have such a "temperature-sensitive" mutation in a gene encoding an enzyme that makes dark pigment in the fur. The mutation results in the breed's distinctive point markings and lighter body color (see the photo). Using this information and what you learned in the chapter, explain the pattern of the cat's fur pigmentation.

MasteringBiology®

Students Go to **MasteringBiology** for assignments, the eText, and the Study Area with practice tests, animations, and activities.

Instructors Go to **MasteringBiology** for automatically graded tutorials and questions that you can assign to your students, plus Instructor Resources.

INDEX

NOTE: A page number in regular type indicates where a topic is discussed in the text; a **bold** page number indicates where a term is bold and defined; an *f* following a page number indicates a figure (the topic may also be discussed in the text on that page); a *t* following a page number indicates a table (the topic may also be discussed in the text on that page).

Index